◎ Harden's

London Restaurants

2020

Survey driven reviews of 1,700 restaurants

29th edition

Put us in your pocket!

Download our app for iPhone or Android

© **Harden's Limited 2019**

ISBN 978-1-916076-10-5

British Library Cataloguing-in-Publication data:
a catalogue record for this book is available from
the British Library.

Printed in Italy by Legoprint

Assistant editors: Bruce Millar, Antonia Russell

Harden's Limited
Beta Space, 25 Holywell Row, London, EC2A 4XE

Would restaurateurs (and PRs) please address
communications to 'Editorial' at the above address,
or ideally by email to: editorial@hardens.com

CONTENTS

RATINGS & PRICES

Ratings

Our rating system does not tell you – as most guides do – that expensive restaurants are often better than cheap ones! What we do is compare each restaurant's performance – as judged by the average ratings awarded by reporters in the survey – with other similarly-priced restaurants. This approach has the advantage that it helps you find – whatever your budget for any particular meal – where you will get the best 'bang for your buck'.

The following qualities are assessed:

F — Food
S — Service
A — Ambience

The rating indicates that, *in comparison with other restaurants in the same price-bracket*, performance is…

5 — Exceptional
4 — Very good
3 — Good
2 — Average
1 — Poor

Prices

The price shown for each restaurant is the cost for one (1) person of an average three-course dinner with half a bottle of house wine and coffee, any cover charge, service and VAT. Lunch is often cheaper. With BYO restaurants, we have assumed that two people share a £7 bottle of off-licence wine.

Telephone number – *all numbers are '020' numbers.*

Map reference – *shown immediately after the telephone number.*

Full postcodes – *for non-group restaurants, the first entry in the 'small print' at the end of each listing, so you can set your sat-nav.*

Website and Twitter – *shown in the small print, where applicable.*

Last orders time – *listed after the website (if applicable); Sunday may be up to 90 minutes earlier.*

Opening hours – *unless otherwise stated, restaurants are open for lunch and dinner seven days a week.*

Credit and debit cards – *unless otherwise stated, Mastercard, Visa, Amex and Maestro are accepted.*

Dress – *where appropriate, the management's preferences concerning patrons' dress are given.*

Food Made Good Star Rating – *the sustainability index, as calculated by the Sustainable Restaurant Association – see page 8 for more information.*

HOW THIS GUIDE IS WRITTEN

Nearly 30 years of the Harden's survey

This guide is based on our 29th annual survey of what 'ordinary' diners-out think of London's restaurants.

This year, the total number of reporters in our combined London/UK survey, conducted mainly online, numbered 7,500, and, between them, they contributed 50,000 individual reports.

At a time when a recent study suggested that as many as 1/3 of the reviews on TripAdvisor are paid for by the restaurants they cover, we believe there is an ever-greater need for trusted sources such as the Harden's annual diner survey. For while obviously folks can attempt to stuff the Harden's ballot too, the high degree of editorial oversight plus the historical data we have both about the restaurants and also about those commenting makes it much harder to succeed. In this way Harden's can socially source restaurant feedback, but – vitally – curate it fully as we do so. It is this careful curation which provides extra 'value-added' for diners.

How we determine the ratings

In the great majority of cases, ratings are arrived at statistically. This essentially involves 'ranking' the average survey rating each restaurant achieves in the survey – for food, service and ambience – against the average ratings of the other establishments in the same price-bracket.

(This is essentially like football leagues, with the most expensive restaurants going in the top league and the cheaper ones in lower leagues. The restaurant's ranking *within its own particular league* determines its ratings.)

How we write the reviews

The tone of each review and the ratings are largely determined by the ranking of the establishment concerned, which we derive as described above.

At the margin, we may also pay some regard to the proportion of positive nominations (such as for 'favourite restaurant') compared to negative nominations (such as for 'most overpriced').

To explain why a restaurant has been rated as it has, we extract snippets from survey comments ("enclosed in double quotes"). On well-known restaurants, we receive several hundred reports, and a short summary cannot possibly do individual justice to all of them.

What we seek to do – *without any regard to our own personal opinions* – is to illustrate the key themes which have emerged in our analysis of the collective view.

If ocean plastic was the issue driving positive change in restaurants in 2018, the climate emergency has been very much front of mind in 2019. Countless reports have been published in the last 18 months highlighting the plight of the planet and the drastic action we need to take to ensure we keep temperature rises below 1.5C.

SUSTAINABLE RESTAURANT ASSOCIATION

The good news for all of us is that our appetites are incredibly powerful. The choices we make about food have the greatest single impact on the planet – greater even than the car we drive or the planes we take. That provides chefs and menu developers with a big slice of power – the ability to influence what we eat and, through that behaviour change, a genuine shift towards less environmentally damaging diets. This chance to grab the sustainability bull by the horns also comes at precisely the time when the great British dining public is looking to satisfy its insatiable appetite to eat wisely.

And grab it they have. Hugh Fearnley-Whittingstall, he of River Cottage fame, described the Greggs vegan sausage roll as the most significant food story of the year. From high street to high end, the shift towards more veg-based dishes is accelerating at serious pace.

Vegetables, the eternal bridesmaids, are at long last taking centre stage. By dishing up more and more delicious and creative plant-based options, chefs are helping reduce the impact of their restaurant while also helping customers eat their way to a better food future. If, as UK citizens we all went plant-based for one more meal a week, it would reduce the nation's carbon footprint by a stunning 8%.

A desire to dine more consciously is growing faster than ever before and restaurants are striving to keep pace.

We've supported the SRA since soon after its launch in 2010 because we too believe in helping diners vote with their forks for a better food future.

Look out for those restaurants serving a One Planet Plate, the chef's sustainable special (www.oneplanetplate.org) and search in the guide for those with an SRA Sustainability Rating, either One, Two or Three Stars, achieved by proving they are doing these ten things:

Support Global Farmers	Source Fish Responsibly
Value Natural Resources	Serve More Veg & Better Meat
Treat People Fairly	Reduce Reuse Recycle
Feed Children Well	Waste no Food
Celebrate Local	Support the Community

w: www.foodmadegood.org / www.oneoplanetplate.org
Twitter: @the_SRA
Instagram: @foodmadegood

SURVEY FAQs

Q. How do you find your reporters?
A. Anyone can take part. Simply register at
www.hardens.com. Actually, we find that many people who
complete our survey each year have taken part before.
So it's really more a question of a very large and ever-
evolving panel, or jury, than a random 'poll'.

Q. Wouldn't a random sample be better?
A. That's really a theoretical question, as there is no
obvious way, still less a cost-efficient one, by which one
could identify a random sample of the guests at each of, say,
5,000 establishments across the UK, and get them to take
part in any sort of survey. And anyway, which is likely to be
more useful: a sample of the views of everyone who's been
to a particular place, or the views of people who are
interested enough in eating-out to have volunteered their
feedback?

Q. What sort of people take part?
A. A roughly 60/40 male/female split, from all adult age-
groups. As you might expect – as eating out is not the
cheapest activity – reporters tend to have white collar jobs
(some at very senior levels). By no means, however, is that
always the case.

Q. Do people ever try to stuff the ballot?
A. Of course they do! A rising number of efforts are
weeded out every year. But stuffing the ballot is not as
trivial a task as some people seem to think: the survey
results throw up clear natural voting patterns against which
'campaigns' tend to stand out.

Q. Aren't inspections the best way to run a guide?
A. It is often assumed – even by commentators who ought
to know better – that inspections are some sort of 'gold
standard'. There is no doubt that the inspection model
clearly has potential strengths, but one of its prime
weaknesses is that it is incredibly expensive. Take the most
famous practitioner of the 'inspection model', Michelin. It
doesn't claim to visit each and every entry listed in its guide
annually. Even once! And who are the inspectors? Often
they are catering professionals, whose likes and dislikes may
be very different from the establishment's natural customer
base. On any restaurant of note, however, Harden's typically
has somewhere between dozens and hundreds of reports
each and every year from exactly the type of people the
restaurant relies upon to stay in business. We believe that
such feedback, carefully analysed, is far more revealing and
accurate than an occasional 'professional' inspection.

SURVEY MOST MENTIONED

These are the restaurants which were most frequently mentioned by reporters. (Last year's position is given in brackets.) An asterisk* indicates the first appearance in the list of a recently opened restaurant.

1	J Sheekey (1)
2	Le Gavroche (4)
3	Chez Bruce (3)
4	Clos Maggiore (2)
5	Scott's (5)
6	The Ledbury (6)
7	Core by Clare Smyth (13)
8	The Wolseley (10)
9	Brasserie Zédel (11)
10	La Trompette (9)

11	Gauthier Soho (8)
12	The River Café (12)
13	Gymkhana (7)
14	Hide (-)
15	The Ivy (14)
16	A Wong (15)
17	Bocca Di Lupo (24)
18=	Indian Accent (-)
18=	Andrew Edmunds (17)
20	The Delaunay (16)

21	Noble Rot (29)
22	Galvin La Chapelle (-)
23	Brat (-)
24	Trinity (18)
25	The Cinnamon Club (21)
26=	Pollen Street Social (23)
26=	La Poule au Pot (22)
28=	The Ritz (40)
28=	Gordon Ramsay (37)
30	Bentley's (31)

31	The Five Fields (25)
32	Bleeding Heart Restaurant (28)
33	Murano (-)
34=	Pied À Terre (33)
34=	Trishna (-)
36	Medlar (-)
37=	Kerridge's Bar & Grill (-)
37=	Trullo (-)
37=	Le Caprice (19)
40	Elystan Street (30)

SURVEY NOMINATIONS

Top gastronomic experience

1 Core by Clare Smyth (6)
2 Le Gavroche (2)
3 The Ledbury (1)
4 Chez Bruce (3)
5 La Trompette (4)
6 Pied À Terre (-)
7 Gauthier Soho (5)
8 Frog by Adam Handling (-)
9 Hide (-)
10 The Five Fields (10)

Favourite

1 Chez Bruce (1)
2 Le Gavroche (7)
3 The Ledbury (3)
4 The River Café (-)
5 La Trompette (8)
6 Gauthier Soho (4)
7 Trinity (-)
8 J Sheekey (9)
9 The Wolseley (5)
10 Clos Maggiore (-)

Best for business

1 The Wolseley (1)
2 Hawksmoor (3)
3 The Delaunay (2)
4 Bleeding Heart Restaurant (5)
5 The Dining Room, The Goring Hotel (-)
6 Scott's (4)
7 The Ivy (10)
8 Galvin La Chapelle (-)
9 Goodman (-)
10 Coq d'Argent (-)

Best for romance

1 Clos Maggiore (1)
2 La Poule au Pot (2)
3 Andrew Edmunds (3)
4 Chez Bruce (7)
5 Bleeding Heart Restaurant (4)
6 Le Gavroche (5)
7 The Ledbury (-)
8 Café du Marché (8)
9 Gauthier Soho (6)
10 The Ritz (-)

Best breakfast/brunch

1 The Wolseley (1)
2 Dishoom (5)
3 Caravan (6)
4 The Delaunay (2)
5 The Ivy Grills & Brasseries (3)
6 Côte (8)
7 Cecconi's (10)
8 Granger & Co (4)
9 Breakfast Club (7)
10 Hawksmoor (-)

Best bar/pub food

1 Harwood Arms (1)
2 The Anchor & Hope (2)
3 The Anglesea Arms (4)
4 The Wells Tavern (5=)
5 Canton Arms (7)
6 The Ladbroke Arms (5=)
7 The Drapers Arms (-)
8 The Guinea Grill (-)
9 The Wigmore, The Langham (-)
10 The Coach (-)

Most disappointing cooking

1 Oxo Tower (2)
2 The Ivy (3)
3 The Ivy Grills & Brasseries (1)
4 Le Gavroche (-)
5 Hide (-)
6 Gordon Ramsay (7)
7 Chiltern Firehouse (9)
8 Kerridge's Bar & Grill (-)
9 Scott's (-)
10 Union Street Café (-)

Most overpriced restaurant

1 The River Café (1)
2 Gordon Ramsay (4)
3 Oxo Tower (3)
4 Sexy Fish (2)
5 Le Gavroche (8)
6 Hide (-)
7 The Ivy Café (-)
8 J Sheekey (-)
9 Sushisamba (9)
10 Hutong (-)

SURVEY HIGHEST RATINGS

FOOD	SERVICE

£100+

	FOOD		SERVICE
1	The Five Fields	1	The Five Fields
2	Bubbledogs, Kitchen Table	2	Pied à Terre
3	Texture	3	The Ledbury
4	The Ledbury	4	Le Gavroche
5	Pied à Terre	5	Bubbledogs, Kitchen Table

£75–£99

	FOOD		SERVICE
1	Zuma	1	Caractère
2	Launceston Place	2	Chez Bruce
3	Roganic	3	Noizé
4	Roux at Parliament Sq	4	Launceston Place
5	Roka	5	Roux at the Landau

£60–£74

	FOOD		SERVICE
1	Frog by Adam Handling	1	Il Portico
2	Cornerstone	2	Caraffini
3	Brat	3	Oslo Court
4	Twist	4	Quilon
5	Anglo	5	Smith's Wapping

£45–£59

	FOOD		SERVICE
1	The Barbary	1	The Barbary
2	Babur	2	Babur
3	Barrafina	3	Barrafina
4	A Wong	4	A Wong
5	Bombay Palace	5	40 Maltby Street

£44 or less

	FOOD		SERVICE
1	Dastaan	1	Monmouth Coffee Co
2	Padella	2	Kaffeine
3	Pizza Pilgrims	3	Paradise Hampstead
4	Homeslice	4	Dastaan
5	Lahore Kebab House	5	Kiln

SURVEY HIGHEST RATINGS

AMBIENCE

1 The Ritz
2 Pied à Terre
3 Bubbledogs, Kitchen Table
4 Oblix
5 The Ledbury

1 Clos Maggiore
2 Spring Restaurant
3 Launceston Place
4 Rules
5 Roux at Parliament Sq

1 La Poule au Pot
2 Andrew Edmunds
3 Rex Whistler
4 The Wolseley
5 Oslo Court

1 Brasserie Zédel
2 San Carlo Cicchetti
3 Barrafina
4 40 Maltby Street
5 Ognisko

1 Dishoom
2 Churchill Arms
3 Kiln
4 Mercato Metropolitano
5 Padella

OVERALL

1 Pied à Terre
2 Bubbledogs, Kitchen Table
3 The Five Fields
4 The Ledbury
5 Core by Clare Smyth

1 Launceston Place
2 Roux at Parliament Sq
3 Caractère
4 Chez Bruce
5 Roka

1 Cornerstone
2 Brat
3 Smith's Wapping
4 Clarke's
5 Cabotte

1 The Barbary
2 Barrafina
3 Babur
4 40 Maltby Street
5 Bombay Palace

1 Padella
2 Monmouth Coffee Co
3 Dishoom
4 Dastaan
5 Kiln

SURVEY BEST BY CUISINE

These are the restaurants which received the best average food ratings (excluding establishments with a small or notably local following).

Where the most common types of cuisine are concerned, we present the results in two price-brackets. For less common cuisines, we list the top three, regardless of price.

For further information about restaurants which are particularly notable for their food, see the area overviews starting on page 262.

British, Modern

£60 and over		Under £60	
1	The Five Fields	1	The Dairy
2	Bubbledogs, Kitchen Table	2	40 Maltby Street
3	The Ledbury	3	Lamberts
4	Launceston Place	4	The Anchor & Hope
5	Roganic	5	Noble Rot

French

£60 and over		Under £60	
1	Le Gavroche	1	Casse-Croute
2	La Dame de Pic London	2	Café du Marché
3	The Ninth London	3	The Wells Tavern
4	La Petite Maison	4	Le Relais de Venise
5	La Trompette	5	Comptoir Gascon

Italian/Mediterranean

£60 and over		Under £60	
1	Theo Randall	1	Padella
2	Bocca Di Lupo	2	Bancone
3	Murano	3	Sorella
4	River Café	4	L'Amorosa
5	Locanda Locatelli	5	San Carlo Cicchetti

Indian & Pakistani

£60 and over		Under £60	
1	Amaya	1	Dastaan
2	Gymkhana	2	Babur
3	Indian Accent	3	Bombay Palace
4	Kutir	4	Lahore Kebab House
5	Café Spice Namaste	5	Dishoom

Chinese

£60 and over
1 Hakkasan
2 Hunan
3 Yauatcha
4 China Tang
5 Min Jiang

Under £60
1 A Wong
2 Singapore Garden
3 Yming
4 Kym's by Andrew Wong
5 Royal China

Japanese

£60 and over
1 Umu
2 Endo at Rotunda
3 Zuma
4 Roka
5 The Araki

Under £60
1 Sushi Tetsu
2 Takahashi
3 Chotto Matte
4 Chisou
5 Jin Kichi

British, Traditional
1 St John Smithfield
2 The Ritz
3 Scott's

Vegetarian
1 Gauthier Soho
2 The Frog
3 Vanilla Black

Burgers, etc
1 Hawksmoor
2 Goodman City
3 Burger & Beyond

Pizza
1 Pizza Pilgrims
2 Homeslice
3 Oliveto

Fish & Chips
1 Toff's
2 fish!
3 North Sea Fish

Thai
1 Smoking Goat
2 Kiln
3 Farang

Steaks & Grills
1 Hawksmoor
2 Goodman City
3 Flat Iron

Fish & Seafood
1 Cornerstone
2 Angler
3 J Sheekey

Fusion
1 Brat
2 Twist
3 108 Garage

Spanish
1 Barrafina
2 Sabor
3 José

Turkish
1 Kyseri
2 Oklava
3 Mangal I

Lebanese
1 Crocker's Folly
2 Maroush
3 Yalla Yalla

THE RESTAURANT SCENE

The squeeze on the market loosens… just

There are 174 newcomers in this year's guide. Although this is the fourth-best year we have recorded, this figure is well off the peaks seen in 2017 and 2018 which scored 200 and 193 respectively.

Closures, however, remain at a near-record level. At 110, they are the third highest-ever recorded since we started keeping count in 1992. They are narrowly exceeded only by last year's chart-topping 117 and the 113 recorded in the 2004 guide, which resulted from the savage hit the trade took as a result of the second gulf war and SARS epidemic.

Net openings (openings minus closures) grew weakly to 64: a rather mediocre performance. In the last ten years only two years have seen a worse result (last year and 2012).

The feeling that the market is still in the doldrums is reinforced by the ratio of openings to closures. At 1.6:1, it represents only a slight gain from last year's 1.4:1, and is well below the 29-year average of 2.1:1. Previous slumps in activity have generally been followed by a sharp rebound either back to, or above, the long-term average. You have to go back to the deep recession of the early 1990s to find as limp a recovery as the one currently underway.

Only the strong survive

One of the eye-catching features of the last year has been the number of high profile casualties. The failure of Jamie's Italian was major news, although it came as a surprise only to those who had not bothered to read this guide, which had awarded it dire marks for six years previously. Eventually gravity intervened.

Jamie's problems have become emblematic of the crisis in casual dining, which has also taken its toll on a slew of other chains, with seemingly daily announcements of CVAs (Creditor Voluntary Agreements) or closures. Abokado, Byron, Polpo, Ed's Easy Diner, Giraffe…

Looking at the more upscale chains and indies that Harden's reporters tend to focus on, what have been notable are the number of casualties amongst long-running well-known names, who chose this year to give up the ghost. Fifteen shuttered itself of course, but also Hedone, The Providores, Shepherd's, Kensington Place, maze, The Red Fort, Sonny's, Asia de Cuba, and Great Queen Street. Also small multiples of quality such as Rök, Picture and Foxlow. Doubtless the glory days of many of the above had passed, but at another time, many of them would have soldiered on.

It is a truism of entrepreneurial texts that just to stand still it is necessary for any business constantly to reinvent itself. That is ever-more the case in the London restaurant scene where any site that is not performing at its peak, will quickly be reformatted under the same brand or a new one.

The tough get going... less so to the burbs

The good news is that London's restaurateurs are a much more formidable bunch than when this guide was first published. The last three decades have seen an incredible rise in the professionalism of the trade. Opportunities continue to present themselves to those with witty new formats or sufficient passion to excel at the old ones.

But whereas in recent years much of the excitement has been focused on hipster enclaves in the East End, this year saw openings much more targeted on Central London (with 82 newcomers).

Away from the centre, activity was very much more evenly spread than it has typically been in recent times. East London led the way, but only by a whisker (with 27 openings) closely followed by both South London (with 26) and West London (25). The only laggard was North London which – after a promising year last year – reverted to being the tail end charlie (with just 14 newcomers).

Modern British cuisine (53) is by far and away the most popular for newcomers, with Italian (17), Indian (10) and Japanese (9) the next most numerous.

A good year for the girls...

Core by Clare Smyth enters the top-10 Most Mentioned restaurants this year. Taylor Bonnyman's Five Fields – head chef Marguerite Keogh – scored the survey's highest food mark. Newcomer of the year at Harden's Restaurant Awards 2019 was Caractère: Emily Roux's venture in partnership with husband Diego Ferrari.

The hottest of the hot

Every year, we do an editors' pick of the ten most significant openings of the year. This year our selection is as follows:

Bancone	Darby's
Bright	Endo at Rotunda
Bob Bob Cité	Emilia
Caractère	Gloria
The Coal Office	Kutir

Prices

The average price of dinner for one at establishments listed in this guide is £59.28 (compared to £55.76 last year). Prices have risen by 6.3% in the past 12 months (up on 4.8% in the preceding 12 months). This rate compares with a general annual inflation rate of 2.1% for the 12 months to July 2019, yet further accelerating the trend seen in the last three years by which London restaurant bills have seen price rises running significantly higher than UK inflation generally. Restaurants are a people-heavy business, though, and with UK wage growth having picked up to 4%, an above-inflation rise in restaurant bills is to be expected.

OPENINGS AND CLOSURES

Openings (174)

Adam Handling Chelsea
Allegra
Angelina
AOK Kitchen
Arcade Food Theatre
Arros QD
Baba G's (NW1)
BabaBoom (N1)
Bancone
Bao & Bing
Baozi Inn (SE1)
Berto
The Betterment
Black Dog Beer House
Black Radish
Bloomsbury Street Kitchen
Brasserie of Light
Bright
Brixton Laundry
Brook House
Bubala
Bun House (WC2H)
Burger & Beyond
by Chloe (SE1, W1)
Casa Fofó
Caviar Kaspia
Le Cellar
Cent Anni
Ceru (W1)
Charlie's
Church House
Circolo Popolare
Coqfighter
Le Comptoir Robuchon
Curry House Coco Ichibanya
Da Terra, Town Hall Hotel
Daffodil Mulligan
Dandy
Darby's
Davies and Brook, Claridge's Hotel
Decimo
Din Tai Fung (WC1)
Double Standard
E&O Chelsea (SW3)
Eggslut
Emilia's Crafted Pasta (E1)

Emilia
Endo at Rotunda
Fare
Farzi Cafe
Fatt Pundit
Fishworks (WC2)
Flat Iron (E1)
Flesh and Buns (W1)
Flor
Folie
Fortnum's Bar & Restaurant, Royal Exchange
400 Rabbits (SE27)
Four Legs at The Compton Arms
Franzina Trattoria
Fucina
Fugitive Motel
Garden Room
Gezellig
Gloria
Gold
Grays & Feather
Gridiron, COMO Metropolitan London
The Halal Guys
Hankies Marble Arch (W1)
Hard Rock Café (W1 x2)
Harlequin
Harrods Dining Hall
Haya
Hello Darling
Heritage
Imperial Treasure
Ippudo London (WC2)
Isla
Kaki
Kanishka
Kin and Deum
Kol
KoolCha
KPH
Kricket (W12, SW9)
Kuku Riku
Lagom at Hackney Church Brew Co.
Laksamania
Legare

Openings (continued)

Lina Stores (N1)
Lino
Locket's
The Lore of the Land
Loyal Tavern
Lucknow 49
Lucky Cat
Madame Pigg
Manzi's
Mao Chow
Maremma
Market Hall Victoria
Master Wei
Mathura
Melabes
Mimo
Moio
Moncks of Dover Street
Monsieur Le Duck
Myrtle
Nandine
No. 5 Social
No. Fifty Cheyne
Norma
Nutshell
O'ver (SW1)
The Oak (SW11)
104 Restaurant
Onima
OOTY
Orasay
Pachamama East (EC2)
Paradise
Parrillan
Passyunk Avenue
Pasta Remoli (W5, E20)
Pasticceria Marchesi 1824
Patri (W13, W6)
Peg
Le Petit Citron
Pick & Cheese
Les Platanes
Poppy's 3 (W6)
Le Pot de Terre
Pucci Mayfair
Roast (W1)
Robata
Roe

Sambal Shiok
The Sea, The Sea
Seabird
Señor Ceviche (W1)
Sette
Shanghai Modern
Silo
Siren
Sloane Street Deli
Snackbar
Soane's Kitchen
Spiritland (SE1, N1)
St Martin's Lane Kitchen
Stem & Glory (EC1)
Suzi Tros
10 Heddon Street
The Buxton
The Restaurant at The Capital
The Yard, Great Scotland Yard Hotel
Top Cuvee
Trivet
Vardo
Vinegar Yard
Wild Food Cafe (WC2)
Wild Rice & Mamasan
Xier
XR
Yeni
Yopo
Zia Lucia (W14)

Closures (110)

L'Absinthe
L'Ami Malo
Andi's
Annies (SW13)
Asia de Cuba, St Martins Lane Hotel
L'Atelier de Joel Robuchon
Babel House
The Balcon, Sofitel St James
Barbecoa (EC4)
Beck at Browns, Browns Hotel
Bellanger
Bonhams Restaurant

The Brackenbury
Bradys
La Buvette
Ceremony
Chilly Katz
Claw Carnaby
Dip in Brilliant
Drakes Tabanco
Edwins
Eight Over Eight
Essence Cuisine
Fayre Share
Fera at Claridge's,
    Claridge's Hotel
Fifteen
Foxlow (W1, EC1, SW12)
Gabys
Gastronhome
Gaylord
Gazelle
Gazette (SW12)
Ginger & White (NW3)
Great Queen Street
Hedone
Heirloom
Jackson & Rye Chiswick (W4)
Jackson & Rye (W1)
James Cochran EC3 (EC3A)
Jamie's Italian (all branches)
Kensington Place
Kensington Square Kitchen
Kerbisher & Malt (SW4)
Kiru
Kulu Kulu (WC2, SW7)
Lantana Cafe (NW1)
Lardo Bebè (E8)
Little Social
Lokhandwala
Londrino
Lupita (WC2)
Magpie
Marianne
MASH Steakhouse
maze
Mint Leaf (SW1)
Morada Brindisa Asador (W1)
Mustard
Neo Bistro
Nuala
On The Bab Express (W1)

On the Dak
The Palmerston
Parabola, Design Museum
Pescatori
Peyotito
Picture (W1 x2)
Pitt Cue Co
Polpetto
Popeseye (N19)
La Porchetta Pizzeria
    (EC1, N4, NW1)
The Providores and Tapa
    Room
Quantus
Red Fort
Rivea, Bulgari Hotel
Rök (N1, EC2)
Rotorino
Rox Burger
Sapling
Schmaltz Truck
Serge et Le Phoque
Shepherds
Social Wine & Tapas
Sonnys Kitchen
Southam Street
Stem
Outlaw's at The Capital
Taylor Street Baristas
    (all branches)
Toms Kitchen (E1, E14)
Tommi's Burger Joint (SW3)
The Trafalgar Dining Rooms
Tratra
28-50 (W1, EC4)
VIVI
Waterloo Bar & Kitchen
Wellbourne
Workshop Coffee Holborn
    (EC1)

DIRECTORY

Comments in "double quotation marks" were made by reporters.

A Cena TW1 £50 3 4 3
418 Richmond Road 020 8288 0108 1–4A
Upmarket local in St Margaret's – close enough to Twickers for a meal before or after the rugby – that earns solid ratings for its "great Italian cooking" and "very friendly service". New owner chef Tom Rowlandson has introduced weekend brunches. / TW1 2EB; www.acena.co.uk; @acenarestaurant; 10 pm; closed Mon L & Sun D; booking max 6 may apply.

A Wong SW1 £59 5 5 3
70 Wilton Rd 020 7828 8931 2–4B
"He's won my heart, and my taste buds…" – Andrew Wong's Pimlico venture "a short walk from Victoria Station" is the survey's No. 1 Chinese nowadays due to its "absolutely amazing", "elevated cuisine, beautifully plated and full of flavour". At lunch time, the attraction is "dim sum as you've never tasted it before" – "mouthwatering and so delicate", with special mention to the "incredible soup dumplings" – while at night there's "a brilliant tasting menu, taking you on a whistle-stop tour of Chinese culinary delights". "Happy" and "super-efficient" staff also rate special mention. "Plush the decor is not" – in fact the ground floor can seem "an oddly canteen-ish environment" – but, by contrast, the basement bar "has a beautiful 'secret club' feel to it". See also Kym's. / SW1V 1DE; www.awong.co.uk; @awongSW1; 10.15 pm; closed Mon L & Sun; credit card required to book.

The Abbeville SW4 £46 3 3 3
67-69 Abbeville Rd 020 8675 2201 11–2D
"Reliable local with better-than-pub fare"; an attractive, and well-established gastropub (which looks more like a wine bar — complete with opening frontage in summer — than a trad boozer), which sits at the heart of 'Abbeville Village' life. / SW4 9JW; www.theabbeville.co.uk; @threecheerspubs; 10.30 pm, Sun 9 pm.

Abd El Wahab SW1 £62 3 3 2
1-3 Pont Street 020 7235 0005 6–1D
Surprisingly little feedback on this posh Lebanese, swankily located near Belgrave Square – the London outpost of a well-known, Beirut-based chain with 18 branches in the Arab world. Such as we have suggests it's good all-round, but doesn't set the world on fire. / SW1X 9EJ; www.abdelwahab.co.uk.

The Abingdon W8 £59 3 3 4
54 Abingdon Rd 020 7937 3339 6–2A
With its "cosy red-leather booths" to the rear and attractive dining room and bar, this posh gastropub has been a "locals' favourite" of chichi backstreet Kensington for 21 years. The food is "above average (fantastic steaks!)" and there's a "decent wine list" – "what's not to like?". / W8 6AP; www.theabingdon.co.uk; @theabingdonw8; Tues-Sat 10.30 pm, Sun-Mon 10 pm.

About Thyme SW1 £56 3 4 3
82 Wilton Rd 020 7821 7504 2–4B
"Like a home away from home", this Pimlico stalwart keeps regulars happy with a "lovely range of tapas" and Spanish classics, "supervised brilliantly by the amazing host, Issy". "In an age of ever-changing restaurants, it's a great pleasure to enjoy such consistency over many years." / SW1V 1DL; www.aboutthyme.co.uk; 10 pm; closed Sun.

Abu Zaad W12 £30 3 3 2
29 Uxbridge Rd 020 8749 5107 8–1C
"Plentiful and delicious Syrian specialities make it worth trying out this Shepherd's Bush café". It has a "slightly unpromising exterior", but a "superb atmosphere" inside, and it's "good value too". "Just go!" – "you won't be leaving hungry". / W12 8LH; www.abuzaad.co.uk; @abuzaaduk; 11 pm, Sat & Sun midnight; No Amex.

Adam Handling Chelsea SW1 NEW 3|3|4

The Belmond Cadogan, 75 Sloane Street   020 7199 8370   6–2D

Sloane Street's old Cadogan Hotel – formerly a creaky, old Chelsea anachronism – has been transformed to join the über-luxurious Belmond portfolio: it now provides a "gorgeous" and luxurious backdrop to a meal ("perfect to impress a client in Chelsea"). Wunderkind chef, Adam Handling, is in charge of the dining room, and fans say that his individualistic cuisine is "knock-out": "from the bread with chicken-butter onwards, everything about this menu is now the best of modern British". However, there's also a slightly worrying proportion of disgruntled reports too: "as a massive fan of Adam Handling's Frog restaurants and even his cooking at Caxton Grill back in the day, I was anticipating greatness from AH Chelsea. But the food was sorely disappointing, confused, and as such, very overpriced. Hoping the food matches its surroundings soon!" / SW1X 9SG; www.adamhandlingchelsea.co.uk; @AHChelseaLDN.

Adams Café W12 £34 3|5|3

77 Askew Rd   020 8743 0572   8–1B

"Greasy spoon by day, North African bistro by night" – this "so friendly" Shepherd's Bush institution run by Anglo-Tunisian couple Frances and Abdel Boukraa has been "treasured by locals for 25 years". "The grills (fish, lamb, chicken) are the high points, all delicious!", but "don't miss the home-made pickles and harissa – they're highly addictive". They are licensed these days, but you can still BYO (wines only, £6 corkage). / W12 9AH; www.adamscafe.co.uk; @adamscafe; 10 pm; closed Sun.

Addie's Thai Café SW5 £38 4|3|2

121 Earl's Court Rd   020 7259 2620   6–2A

"Fantastic Thai food at very reasonable prices" is the reason this basic Earl's Court canteen "has been around for over 20 years". "You can't fault it" for "real street food" that "far outperforms rivals and chains". / SW5 9RL; www.addiesthai.co.uk; 11 pm, Sun 10.30 pm; No Amex.

Addomme SW2 £54 4|3|3

17-21 Sternhold Avenue   020 8678 8496   11–2C

"They use the best ingredients, the pizzas are extremely good, and Nadia and her husband are always lovely hosts" at their family-run joint, next to Streatham Hill station. "Sometimes it can get a bit crammed and noisy, but hey, it's a pizza place". / SW2 4PA; www.addomme.co.uk; @PizzAddomme; 11 pm.

The Admiral Codrington SW3 £55 3|3|3

17 Mossop St   020 7581 0005   6–2C

In a chichi backstreet, a posh boozer that's well-known to the denizens of Chelsea: it serves "a revisited version of typical pub food" in its rear dining room, which boasts a big, retractable glass skylight for warm days. / SW3 2LY; www.theadmiralcodrington.co.uk; @TheAdCod; 10 pm, Thu-Sat 11 pm, Sun 9 pm; No trainers.

Afghan Kitchen N1 £29 3|3|2

35 Islington Grn   020 7359 8019   9–3D

"Decent food but seriously cramped!" – that's long been the trade-off at this tiny, barely decorated caff, by Islington Green, whose small selection of interesting curries makes it a "great local". / N1 8DU; 11 pm; closed Mon & Sun; Cash only; no booking.

Aglio e Olio SW10 £47 3|3|2

194 Fulham Rd   020 7351 0070   6–3B

"Honest", "fresh-tasting pasta and Italian staples" have won a major fanclub for this "unobtrusive" but "buzzy and very good-value institution" near Chelsea & Westminster Hospital. "Service is high-speed" and there's a "fun atmosphere" – but be warned, it's "not for the hard of hearing". / SW10 9PN; www.aglioeolio.co.uk; 11.00 pm.

Akira at Japan House W8 £88 ②③③
101-111 Kensington High Street 020 3971 4646 6–1A
"Would have expected a lot more from a Japanese restaurant within Japan House" is too often the verdict on this venue within the Japanese Government's year-old showcase for all things Nipponese, which occupies Kensington's former Derry & Toms department store. The place is not without advocates of its "attractive" design and "beautiful presentation" but even fans acknowledge it's "on the expensive side" and some critics report really bad trips with "overly complex and heavy", or even "shockingly bad" dishes. / W8 5SA; www.japanhouselondon.uk; @japanhouseldn.

Al Duca SW1 £59 ②②②
4-5 Duke of York St 020 7839 3090 3–3D
To avoid breaking the bank in swanky St James's, this long-established Italian is worth remembering thanks to its "reasonable food at sensible prices". On the downside, "there's no real ambience, but it can be fun to take a coffee at a pavement table and watch the world walk by". / SW1Y 6LA; www.alduca-restaurant.co.uk; 11 pm; closed Sun.

Al Forno £43 ③④④
349 Upper Richmond Rd, SW15 020 8878 7522 11–2A
2a King's Rd, SW19 020 8540 5710 11–2B
These "buzzing family-run Italians" in southwest London create "an exceptional atmosphere" for large parties of all ages – and "they won't break the bank". "Despite the celebratory brouhaha, they produce a very respectable menu of traditional dishes – fish stew, duck, pizza on demand" – "even the veggies are catered for". "Expect noise and old people dancing." / 10 pm-11 pm.

Alain Ducasse at The Dorchester W1 £133 ②③③
53 Park Ln 020 7629 8866 3–3A
Now a dozen years old: Alain Ducasse's UK flagship is a "subtly decorated and beautiful" – some would say "spectacular" – looking chamber on Park Lane, which perennially divides opinion between those who say it "never lets you down" and opponents who say it "never fails to disappoint". The latter camp have had the upper hand pretty much since the day it opened: they acknowledge a meal here is "a treat", but focus their fire on the "ludicrous prices", and the fact that its level of achievement is so "overhyped" by Michelin, who – seemingly on the grounds of Gallic cultural imperialism – insist on awarding this superstar Frenchman three stars, when one or two would be more than adequate! / W1K 1QA; www.alainducasse-dorchester.com; 9.30 pm; closed Mon, Sat L & Sun; Jacket required.

Albertine W12 £50 ③③⑤
1 Wood Lane 020 8743 9593 8–1C
The attractively "louche and convivial atmosphere" of this Shepherd's Bush veteran, opposite and long pre-dating Westfield shopping centre, is redolent of the 1970s, when the "great little wine bar" was opened by chef Allegra McEvedy's mother. Now co-owned by McEvedy, whose "interesting short seasonal menu" is available in the bar and upstairs restaurant. / W12 7DP; albertine.london; @albertineLDN; closed Sat L & Sun; No Amex.

Aleion N10 £48 ③③③
346 Muswell Hill Broadway 020 8883 9207 1–1B
"A very small, friendly local" in the centre of Muswell Hill for over two years now; mostly it serves "delicious", light brunch-friendly fare from breakfast onwards ("lovely healthy salad options"), but there's a more substantial menu of simple, modern bistro dishes by night. / N10 1DJ; www.aleion.co.uk; @Aleion346.

The Alfred Tennyson SW1 £64 🗲

10 Motcomb Street   020 7730 6074   6–1D

Smartly kitted-out and scenically located Belgravia pub, originally launched (under the same owners) as the Pantechnicon Dining Rooms, with a happening ground-floor bar and less frenetic first-floor dining room. Upstairs in particular, the quality of the fit-out is much plusher than your typical corner-boozer. / SW1X 8LA; thealfredtennyson.co.uk; @TheTennysonSW1; 10 pm, Sun 9.30 pm.

Ali Baba NW1 £29 3️⃣2️⃣2️⃣

32 Ivor Pl   020 7723 5805   2–1A

"An enduring curio that never disappoints and is so engagingly different" – this family run dining room, off the top end of Baker Street, is entered through a take-away, and offers genuine Egyptian cooking at prices that are a snip, in a genuinely Egyptian (if not always particularly polished) manner. / NW1 6DA; alibabarestaurant.co.uk; @alibabalondon; midnight; Cash only.

Allegra E20 NEW

Manhattan Loft Gardens, 20-22 International Way   14–1D

Ex-Chiltern Firehouse head chef Patrick Powell's first solo venture, on the seventh floor of Stratford's new Manhattan Loft Gardens building, opened too late for any reports in our survey. Powell's dedication to sustainability has extended to buying Kent farmland with local ingredients. / E20 1GQ; www.allegra-restaurant.com; @allegraLDN.

Alounak W14 £27 3️⃣3️⃣3️⃣

· 10 Russell Gdns   020 7603 1130   8–1D

"I started eating at Alounak when it was in a container in a car park round the corner" twenty-five years ago, and this Iranian café over the tracks from Olympia remains a "favourite BYO" to this day, with its "consistently good Persian comfort food": in particular "superb kebabs". (A Bayswater 'Alounak' is still in operation, but seems now to operate independently of W14.) / W14 8EZ; alounakrestaurant.com; 11.30 pm; No Amex.

Alyn Williams,
Westbury Hotel W1 £107 4️⃣5️⃣3️⃣

37 Conduit St   020 7183 6426   3–2C

"Outstanding cooking, with first-class service" consistently hits the bullseye at this relatively unsung venue, tucked away at the back of a luxury Mayfair hotel. There's a "thoughtful" approach to the meal, with "chefs coming out to tell you about dishes" – while some diners are "invited into the kitchen to meet Alyn". It's a "very comfortable" set-up and "the space between tables is incredible by modern restaurant standards, which creates the intimacy that a romantic meal requires". And, especially at lunch, the elegant room's lack of windows and natural light adds to the cocooning nature of the experience. / W1S 2YF; www.alynwilliams.com; @Alyn_Williams; 10.30 pm; closed Mon & Sun; Jacket required.

Amaya SW1 £87 5️⃣3️⃣3️⃣

Halkin Arcade, 19 Motcomb St   020 7823 1166   6–1D

"Cracking Indian fine dining with-a-twist" is to be had at this "congenial" and moodily "cavernous" Belgravia fusion-venture (under the same ownership as Chutney Mary and Veeraswamy). The tapas-style dishes, prepared in an open kitchen over the grill, deliver "vibrant" and "fabulous flavours", and rank amongst London's very best. Overall, it's "a bit expensive", but a "super, super, super-lovely experience". / SW1X 8JT; www.amaya.biz; @theamaya_; 11.30 pm, Sun 10.30 pm.

The American Bar SW1 £80 2️⃣4️⃣3️⃣

16 - 18 Saint James's Place   020 7493 0111   3–4C

"The beautiful cocktails are the best" at this plush and cosy hideaway, at the end of a St James's mews. Foodwise, there's a Mediterranean-inspired brasserie menu, or hold out for the summer BBQs in the courtyard. / SW1A 1NJ; thestaffordlondon.com/the-american-bar; @StaffordLondon; 10 pm.

Ametsa at COMO The Halkin SW1 £83 3 3 2
5 Halkin St   020 7333 1234   2–3A
*Notable for its associations with San Sebastian superstar chef Arzak,
this hotel dining room, a chic-but-austere space near Belgrave Square,
suffers from a "disappointing lack of atmosphere" (just like its predecessor,
Nahm, long RIP). Opened with great fanfare five years ago, its highly
ambitious Basque-inspired cuisine has never really won it the reputation
anticipated for it on opening, but gradually improving ratings year-by-year
suggest that it shouldn't be written off, and that the tyre men were wrong
to deprive Ruben Briones of his star last October. "Having been with
different friends, we realise it is not to everyone's taste, but we love offbeat
elements throughout the menu, and everything looks so beautiful. They
lost their Michelin star but we think the food is better than ever".
/ SW1X 7DJ; www.comohotels.com/thehalkin/dining/ametsa; 10 pm; closed
Mon L & Sun.*

L'Amorosa W6 £54 4 4 3
278 King St   020 8563 0300   8–2B
*"It's a privilege to have such a high-class local Italian on our doorstep –
I love it!", say Hammersmith foodies, thrilled by the "authentic food
at affordable prices" ("fab pasta" in particular) which draws fans from
across West London; it's prepared by ex-Zafferano chef/patron,
Andy Needham, in slightly quirky, split-level premises, in a row of shops near
Ravenscourt Park. The "warm welcome" from staff helps the occasion feel
"special". / W6 0SP; www.lamorosa.co.uk; @LamorosaLondon; Tues - Sat 10pm;
closed Mon & Sun D.*

Amrutha SW18 £31 4 4 2
326 Garratt Lane   020 8001 4628   11–2B
*"Deservedly loved" – this "friendly, little 'vegan soul food'" yearling
in Earlsfield serves "delicious", meat-free dishes, created by Arvin
Suntaramoophy and Shyam Kotecha. It's a total bargain too – not only can
you BYO (no corkage) but you pay as much as, or little as you feel the meal
is worth. You may have to queue: not only do the locals love it, but it
regularly features as #1 in TripAdvisor's London rankings. / SW18 4EJ;
www.amrutha.co.uk.*

Anarkali W6 £33 3 2 2
303-305 King St   020 8748 1760   8–2B
*After a "welcome return" and revamp following an extended period
of closure, this stalwart of Hammersmith's restaurant row (est 1972)
continues to provide a "very relaxing" setting for chef Rafiq's consistently
"enjoyable" curries. / W6 9NH; www.anarkali-finedining.com; @anarkalidining;
midnight; closed Mon L & Sun L; No Amex.*

The Anchor & Hope SE1 £54 4 3 2
36 The Cut   020 7928 9898   10–4A
*"Still nailing it after all these years" – this "unpretentious but brilliant"
Southwark boozer near the Young Vic was again very narrowly beaten into
No. 2 place amongst London's best gastropubs (by the Harwood Arms), but
maintains a massive fanclub, and "you still have to queue to get
a table". The draw is its "hearty" British cooking – "always-fascinating-and-
unusual" dishes (often using game or offal) "delivering great flavours and
textures". Top Tip – you can book for Sunday lunch. / SE1 8LP;
www.anchorandhopepub.co.uk; @AnchorHopeCut; 10.30 pm, Sun 3.15 pm; closed
Mon L & Sun D; No Amex; no booking.*

Andina £52 **4**|**3**|**3**
31 Great Windmill Street, W1   020 3327 9464   4–3D
157 Westbourne Grove, W11   020 3327 9465   7–1B
1 Redchurch St, E2   020 7920 6499   13–1B
"Quite stunning food at a consistently high level", led by "fresher-than-fresh ceviche" and other "flavoursome dishes", earns improving ratings for Martin Morales's small Peruvian group, inspired by the cooking of the Andes. "Fabulous to visit" – "the room is permanently sunny – or is that just the pisco sours?". The Notting Hill venue includes a bakery. / www.cevichefamily.com/andina; @AndinaLondon.

The Andover Arms W6 £49 **3**|**4**|**4**
57 Aldensey Rd   020 8748 2155   8–1B
A "great", "traditional pub" in a cute warren of Hammersmith backstreets, which has been somewhat gentrified by successive managements, but which has 'kept it real' as a community boozer better than most. Steak is the top tip on the "good value" menu. / W6 0DL; www.theandoverarms.com; @theandoverarms; 10 pm, Sun 9 pm; No Amex.

Andrew Edmunds W1 £61 **3**|**3**|**5**
46 Lexington Street   020 7437 5708   4–2C
"Perfect for dîner à deux" – the "quaint", "rustic and candle-lit" interior of this "Dickensian" Soho "staple" remains one of the capital's most romantic destinations, and its long-term ownership by antique print dealer Andrew Edmunds gives it a "charming and unpretentious" style of a rare kind, and fostered by his "genial" staff. "Yes, it's cramped" ("you squeeze in at a tiny table with lots of noise") and the "honest" and "straightforward food" – though "perfectly decent" – avoids fireworks. As an overall experience, though, it offers "excellent value" particularly due to the owner's collection of wine: "Andrew still makes other lists look a rip-off" with "prices not much more than retail" for some fine vintages and "ever changing additions to the blackboard that are a pleasure to explore". The ground floor is the safest bet – by comparison the basement can appear "dull". / W1F 0LP; www.andrewedmunds.com; 10.45 pm, Sun 10.30 pm; No Amex; booking max 6 may apply.

Angelina E8 NEW £54 **5**|**4**|**3**
56 Dalston Lane   020 7241 1851   14–1A
"A clever, Italian-Japanese fusion that actually works well, who knew!?" – this tiny and original six-seater in Dalston inspires nothing but love amongst early reporters. "If you're bored of the endless tasting-menus trend in the food scene, the one here is top notch" – with five courses for £39 (or you can order individually at £9 per plate). "Bargain!" – "I went back the next day..." / E8 3AH; angelina.london.

Angelus W2 £75 **3**|**4**|**2**
4 Bathurst Street   020 7402 0083   7–2D
"A serious wine list complements the good-quality Gallic cuisine" at former Gavroche sommelier Thierry Tomasin's clever conversion of a Lancaster Gate mews pub into an art nouveau bistro. The "old-fashioned service" is excellent, but prices are high, given the slightly off-the-beaten-track location. / W2 2SD; www.angelusrestaurant.co.uk; @AngelusLondon; 11 pm, Sun 10 pm.

Angie's Little Food Shop W4 £44 **3**|**2**|**2**
114 Chiswick High Road   020 8994 3931   8–2A
"Sublime blueberry pancakes… flavour-packed avocado toast… luscious cakes" – typical of the light-ish bites that make Angie Steele's artfully distressed café a Chiswick brunch, light lunch and coffee favourite. / W4 1PU; www.angieslittlefoodshop.com; 7 pm, Sun 6 pm; L only.

Angler,
South Place Hotel EC2 £92 **4 3 3**
3 South Pl 020 3215 1260 13–2A

Gary Foulkes's "classy" cuisine – "always perfect" fish and seafood, from a menu showcasing sustainable British Isles produce – maintains this "City gem" as the culinary star of D&D London at present. Occupying the "cool and refined" top floor of a hotel near Broadgate, it's "a great place for a business lunch, with excellent light": "one wall is virtually all window, overlooking the neighbouring blocks" (and there's a terrace for sunny days). "It's pricey, but you are slap bang in the heart of the Square Mile." / EC2M 2AF; www.anglerrestaurant.com; @Angler_London; 10 pm; closed Sat L; May need 8+ to book.

The Anglesea Arms W6 £62 **4 4 4**
35 Wingate Rd 020 8749 1291 8–1B

"The perfect pub" – this "brilliant all-round" hostelry, in a leafy sidestreet near Ravenscourt Park, is one of London's top gastropubs: a status it's maintained for two decades now. Its "seasonal" cooking is "unfussy but universally well-prepared and tasty", "the wine list is very reasonable, there's great cask beer" and it's "always full and humming". Service has had its ups and downs over the years: "it's better than ever" at present: "friendly but not overwhelming". Top Tip – "T-bone night is fantastic and exceptional value". / W6 0UR; www.angleseaarmspub.co.uk; @_AngleseaArmsW6; 10 pm, Fri 11 pm, Sat & Sun 10 pm; closed weekday L; no booking.

Anglo EC1 £71 **5 3 2**
30 St Cross Street 020 7430 1503 10–1A

"It's all about the food" – "thought-provoking flavour combinations that hit all the right notes" – at Mark Jarvis's "incredible" venture, where the main options (other than a three-course menu at lunch) are its six- or seven-course tasting menus (alongside "drink pairings which segue into cider and sour beers for dessert – another sign of a willingness to break the mould"). "Service is less polished" though: ditto the surroundings – a "soulless", "minimal room stuck in lawyer-land" near Hatton Garden. Still, "it's hard to find the words to describe just what good value it is". Come on Michelin, wake up and give the lad a star. / EC1N 8UH; www.anglorestaurant.com; @AngloFarringdon; 9.30 pm; closed Sun; booking max 4 may apply.

Anima e Cuore NW1 £49 **5 5 2**
129 Kentish Town Rd 07590 427171 9–2B

"Fab creative Italian food" – "an ever-changing menu with great homemade pasta" – is "served with charm in the most unpretentious environment", at this "tiny BYO café" in Kentish Town. With ratings improving every year, locals are smitten by this "lovely hidden gem", so the only problem is the increasing difficulty of grabbing a seat – but then again "they're expanding, so perhaps it'll become a little easier to get a table". / NW1 8PB; @animaecuoreuk; 9 pm, Sun 2.30 pm.

Anjanaas NW6 £38 **4 2 2**
57-59 Willesden Lane 020 7624 1713 1–1B

"Humble, family-run" venture that's become a "go-to Indian in Kilburn" on the strength of the "beautiful flavours" on its "superb Keralan menu": "great value for such high quality", which some even compare favourably with nearby legend Vijay. A word of warning: "they need to make sure the Deliveroos don't take precedence over customers present". / NW6 7RL; www.anjanaas.com.

Annie's W4 £52 3 4 4
162 Thames Rd 020 8994 9080 1–3A

This "enviable local star" from former Sticky Fingers director Lorraine Angliss knows exactly its doing after more than 15 years in Strand-on-the-Green – and its ratings are always very dependable. The menu may not be the most exciting in town, but it's "varied" and contributes to a "totally relaxing" meal. In September 2019, its Barnes sibling gave up the ghost – perhaps the closure of Hammersmith Bridge was knocking trade? / W4 3QS; www.anniesrestaurant.co.uk; @annieschiswick; 10 pm, Fri & Sat 10.30 pm.

The Anthologist EC2 £56 2 2 2
58 Gresham St 0845 468 0101 10–2C

This very "convenient" and sizeable bar-restaurant from Drake & Morgan, near the Guildhall, is valued for its efficiency and reliable (if pretty standard) menu. Nothing about it will set the world on fire, but it's a pleasant and versatile standby that can be pressed into action for any number of occasions. / EC2V 7BB; www.theanthologistbar.co.uk; @theanthologist; 11 pm, Thu & Fri 1 am; closed Sat & Sun.

L' Antica Pizzeria NW3 £49 4 4 3
66 Heath St 020 7431 8516 9–1A

"A Hampstead institution", this "small" Neapolitan with a "classic, buzzy-pizzeria ambience" is "the real deal and excellent value" – so it's "always packed, especially at weekends (when you can't reserve)". There's also a range of appetizers and pasta dishes, and a spin-off branch in New Barnet. / NW3 1DN; www.anticapizzeria.co.uk; @AnticaHamp; 10.30 pm; Mon-Thu D only, Fri-Sun open L & D.

L'Antica Pizzeria da Michele NW1 £47 3 2 3
199 Baker Street 020 7935 6458 2–1A

The London franchise of the 19th-century Neapolitan pizzeria that featured in the film 'Eat, Pray, Love' is a "buzzy, noisy" crowd-pleaser in touristy Baker Street that serves "delicious and massive pizzas". / NW1 6UY; anticapizzeriadamichele.co.uk.

Antipodea Richmond TW9
30 Hill Street 020 8940 4727 1–4A

"An excellently seasoned burger" is typical of the "big portions of rather tasty" food at this popular, "friendly and pleasantly appointed", all-day modern bistro in Richmond. There are also (less commented-on) branches in Kew, Putney and Notting Hill. / TW9 1TW; antipodea.co.uk; @AntipodeaLondon.

AOK Kitchen W1 NEW £86 2 2 4
52-55 Dorset Street 020 3889 9400 2–1A

A "beautiful room", with Instagram-friendly blossom trailing from the ceiling, helps win positive early reports on this ambitious (rather clunkily-named) new Marylebone restaurant (upstairs) and bakery (downstairs), where the focus is on "healthy cooking that's 100% free from gluten, dairy and refined sugar". Some negative feedback, however, although not massively so, contributes to a slightly mixed rep overall: "no pun intended, it was only OK". / W1U 7NQ; www.aokkitchen.co.uk.

Applebee's Fish SE1 £64 4 2 2
5 Stoney St 020 7407 5777 10–4C

"Superb fish – not overcooked – in generous portions" is the USP at this Borough Market café, where you can "sit outside for a lovely lunch". Service came under fire from several reporters this year: "are they becoming a little slapdash?" / SE1 9AA; www.applebeesfish.com; @Applebeesfish; 10 pm, Thu-Sat 11 pm; closed Sun; No Amex.

Apulia EC1 £56 **3** **3** **2**
50 Long Ln   020 7600 8107   10–2B
This "friendly little place" on the edge of Smithfield Market "serves delicious, hearty Puglian-style food", including "proper southern Italian pizza with fresh and authentic ingredients". This year's worst report? – "A likeable place: the sort you would want round the corner." / EC1A 9EJ; www.apuliarestaurant.co.uk; 10 pm; closed Sun D.

aqua kyoto W1 £85 **2** **2** **4**
240 Regent St (entrance 30 Argyll St)   020 7478 0540   4–1A
"This huge restaurant above Regent Street" with a sizeable rooftop setting (from the Hong Kong-based group also at The Shard) serves "surprisingly good Japanese food" and "feels like a nightclub, with bouncers, red carpets, loud music, moody lighting and a sexily groomed, exuberant clientele". It's "very buzzy, very loud and great for people-watching". A neighbouring rooftop sibling, aqua nueva, does similar things with a Hispanic menu but doesn't inspire the same level of feedback. / W1B 3BR; www.aqua-london.com; @aqualondon; 10.30 pm, Thu-Sat 11 pm; closed Sun D.

Aqua Shard SE1 £112 **1** **1** **4**
Level 31, 31 St Thomas St   020 3011 1256   10–4C
"The views are fantastic from the top of the Shard", but prices for the "very ordinary food" are "totally outrageous" – "hardly value for money unless you're a hedge-fund manager". Some reporters "would never return", but others are "glad they went". Just remember – "this is a place to be seen and to see from, rather than a magnet for food-lovers". Top Tip – "don't miss the urinals – they're the best in London". / SE1 9RY; www.aquashard.co.uk; @aquashard; 10.45 pm.

Aquavit SW1 £83 **3** **2** **3**
St James's Market, 1 Carlton St   020 7024 9848   4–4D
This two-year-old, near Piccadilly Circus – in the glossy St James's Market development – is an offshoot of one of Manhattan's most celebrated restaurant stalwarts, and here, as in NYC, "everything is made following Nordic traditions creating really delicious dishes" with "great Scandinavian fish and meat" ("even the bread is something you won't forget"). But while to some reporters its big windows and expensive decor are "truly glamorous", to others the ambience is "cold" – "a bit see-and-be-seen, and somehow a bit soulless". / SW1Y 4QQ; www.aquavitrestaurants.com; @aquavitlondon.

Arabica Bar and Kitchen SE1 £52 **3** **4** **3**
3 Rochester Walk   020 3011 5151   10–4C
"Outstandingly flavoursome Middle Eastern fare" is delivered "fast" – and with "warm and helpful service" – at this "lively and noisy" venue on the edge of foodie Borough Market. "Just the place after visiting the market stalls, or the Shard". A second 100-seater site is planned to open in autumn 2019 in King's Cross, but the menu will be quite a departure. / SE1 9AF; www.arabicabarandkitchen.com; @ArabicaLondon; 10.30 pm, Sat 11 pm, Sun 8.30 pm; closed Sun D.

The Araki W1 £369 **5** **3** **2**
Unit 4 12 New Burlington St   020 7287 2481   4–3A
"Sushi as an art form, with every piece designed to the last detail" is at the heart of an unforgettable trip to this illustrious Mayfair nine-seater, where Marty Lau is the new master after maestro Matsuhiro Araki returned to Japan in spring 2019. The place is "soooooooooo expensive", but what's been striking ever since its debut in 2014 is how few diners begrudge the mesmerising bill, instead appreciating the intense, personal theatricality of the endeavour; and the "exceptional quality and sourcing of the ingredients". Early feedback on the new regime says it's "not affected by the

*loss of Mr Araki, and still a very special experience" – whether Michelin
maintain its three-star rating in autumn 2019 remains to be seen...*
/ W1S 3BH; www.the-araki.com; seatings only at 6 pm and 8.30 pm; D only,
closed Mon.

Arcade Food Theatre WC2 NEW
Centre Point, 103-105 New Oxford Street   5–1A
*A new style of food hall for central London; this industrial-chic space on the
ground floor of Centre Point has seven kitchens, three bars, a coffee shop
and bakery and an 'incubation-focused space'. Stalls at the summer 2019
opening were Lina Stores, Pophams, TOU by TA TA, Pastorcito, Oklava,
Flat Iron, Casita do Frango and Chotto Matte.* / WC2H 8LH;
www.arcade-london.com.

Ariana II NW6   £25   3 3 2
241 Kilburn High Rd   020 3490 6709   1–2B
*"Seriously tasty Afghan food" has made this "niche venue" a long-time north
London favourite (the original Ariana was founded by another branch of the
family in New York in the 1980s). It's "handy for the Kiln Theatre" (formerly
the Tricycle) and "BYO so very cheap 'n' cheerful indeed". Top Tip –
"the mantu (minced lamb in steamed pastry) are worth the trip alone".*
/ NW6 7JN; www.ariana2restaurant.co.uk; @Ariana2kilburn; midnight.

Ark Fish E18   £40   3 4 2
142 Hermon Hill   020 8989 5345   1–1D
*Solidly high ratings again this year for this South Woodford chippy, whose
owning family are fish 'n' chips royalty (having previously run Lisson Grove's
famous Seashell); fish comes daily from Billingsgate.* / E18 1QH;
www.arkfishrestaurant.co.uk; @ArkfishLondon; 9.45 pm, Fri & Sat 10.15 pm,
Sun 8.45 pm; closed Mon; No Amex; no booking.

Arlo's   £51   3 2 2
47 Northcote Road, SW11   11–2C
1 Ramsden Road, SW12   020 3019 6590   11–2C
*"Top-quality steaks" – "cooked to perfection" – and at "reasonable prices"
make this three-year-old Balham steakhouse and its Battersea satellite
"great for carnivores". Non-meat-eaters are catered for on a daily
brunch menu.*

Arros QD W1 NEW   £86   4 4 4
64 Eastcastle Street   020 3883 3525   3–1D
*"A fantastic paella" is the signature dish at Quique Dacosta's very well-
publicised (well, he does have three Michelin stars back in Alicante) two-
floor, Spanish newcomer, which opened in June 2019: too late to receive
a huge volume of survey feedback (so the ratings should be seen
as indicative). Such as we have is brimming with enthusiasm all-round,
both for results from the extensive menu (not just paella, but skewers, grilled
and roasted fish and meats) and for the "really good atmosphere for
a restaurant just north of Oxford Street". The newspaper critics have
painted a mostly upbeat, but more mixed, picture.* / W1W 8NQ;
www.arrosqd.com; @QiqeDacosta.

Arthur Hooper's SE1   £50   3 3 3
8 Stoney St   awaiting tel   10–4C
*"Brilliant value... market bustle... great modern menu – we love it",
declare fans of this "upmarket" wine bar with (mainly Italian) small plates –
"another good option for a great tapas meal in Borough Market". It took the
name of the greengrocer who previously occupied the site.* / SE1 9AA;
www.arthurhoopers.co.uk; @arthurhoopers; 10.30 pm, Fri & Sat 11.30 pm; booking
max 6 may apply.

L'Artista NW11 £43 3 3 3
917 Finchley Rd 020 8731 7501 1–1B

"Tucked under the railway arches", by the tube at Golders Green, this very family-friendly local landmark and celebration spot has been serving "great pasta and pizza" along with a good dose of old-school jollity for 35 years. "You won't be disappointed" – "cheap 'n' cheerful it really is". / NW11 7PE; www.lartistapizzeria.com; 11.30 pm.

Artusi SE15 £48 4 3 2
161 Bellenden Rd 020 3302 8200 1–4D

A "limited seasonal menu knocks it out of the park" at this "star neighbourhood restaurant" in Peckham (named after Pellegrino Artusi, the 19th-century 'godfather of Italian cuisine'). There's a "laid-back, hipster" vibe, while the "simple and cheap ingredients are well chosen and delivered at a compelling price". / SE15 4DH; www.artusi.co.uk; @artusipeckham; 10.30 pm, Sun 8 pm; closed Mon L.

Asakusa NW1 £33 5 2 2
265 Eversholt St 020 7388 8533 9–3C

Vaguely Tyrolean, beamed decor is nobody's idea of a Japanese restaurant at this slightly odd venture, near Mornington Crescent tube. No complaints about the outstanding value sushi and other fare though: "good and varied as ever, with many choices for Japanese drinks too, including sake". / NW1 1BA; asakusa.has.restaurant; 11.30 pm, Sat 11 pm; D only, closed Sun.

Assaggi W2 £68 3 3 1
39 Chepstow Pl 020 7792 5501 7–1B

"Having been the biggest fan since the first day Assaggi opened, I'm now struggling with the prices!" – a constant refrain in feedback on this offbeat, first-floor Bayswater pub dining room, which for many years was a contender as London's top Italian. No-one's suggesting the cooking's gone down the tubes – in fact some regulars believe that "standards are as good as they were fifteen years ago" – but "the room and ambience need updating", and even many reporting an "excellent" meal nevertheless leave feeling "fleeced". / W2 4TS; www.assaggi.co.uk; @assaggi3; 11 pm; closed Sun; No Amex.

Assaggi Bar & Pizzeria W2 £62 3 3 3
39 Chepstow Place 020 7792 5501 7–1B

"Extraordinarily good pizzas", "very good negronis" and "no burgers" are served at this bar, which boasts "the style of Mayfair transplanted to Notting Hill". It's upstairs from Assaggi, and from the same team, in the former pub they share, and these days seems the less risky bet. Top Tip – "try the truffle pizza in winter and English asparagus with San Daniele ham in summer". / W2 4TS; www.assaggi.co.uk; @Assaggi3; No bookings.

Aster Restaurant SW1 £68 2 2 2
150 Victoria St 020 3875 5555 2–4B

"For a pre-Hamilton meal", this D&D London operation has proved "a welcome addition to Victoria eating choices": "perfect for a better-than-quick, better-than-casual, meal". It's not an area over-blessed with options, though, and there is an element of 'in the land of the blind, the one-eyed man is king'. The cuisine – no longer with Nordic influences since Helena Puolakka left in early-2019, but now, under Bjoern Wassmuth, in the 'Grand European Café' mould – is "variable, if nothing to complain about". And the modern setting – to fans "the most characterful option in the new Nova development canyons" – can feel "like eating in an airport". / SW1E 5LB; www.aster-restaurant.com; @AsterVictoria; 9.30 pm.

Atari-Ya £43 **4 2 1**
20 James St, W1   020 7491 1178   3–1A
1 Station Pde, W5   020 8896 3175   1–3A
75 Fairfax Road, NW6   020 7328 5338   9–2A
Some of "the best (reasonably affordable) sushi in London" can be found
at these supermarket/cafés operated by a Japanese food importer. But it's
all about the "fresh and addictive" plates – "service is a bit rough and ready
when they're busy" and the ambience "lacks soul". / www.sushibaratariya.co.uk;
W1F Mon-Wed 10 pm, Thu-Sat 10.30 pm, W1T Mon-Sat 10 pm, E8 Sat 4 pm;
NW6 closed Mon, W5 closed Mon .

The Atlas SW6 £49 **4 4 4**
16 Seagrave Rd   020 7385 9129   6–3A
This "cracking, traditional English pub", "tucked away in the backstreets"
a short walk from West Brompton tube, has earned an enviable reputation
for "interesting" Mediterranean cooking, backed up by "premium wines"
and "some of London's best real ale", over more than two decades.
"The Victorian-style cosy interior and spacious, sunny terrace makes
it perfect for all occasions" – the outside is now even more of an attraction
given the smart and expanded garden enabled by the new development
next door. / SW6 1RX; www.theatlaspub.co.uk; @theatlasfulham; 10 pm.

Augustine Kitchen SW11 £54 **4 4 3**
63 Battersea Bridge Rd   020 7978 7085   6–4C
This "great local French bistro" offers "well priced and very well executed"
dishes, based on the cuisine of Evian on the shore of Lake Geneva. It's
"easily missed in its location" just south of Battersea Bridge. / SW11 3AU;
www.augustine-kitchen.co.uk; @augustinekitchen; closed Mon & Sun D.

Aulis London W1 £195 **5 5 4**
Soho - address on booking   020 3948 9665   –
Lakeland-based uber-chef Simon Rogan's eight-seater development kitchen
offers "a fascinating and unique experience", featuring "some of the
most creative dishes in London". Diners pre-book (at £195 a head) and
go to a secret Soho address, where a dozen surprise courses and paired
wines are prepared in front of them by two chefs. "We went for our
anniversary but the other six diners pulled out; what could have been
awkward became a once-in-a-lifetime exclusive pampering!". / W1;
aulis.london; @AulisSimonRogan.

Authentique Epicerie & Bar NW5 £46 **3 4 3**
114-116 Fortress Road   020 3609 6602   9–2C
"A must for wine-lovers" – this year-old combination of wine bar, restaurant
and shop in Tufnell Park is a "real treasure-trove", showcasing the produce
of the French-speaking world, including 650 wines. "Given the retail side
of the operation, you could just buy the stuff and eat it all at home, but it
would be a shame to miss out on the buzz" – and the "fresh and well-
presented small menu". Top Tip – "book a table if you don't want to sit
on a stool". / NW5 5HL; authentique-epicerie.com.

The Avalon SW12 £53 **3 4 4**
16 Balham Hill   020 8675 8613   11–2C
"A great pub!" (part of the Three Cheers Pub Co) down Balham way,
with smart interior and gorgeous, big outside garden, and where steaks and
'artisan pizzas' are mainstays of a comprehensive menu: "even if the pub
was boring, I'd come back time and again for the fantastic food!"
/ SW12 9EB; www.theavalonlondon.com; @threecheerspubs; 10.30 pm, Sun 9 pm.

L'Aventure NW8 £72 345
3 Blenheim Terrace   020 7624 6232   9–3A
*"A romantic hideaway obscured, by climbing plants, from passers-by" –
Catherine Parisot's St John's Wood institution has just celebrated its 40th
anniversary, serving "classic French cuisine" that is "unchanged in years".
"It is old-fashioned but never boring, conventional but not too formal, simple
but not too basic, traditional but still progressive". To the relief of her many
fans, Madame C is targeting her half-century here: "she is always there
to come and talk to you, the waiters are very friendly and they want you
to have a good time". / NW8 0EH; www.laventure.co.uk; 11 pm; closed
Sat L & Sun.*

The Avenue SW1 £53 333
7-9 St James's Street   020 7321 2111   3–4D
*This "slick and professional" modern brasserie in the heart of St James's
from D&D London is "very popular at lunchtime with business people" –
in particular for the "glass-fronted private room which allows for confidential
conversation without being stuffy". "The location is easy to get to", and the
food "caters for all tastes". / SW1A 1EE; www.avenue-restaurant.co.uk;
@avenuestjames; 10.30 pm; closed Sat L & Sun.*

Aviary EC2 £64 223
10th Floor, 22-25 Finsbury Square   020 3873 4060   13–2A
*"A pleasant location overlooking the City" is the headline attraction at this
10th-floor eyrie on Finsbury Square, which has a big outside terrace.
"The food is fine but not very inspiring, and service can be a bit away with
the fairies" – maybe try it out for brunch. / EC2A 1DX; aviarylondon.com;
@AviaryLDN.*

Awesome Thai SW13 £32 342
68 Church Rd   020 8563 7027   11–1A
*"Family-run, friendly and popular" – an easy-going but efficient Thai local,
which does a roaring trade at least in part due to its location, bang opposite
the busy Olympic Studios indie cinema in Barnes. That said, the food
is "delicious and not expensive", and "feels like authentic home cooking".
/ SW13 0DQ; www.awesomethai.co.uk; 10.30 pm, Sun 10 pm; Mon-Thu D only,
Fri-Sun open L & D.*

Le Bab W1 £47 423
Top Floor, Kingly Court   020 7439 9222   4–2B
*"Posh kebabs bring the late-night, post-pub favourite to a new level" at this
"fun little place at the top of Kingly Court", thanks to "quality ingredients
and a standard of cooking (and imagination) not available elsewhere".
/ W1B 5PW; www.eatlebab.com; @EatLeBab; 10 pm, Sun 7 pm; booking max 6 may
apply.*

Baba G's 43-
724 Stables Market, NW1   07725 230995   9–2B NEW
Pop Brixton, 49 Brixton Station Road, SW9   07725 230995   11–1D
*"Everything here is great, but I totally loved the paneer burger" –
an alternative to the best-selling bhangra burger on the menu of these
popular pop-ups, in POP Brixton and now also Vinegar Yard, SE1. After over
ten years in the game, the business shifted up a gear in May 2019 (too late
for survey feedback) with the opening (flush with £300k of investment
having won BBC2's 'My Million Pound Menu') of the new forever-home listed
here: a 50-seater in Camden Town's Stables Market. / www.bhangraburger.com;
@BabaGsfood.*

BabaBoom £34 **3 2 2**

189 Upper Street, N1   07715 525203   9–2D **NEW**
30 Battersea Rise, SW11   07809 903181   11–2C
"A great local for a quick dinner" – these cheery pitstops in Battersea and Islington offer superior kebabs and mezze, alongside craft beer and other drinks. Top Tip – bottomless frozen margaritas with their weekend brunch deal. / www.bababoom.london; @bababoomlondon.

Babette SE15 £45 **3 3 3**

57 Nunhead Lane   020 3172 2450   1–4D
Nunhead ain't overburdened with super eating options, and this French-owned, converted old Truman pub is one of the best: "its sharing boards are tops for a cheap 'n' cheerful meal"; and "it never fails to give great customer service". / SE15 3TR; www.babettenunhead.com; @babettenunhead; 11 pm, Fri & Sat midnight, Sun 5 pm; closed Mon & Tue, Wed & Thu D only, Fri & Sat L & D, Sun L only.

Babur SE23 £57 **5 5 4**

119 Brockley Rise   020 8291 2400   1–4D
"In Forest Hill... who knew?"; this "off-the-beaten-track" culinary mecca has, in fact, been "brilliant for years" (it opened in 1985) and "these guys just keep on delivering the goods". It's not just the "magnificent cooking", often featuring game, or "seriously divine cocktails" (some of them "super spicy") – the ambience too "is strikingly elegant given the mundane locale" of the distant south London 'burbs. Top Tip – "best experienced when they do their special seasonal menus and events". / SE23 1JP; www.babur.info; @BaburRestaurant; 11.30 pm; No shorts.

Bacco TW9 £59 **3 3 2**

39-41 Kew Rd   020 8332 0348   1–4A
The well-priced pre-show menu is popular with Richmond's theatre-goers at this "excellent local Italian" – handy for both the Orange Tree and Richmond Theatres – it's a "calm and pleasant" standby for "well-cooked cuisine". / TW9 2NQ; www.bacco-restaurant.co.uk; @BaccoRichmond; 11 pm; closed Sun D.

Bageriet WC2 £12 **4 3 3**

24 Rose St   020 7240 0000   5–3C
"The best cinnamon buns", "freshly cooked cakes" and "good coffee" make this "tiny Swedish café a good pitstop for cultural activities in Covent Garden". "Just a pity it's so small you can't always get in". / WC2E 9EA; www.bageriet.co.uk; @BagerietLondon; 7 pm; L & early evening only, closed Sun; No bookings.

Bala Baya SE1 £64 **3 2 2**

Arch 25, Old Union Yard Arches, 229 Union Street   020 8001 7015   10–4B
"Unusual, imaginative and tasty Israeli cuisine" takes centre stage at this "lively modern Tel Aviv-style café" with cocktail bar, in a Southwark railway arch, from former Ottolenghi chef Eran Tibi. / SE1 0LR; balabaya.co.uk; @bala_baya; 11.30 pm, Sun 5 pm; closed Sun D.

Balady NW11 £23 **3 4 2**

750 Finchley Road   020 8458 2064   1–1B
"Israeli street food with attitude" – in particular the "lovely falafels" – win nothing but praise for this top "cheap 'n' cheerful" kosher bar in Temple Fortune (where most surfaces are wipe clean). It's no criticism of the place to say that Giles Coren awarding it 9/10 this year may have been over-egging the shakshuka a little. / NW11 7TH.

Balthazar WC2 £73 2 2 4

4 - 6 Russell Street 020 3301 1155 5–3D

"This American-style French brasserie" in Covent Garden – an offshoot of Keith McNally's downtown NYC institution – has a "great atmosphere any time of day": "love the decor as you enter". It's "a large space but a very cosy one", and, say fans, "not outrageously priced considering its position and what it must have cost to create". But at times it's "a victim of its own success – packed, loud and slow, with staff trying heroically to cope", and "the food is not exactly world-shattering", just "fine in a 'here's one I prepared earlier and heated up' sort of way". Top Tip – "it's very good for breakfast, which is less costly than other meals here". / WC2B 5HZ; www.balthazarlondon.com; @balthazarlondon; midnight, Sun 11 pm.

Baltic SE1 £66 3 3 4

74 Blackfriars Rd 020 7928 1111 10–4A

"A real surprise" near The Cut – this well-established fixture (which opened in 2001) has a relatively "humble entrance", which opens onto a "great space": an intriguingly converted Georgian factory, with a fun bar, and an unexpectedly large, "light-filled" dining room. The cuisine is enjoyably unusual too: "modern Polish – not the usual heavy, East European dishes", but "gutsy" and "always imaginative, with new and traditional choices". Go easy on the vodka though: over 60 varieties, all served straight from the deep freeze in frozen glasses. / SE1 8HA; www.balticrestaurant.co.uk; @balticlondon; 11.15 pm, Sun 10.30 pm; closed Mon L

Bancone WC2 NEW £47 5 4 3

39 William IV Street 020 7240 8786 5–4C

"Superbly-flavourful" pasta dishes at "extremely good-value" prices – especially for the West End – make Louis Korovilas's "handy" yearling "one of the better options in the tourist centre" of town, just off Trafalgar Square. Some reporters feel it's "let down by the long, narrow shape of the restaurant", but more commonly it's judged an "elegant, buzzing, if packed space". / WC2N 4DD; www.bancone.co.uk; @bancone.pasta.

Bang Bang Oriental NW9 £43 2 2 3

399 Edgware Road no tel 1–1A

"A recreation of a Singapore food court", this vast space in Colindale has a "huge choice of different Oriental foods" – "everything from dim sum to Korean". The main challenge is that "quality varies hugely" – "not everything is a hit but it's never dull, kids love it, and it's full of Asian families". Top Tip – "the bao from mainland China are excellent". / NW9 0AS; www.bangbangoriental.com; @Bangbangofh.

Bánh Bánh £42 3 3 2

46 Peckham Rye, SE15 020 7207 2935 1–4D
326 Coldharbour Lane, SW9 020 7737 5888 11–2D

"A small but well-executed menu" and "great cocktails" win general applause for this "tasty, cheap 'n' cheerful local Vietnamese" in Peckham Rye, now with a Brixton spin-off. The Nguyen family use their chef-grandmother's recipes from 1940s Saigon. / www.banhbanh.com; @BanhBanhHQ.

Banners N8 £52 2 3 4

21 Park Rd 020 8348 2930 9–1C

"Perfect for breakfast" – Juliette Banner's "very family-friendly", neighbourhood diner has been a treasured staple of Crouch End life since it opened in 1992 (and chef Tim Peterman has been in charge of the stoves all this time too). By contrast, its wacky mix of world food cuisine makes it "a bit of an unreliable option for dinner" though. / N8 8TE; www.bannersrestaurant.com; 11 pm, Fri 11.30 pm, Sat midnight, Sun 10.30 pm; No Amex.

Bao £38 **4** **3** **3**
31 Windmill St, W1   020 3011 1632   5–1A
53 Lexington St, W1   07769 627811   4–2C
13 Stoney Street, SE1   020 3967 5407   10–4C NEW
Netil Market, 13-23 Westgate Street, E8   no tel   14–2B
*"A hole-in-the-wall type place, but some of the best buns in London!" –
these "hipsterish", if "haphazard" Taiwanese cafés in Soho, Fitzrovia,
and now also Borough, have made a big name for their "sensationally tasty"
steamed buns and other "inventive, delicious plates": superb "homely food
at very reasonable prices". The new SE1 branch, opened in Spring 2019,
has a grab-and-go delivery hatch and a karaoke room upstairs; and both
here and in Fitzrovia you can book – at Soho you run the gauntlet of a big
queue and it's more "rushed". / baolondon.com; @bao_london; W1F Mon-Wed
10 pm, Thu-Sat 10.30 pm, W1T Mon-Sat 10 pm, E8 Sat 4 pm; W1F & W1T closed
Sun, E8 open Sat L only; W1 no bookings, E8 takeout only.*

Bao & Bing W1 NEW £40 **3** **3** **4**
22 Paddington Street   020 3873 7271   2–1A
*For a fun night out with the girls, promising early-days reports on this slick
new cocktail and dining concept, in Marylebone, from the former CEO
of the Ping Pong dim sum chain (similar DNA here), which mixes tasty bao
buns and other Taiwanese, street-food fare ('inspired by night street markets
of Taipei and Jiufen', apparently) with yummy cocktails, and sleek design
(to 'take you all the way back to the 1950s and 1960s teahouses of Xinyi
district'). / W1U 5QY; www.baoandbing.com; @baoandbing.*

Baozi Inn **3** **3** **3**
24 Romilly Street, W1   020 7287 6877   5–3A
8 Southwark Street, SE1   10–4C NEW
*"Spicy noodles and tasty bao make for a dependable staple for quick eats
in Chinatown" at the original Newport Court branch of this growing chain:
the brainchild of Wei Shao, who helped popularise Sichuan cuisine with Bar
Shu back in the day. A Soho offshoot followed in 2018, and mid-
August 2019 saw the launch of a new three-storey, 120-cover, flagship near
Borough Market (and there's also a stall in Market Halls Victoria). The exact
offering varies from branch to branch but, in general, meals are "extremely
satisfying and reasonably priced". / baoziinn.com.*

**The Baptist Grill,
L'Oscar Hotel WC1** £91 **3** **4** **4**
2-6 Southampton Row   020 7405 5555   2–1D
*A former HQ of the Baptist Church provides the gracious quarters for this
swish, new Holborn hotel, whose luxurious dining room's cuisine is produced
by Tony Fleming (who held a Michelin star at his former gaff, The Angler).
Thin feedback supports the view that this late-2018 opening remains
somewhat off-the-radar for many Londoners, but such as we have suggests
it's worth discovering: "I used to go to Baptist Council meetings in the
building so was intrigued to see how it had worked out: the answer is well!
I also worried from some of the hotel's descriptions that it would all be a bit
up-itself, but it was better than I expected: the cooking was very good
indeed – not too fussy and full of flavour – and there's a very good wine
list too. Service was OK: I could have just done without the waiters'
psychedelic jackets…" / WC1B 4AA; baptistgrill.com.*

**Bar Boulud,
Mandarin Oriental SW1**   £72   **3****3****3**

66 Knightsbridge   020 7201 3899   6–1D

"Consistency has always been key" at this NYC-import in the basement of a
landmark Knightsbridge hotel, "so it's not surprising it reopened after the
fire here and did not skip a beat". Oft touted by some for
"the best hamburger in town" ("beating the specialist chains"), it actually
"offers a surprisingly wide range of dishes, although the French bistro
options tend to be best", and fans say they are delivered "with just the right
amount of friendliness". It's very much casual luxury, however, and there's
also quite a widely held view that "for such a glamorous hotel, everything
here is distinctly average", especially at very Knightsbridge prices. Top Tip –
in summer, you can now dine outside on the 'Bar Boulud Terrace'
overlooking Hyde Park (first-come first-served, weather permitting).
/ SW1X 7LA; www.barboulud.com; @barbouludlondon; 11.45 pm, Sun 10.45 pm;
No trainers.

Bar Douro SE1   £56   **4****4****4**

Arch 25b Flat Iron Square, Union St   020 7378 0524   10–4B

A "unique menu" of "delicious Portuguese tapas" that "really pack flavour"
makes this authentically tiled bar near Borough Market "just a delight";
especially in summer when its "lovely outdoor seating area" makes
it "an ideal place to spend an afternoon". "The knowledgeable staff have
great wine recommendations" from the "interesting" all-Portuguese list.
/ SE1 1TD; www.bardouro.co.uk; @BarDouro; 11.30 pm; booking max 4 may apply.

Bar Esteban N8   £53   **3****4****3**

29 Park Rd   020 8340 3090   1–1C

"Brilliant upmarket tapas" have Crouch Enders purring that "we're lucky
to have this as our local Spanish restaurant". It's run by "lovely people" and
has some "really interesting Spanish wines from smaller vineyards". Top Tip
– "paella lunches at the weekend are great fun with the kids". / N8 8TE;
www.baresteban.com; @barestebanN8; 9.30 pm, Fri & Sat 10.30 pm, Sun 9 pm;
closed weekday L; booking max 8 may apply.

Bar Italia W1   £34   **2****3****5**

22 Frith St   020 7437 4520   5–2A

"A special place" – "frozen in time and all the better for it" –
this atmospheric Soho institution defies caffeine fashion and is as perfect
a location for a cup of coffee today as it was when it opened in 1949.
It operates 24/7 – and don't even think of bringing your laptop... / W1D 4RF;
www.baritaliasoho.co.uk; @TheBaristas; open 24 hours, Sun 4 am; No Amex;
no booking.

The Barbary WC2   £52   **5****5****4**

16 Neal's Yard   awaiting tel   5–2C

"If fantastic food is your priority rather than comfort", make a bee-line for
The Palomar's "fun" and "intimate" younger sibling in Neal's Yard, which
majors in "the most tasty and exciting" North African-inspired tapas,
all served at the bar. "In theory this is everything I dislike in a restaurant:
countertop seating only, loud music, and sharing-plates. But it blew every
prejudice out of the water. The food was exquisite – lots of flavours I hadn't
had before – and the ones I had, perfectly produced. Fantastic wine,
wonderful atmosphere; and despite being alongside fellow diners at the
counter, it felt private and relaxed. A really special evening". "I'd go all the
time if only you could book!" / WC2H 9DP; www.thebarbary.co.uk;
@barbarylondon; 10 pm, Sun 9 pm; no booking.

La Barca SE1 £68 3️⃣3️⃣3️⃣

80-81 Lower Marsh   020 7928 2226   10–4A

"A lovely and cosy, family-run Italian", "handily placed near Waterloo", which "has been a feature of the area for years" (well over 30). It's always been "quite expensive", but for traditional trattoria fare it's a "go-to" for some diners, including as a business lunch spot. / SE1 7AB; www.labarca-ristorante.com; @labarca1976; closed Sat L & Sun; Booking max 12 may apply.

Barrafina £59 5️⃣5️⃣5️⃣

26-27 Dean Street, W1   020 7813 8016   4–1D
10 Adelaide St, WC2   020 7440 1456   5–4C
43 Drury Ln, WC2   020 7440 1456   5–2D
Coal Drops Yard, N1   9–3C

"The tapas is perfection and the equal of Cal Pep in Barcelona" at the Hart Bros' "vibrant" chain of small (typically 30 covers) no-bookings bars, which its vast fanclub acclaim as "the best tapas in London or in the UK or perhaps even in Europe north of the Pyrenees!", with "delicious, ultra-fresh seafood" a particular highlight. The preparation at the counter is "still a great piece of theatre" and – buoyed by its "exceptional, friendly, enthusiastic and knowledgeable staff" – helps create a feelgood experience. "Don't be put off by the queuing – it's part of the fun: sipping on Cava and nibbling on Jamon as you snake your way to the front of the line!". This year, the group added a "slick outfit in the new Coal Drops Yard development" – "it lacks a bit of the charm and vibe of those in Soho and Covent Garden, but the edibles are still very edible!" / www.barrafina.co.uk; 11 pm, Sun 10 pm; no booking, max group 4.

Barrica W1 £55 3️⃣3️⃣3️⃣

62 Goodge St   020 7436 9448   2–1B

"Popular for a good reason", this Goodge Street spot is valued for "authentic tapas, served fast and fresh, with knowledgeable and friendly Spanish staff to guide you through the choices". It's "great value" for central London, but can get "hot and cramped", with the "buzzy and loud" atmosphere rising to "raucous" on busy evenings. / W1T 4NE; www.barrica.co.uk; @barricatapas; 10.30 pm; closed Sun.

Barshu W1 £47 4️⃣2️⃣2️⃣

28 Frith St   020 7287 6688   5–3A

"Spice heaven!" – this "old favourite" is "worth a detour north of Shaftesbury Avenue" to "experience genuinely interesting and mouth-popping Sichuan specials" – so "be brave when you order". The food-writer, China expert and consultant "Fuchsia Dunlop's touch makes it a regional Chinese diamond in the Chinatown rough". / W1D 5LF; www.barshurestaurant.co.uk; @BarshuLondon; 10.30 pm, Fri & Sat 11 pm.

Bears Ice Cream W12 £7

244 Goldhawk Road   020 3441 4982   8–1B

An ice cream parlour with a difference – a mouthwatering selection of toppings, all mixed with just one flavour of ice – from an Icelandic recipe – at this simple little shop (with small garden), on the busy gyratory north of Ravenscourt Park. More reports please! / W12 9PE; www.bearsicecream.co.uk; @bears_icecream; 8.30 pm; L & early evening only; No bookings.

Beast W1 £107 2️⃣2️⃣2️⃣

3 Chapel Pl   020 7495 1816   3–1B

"An amazing place for steaks and spider crab… but, my god, is it expensive!" Nothing changes at Goodman group's candle-lit, surf 'n' turf extravaganza, just off Oxford Street, which bills itself as 'a unique gastronomic experience featuring Norwegian King Crab and hand-selected, dry-aged Nebraskan Angus beef. But, after five years in operation, what's actually most striking is how little feedback we receive nowadays… / W1G 0BG; www.beastrestaurant.co.uk; @beastrestaurant; 10.30 pm; closed Mon & Sun; May need 7+ to book.

Beef & Brew   £47   3 4 3
33 Downham Road, N1   020 7254 7858   14–2A
323 Kentish Town Rd, NW5   020 7998 1511   9–2B
"Really good-value steaks" – "surprisingly excellent" – are matched with
"tremendous chips and interesting wine and beer pairings" at this "small
canteen" in Kentish Town. Staff are "lovely" but the bare walls make for
"an uncompromising acoustic". Its popularity has led to a spin-off
in Haggerston. / www.beef-and-brew.co.uk; @BeefandBrewLDN.

The Begging Bowl SE15   £49   4 3 2
168 Bellenden Rd   020 7635 2627   1–4D
Spicy scoff "continues to impress at this authentic and very busy Peckham
fixture" – a corner site with terrace, which has been a well-known feature
of the local food scene since 2012 (and was refurbed in December 2018).
It's not Thai-run: chef and co-owner Jane Alty worked at David Thompson's
much-vaunted Nahm (long RIP) back in the dim and distant past.
/ SE15 4BW; www.thebeggingbowl.co.uk; @thebeggingbowl; 9.45 pm, Sun 9.15 pm;
no booking.

Bellamy's W1   £62   3 4 4
18-18a Bruton Pl   020 7491 2727   3–2B
"Everybody is smartly attired which makes a nice change" at Gavin Rankin's
(ex-MD of Annabel's) "old-fashioned-in-a-good-way" bastion: "a picture-lined
dining room", tucked away in a quiet mews, which – to those of a
blueblooded disposition – makes "a much more attractive choice than some
of its flashier Mayfair rivals". "Well-drilled", traditionally-attired staff deliver
"classic" – if "fairly simple" – Anglo/French cuisine and, in particular,
the package makes "an excellent choice for a business lunch" (of the kind
where "a couple of dry Martinis before you get started will not raise
an eyebrow"). / W1J 6LY; www.bellamysrestaurant.co.uk; 10.30 pm; closed
Sat L & Sun.

Belvedere Restaurant W8   £72   2 4 5
off Abbotsbury Rd in Holland Park   020 7602 1238   8–1D
"There's not a better setting in London for romance" than this 17th-century
former ballroom inside Holland Park: "a walk to the restaurant through the
greenery is a joy, the space itself is elegant and light; and in the summer,
the terrace offers al fresco dining overlooking the formal gardens". Some
reports still talk of the "pretty ordinary" modern British food and
"adequate" service that's often dogged the place, but overall feedback was
more positive this year: "its lean years of so-so food and service are behind
it" – "it's a shame more people don't go". / W8 6LU;
www.belvedererestaurant.co.uk; @BelvedereW8; 11 pm, Sun 3.30 pm; closed Sun D.

Benares W1   £104   2 2 2
12a Berkeley Square House,   020 7629 8886   3–3B
Mixed reports this year on this swish first-floor Indian, in the heart
of Mayfair, which severed ties in August 2018 with its original founder. Fans
say it's "still excellent, despite Atul Kochhar's departure", serving "very nicely
balanced, spiced and well-prepared" Indian cuisine that offers "a real
twist compared to what's usually found in the UK". Its ratings have waned,
though, with gripes re-emerging about its "windowless", slightly "dull"
interior, but more concerningly about cooking that "may not justify the price
tag": "just go to Dishoom, get better food, have more fun and save your
cash!" / W1J 6BS; www.benaresrestaurant.co.uk; @benaresofficial; 10.45 pm,
Sun 9.45 pm; closed Sun L; No trainers; booking max 10 may apply.

Bentley's W1 £90 3 3 3
11-15 Swallow St   020 7734 4756   4–4B

"We always sit at the bar and enjoy superb oysters!" – so say fans of the *"more casual downstairs"* at Richard Corrigan's *"elegant"* stalwart, near Piccadilly Circus, which some diners prefer over the *"quieter"* (prettier) upstairs dining rooms. Now over a century old, this remains one of the capital's favourite destinations for fish that's *"invariably good"* and *"classic seafood"* (with lobster, oysters, *"epic fish pie"*, *"top fish 'n' chips with mushy peas"* and *"the best dressed crab in town"* all rating mention). Most diners love its *"very relaxed"* style (although one or two feel staff can be a bit *"over-familiar"*), and there are pitfalls to its super-handy West End location: it can seem *"rather touristy"*; *"tables are closely packed"*; and prices are a bit *"elevated"*. Top Tip – *"fabulous outside terrace: summer lunch in the alleyway is bliss"*. / W1B 4DG; www.bentleys.org; @bentleys_london; 10.30 pm, Sun 10 pm; No shorts; booking max 8 may apply.

Berber & Q £52 4 4 4
Arch 338 Acton Mews, E8   020 7923 0829   14–2A
Exmouth Market, EC1   020 7837 1726   10–1A

The tang of Tel Aviv-meets-North African tastes infuse the lipsmacking charcoal-grilled meats (and also the veg) at Josh Kat's Haggerston railway arch, which is mostly a walk-in style place (though there are a few tables for bookings). But, in fact, it's the more recent Exmouth Market spin-off that inspires more feedback nowadays: *"Having Shawarma Bar in the title might make it sound like a kebab-shop but, it's actually an unassumingly intimate restaurant, with great sharing plates and grill dishes that don't break the bank"*. And *"it really punches above its weight in terms of the seriously delicious Israeli/Eastern Mediterranean dishes it turns out (the rotisserie chicken is amazing) complemented by an exciting, low-intervention wine list"*.

Berenjak W1 £57 4 4 4
27 Romilly Street   5–2A

"Fun and trendy" Persian newcomer in Soho – a busy, small (35-seater), no-bookings dive that's part of JKS Restaurants's portfolio, where the seats at the counter look onto a grill, rotisserie and clay oven. On the menu from Iranian chef Kian Samyani, *"gentrified"* kebabs (arguably *"it's really all about the meat"*, this place), flatbreads and mezze that are *"interesting and full of flavour"*. / W1D 5AL; berenjaklondon.com.

Bernardi's W1 £66 3 4 3
62 Seymour Street   020 3826 7940   2–2A

A stylish modern Italian where Marylebone meets Bayswater. It's *"particularly good for a late, louche lunch"*, although it can be *"difficult to carry on a conversation"* with the associated *"buzz"*. The food? – *"inconsistent but really enjoyable nevertheless"*. / W1H 5BN; www.bernardis.co.uk; @BernardisLondon; Mon - Sat 10.30pm, Sun 9.30pm.

The Berners Tavern W1 £93 2 1 4
10 Berners St   020 7908 7979   3–1D

To be *"blown away by the decor"* – with its *"beautiful high ceiling and sense of spaciousness"* – is still the dominant reaction to Jason Atherton's glam dining room inside Ian Shrager's Edition hotel, north of Oxford Street. *"Wish the food could be at the same level as the interior"* is another common theme, however, as is ever-more *"arrogant"* or *"haphazard"* service, and there's a general feeling that, on current form, the place is *"serving a transient market with its glorious setting rather than focussing on the product and delivery"*. / W1T 3NP; www.bernerstavern.com; @bernersTavern; 11.45 pm, Sun 10.15 pm.

Berto N7 NEW
155 Holloway Road   9–2D
From the owners of Zia Lucia, this smallish (40-cover), summer 2019 newcomer aims to bring a similar experimental approach to pasta to that which has won Zia Luca a following for pizza, using different flours for its homemade creations. 'Pasta – Roll with it' is the catchy motto. / N7 8LX; berto.uk.

Best Mangal   £40   4 3 2
619 Fulham Rd, SW6   020 7610 0009   6–4A
104 North End Rd, W14   020 7610 1050   8–2D
66 North End Rd, W14   020 7602 0212   8–2D
Every postcode boasts its own "best kebab in London", but this trio in Fulham haa a better claim than most after 23 years' service: "all freshly made and truly delicious", fans say they're "one in a million!" / www.bestmangal.com; midnight, Sat 1 am; no Amex; book online.

The Betterment W1 NEW
The Biltmore, 39-44 Grosvenor Square   020 7629 9400   3–2A
Due to open in September 2019, Hilton's new luxury Mayfair hotel has signed Jason Atherton's Social Company to oversee all the food; former City Social head chef Paul Walsh will be heading up the stoves at this all-day, brasserie-style operation. The debut is bang opposite the recent opening from Atherton's former employer, Gordon Ramsay's Lucky Cat, and much has been made in the press of the two 'going head-to-head'. / W1K 2HP; lxrhotels3.hilton.com/lxr/biltmore-mayfair/dine.

Bibendum SW3   £134   3 3 4
81 Fulham Rd   020 7589 1480   6–2C
"The iconic architecture of the Michelin building", in South Kensington, helps make its first-floor dining room (converted by Sir Terence Conran, and opened in 1987) a modern classic, and provides a "stunning" location for a meal (in particular at lunch). Claude Bosi is entering his third year at the stoves now, and wins strong praise from most diners for his "first-class-but-rich" French cuisine, which creates some "wow" moments. A minority, though, feel the cooking here "is not up to the very high standard Bosi set when in Ludlow and Mayfair", and consider prices "exorbitant": "I thought tiny, overpriced portions of nouvelle cuisine were a thing of the past… until I ate here". / SW3 6RD; www.bibendum.co.uk; @bibendumltdSW3; 11 pm, Sun 10.30 pm; booking max 12 may apply.

Bibendum Oyster Bar SW3   £55   3 3 4
Michelin House, 81 Fulham Road   020 7581 5817   6–2C
"Expensive for what it is but very enjoyable" – the unchanging equation over the years at this luxurious seafood café, off the beautiful and atmospheric foyer of the Michelin building. Nowadays part of Claude Bosi's regime, he has added hot items (fish pie, moules, fish 'n' chips etc) to an offer that has traditionally focussed on raw seafood and cold platters. / SW3 6RD; www.bibendum.co.uk; @bibendumrestaurant; 10 pm; closed Sun D; no booking.

Bibimbap Soho   £34   3 3 2
10 Charlotte St, W1   020 7287 3434   2–1C
11 Greek St, W1   020 7287 3434   5–2A
39 Leadenhall Mkt, EC3   020 72839165   10–2D
For a Korean bite on the go, try these Soho and Fitzrovia canteens (and there's also a take-away in the City's Leadenhall Market), whose trade bibimbaps (rice with a topping) make for "delicious food, served quickly and at great prices". Top Tip – "Korean Fried Chicken is a naughty-but-nice treat packed full of flavour". / 11pm, EC3 3 pm; W1 Sun, EC3 Sat & Sun; no bookings.

Big Easy £61 3 2 3
12 Maiden Ln, WC2   020 3728 4888   5–3D
332-334 King's Rd, SW3   020 7352 4071   6–3C
Crossrail Pl, E14   020 3841 8844   12–1C
"Good basic BBQ and fried foods" plus "similar lobster and seafood options"
(and "live music is another plus") have kept this gen-u-ine American
crabshack an always-packed-and-noisy feature of the King's Road for nearly
30 years. "Good-sized portions" and good times are also reported at its
newer, if less-established ,spin-offs in Covent Garden and Canary Wharf.
/ www.bigeasy.co.uk; @bigeasytweet; Mon-Thu 11 pm, Fri & Sat 11.30 pm,
Sun 10.30 pm.

The Bingham TW10 £66 3 4 5
61-63 Petersham Road   020 8940 0902   1–4A
"A super-pretty location" helps make the dining room of this Richmond
boutique hotel – rebranded this year as the Bingham Riverhouse –
"unbeatable for a special meal". To accompany the "lovely ambience",
and "great views over the Thames", the food is an attraction in itself:
"the menu reflects the seasons well and is always delivered to a high
standard". / TW10 6UT; www.thebingham.co.uk; @thebingham; 10 pm; closed
Sun D; No trainers.

The Bird in Hand W14 £53 4 3 4
88 Masbro Road   020 7371 2721   8–1C
"Not your average pub selling pizzas... these are the real deal... some
of the best ever!" This stylish pub-conversion in the backstreets of Olympia
is cousin to the Oak chain, and has a similarly high quality offering.
"The locals obviously know they're onto a good thing as it's busy on a
Tuesday night..." / W14 0LR; www.thebirdinhandlondon.com; @TBIHLondon;
10 pm, Sun 9.15 pm; booking weekdays only.

Bistro Aix N8 £62 2 2 3
54 Topsfield Pde, Tottenham Ln   020 8340 6346   9–1C
A "long-time, local favourite" – this "relaxed", retro bistro brings the classic
flavours of France to Crouch End. Chef-proprietor Lynne Sanders and her
team send "reliably good food" out from the kitchen. / N8 8PT;
www.bistroaix.co.uk; @bistroaixlondon; 10 pm, Fri & Sat 11 pm; Mon-Thu D only,
Fri-Sun open L & D; No Amex.

Bistro Mirey SW6 £55 4 3 3
98 Lillie Road   020 3092 6969   8–2D
"Striving hard" in a tough location – near the gyratory at the top of North
End Road Market – your heart goes out to this "useful and pleasant", small
'Franco-Japanese bistro' owned by Gerald Mirey and Ko Ito. "Simple classics
like steak and chips are well executed", but there are also Japanese notes
that add an interesting slant to familiar dishes. / SW6 7SR;
www.bistromirey.com; @bistromirey.

Bistro Union SW4 £57 3 2 2
40 Abbeville Rd   020 7042 6400   11–2D
Clapham-star Trinity's younger sibling gains solid ratings for bringing
affordable British bistro fare to the smart 'Abbeville Village' enclave. One
or two diners "expect slightly better" from a patron of Adam Byatt's calibre
though – "adequate but didn't quite hit the spot". / SW4 9NG;
www.bistrounion.co.uk; @BistroUnion; 10 pm, Sun 8 pm; booking max 8 may apply.

Bistro Vadouvan SW15 £63 4 4 3
30 Brewhouse Lane   020 3475 3776   11–2B
"Really interesting, Asian-fusion notes" to the essentially modern European
dishes – "serious cooking, bursting with flavour" – aren't the only good
feature of this Indian-run two-year-old: it has a "great location near Putney
Bridge", and service is "super-friendly". "It's good to have somewhere
reasonable in Putney, which is not well served by restaurants". / SW15 2JX;
bistrovadouvan.co.uk; @BistroVadouvan; 10 pm.

Bistrotheque E2 £68 **3** **2** **4**

23-27 Wadeson St   020 8983 7900   14–2B

"This crisp, clean, chic warehouse" with *"big industrial windows"* in Cambridge Heath is, say fans, the *"perfect, perfect, perfect spot for a lovely weekend brunch"* or a *"lush lunch with oysters and Champagne"*. A hipster haven for 15 years, it still rates well for its *"delicious food"* and an atmosphere boosted by live music. / E2 9DR; www.bistrotheque.com; @Bistrotheque; 10.30 pm, Fri & Sat 11 pm; closed weekday L.

Black Axe Mangal N1 £53 **4** **3** **3**

156 Canonbury Road   no tel   9–2D

"Unique! Hard rock, offal, penises on the walls, skateboards… all plus rocking cooking from an ex-St John chef" – KISS fan, Lee Tiernan's tiny kebab dive near Highbury Corner is *"not a place for everyone"*, but his massively spicy flatbreads *"take this kind of dish to the next level"*, and, for its adoring fanclub, *"a brilliant vibe and superb food make it a must-go"*. / N1; www.blackaxemangal.com; @blackaxemangal; 10.30 pm, Sun 3 pm; D only Mon-Fri, Sat L & D, Sun L only; no booking.

Black Bear Burger E1 £10 **5** **3**–

Boxpark Shoreditch, 2-10 Bethnal Green Road   no tel   13–2B

"Amazing and well-considered burgers, plus delicious, crunchy chips" help win very high ratings for this pop-up brand, which has now graduated to Boxpark Shoreditch. The backstory works well: one of the founders grew up on a Devon beef farm: all meat is sourced from the south west from native breeds that are grass-fed and dry-aged on the bone; bacon is from outdoor-bred pigs in the east of England… / E1 6GY; www.blackbearburger.com; @BlackBearBurger.

Black Dog Beer House TW8 NEW £52 **4** **3** **3**

17 Albany Road   020 8568 5688   1–3A

"An amazing newcomer, head and shoulders above the competition locally" – this autumn 2018 opening in Brentford is the brainchild of an Aussie and Canadian couple, Pete and Ash, who have gone for it with their 14 kegs, five real ales, five real ciders and in-house brewery (Fearless Nomad). All this plus a consistently highly-rated menu serving an eclectic mix of funked-up gastro-fare. *"You need to book but it's totes fab"*. / TW8 0NF; www.blackdogbeerhouse.co.uk; @blackdogbeerhse.

Black Prince SE11 £46 **3** **3** **2**

6 Black Prince Rd   020 7582 2818   2–4D

"Good-quality bar food and an exceptional Sunday lunch" continue to win tips for this Kennington hostelry (which film buffs will recognise from the 2014 movie Kingsman). / SE11 6HS; www.theblackprincepub.co.uk; 11 pm.

Black Radish SW19 NEW £68 **4** **4** **3**

28 Ridgway   020 8617 3960   10–2B

"No choice, but it doesn't matter as everything is delicious" – on weekend evenings there's only a five-course tasting option available at this Wimbledon Village newcomer, and at other services choice is very limited: but judging by the high marks awarded by its local fanclub, no-one minds (in contrast to The Evening Standard's Fay Maschler, who panned the place). / SW19 4QW; www.blackradishsw19.com; @BlackRadishSW19.

Black Roe W1 £76 **3** **3** **3**

4 Mill Street   020 3794 8448   3–2C

"A club vibe" and *"amazing cocktails"* help fuel the fun scene at this Hawaiian-inspired Mayfair fixture. The speciality is poké and other *"expensive Pacific Rim foods"* – sceptics feel dishes are *"well done but on the whole lack that special something"* but on most accounts results are *"very flavoursome"*. / W1S 2AX; www.blackroe.com; @blackroe; 10.45 pm; closed Sun.

Blacklock £45 **3** **4** **4**
24 Great Windmill St, W1   020 3441 6996   4–3D
28 Rivington Street, EC2   awaiting tel   13–1B
13 Philpot Lane, EC3   020 7998 7676   10–3D
"Oh my! A meat-lovers' feast awaits!" at these "carnivorous havens", where "evidently very well-sourced produce is expertly cooked and served in great platters of meaty delight!" ("go when you are hungry!"). There are "superb-value steaks", but it's the "mouthwateringly scrumptious" chops that inspire more feedback. Soho and the City occupy "urban-chic" basements, whereas Shoreditch is above-ground and more "warehouse-y". Top Menu Tip – "bargain basement prices on Butchers Block Monday, with £10 corkage if you bring your own wine!" / theblacklock.com; @BlacklockChops.

Blanchette £56 **4** **2** **3**
9 D'Arblay St, W1   020 7439 8100   4–1C
204 Brick Lane, E1   020 7729 7939   13–1C
"Just fab!", say fans of this pair of "rather crammed" French bistros in Soho and Brick Lane offering "delightful and different dishes in a good atmosphere". Served as small or sharing plates, the food is generally "interesting and imaginative", and the "service friendly, if a tiny bit flaky at times". / 11 pm, Sun 9 pm.

Blandford Comptoir W1 £66 **3** **3** **3**
1 Blandford Street   020 7935 4626   2–1A
"Wonderful bistro food" – "surprisingly fancy, but very well executed" – matches up to a notably "interesting and well-priced wine list" at this "delightful little wine bar" in Marylebone from Xavier Rousset, the youngest-ever Sommelier of the Year. / W1U 3DA; blandford-comptoir.co.uk; @BlandfordCompt; 10 pm; No Amex.

Bleecker Burger £22 **5** **2** **1**
205 Victoria St, SW1   no tel   2–4B
Unit B Pavilion Building, Spitalfields Mkt, E1   07712 540501   13–2B
Bloomberg Arcade, Queen Victoria Street, EC4   awaiting tel   10–3C
"There is no finer burger in town: end of!" – Zan Kaufman's tiny group "keeps things simple… and they smash it!". "If you want mega-stacked, crazy combos, with layers and layers of toppings falling out of the side, there are numerous other (excellent) options in London. But if you want the best patties, made with the best aged beef, un-mucked-about-with and served by a bunch of nice people, then Bleecker is just the best there is".

Bleeding Heart Restaurant EC1 £76 **3** **3** **4**
Bleeding Heart Yd, Greville St   020 7242 8238   10–2A
"A bit of a one-off" – this sprawling, Dickensian, subterranean warren is "hidden away in a cobbled yard that itself is tucked away behind Hatton Garden". "Though very handy for the City, it has a very romantic feel to it", with "quiet out-of-the-way arches and alcoves", but is as well-suited to conspiratorial business lunches as it is to "evening romance". A "superb wine list" adds lustre to fairly traditional Gallic cuisine that's a little "pricey" but "dependable". Top Tip – "excellent-value set menu". / EC1N 8SJ; bleedingheart.co.uk; @bleedingheartyd; 10.30 pm; closed Sat & Sun.

Blixen E1 £59 **2** **2** **3**
65a Brushfield Street   020 7101 0093   13–2C
Elegant styling – the venue is a former bank made over in the style of a European brasserie – and a handy position by Spitalfields Market help win brunch and business recommendations for this all-day venture. Its ratings are indifferent though, and it takes some flak for "poorly executed food that doesn't merit the price charged". / E1 6AA; www.blixen.co.uk; @BlixenLondon; 11 pm, Sun 8 pm.

Bloomsbury Street Kitchen WC1 NEW
9-14 Bloomsbury Street   020 7666 2044   2–1C
The promising, but hitherto under-exploited mix of Mediterranean and Japanese small plates is the crux of the menu offering at this August 2019 opening, which promises 'a modern, day-to-night, neighbourhood restaurant and bar… complemented by a diverse variety of wines, sake and signature cocktails'. / WC1B 3QD; bloomsburystreetkitchen.co.uk; @BloomsStKitchen.

Bluebird SW3   £83   2 3 4
350 King's Road   020 7559 1000   6–3C
This smart D&D London conversion of a Modernist 1920s car showroom on a prominent King's Road site leaves reporters impressed by the venue if rather underwhelmed by the cuisine – "beautiful restaurant and nice service, they just need to up their game food-wise". Situation normal, then, at this large space, which has never really capitalised fully on its potential. / SW3 5UU; www.bluebird-restaurant.co.uk; @bluebirdchelsea; 10.30 pm, Sun 9.30 pm.

Blueprint Café SE1   £62   3 3 4
28 Shad Thames, Butler's Wharf   020 7378 7031   10–4D
"One of the best views in the capital", over Tower Bridge and the Thames, is the highlight of any meal at this venue from D&D London, on the first floor of the former Design Museum. Beyond that, there's "no problem with the food or cooking", which can be "surprisingly delicious" nowadays. / SE1 2YD; www.blueprintcafe.co.uk; @BlueprintCafe; 10.30 pm; closed Mon & Sun; no booking.

Bob Bob Cité EC3   £88
Level 8, 122 Leadenhall Street   020 3928 6600   10–2D
Three years and £25m later, Leonid Shutov's City sibling to Soho fave-rave, Bob Bob Ricard, finally burst forth onto the London restaurant scene just as our survey was closing in June 2019. Occupying the third floor of the City's 'Cheesegrater' (aka the Leadenhall Building), it looks a little like a Sci-Fi re-imagining of the decadent Soho original, complete with booths, and new-look 'Presser pour Champagne' buttons. Early feedback (too thin for a full rating) is ecstatic in terms of its potential for business entertaining – bolstered by a comprehensive wine list (with options up to £10k), and Eric Chavot's luxury-brasserie menu – but that fit-out's not going to pay for itself, and the bill is confirmation of the fact. / EC3V 4PE; www.bobbobcite.com; @bobbobcite.

Bob Bob Ricard W1   £98   2 3 5
1 Upper James Street   020 3145 1000   4–2C
"OTT-opulent decor, with a 'push for champagne' button in each booth" have carved a big name for Leonid Shutov's fantastical Soho haunt, whose "high novelty factor" is extremely romantic ("you just have to take a date"). When it comes to Eric Chavot's menu of luxurious classics ("amazing beef Wellington" for example) results undisputedly taste "very nice", but the food is "expensive for what it is, and you get more adventurous cooking at the same price-bracket elsewhere". / W1F 9DF; www.bobbobricard.com; @BobBobRicard; 11.15 pm, Sat midnight, Sun 11.15 pm; closed Sat L; Jacket required.

BOB's Lobster SE1   £37   3 4 3
Unit 71, St Thomas Street   10–4C
"Very fresh lobster, oysters, crab, etc, plus a good choice of wines by the glass" (as you'd expect from the team behind Bedales of Borough) win praise from a small fanclub for this railway arch below London Bridge station – the permanent site for a pop-up whose hallmark is a roving fleet of VW camper vans. / SE1 3QX; www.bobslobster.com; @BOBs_Lobster.

Bocca Di Lupo W1 £61 **5 4 3**

12 Archer St 020 7734 2223 4–3D

"Italian peasant-food fit for a king" – Jacob Kenedy's *"exceptional and distinctive"* fixture, a short stroll from Piccadilly Circus, has carved a massive foodie following with its *"wonderfully eclectic and ever-changing range of traditional dishes from across the country"* (categorised by region, and available in 'small' or 'large sizes'), with the *"exciting"* results *"so simple and delicious you cannot believe it"*. *"And they're complemented by a staggering wine list"* which *"is itself a trip through Italy"* (*"it's worth having a detailed conversation with the wine waiter to discover outstanding vintages at sensible prices"* with *"lots of interesting options by the glass"*). *"Unsurprisingly, the place is always jammed"*, and the *"busy, café-style"* interior with *"closely packed tables"* is such that *"while mostly delightful, it's bloody noisy"* (*"if not slightly manic"*). But the *"efficient and friendly staff"* help keep the mood upbeat. Some guests *"prefer the counter"* – *"there's great kitchen theatre perched on the bar stools"*. / W1D 7BB; www.boccadilupo.com; @boccadilupo; 11 pm, Sun 9.30 pm; booking max 10 may apply.

Bocconcino Restaurant W1 £108 **2 2 2**

19 Berkeley St 020 7499 4510 3–3C

In a prime Mayfair location, this "noisy", Russian-owned Italian wins acceptable ratings, but divides reporters on the subject of value: fans hail it as "wonderful all-round, with a variety of choice and well-presented dishes" (including "top pizza"), but to sceptics "although the food is decent, it's majorly overpriced, in particular the wine list". / W1J 8ED; www.bocconcinorestaurant.co.uk; @BocconcinoUK; 10.45 pm.

Al Boccon di'vino TW9 £66 **4 4 5**

14 Red Lion Street 020 8940 9060 1–4A

"Always a surprise" – you get what you're given (there's no menu choice) at chef Riccardo Grigolo's set-price Venetian feast in Richmond: an unqualified delight, with multiple courses of *"amazing, delicious food"* and *"excellent service"*, creating *"an atmosphere rarely found elsewhere"*. / TW9 1RW; www.nonsolovinoltd.co.uk; @alboccondivino; 11 pm; closed Mon, Tue L & Wed L; No Amex.

Bodean's £45 **2 2 2**

10 Poland St, W1 020 7287 7575 4–1C
25 Catherine St, WC2 020 7257 2790 5–3D
4 Broadway Chambers, SW6 020 7610 0440 6–4A
225 Balham High St, SW17 020 8682 4650 11–2C
169 Clapham High St, SW4 020 7622 4248 11–2D
201 City Rd, EC1 020 7608 7230 13–1A
16 Byward St, EC3 020 7488 3883 10–3D

"A nice, laid-back American buzz" has helped win a loyal following over the years for this small chain of Kansas City-style diners: one of the first in London to bring BBQ indoors. *"It's a fun place"* (in the right mood) and the food is *"decent"* and in man-sized portions, but *"not particularly special"*. / www.bodeansbbq.com; 11 pm, Sun 10.30 pm, NW10 10 pm, Fri & Sat 11 pm; booking: min 8.

Boisdale of Belgravia SW1 £77 **3 2 3**

15 Eccleston Street 020 7730 6922 2–4B

"High-quality manfood" (steaks, burgers and other 'proper' main dishes) and a *"clubby atmosphere"* of whisky, cigars (on a dedicated terrace) and live jazz are the key ingredients at Ranald MacDonald's Scottish-themed Belgravia haunt, which has offshoots in Mayfair, the City and Canary Wharf. It's *"not for everyone"* – one nay-sayer complained of *"worse than pub food"* – but for a certain sort of bloke it's *"the perfect place – he'll leave happy, content and very satisfied"*. / SW1W 9LX; www.boisdale.co.uk/belgravia; @boisdale; midnight; closed Sat L & Sun.

Boisdale of Bishopsgate EC2 £75 3 2 2

Swedeland Court, 202 Bishopsgate   020 7283 1763   10–2D

"A complete contrast from the exterior bustle of Bishopsgate" –
this Caledonian-themed wine bar (ground floor) and restaurant (basement)
provides the same gutsy (some feel "heavy"), meaty Scottish fare of the
Belgravian original, and is consistently decently rated food-wise. / EC2M 4NR;
www.boisdale.co.uk; @Boisdale; 11 pm; closed Sat & Sun.

Boisdale of Canary Wharf E14 £69 2 3 4

Cabot Place   020 7715 5818   12–1C

"For a total dining experience, night out, or even Saturday BBQ", fans of the
"spacious-yet-intimate" E14 spin-off from Ranald Macdonald's well-known
Belgravian applaud its "eclectic brilliance", and cigar-lovers particularly enjoy
the "wonderful humidor and private smoking balcony". The cuisine can
seem "expensive for what it is", but even some critics acknowledge:
"you don't really go for the food – the entertainment is top-notch, and the
great selection of spirits helps dampen any pain from the bill". / E14 4QT;
www.boisdale.co.uk/canary-wharf; @boisdaleCW; 11 pm, Wed-Sat midnight,
Sun 4 pm; closed Sun D.

Bombay Brasserie SW7 £72 3 3 2

Courtfield Road   020 7370 4040   6–2B

This upmarket fixture in South Kensington – on the Indian dining scene
in London since 1982 – doesn't make waves nowadays, but still earns solid
praise by producing consistently "very good food". Current owner Taj Hotels
have spruced up the interior, although the odd reporter is "not keen on the
current look". / SW7 4QH; www.bombayb.co.uk; @Bbsw7; 11 pm, Sun 10.30 pm;
closed Mon L.

Bombay Bustle W1 £73 4 3 3

29 Maddox Street   020 7290 4470   4–2A

The "fantastic", "properly spicy and tasty" Indian cooking at this Mayfair
two-year-old is "definitely of the quality and invention of Jamavar" –
its celebrated stablemate nearby. Taking inspiration from Mumbai street and
comfort food invites the comparison to an "upmarket Dishoom", while the
departure of founding chef Rohit Ghai has thus far only had limited impact
on the excellent ratings. / W1S 2PA; www.bombaybustle.com; @BombayBustle.

Bombay Palace W2 £47 5 4 3

50 Connaught St   020 7723 8855   7–1D

"A wonderful taste of India!" – the cooking at this plush venue tucked away
behind Marble Arch has returned to the heights following an extended
period of closure after a fire a few years ago. "The makeover looks great"
and "the food is still consistent and authentic", according to relieved
regulars. / W2 2AA; www.bombay-palace.co.uk; @bombaypalaceW2; 10.45 pm.

Bon Vivant WC1 £57 3 2 3

75-77 Marchmont Street   020 7713 6111   9–4C

"Like an everyday restaurant in a minor French town", this "very busy"
Bloomsbury bar/bistro is a "noisy but great fun" neighbourhood amenity:
"some dishes are more successful than others" but most are délicieux.
/ WC1N 1AP; www.bonvivantrestaurant.co.uk.

Bone Daddies £40 3 3 3

Nova, Victoria St, SW1   no tel   2–4B
30-31 Peter St, W1   020 7287 8581   4–2D
46-48 James St, W1   020 3019 7140   3–1A
Whole Foods, Kensington High St, W8   020 7287 8581   6–1A
24 Old Jamaica Road, SE16   10–4D **NEW**
The Bower, 211 Old Street, EC1   020 3019 6300   13–1A

"Incredibly filling bowls of ramen" – backed up by "interesting menus
of delicious food, served quickly with a smile" – attract an enthusiastic
crowd to this small chain of hip Japanese-style fast-food bars, although
feedback supports the view that "the original in Soho is by far the best".

The founder, Aussie-born, Nobu-trained chef Ross Shonhan, has spun off a series of "Asian-fusion" concepts – Flesh & Buns, Shack-Fuyu and his latest, Poke-Don. / www.bonedaddies.com/restaurant/bermondsey; 10 pm, Thu-Sat 11 pm, Sun 9.30 pm; W1, W8, SE16 no bookings.

Bonnie Gull £59 533

21a Foley St, W1   020 7436 0921   2–1B
22 Bateman Street, W1   020 7436 0921   5–2A

"Like being by the sea in the centre of London!" – this "tiny-but-perfectly-formed" Fitzrovian offers a "wide range of carefully sourced, skilfully prepared, seasonal fish"; and "if the dining room's a bit noisy and crowded, that's part of the experience" ("you get to know the adjoining table pretty well"), although in the summer months there's also "outside seating in the quiet street". Its even smaller Soho 'shack' spin-off – with a counter at the front and a few tables to the rear – opened a couple of years ago, and scores similarly highly. / www.bonniegull.com; @BonnieGull.

Bonoo NW2 £51 443

675 Finchley Road   020 7794 8899   1–1B

"The consistently excellent Indian street food" at this family-run local in Child's Hill – "mostly sharing-plates served tapas-style" – "is tastier and more varied than what's on offer at fancier places in central London". / NW2 2JP; www.bonoo.co.uk; @bonoohampstead; 10.30 pm.

The Booking Office, St Pancras Renaissance Hotel NW1 £78 214

Euston Road   020 7841 3566   9–3C

A "beautiful location" is the particular reason to seek out this this all-day operation, which oldies still recall as the grand ticket office of St Pancras station: nowadays converted in all its Victorian splendour, with an attractive atrium attached. It's "a bit pricey" and "service is all over the place", but – particularly for breakfast, or Sunday lunch – it can be an atmospheric choice on account of food that's "reliable if not spectacular". / NW1 2AR; www.bookingofficerestaurant.com; @StPancrasRen; 11 pm.

Boqueria £50 433

192 Acre Ln, SW2   020 7733 4408   11–2D
278 Queenstown Road, SW8   020 7498 8427   11–1C

"A really interesting menu" of "wonderful modern-style tapas and sharing plates" contributes to "a Spanish gastronomic experience" at this "vibrant" duo in Battersea and Clapham. "The young staff are always so friendly and welcoming". / www.boqueriatapas.com; @BoqueriaTapas.

Il Bordello E1 £52 333

Metropolitan Wharf, 70 Wapping Wall   020 7481 9950   12–1A

"Wapping's favourite" for more than 20 years – this "classic local Italian trat" scores well for its "friendly service", "and the food remains terrific". There's a recurrent complaint – rare elsewhere – that "portions are too large", but to both management and happy regulars this is without doubt a badge of honour. / E1W 3SS; www.ilbordello.com; 11 pm, Sun 10.30 pm; closed Sat L

Boro Bistro SE1 £44 233

6-10 Borough High St   020 7378 0788   10–3C

"Interesting and very edible food in 'tapas mode'", at "very reasonable prices", is on offer at this contemporary Franco-Hispanic bistro in Borough Market. "Charming service" from "efficient and friendly staff" adds to its attractions – along with "plenty of outdoor tables" for summer scoffing. / SE1 9QQ; www.borobistro.co.uk; @borobistro; 10.30 pm, Mon & Sun 9 pm; closed Mon & Sun; booking max 6 may apply.

The Botanist £55 ② ② ②
7 Sloane Sq, SW1   020 7730 0077   6–2D
Broadgate Circle, EC2   020 3058 9888   13–2B
This pair of "casual", well-located all-day brasseries serve an "eclectic
menu" from breakfast on, but it's the "friendly ambience that's a real
winner". The Sloane Square branch is "very Chelsea" – "great for lunch"
and "wonderfully convenient pre- and post-show for Cadogan Hall or Royal
Court". / thebotanist.uk.com; @botanistchester; SW1 breakfast 8, Sat & Sun
9, SW1 & EC2 11 pm.

Boudin Blanc W1 £71 ③ ③ ④
5 Trebeck St   020 7499 3292   3–4B
"It feels like a proper Gallic bistro"; and this 'petit coin' of Mayfair's cute and
atmospheric Shepherd Market is reasonably "authentic" all-round –
"the classic French cooking takes you away on holiday" all without leaving
W1, and it's most popular as a place for wooing a date. / W1J 7LT;
www.boudinblanc.co.uk; 11 pm.

Boulestin SW1 £76 ② ② ②
5 St James's St   020 7930 2030   3–4D
A "perfect courtyard – practically unique for the West End" is a good
feature of this "expensive French bistro", which serves "classic but well-
executed food". Named after an iconic Covent Garden dining room of the
1920s, it was revived on this site in St James's (once L'Oranger, RIP) a few
years ago, but never really made waves and went into administration
last year. "Under new management (and it shows)", it still seems "slightly
overpriced" but elicited supportive, if mixed feedback this year: "They didn't
know what a Kir is. Not great for a restaurant named after a famous chef.
Will try again but for now, a work in progress…" / SW1A 1EF;
www.boulestin.com; @BoulestinLondon; 10.30 pm; closed Sun; No trainers.

Boulevard WC2 £53 ② ③ ③
40 Wellington St   020 7240 2992   5–3D
In the tourist hell of Covent Garden, this traditional brasserie is easily missed
but worth remembering for a "cheap 'n' cheerful" bite. Even those who say
"it's not too inspiring" feel it's "hard to fault for a speedy pre-theatre meal":
"just like half the brasseries in France – classic dishes, realisation can
be mediocre, but very reasonably priced". / WC2E 7BD;
www.boulevardbrasserie.co.uk; @BoulevardWC2; 11 pm, Fri & Sat 11.30 pm,
Sun 10.30 pm.

Bourne and Hollingsworth Buildings EC1 £54 ③ ② ④
42 Northampton Rd   10–1A
"Lush surroundings" set a stylish tone at this "trendy", five-year-old venue
on a "hard-to-find" Farringdon corner, not far from Exmouth Market. It's
a 'multi-faceted' venue – a jumble of bar, café, restaurant, club, and private
dining space – from a design team whose portfolio includes Pizza East and
Riding House Café. "Fab cocktails" are maybe its most reliable attraction,
although the food is consistently well-rated too. / EC1R 0HU;
www.bandhbuildings.com.

Bowling Bird EC1 £51 ④ ④ ③
44 Cloth Fair   020 7324 7742   10–2B
"Ranks with the best beef I've ever had in London" is typical of the high
praise earned by this smart two-year-old. "Mind you, it is right next
to Smithfield" – a fact reflected in its straight-to-the-point menu – "and the
maître d' knows just the right wine to wash it down with". It occupies
an architectural gem of a townhouse once home to Sir John Betjeman.
/ EC1A 7JQ; bowlingbird.com.

Boxcar Butcher & Grill W1   £56   4 4 3
23 New Quebec St   020 3006 7000   2–2A
*"Top burgers…", "good-value and tasty steaks…", "good Sunday roast…"
– such are the attractions of this all-day Marylebone butcher, deli and
steakhouse (part of the Cubitt House group). / W1H 7SD; boxcar.co.uk;
@BoxcarLondon.*

Brackenbury Wine Rooms W6   £58   2 3 3
111-115 Hammersmith Grove   020 3696 8240   8–1C
*An "interesting wine list" is backed up by "reliable and quite imaginative
food" at this modern and "very friendly" wine bar (with a sunny terrace)
on a leafy Hammersmith corner. Wines are available pre-paid and by the
glass to encourage experimentation, and can be bought by the bottle from
the attached shop. There's another branch in Kensington. / W6 0NQ;
winerooms.london/brackenbury; @Wine_Rooms; 11.30 pm, Sun 10.30 pm.*

Bradley's NW3   £64   2 2 2
25 Winchester Rd   020 7722 3457   9–2A
*This "friendly" neighbourhood spot with a "tasty" modern European menu
has done stalwart service in a Swiss Cottage sidestreet for the best part
of three decades. "They have a monopoly for convenience to the nearby
Hampstead Theatre", and serve an "efficient and stress-free" pre-theatre
spread. The harsh would say the quality of the cooking can be "so so" – if it
was a notch higher, this could be quite a destination. / NW3 3NR;
www.bradleysnw3.co.uk; @bradleysnw3; 10 pm; closed Sun D.*

Brasserie Blanc   £56   2 2 2
*"Fair all-round, if by no means special" is a justifiable, if slightly harsh verdict
on Raymond Blanc's contemporary brasserie chain, whose branches are
generally handy and well-appointed, and whose EC2 and SE1 outlets are
often voted as "a decent place for a business meet up/dinner". If it were not
"trading on the name" of one of the country's most famous chefs,
its "reasonable" level of cooking might seem more laudable and less
"formulaic". / www.brasserieblanc.com; most branches close between 10 pm &
11 pm; Threadneedle and Chancery lane closed Sun.*

Brasserie of Light W1 NEW   £64   2 2 4
400 Oxford Street   020 3940 9600   3–1A
*"For sheer glamour and Damien Hirst's Pegasus, this gets my vote" –
Richard Caring's "lavish" and "wonderfully buzzy" (at times "ear-splittingly
loud") newcomer on the first floor of Selfridges (but with its own entrance)
is "visually stunning, with a fit-out that creates talking points and enjoys
marvellous views of Oxford Street". Its brasserie fare ranks somewhere
between "better-than-you-might-expect" and "mediocre", and service can
be "amateur", but serious criticisms are absent. "Populated mostly by ladies
who shop and lunch", it was also nominated by numerous reporters for
"a great and glitzy date": "something about department store dining can
actually be quite sexy, and this extravagant presentation kind-of works…"
Top Tip – "Would recommend for a drink at the bar as the space
is gorgeous, and with pink loos being so OTT it made us smile". / W1A 1AB;
www.brasserie-of-light.co.uk.*

Brasserie Toulouse-Lautrec SE11   £61
140 Newington Butts   020 7582 6800   1–3C
*Nightly live entertainment jazzes up this bravely-located fixture,
near Kennington's cinema museum, which serves a variety of brasserie fare,
majoring in steaks and other meaty, traditional Gallic dishes. Limited
feedback this year, but all positive, including as a breakfast option.
/ SE11 4RN; www.btlrestaurant.co.uk; @btlrestaurant; 10.30 pm, Sat & Sun 11 pm.*

Brasserie Zédel W1 £45 2 3 5

20 Sherwood St   020 7734 4888   4–3C

"You'll be so dazzled by the place that you may be inclined to overlook the food" – Corbin & King's "improbably glamorous" recreation of an "archetypal buzzing Parisian brasserie" is "so handy, being just by Piccadilly Circus tube" and provides "unmistakable value for such opulent and elegant surroundings in the very centre of London". The "huge", Grade I listed chamber is an "amazing Art Deco underground ballroom"; "a wonderfully blingy, brightly-lit space with gold everywhere". The "straightforward" French brasserie fare (soupe à l'oignon, boeuf bourguignon, steak haché…) from a huge menu is mundane by comparison… in fact it's pretty mundane full stop. But whereas the odd critic brands results as "terrible", most reporters feel that "you'd have to be a miserable sod to complain about anything at these prices" – "inevitably there are slips along the way and food can be inconsistent, but you get more bang for your buck here than at virtually any other London restaurant" (in particular "prix-fixe menus are astonishing value"). Top Tip – "there is also a beautiful Bar Americain". / W1F 7ED; www.brasseriezedel.com; @brasseriezedel; 11.45 pm, Sun 10.45 pm.

Brat E1 £61 5 5 4

First Floor, 4 Redchurch Street   no tel   13–1B

"Totally living up to the hype!" – Tomos Parry's "cool ex-pub, first-floor dining room" (above Smoking Goat) was Harden's top newcomer last year, and "pulls off what so many Shoreditch restaurants aspire to" with "its phenomenal food from the open kitchen; its relaxed-but-highly-competent style; and its lack of expense". "And the wood-panelled dining room is a welcome change from the usual warehouse-style in the area". The Basque-influenced cuisine, much of it cooked over an open wood fire, majors in fish – "never overcooked, with a hint of smokiness after a roasting over hot embers" – in particular the "to-die-for", signature turbot (for which the restaurant is named) which is "positively Mediterranean in its fresh deliciousness". "The room is small and tables are close together" but no-one seems to care: "the buzz of the place simply tells you that here are a lot of folks really enjoying their dinner". It helps that "the staff are almost as good as the food: enthusiastic, knowledgeable, and clear in their explanations of the menu". All this, plus a "brilliant, wide-ranging and value-for-money wine list". / E1 6JJ; www.bratrestaurant.com; @bratrestaurant.

Brawn E2 £61 5 3 4

49 Columbia Road   020 7729 5692   14–2A

"By rights this place ought to have gone off by now, it's been going too long still to be fashionable!" But this East End sibling to the West End's Terroirs – "a gorgeous modern space" on Columbia Road – shows no sign of going downhill like its stablemate. "Ed Wilson is back at the helm full time and the kitchen purrs like a Rolls". "Every week brings different choices, but always with amazing products and a quality of small plates that's without a doubt at the top level". And there's a "great selection of natural wines" from all over Europe. "Why doesn't it have a Michelin star yet? They have delivered on an exceptional level of cooking for almost a decade now, and managed to remain creative, inventive and original in the meantime". / E2 7RG; www.brawn.co; @brawn49; 11 pm; closed Mon L & Sun D; No Amex.

Bread Street Kitchen EC4 £74 2 2 3

10 Bread Street   020 3030 4050   10–2B

This "warehouse-style" outfit from Gordon Ramsay near St Paul's provides a handy amenity for business-lunchers and, out of business hours, has a "great atmosphere for families and groups". But while it's generally decent, especially for brunch, it's rather "overpriced for what it offers" and apt to be "let down by average cooking and service". / EC4M 9AJ; www.breadstreetkitchen.com; @breadstreet; 11 pm, Sun 8 pm.

Breakfast Club £42 **3** **3** **3**
33 D'Arblay St, W1   020 7434 2571   4–1C
2-4 Rufus St, N1   020 7729 5252   13–1B
31 Camden Pas, N1   020 7226 5454   9–3D
12-16 Artillery Ln, E1   020 7078 9633   13–2B
An "outstanding array of breakfasts" – "from egg and chips to huevos rancheros" – "in a buzzing atmosphere" that lasts well into the evening has driven the enormous popularity of this café chain. "Book ahead though, or be ready for a long queue at the door". The convivial party feel is fuelled by cocktails as the day wears on. / www.thebreakfastclubcafes.com; @thebrekkyclub; SRA-Food Made Good – 3 stars.

Breddos Tacos £49 **4** **2** **3**
26 Kingly Street, W1   4–2A
82 Goswell Road, EC1   020 3535 8301   10–1B
"We were taken there by a Mexican who reckons it's the most authentic in London!" – these "friendly-if-chaotic, little taco stops" hit the spot with "interesting flavour combinations" on "a tiny menu that manages to have something for everyone". / breddostacos.com; @breddostacos.

Briciole W1 £52 **3** **3** **2**
20 Homer St   020 7723 0040   7–1D
"Fresh, interesting and authentic Italian dishes" make this Marylebone deli/trattoria "an easy choice for family gatherings". It started out as a spin-off from Latium in Fitzrovia, which closed last year (RIP). / W1H 4NA; www.briciole.co.uk; @briciolelondon; 10.15 pm.

Brick Lane Beigel Bake E1 £5 **4** **1** **1**
159 Brick Ln   020 7729 0616   13–1C
This epic, "super-cheap" Jewish deli (nowadays "obviously in overseas guide books given the numbers of tourists in the line") has been famous forever, thanks to its "delicious home-made beigels" and "incredible salt beef", plus its 24/7 opening (and queue). Staff "can be very rude", but "the brutal service is part of the charm". Top Tip – "forget the beigel and have salt beef in a superb onion platzel – at £4.50 it's one of London's culinary bargains". / E1 6SB; www.beigelbake.com; @BeigelBake; open 24 hours; Cash only; No bookings.

Brigadiers EC2 £55 **5** **4** **4**
Bloomberg Arcade, Queen Victoria Street   020 3319 8140   10–3C
"Mindblowing!" – this "colonially-themed" yearling in the City's Bloomberg Arcade is "another smash hit from JKS" and "probably the best place to eat in the Square Mile" right now. Occupying a "comfortable (slightly macho) sequence of little rooms", staff are notably "patient and helpful", while foodwise "the focus is on Indian sharing plates" with "insanely good" grilled meats (lamb chops in particular), plus "all your local curry favourites, dressed up with wonderful, perfumed aromatics and dazzling dips". "They don't pull any punches when it comes to heat in dishes either", and "there's a strong drinks menu too" – you can see "thought has gone into the beer selection". With numerous TV screens, "it's a great place to watch sports" ("they even have a pool table!") / EC2R; brigadierslondon.com; @brigadiersldn.

Bright E8 £74 **5** **4** **3**
Netil House, 1 Westgate Street   020 3095 9407   14–2B
"Beautiful food, with elegance and full, intense flavours" from a menu of "simple, high-quality dishes", backed up by a list of "natural wines from top importers" – all served in a "laid back", semi-industrial space (formerly Ellory, RIP) – wins adulation for this yearling in London Fields, from the team behind fooderati fave-rave P Franco. / E8 3RL; www.brightrestaurant.co.uk.

The Bright Courtyard W1 £70 **3**22
43-45 Baker St   020 7486 6998   2–1A
North of Portman Square, in a somewhat nondescript office block setting (complete with atrium seating for some diners), this Marylebone Chinese has won a big reputation for its innovative cuisine. Its ratings were more middling this year, however, with one or two reporters feeling that "even if the food is exceptional, it does not warrant such high prices". / W1U 8EW; www.lifefashiongroup.com; @BrightCourtyard; 10.45 pm, Thu-Sat 11.15 pm.

Brinkley's SW10 £64 22**3**
47 Hollywood Rd   020 7351 1683   6–3B
John Brinkley's "stalwart of Chelsea nightlife" provides "a good service to the Eurotrash and ageing lotharios brigade". "The food won't set the world alight", but it's a "buzzy" venue, with a "great garden conservatory". / SW10 9HX; www.brinkleys.com/brinkleys-restaurant.html; @BrinkleysR; 11.30 pm; closed weekday L.

Brixton Laundry SW9 NEW
374 Coldharbour Lane   11–2D
Opening in November 2019, at Walton Lodge in Brixton: an all-day neighbourhood café, restaurant and wine shop from Melanie Brown, who used to work with Peter Gordon and launched The New Zealand Cellar and Australian Cellar. In the morning it will offer pastries and other light bites, and in the evening cocktails and a menu of more substantial dishes. / SW9 8PL.

Brook House SW6 NEW £59 **3**2**4**
65 New King's Road   11–1B
Mark Dyer and Eamonn Manson (formerly of The Sands End and The Brown Cow) have taken over this traditional pub overlooking Eel Brook Common, which wins praise for its "top-class" cooking (too posh to be called pub grub) and "super ambience". "They need to improve the inconsistent service", however. / SW6 4SG; brookhousefulham.com.

Brookmill SE8 £43 2**33**
65 Cranbrook Road   020 8333 0899   1–4D
It's worth knowing about this "light, airy and comfortable renovation" of a Victorian boozer complete with cute beer garden, according to Deptford-based regulars: "nothing will unduly quicken the pulse but everything's reassuringly pleasant: solidly-executed pub-grub, a decent selection of beers on tap, and BT Sport & Sky for the footie (though it never gets too rowdy)". / SE8 4EJ; www.thebrookmill.co.uk; @thebrookmillpub; 10 pm, Sun & Mon 9 pm.

The Brown Dog SW13 £52 **333**
28 Cross Street   020 8392 2200   11–1A
This "hidden gem" in the cute 'Little Chelsea' enclave of Barnes is "awkward to find if you're not a local, but that's probably why it's retained its character". It changed hands last year, but seems to have held onto its rep as a "reliable gastropub" – you need to book for the "great Sunday lunch". There's outdoor seating in the backyard, and dogs and children are welcome. / SW13 0AP; www.thebrowndog.co.uk; @browndogbarnes; 10 pm, Sun 9 pm.

Brown's Hotel, The English Tea Room W1 £79 **3**4**4**
Albemarle St   020 7493 6020   3–3C
"So comfortable and homely, yet chic and stylish too" – this "classic" British hotel lounge is not quite as famous or grand as the nearby Ritz Palm Court, but nevertheless has a massive following for its "scrumptious afternoon tea" ("if at a price", of course). Top Tips – it's "'Teatox' is decadently delicious whilst not being too heavy"; and this is also "a central location for a business breakfast, with very good food". / W1S 4BP; www.roccofortehotels.com; No trainers.

Brunswick House Café SW8 £60 3 2 5
30 Wandsworth Rd   020 7720 2926   11–1D
This Georgian mansion-turned-architectural salvage shop is a "wonderful old building in a location you'd least expect it, overlooking Vauxhall Cross's huge gyratory system – and worth the trip!" for the "fun" and unexpected discovery of the "vibrant, buzzy bohemian bistro" it contains. Eating "amidst antiques a-plenty", you can enjoy "unusual breakfasts", "decent cocktails" and "excellent southwest French cuisine", the work of well-known chef, Jackson Boxer. Service, though, can be "a bit off the ball". / SW8 2LG; www.brunswickhouse.london; 10 pm; closed Sun D.

Bryn Williams at Somerset House WC2 £66 3 3 3
Somerset House   020 7845 464   2–2D
This avowedly 'veggie-centric' concept from Welsh chef Bryn Williams (of highly rated Odette's in Primrose Hill) gives top billing to vegetables and fruit, although the menu still offers plenty for carnivores to chew on. It occupies the quirky chamber, right at the back of Somerset House with Thames views, that once housed The Admiralty (RIP) – an intriguing location, but also one smart enough for doing business. From a fair number of reports, there is mostly praise for dishes that are "beautifully prepared and served" – a "detox set lunch with no meat or fish in sight was really inspiring and exciting". / WC2R 1LA; www.bryn-somersethouse.co.uk; @bwsomersethouse.

Bubala E1 NEW
65 Commercial Street   13–2C
Following a number of sell-out events across London, this Middle Eastern venture's first permanent site opened near Spitalfields as we went to press. The team's CVs incorporate Berber & Q and also The Palomar family; a boldy-flavoured, fully vegetarian menu of sharing plates is promised, inspired by Tel Aviv's modern cafés. / E1 6BD; www.bubala.co.uk.

Bubbledogs W1 £52 3 4 4
70 Charlotte St   020 7637 7770   2–1C
"Hot dogs and Champagne – how could that be wrong?", asks a fan of Sandia Chang's unlikely-sounding Fitzrovia concept bar, which shares premises with her husband James Knappett's tasting-menu-only Kitchen Table (see also). What's more, "excellent burgers" paired with "London's most accessible list of Champagnes (including some crackers by the glass) qualifies as cheap and ridiculously cheerful". / W1T 4QG; www.bubbledogs.co.uk; @bubbledogsUK; 9 pm; closed Sun.

Bubbledogs, Kitchen Table W1 £179 4 4 4
70 Charlotte St   020 7637 7770   2–1C
"One of a kind!": James Knappett's "phenomenal" Fitzrovia 20-seater – entered via the hotdog-and-Champagne bar that shares its name (see Bubbledogs) – "takes creative gastronomy to a new level" and is "well deserving of its second Michelin star". Cooking behind a horseshoe-shaped counter with the kitchen at its centre, "the chefs are good company", and their conversation helps "nail the balance between a very interesting gastronomic journey and a lovely 'feel-at-home' atmosphere". Dishes "celebrating high quality produce are effortlessly executed and perfectly sized"; and "with enough innovation to keep you interested, while not alienating anyone". "One of the best meals of my life" – "I barely noticed that it lasted three hours!" / W1T 4QG; www.kitchentablelondon.co.uk; @bubbledogsKT; seatings only at 6 pm & 7.30 pm; D only, closed Mon & Sun.

Bucket W2 £50 **3** **4** **3**

107 Westbourne Grove   020 3146 1156   7–1B

Mussels, prawns, calamari and other seafood by the, er, bucket-load is the promise at this "lovely local" yearling on the Bayswater/Notting Hill border – a "comfortable" modern bistro with simple-but-effective decor, serving "a wide selection of very fresh fish and seafood" (in small metal pails) that's "very good value". Top Tip – oyster happy hour 4pm-7pm weekdays and 4pm-6pm on weekends, when oysters are £1 each with any bottle, jug, cocktail or bucket of beers. / W2 4UW; www.bucketrestaurant.com.

Buen Ayre E8 £61 **4** **3** **2**

50 Broadway Market   020 7275 9900   14–2B

"As close as you can get to Buenos Aires without leaving London" – this Argentinian parrilla is one of hip Broadway Market's longest-serving foodie hotspots, and serves "amazing steaks, and a great wine list for reds". / E8 4QJ; www.buenayre.co.uk; 10 pm, Fri & Sat 10.30 pm, Sun 10 pm; No Amex.

The Builders Arms SW3 £58

13 Britten St   020 7349 9040   6–2C

This attractive Chelsea backstreet pub – "good food"; "a good place to watch the rugby" – closed for a refurb this summer, following our survey. Its sale to Hippo Inns returns it to the ownership of Rupert Clevely, who sold former owner Geronimo to Young's in 2010. / SW3 3TY; www.thebuildersarmschelsea.co.uk; @BuildersChelsea; 10 pm, Thu-Sat 11 pm, Sun 9.30 pm; no booking.

The Bull N6 £51 **3** **4** **3**

13 North Hill   020 8341 0510   9–1B

This grand old Highgate pub with an in-house microbrewery has a "great range of their own beers, and some good nibbles to go along with them". More substantial fare includes "very good roasts", and staff are "particularly helpful". / N6 4AB; thebullhighgate.co.uk; @Bull_Highgate.

Bull & Last NW5 £66 **3** **3** **3**

168 Highgate Rd   020 7267 3641   9–1B

"Cannot wait for this gem of a place to reopen!" – Kentish Town's brilliant Heath-side destination has been closed for most of the last year, as it turns itself into a six-bedroom pub-with-rooms. Set to re-open in late-2019, here's hoping they haven't mucked up what's ranked as north London's top gastropub in recent years. / NW5 1QS; www.thebullandlast.co.uk; @thebullandlast; 10 pm, Sun 9 pm.

Bumpkin £58 **2** **2** **3**

102 Old Brompton Rd, SW7   020 7341 0802   6–2B

Westfield Stratford City, The Street, E20   020 8221 9900   14–1D

"A sort of neighbourhood bistro, just beyond the touristy influence of the South Kensington museums" – the main survivor of an erstwhile chain (there's also a Stratford sibling no-one talks about) "offering British upmarket pub food", which is variable to good. It's "a nice and warming place", but it can become "rather busy and noisy"; and "service, while cheerful and pleasant, is extremely variable". / www.bumpkinuk.com; 10 pm, Sun 9 pm; closed Mon.

Bun House WC2 NEW £14 **4** **3** **3**

26-27 Lisle Street   5–3A

"Recently moved from Soho to Chinatown into a new, bigger and better space" – Z He and Alex Peffly's venture is a "#1 spot for a quick, cheap meal": "buns are filled with authentic Chinese flavours and the dough is so soft it feels like you're eating clouds!". Meanwhile, back at the original Greek Street site, this husband-and-wife team have transformed their old premises into Wun's, which opened in July 2019: see also. / WC2H 7BD; bun.house; @8unhouse.

Burger & Beyond E1 NEW £53 5 3 3
147 Shoreditch High Street 13–1B
"Some of the best burgers in London" – including a "sublime, fried, hot fish burger" and "a real vegetarian burger (that isn't pretending to be anything other than a real, delicious vegetarian burger)" – make it well worth discovering this hip new Shoreditch diner. When it comes to going 'beyond', "some of the tapas style starters are worth trying too" (cauliflower cheese balls, fried chicken bites…) / E1 6JE; burgerandbeyond.co.uk; @burgerandbeyond.

Burger & Lobster £60 3 2 3
Harvey Nichols, 109-125 Knightsbridge, SW1 020 7235 5000 6–1D
26 Binney St, W1 020 3637 5972 3–2A
29 Clarges St, W1 020 7409 1699 3–4B
36 Dean St, W1 020 7432 4800 3–2A
6 Little Portland St, W1 020 7907 7760 3–1C
18 Hertsmere Road, E14 020 3637 6709 12–1C
40 St John St, EC1 020 7490 9230 10–1B
Bow Bells Hs, 1 Bread St, EC4 020 7248 1789 10–2B
52 Threadneedle Street, EC2 020 756 9755 NEW
The cut-price surf 'n' turf at this "fun, relaxed and reliable" operation "never fails" – "have a lobster roll as a starter, then a burger as a main". Under the same ownership as the Goodman steakhouses, the London-based chain has consolidated to nine domestic branches plus the Smack lobster roll delivery-only spinoff, while expanding internationally in the US, Middle East and southeast Asia. / www.burgerandlobster.com; @Londonlobster; 10.30 pm-11 pm, Sun 8 pm-10 pm; WC1 & EC2 closed Sun; booking: min 6.

Busaba Eathai £51 3 2 2
"Decent Thai food from a regularly changing menu" has earned solid ratings this year for this chain of communal Asian diners, which has seen improved feedback since the closure of its branches outside London last year. The group was founded 20 years ago by Alan Yau as the follow-up to his hit creation Wagamama, and has its strongest presence in the West End, where the branches are "a useful pre-theatre pitstop". / www.busaba.co.uk; @busabaeathai; 11 pm, Fri & Sat 11.30 pm, Sun 10 pm; W1 no booking; WC1 booking: min 10.

Butlers Wharf Chop House SE1 £70 3 3 4
36e Shad Thames 020 7403 3403 10–4D
This business-friendly D&D London venue plays to its strengths: the spectacular Tower Bridge setting, plus a well-constructed menu of meaty, classic British dishes. Originally part of Sir Terence Conran's 'Gastrodome' project in the 1990s, fans "have been coming here for years" and for a simple grill in prime Thames-side territory, it's worth remembering. / SE1 2YE; www.chophouse-restaurant.co.uk; @BWChophouse; 11 pm.

by Chloe 3 2 2
4-5 Langham Place, W1 3–1C NEW
Drury House, 34-43 Russell Street, WC2 020 3883 3273 5–2D
ICON at the O2, Peninsula Square, SE10 12–1D NEW
6 Duchess Walk, One Tower Bridge, SE1 10–4D NEW
A single Covent Garden branch has quickly become a chain of four for Chloe Coscarelli and Samantha Wasser's NYC-based, fast-food, vegan chain, with openings this year near Tower Bridge, by Oxford Circus and in the O2. It's mass catering for sure (with salads, fish 'n' chips, sarnies), junk-ish even (burgers, mac 'n' cheese, fries, cupcakes) but, for an everyday vegan fix from brunch onwards, no chain is covering the ground quicker. / www.eatbychloe.com; @eatbychloe.

Byron £37 122

Will the July 2019 adoption of a vegan burger option help turn around the fortunes of this once-market-leading burger chain, which lost nearly 1/3 of its branches in 2018 during a much-publicised CVA (Company Voluntary Agreement)? Still-plummeting ratings suggest it still has a mountain to climb with reports of food that's "not up to scratch" and "branches that seem unloved". But even so, it maintains a big following who want to see management succeed: the "formula may need a bit of refreshment", they say, but "it's a brand that does not deserve to be sneered at!" HOLD THE FRONT PAGE: In August 2019, the chain took a dramatic further step towards a complete turnaround… a new logo! / www.byronhamburgers.com; most branches 11 pm.

C&R Café W1 £31 422

3-4 Rupert Ct   020 7434 1128   4–3D

"Cheap but very tasty Malaysian food" provides a "compelling reason" to choose this well-established fixture in a Chinatown alleyway. (Its former Bayswater sibling still has 'C&R' in the title, but is now separately run as a Japanese izakaya.) / W1D 6DY; 11 pm.

Cabotte EC2 £71 454

48 Gresham St   020 7600 1616   10–2C

"A stunning treasure trove of Burgundy wine" is just one of the attractions of this "buzzy and down-to-earth" two-year-old, near the Guildhall. The serving crew are "super friendly" and "knowledgeable", while the regional French cuisine from head chef Edward Boarland is "luscious, beautiful, and nourishing (almost comfort food, but the quality is super-high)". Often tipped as a top choice for business entertaining, it's nevertheless "one of the very few such City restaurants in which you would want to actually spend your own money!" / EC2V 7AY; www.cabotte.co.uk; @Cabotte_; 9.30 pm.

Café Below EC2 £35 333

St Mary-le-Bow, Cheapside   020 7329 0789   10–2B

"Escape the feel of the City for very reasonable home cooked-food" in the ancient crypt of Bow Bells church. "There are no better dining establishments in the Square Mile: affordable, great service, good food with delicious daily changing salads" including "excellent veggie and vegan options". Depending on when you go, it's either a "quiet" space or quite a "noisy" one. / EC2 6AU; www.cafebelow.co.uk; @cafebelow; 2.30 pm; L only.

Café del Parc N19 £47 553

167 Junction Road   020 7281 5684   9–1C

"What an amazing find" in Tufnell Park – "a tiny kitchen behind a small counter in a converted Victorian shop that turns out delicious, flavour-packed, tapas-style, Moorish-influenced dishes to a handful of tables". There's "no menu, they just bring what they think you'll like" – and reporters are unanimous that it is "beautifully inspired and enjoyable": "the best Mediterranean cooking I've had outside the Med". / N19 5PZ; www.delparc.com; @delParc; 10.30 pm; open D only, Wed-Sun; No Amex; booking D only.

Café du Marché EC1 £52 335

22 Charterhouse Sq   020 7608 1609   10–1B

"Just the kind of spot you expect on the market square of a small French town" – this "delightful stalwart, hidden at the back of a cobbled mews off Charterhouse Square", is an "unchanging old friend" to its big fanclub. "Convivial, candlelit and very romantic", its menu is "not gourmet, but it delivers classic Gallic cuisine served with a lot of charm"; and regular jazz helps "adds to the great ambience" in the evening. / EC1M 6DX; www.cafedumarche.co.uk; @cafedumarche; 10 pm; closed Sat L & Sun.

Café East SE16 £28 **5** 2 2
100 Redriff Rd   020 7252 1212   12–2B
*"The pho served here is the real thing – authentic, tasty and never fails",
is a commonly held view of this long-running and good-value Vietnamese
canteen in Surrey Quays. "They also serve the best summer rolls I've ever
encountered".* / SE16 7LH; www.cafeeastpho.co.uk; @cafeeastpho; 10.30 pm,
Sun 10 pm; closed Tue; No Amex; No bookings.

Café in the Crypt,
St Martin in the Fields WC2 £32 **2** 1 **4**
Duncannon St   020 7766 1158   2–2C
*"Lovely, airy underground café" in the large, rambling and atmospheric crypt
of St Martin-in-the-Fields that's "very useful for a quick lunch" by Trafalgar
Square. There's always "something for everyone", including "good and
varied soups" – and "it's for a good cause".* / WC2N 4JJ;
stmartin-in-the-fields.org/cafe-in-the-crypt; @smitf_london; 8 pm, Wed 10.30 pm,
Thu-Sat 9 pm, Sun 6 pm; L & early evening only; No Amex; May need 5+ to book.

Café Monico W1 £49 2 2 **4**
39-45 Shaftesbury Avenue   020 3727 6161   5–3A
*This would-be-instant-classic Theatreland brasserie – artfully designed by the
Soho House group using the name of an 1877 original – "could be great for
its location", right amongst the bright lights of Shaftesbury Avenue, and has
a fine interior. But the food falls very short – which is "a real shame": the
menu of French and Italian classics "promises so much" but too often
"delivers nothing!"; and, for somewhere so central, the venue inspires
remarkably little feedback.* / W1D 6LA; www.cafemonico.com; @cafemonico;
midnight, Fri & Sat 1 am.

Cafe Murano £63 2 2 2
33 St James's St, SW1   020 3371 5559   3–3C
34 Tavistock Street, WC2   020 3535 7884   5–3D
36 Tavistock St, WC2   020 3371 5559   5–3D
*"Perhaps hopes were too high?" – Angela Hartnett's spin-off Italians
in Covent Garden and St James's inspire a lot of feedback, but much of it
is mixed. Fans do applaud her for "succeeding where most others fail
in establishing a couple of cheaper ventures that follow her style, but do not
feel part of a factory-made chain; and which provide some excellent, simple
Italian cooking and carefully chosen wines". But for many sceptics, the gloss
is taken off the experience either by "food that's fine but not exceptional;
not-wholly-interested service; or a lack of ambience" (WC2 can
be "very noisy"). She must be doing something right however, as in June
2019 she submitted plans to take over the Bermondsey site some will recall
as Zucca (RIP) to become her next outlet. Top Tip – "a useful stop pre-
theatre but the set menu never seems to meet expectations, so it's better
to stick with the à la carte".* / www.cafemurano.co.uk; 11 pm, Sun 4 pm, Pastificio
9 pm, ; Pastificio closed Sun.

Café Spice Namaste E1 £62 **5** **4** **3**
16 Prescot St   020 7488 9242   12–1A
*"Some of the best Indian food in town" – "Cyrus and Pervin Todiwala are
delightful hosts" and the "dated outside" of their City-fringe HQ "gives
no clue that a meal here will be so delicious". The cuisine offers "a different
take on traditional Indian" (mixing Parsi and Goan dishes with more pan-
Indian inspirations) and its longstanding "authenticity" and "creativity" is a
continued joy, as is the "genuinely friendly way that TV-chef Cyrus
T, OBE comes out to chat with guests". "As good as you'll get in Mumbai...
and the traffic isn't as bad!"* / E1 8AZ; www.cafespice.co.uk; @cafespicenamast;
10.30 pm; closed Sat L & Sun.

Caffè Caldesi W1 £75 3 2 3
118 Marylebone Ln   020 7487 0754   2–1A
*"Authentic and exceptional" Italian cuisine, with "classics done well"
alongside "seasonal and Tuscan specials", hits the spot at this family-run
Marylebone venue. The upstairs dining room "can be a bit austere if less
than half full", and there's also an informal bar and café downstairs.
/ W1U 2QF; www.caldesi.com; 10.30 pm, Sun 9.30 pm.*

Cakes and Bubbles W1 £86 3 4 4
Hotel Cafe Royal, 10 Air St   020 7406 3310   4–4C
*Albert Adrià (pastry chef back in the day at his brother Ferran's world
famous El Bulli) operates this marbled café, overlooking Regent Street,
near Piccadilly Circus. When it comes to the menu, the clue is in the name,
and on most accounts his "original", delectable sweet creations – including
the signature cheesecake – may be "a little pricey", but are "simply
legendary". / W1B 4DY; www.cakesandbubbles.co.uk.*

The Camberwell Arms SE5 £50 5 3 3
65 Camberwell Church St   020 7358 4364   1–3C
*"The menu is SO enticing and the food SO delicious that it is difficult
to imagine better pub food than at The Camberwell Arms" – "buzzy" sibling
to the famous Anchor & Hope. "When on song (and not full of refugees
from nearby Peckham) this is one of the best gastropubs in London".
"The wine list is very interesting, with some out-of-the-norm bottles that are
modestly priced; and the cocktails are gluggable too". / SE5 8TR;
www.thecamberwellarms.co.uk; @camberwellarms; 10 pm; closed Mon L & Sun D.*

Cambio de Tercio SW5 £68 4 3 3
161-163 Old Brompton Rd   020 7244 8970   6–2B
*Abel Lusa's "little corner of Spain on the Old Brompton Road" has pioneered
upscale Hispanic cuisine in London for 25 years with "tasty creations that
wow the diner" alongside "a joy of a wine list – not cheap but with
an exceptional selection". It's a "destination of choice for every mood and
occasion, be it just for tapas or a full meal" – or, if you're Rafa Nadal,
if you're in town for a game of tennis... / SW5 0LJ; www.cambiodetercio.co.uk;
@CambiodTercio; 11.15 pm, Sun & Mon 10.45 pm.*

Cambridge Street SW1 £66 3 3 4
52 Cambridge St   020 3019 8622   2–4B
*This "fun" all-day haunt in an otherwise dull corner of Pimlico has "all the
on-trend gastropub menu options you could hope for, but everything is done
really well for once". It makes "the perfect breakfast/brunch spot" –
when "trade can be manic". / SW1V 4QQ; www.cambridgestreetcafe.co.uk;
@TheCambridgeSt; 9.30 pm, Sat 10 pm, Sun 8.30 pm.*

Camillo Benso W1 2 2 3
8-10 Blenheim Street   020 7629 8889   3–2B
*This formal Mayfair yearling – offshoot of a top Milanese establishment –
achieved very limited and mixed survey feedback, in keeping with the
drubbing it received from The Sunday Times's Marina O'Loughlin: "portions
seem small... the food's good but not exceptional, and expect to pay dearly
for it". / W1S 1LJ; www.camillobenso.co.uk; @camillobensoLDN.*

Camino £53 2 2 2
3 Varnishers Yd, Regent Quarter, N1   020 7841 7330   9–3C
The Blue Fin Building, 5 Canvey St, SE1   020 3617 3169   10–4B
2 Curtain Road, EC2   13–2B
15 Mincing Ln, EC3   020 7841 7335   10–3D
*A "good choice of drinks" helps fuel the "buzzy" style of this "good value"
Hispanic group. Some reporters feel its tapas offering is rather "standard",
but most reports are of "good tapas at good prices". / www.camino.uk.com;
11pm, EC3 Sat 10 pm, Sun 10pm; EC2 closed Sun, EC3 closed Sat & Sun.*

Campania & Jones E2 £43 444 3
23 Ezra St   020 7613 0015   14–2A
*Rustic former cowshed that's one of the quainter diversions when visiting
Columbia Road Flower Market. On limited feedback, we received nothing
but good ratings this year for its Italian cooking, but the weight of custom
at busy times means service can suffer. / E2 7RH; www.campaniaandjones.com;
10.30 pm.*

Cannizaro House,
Hotel du Vin SW19 £60 111 3
West Side, Wimbledon Common   0871 943 0345   11–2A
*The "very pleasant surroundings" of an "excellent dining room overlooking
Cannizaro Park" are let down by the consistently disappointing meals and
"don't care" attitude of staff at this Hotel du Vin outfit. "Someone rescue
it – it's a waste of a fantastic space". / SW19 4UE;
www.hotelduvin.com/locations/wimbledon; @HotelduVinBrand; 10 pm.*

Cantina Laredo WC2 £62 222
10 Upper St Martin's Lane   020 7420 0630   5–3C
*"Sitting by the windows on a summer's evening makes for a great pre-
theatre outing" at this American-owned Mexican in Covent Garden.
"Top frozen margaritas" and "guacamole made at your table" add to the
experience. / WC2H 9FB; www.cantinalaredo.co.uk; @CantinaLaredoUK; 10 pm,
Fri & Sat 10.30 pm, Sun 9 pm.*

Canto Corvino E1 £63 323
21 Artillery Lane   020 7655 0390   13–2B
*"Outstanding seasonal food with very helpful and friendly service" gets
a thumbs-up for this modern Italian by Spitalfields Market. There's a "great
wine list – including by-the-glass from the Coravin system", and it's also
highly recommended for a business breakfast – "much better than the
Breakfast Club opposite, and no queue". / E1 7HA; www.cantocorvino.co.uk;
@cantocorvinoE1; 10 pm.*

Canton Arms SW8 £51 434
177 South Lambeth Rd   020 7582 8710   11–1D
*"The best gastropub I've found in London" – this Stockwell operation
is "a winner for an uncomplicated but thoroughly satisfying meal", especially
"for those who enjoy expertly prepared cuts of high-quality meat".
"It's similar in standard to the Anchor & Hope (its famous Southwark
sibling) but better because it's quieter, with a more relaxed atmosphere".
To cap it all, it's "still a proper pub, where you're welcome for a quiet pint".
/ SW8 1XP; www.cantonarms.com; @cantonarms; 10.30 pm; closed Mon L & Sun D;
No Amex; no booking.*

Capeesh E14 £56 333
4 Pan Peninsula Square   020 7538 1111   12–2C
*On the 48th-floor of a Canary Wharf skyscraper, right by South Quay DLR
– this glossy two-year-old, Italian restaurant and 'Sky Bar' certainly enjoys
amazing panoramas. As yet, it still generates only relatively limited feedback,
but such as there is says it avoids the usual curse of rooms with a view,
serving decent pizza, steaks and other Italian fare. There's ent's at the
weekend, with live DJs on Friday, and Saturday is club night. / E14 9HN;
www.capeesh.co.uk; @capeeshlondon.*

Le Caprice SW1 £75 2 4 4
20 Arlington St 020 7629 2239 3–4C

"Even at the bar, one feels like a star… and there are often real stars eating as well!" – this "timeless and elegant" brasserie, tucked away near The Ritz has endured well within Richard Caring's empire and, although the cooking "has fallen away a bit", the overall package remains many a savvy Londoner's favourite. "Staff are upbeat" and "make you feel well looked after", and its buzzy atmosphere "makes other posh rivals feel flat and stuffy": "some nights it zings, sometimes it just feels like an efficient machine, but either way, it's a top night out", particularly on a date. (A spin-off brand, Caprice Café, is due to open its first branch in late 2019 in North Audley Street in Mayfair). / SW1A 1RJ; www.le-caprice.co.uk; @CapriceHoldings; 11.30 pm, Sun 10.30 pm; May need 6+ to book.

Caractère W11 £83 5 5 4
209 Westbourne Park Road 020 8181 3850 7–1B

"Absolutely the best new restaurant in the past year or so" – the Roux dynasty have come up trumps with this "great newbie in the Notting Hill 'hood", on the site of Bumpkin (RIP). It's the brainchild of Michel Roux's daughter Emily Roux and her husband Diego Ferrari (former head chef at Le Gavroche). "Just around the corner from The Ledbury, but half the price and less formal" – it provides a "fabulous all-round experience", founded on "outstanding" and "creative" cooking "born out of two great cuisines: French and Italian". (However, "the unusual menu layout does take a moment to puzzle out", with headings like Curious, Subtle and Greedy). "Impeccable service" and the "very comfortable" space, decorated with "quirky touches" complete the experience. Top Tip – "don't miss the celeriac 'cacio e pepe'". / W11 1EA; www.caractererestaurant.com.

Caraffini SW1 £62 3 5 4
61-63 Lower Sloane St 020 7259 0235 6–2D

"The maitre d' remembered me from over 10 years ago and treated me like I'd given him my patronage every day of those 10 years!" – this "neighbourhood" stalwart trattoria is "a staple of the area" south of Sloane Square: "unchanging from year to year" and "like a home from home" for its many (generally silver-haired) regulars. "The menu may not have changed in years, but who cares?" – it's "always reliable, and well-priced for the locale" – and its USP is its "wonderful staff", who "treat you like royalty" and are so "friendly" ("they knew exactly how to banter with my grumpy daughter and exactly when to point out a good wine on the list"). "Heaven help us when it finally changes hands…" / SW1W 8DH; www.caraffini.co.uk; 11 pm; closed Sun.

Caravaggio EC3 £60 3 2 2
107-112 Leadenhall St 020 7626 6206 10–2D

"Smart and rather business-like" stalwart, near Leadenhall Market, that's one of the City's longer-established expense-account venues. Even those who feel that the experience is "all a bit 'staged'" say it "nevertheless serves great Italian cuisine"; and reporters who feel that "after 20 years it's a tad tired" still say that "it's always a pleasant visit". / EC3A 4DP; www.etruscarestaurants.com; 10 pm; closed Sat & Sun.

Caravan £54 2 2 3
Yalding House, 152 Great Portland Street, W1 020 3963 8500 2–1B
1 Granary Sq, N1 020 7101 7661 9–3C
30 Great Guildford St, SE1 020 7101 1190 10–4B
11-13 Exmouth Mkt, EC1 020 7833 8115 10–1A
Queen Victoria Street, EC4 020 3957 5555 10–3C

"So many amazing, creative options for brunch" together with "renowned coffee" ("meticulously sourced and roasted in-house") have made these "loud", "brash", "buzzy" and "quite hip" haunts – particularly the well-known Granary Square branch – key destinations, particularly at the weekend. When busy, however, service can be "hit and miss"; and the food has sometimes been a let-down of late: "it feels like random, trendy ingredients are thrown into dishes so they can charge more for them, rather than for culinary interest or flavour". / www.caravanonexmouth.co.uk; @CaravanResto; 10.30 pm, Sun 4 pm; closed Sun; no bookings for weekend brunch.

Carousel W1 £52 4 4 3
71 Blandford St 020 7487 5564 3–1A
"A brilliant idea that never disappoints" – this Marylebone venue hosts "a different guest chef every week", flying in "some of the most exciting cooks in the world, who deliver an astonishing range of food". Lunch from the crack in-house team is also "terrific and great value", comprising "small plates full of original flavours". / W1U 8AB; www.carousel-london.com; @Carousel_LDN; one seating only, at 7 pm; closed Mon L & Sun L.

The Carpenter's Arms W6 £57 3 3 3
91 Black Lion Ln 020 8741 8386 8–2B
"If Carlsberg made gastropubs...", fans of this backstreet Hammersmith hostelry near leafy St Peter's Square say it would be just like this, with a "roaring fire, beautifully-lit room, well-assembled wine list, and a menu which is driven by quality ingredients (and also with a garden that's perfect for a romantic summer evening: twinkling lights and lots of greenery")". Not all feedback is so upbeat though: critics say it's "rather expensive for what it is, with hit and miss service". / W6 9BG; www.carpentersarmsw6.co.uk; 10 pm, Sun 9 pm.

Casa Brindisa SW7 £56 3 3 4
7-9 Exhibition Rd 020 7590 0008 6–2C
Acres of pavement seating are the most eye-catching feature of this "buzzing" operation (run by the well-known Spanish food importers), which sits on the ant-trail between South Kensington tube station and the museums (go on a sunny day). It's "reliably enjoyable" for a "cheap 'n' cheerful" meal as the dishes are reliably good, but it's mostly chosen for its convenience rather than its foodie potential. / SW7 2HE; www.brindisatapaskitchens.com/restaurant/casa-brindisa-south-kensington; @TapasKitchens; 11 pm, Sun 10 pm; booking max 8 may apply.

Casa do Frango SE1 £44 3 4 4
32 Southwark Street 020 3972 2323 10–4C
"Grilled chicken is the centrepiece" (frango means chicken in Portuguese) and is done in three different ways: peri peri, lemon, and garlic-and-oregano – at this "buzzing", airy and artfully converted yearling, not far from Borough Market. "Sides, salads and especially the custard tarts are of a very high standard too, and service, like the room, is bright and cheery". A sibling stall is now open in Centre Point's Arcade Food Theatre, see also. / SE1 1TU; www.casadofrango.co.uk; No bookings.

Casa Fofó E8 NEW £57 5 3 3
158 Sandringham Road 020 8062 2489 14–1B
"Paradise for serious foodies" – "a street notorious for once being crime-ridden is now home to Hackney's best-value dining experience: £39 for a seven-course tasting menu", according to practically all reports on ex-Pidgin chef, Adolfo de Cecco's "intimate-feeling" foodie venture. "Thoughtful food is excellently executed by a team with evident passion" and if "a few technical slip-ups can creep in, the charming, passionate service (often by the chefs themselves) more than makes up for this". / E8 2HS; www.casafofolondon.co.uk.

Casa Pastór & Plaza Pastór N1 £64 3 2 3
Coal Drops Yard 9–3C
"Decent Mexican finally arrives in the 'hood" – the Hart Bros' Latino newcomer in the new Coal Drops Yard development mixes "a bit of party atmosphere" with the "authentic" flavours of Central America ("the frijoles charros give me that beany homey hit that has finally filled the void left when I moved to London from San Francisco!"). Top Tip "great kids menu with DIY tacos". / N1C 4AB; www.tacoselpastor.co.uk; @Tacos_El_Pastor.

Casa Tua WC1 £41 4 3 3
106 Cromer Street 020 7833 1483 9–4C
"Delicious, fresh pasta" is a particular highlight of the *"reasonably-priced homemade food"* at this *"cosy corner-Italian in the atmospheric backstreets of Bloomsbury"* (within walking distance of King's Cross). / WC1H 8BZ; www.casatuacamden.com/kings-cross; @casatuagastro.

Casse-Croute SE1 £56 4 4 4
109 Bermondsey St 020 7407 2140 10–4D
"The Gallic bistro you kept looking for on holiday in France, but never found…" – this *"tiny"* and *"cramped"* Bermondsey venue provides a *"small but ever-changing menu"* of *"the kind of memorable, old-school, traditional regional dishes it can be hard to find in Paris these days"* (*"boeuf en croute with gorgeous jus, tarte tatin etc"*). *"Booking is a must"*. / SE1 3XB; www.cassecroute.co.uk; @CasseCroute109; 10 pm, Sun 4 pm; closed Sun D.

Catford Constitutional Club SE6 £40 3 3 4
Catford Broadway 020 8613 7188 1–4D
"An oasis in the middle of the culinary desert" that is downtown Catford: the atmosphere – like the name – at this big (*"cavernous"*) and retro-looking gastropub channels the 1950s by the simple expedient of retaining the decor of the former Conservative club on the site. A smart modern menu is backed up by craft ales and ciders. (Lewisham Council owns the freehold and plans to redevelop it to provide affordable housing, while leaving CCC intact.) Top Tip – cute suntrap garden. / SE6 4SP; catfordconstitutionalclub.com; @CatfordCClub; 10 pm.

Caviar Kaspia W1 NEW
1a Chesterfield Street awaiting tel 3–4B
Since it closed in 2000 (on the site which became Bellamy's), this luxury Parisian-based brand (fondée 1927) has lacked a London outlet. Following a successful pop-up last year, this opening on the site of Mayair's former Chess Club aims to bring it back more permanently. Originally scheduled for April, the actual launch date had yet to be announced in September 2019. / W1J 5JF; www.caviarkaspia.com.

Cay Tre £43 3 3 2
42-43 Dean St, W1 020 7317 9118 5–2A
301 Old St, EC1 020 7729 8662 13–1B
The *"fantastic"* Vietnamese food at these canteens *"is by far the best I've found, and I've tried a number of places in London"* – although *"it isn't the best for ambience"*. There are two to choose between, although the Soho site attracts more feedback than the Hoxton original these days. Top Tip – *"the banh cuon (steamed rice roll) has me travelling across town with a craving!"*. / www.caytrerestaurant.co.uk; @CayTreLondon; 11 pm, Fri & Sat 11.30 pm, Sun 10.30 pm; booking: min 8.

Cecconi's £85 2 2 4
19-21 Old Compton Street, W1 020 7734 5656 5–2A
5a Burlington Gdns, W1 020 7434 1500 4–4A
58-60 Redchurch Street, E2 020 3841 7755 13–1C
The Ned, 27 Poultry, EC2 020 3828 2000 10–2C
"There's always such a buzz at any time" at the original Cecconi's, *"tucked away behind the Royal Academy"* – a *"bustling"* and *"sophisticated"* all-day Italian brasserie, whose *"open, bright, pavement terrace"* helps make it a big favourite amongst the St James's set, be it *"for an upmarket business breakfast"*, or as *"a treat during a day's shopping in the West End"*. When it comes to the cooking, it *"can be a bit hit or miss, but is generally good"*. Nowadays owned by Soho House, the brand is being rolled out, but its diverse family of spin-offs echo rather than replicate the original. There's a City outlet in The Ned's capacious food hall, which like Mayfair is *"fun"* and *"an excellent place to do business"* of a less formal kind. Beyond that, the food is *"reliable"* but pretty *"basic at the price"*, and the setting can

be "the noisiest ever". A Soho pizza spot carries the name, on which there's little feedback. New in September 2018, the Shoreditch branch is "a very good addition as a real neighbourhood restaurant", with a "nice bar", and a generally "winning formula", including for brunch. / cecconis.co.uk.

The Cedar Restaurant £41 **3****3****2**
65 Fernhead Road, W9 020 8964 2011 1–2B
202 West End Lane, NW6 020 3602 0862 1–1B
81 Boundary Road, NW8 020 3204 0030 9–3A
Understated trio of "good neighbourhood Lebanese" in Hampstead, Maida Vale and St John's Wood; "consistently tasty food" is served "in huge portions for the hungry at reasonable prices". / www.thecedarrestaurant.co.uk; @Cedarlebanese.

Celeste at The Lanesborough SW1 £131 **2****2****4**
Hyde Park Corner 020 7259 5599 6–1D
Dining in this grand hotel by Hyde Park Corner is a "truly amazing experience" and the food – overseen by Paris-based uber-chef Eric Fréchon – is by most accounts "lovely". But this "most exceptional night out" requires you "to forget what it will inevitably cost!" – "it would be hard to be good enough to justify these prices" – which might explain why there can be "quite a few empty chairs". / SW1X 7TA; @TheLanesborough; 10.30 pm.

Le Cellar EC1 NEW £37 **3****4****3**
130 St John Street 020 7689 9115 10–1A
Promising initial feedback on this tiny, wine, cheese, charcuterie and tapas newcomer in Clerkenwell, whose backers include wine buyer Anthonin Charlier (formerly at Cellar and Club Gascon). French and Spanish flavours are to the fore – "a really happy discovery: both food and wine are great, but the service makes the place". / EC1V 4JS; lecellar.co.uk.

Cent Anni SW19 NEW £53 **3****3****3**
33 High Street 020 3971 9781 11–2B
A new 100-seater Italian in Wimbledon village (in the site that was formerly Cau, RIP), which avoids pizza, and serves 'proper' dishes at relatively affordable prices. Some results are "so so", but its initial ratings are promising. / SW19 5BY; centanni.co.uk.

Cepages W2 £64 **4****3****4**
69 Westbourne Park Road 020 3602 8890 7–1B
"Sexy sharing dishes and a dark romantic setting" earn a big thumbs-up for this "fabulous French tapas bistro in deepest Westbourne Park", with an "open brickwork vibe and a couple of coveted tables outside for the hot weather". Wine is taken seriously, prices are "gentle", and it's "one of the few places one can enjoy fresh foie gras cooked rare or à point". / W2 5QH; www.cepages.co.uk; @cepagesWPR; 11 pm, Sun 10 pm.

Ceru £35 **4****3****4**
11 D'Arblay Street, W1 020 3195 3002 4–1C NEW
7-9 Bute St, SW7 020 3195 3001 6–2C
"Brilliant", "fresh" and "unusual" Levantine flavours; "cheerful and helpful staff"; and "sunnily charming decoration" ensure these "above-average", modern Middle Eastern bistros are "invariably lively and bustling". The SW7 branch is a well-known fixture of the 'Petit France' enclave of South Kensington, while its year-old spin-off has made a good start establishing itself at the top end of Soho – "you can understand the popularity when food of such a high standard is produced at such very reasonable prices". / www.cerurestaurants.com; @CeruLondon.

Ceviche £60 **3** **3** **4**
17 Frith St, W1   020 7292 2040   5–2A
Alexandra Trust, Baldwin St, EC1   020 3327 9463   13–1A
"Still the best Peruvian cuisine in London and still a go-to for a reliable, enjoyable meal out" with "tons of atmosphere" – so say fans of Martin Morales's "vibrant and fun" Latino cantinas in Soho and Shoreditch, known for their "street-ish dishes with interesting combos" and "lovely pisco sours". Ratings came off the boil a little this year, though, with the view aired by one or two reporters that "you can get much better ceviche at much better prices elsewhere". / www.cevicheuk.com; @cevicheuk; W1D 11pm, Fri & Sat 11.30 pm, Sun 10 pm, EC1V 10.30 pm, Fri & Sat 11.30 pm; EC1V closed Sun.

Champor-Champor SE1 £58 **3** **3** **2**
62 Weston St   020 7403 4600   10–4C
"Unusual Thai cooking with interesting Malay influences" has for many years drawn a steady flow of diners to a sidestreet near Guy's Hospital, now in the shadow of the Shard. "Service is quick and helpful", and the "small, slightly cramped" restaurant "has a lovely hideaway table for a romantic dinner". / SE1 3QJ; www.champor-champor.com; @ChamporChampor; 10 pm; D only.

Charlie's W1 NEW
Brown's Hotel, Albemarle Street   020 7493 6020   3–3C
Trinity's celebrated chef, Adam Byatt, is set to relaunch this stately panelled dining room of the foyer of one of Mayfair's most historic hotels, nowadays owned by Rocco Forte (whose late father, Lord Charles Forte inspired the name of this new venture). Adam is the latest in a succession of chefs (most recently Heinz Beck, of Beck at Browns, RIP) who have somehow failed to hit a home-run in this potentially splendid, traditional chamber. According to the PR we should expect an 'evolution of great British cuisine… while embracing a bygone era of service with a sense of theatre'. / W1S.

Charlotte's £54 **3** **2** **3**
6 Turnham Green Ter, W4   020 8742 3590   8–2A
This "reliable" bistro and gin bar near Turnham Green tube has always been "a pleasure to eat in" for 10 years, with "very good cooking, decent wines, and friendly, helpful staff". It is part of the long-established Ealing-based group whose original venue, Charlotte's Place, has closed down following a disastrous fire last year (RIP). / www.charlottes.co.uk; W4 midnight, Sun 11 pm, W5 9.30pm, Sun 4pm, W5 midnight.

Chelsea Cellar SW10 £46 **4** **4** **4**
9 Park Walk   020 7351 4933   6–3B
"Romantic, quaint and cosy basement" near Chelsea & Westminster Hospital that earns high marks across the board for its "classy and delicious" Italian cicchetti, plus a seasonal menu of larger plates and 250 wines (also available as off sales). "The owners really take care to look after you" and "clearly put everything into this place". / SW10 0AJ; www.thechelseacellar.co.uk; @chelseacellar; midnight.

Chettinad W1 £43 **4** **3** **2**
16 Percy St   020 3556 1229   2–1C
"Simply delicious south Indian cuisine" from the state of Tamil Nadu – including "the best dosas ever" – means this "justly popular independent" in Fitzrovia "is very different from your usual curry house". "I'm slowly working my way through the menu and have yet to find something I don't like". / W1T 1DT; www.chettinadrestaurant.com; @chettinadlondon; 11 pm, Sun 10 pm; No Amex.

Chez Bruce SW17 £84 5 5 4
2 Bellevue Rd   020 8672 0114   11–2C

"Still peerless as a neighbourhood restaurant delivering exquisite, modern French cuisine" – Bruce Poole's immaculate "mainstay of South West London", by distant Wandsworth Common, is – for the 15th year in succession – the survey's No.1 favourite restaurant, and "well worth the trip south of the river". "Whether you are going for a celebratory meal, or just a casual lunch or supper", "its consistency is astonishing, and comes at fabulously reasonable prices" (especially given the "little extra touches like Parmesan biscuits at the beginning of a meal, and chocolate truffles and palmiers at the end"). "What's brilliant about the seasonal cooking is its perfect, pure – not gastronomic – tastes and palate: classics are flawlessly cooked, and there is innovation without it being bound in any way to the latest fads and fashions". And "although there must be heaps going on behind the scenes, the set-up manages to be effortlessly elegant in an unpretentious style that feels like it comes easy to them", with "engaging" staff who are "professional without being obsequious". IF there's a gripe, it's that the "bright and compact" room that most reporters feel is "delightful" and "fitting for pretty much any occasion" (especially a romantic one) is, for a small minority, too "cramped" and un-fancy. / SW17 7EG; www.chezbruce.co.uk; @ChezBruce; 10 pm, Fri & Sat 10.30 pm, Sun 9 pm.

Chez Elles E1 £58 4 4 4
45 Brick Ln   020 7247 9699   13–2C

"Top-quality French food in a totally unpretentious environment is served up with knowledge" at this really charming Brick Lane bistro, with an inviting selection of croques monsieurs at lunch. / E1 6PU; www.chezellesbistroquet.co.uk; @chezellesbistro; 10.30 pm; closed Mon, Tue L & Sun D.

Chicama SW10 £60 4 2 4
383 King's Road   020 3874 2000   6–3C

"Terrific ceviche" – and other "interesting and generally excellent Peruvian-style fish dishes" – dominate the menu at this "really busy and buzzy place" on the King's Road; a two-year-old offshoot of Marylebone's Pachamama. / SW10 0LP; www.chicamalondon.com; @chicamalondon.

Chick 'n' Sours £43 4 3 3
1 Earlham Street, WC2   020 3198 4814   5–2B
62 Upper Street, N1   020 7704 9013   9–3D
390 Kingsland Rd, E8   020 3620 8728   14–2A

"Massive flavours, great vibe" and the "best chicken wings tasted in a long time" (#nextlevel) add up to "heaven in a chintzy, porcelain bowl", say fans of this "great value" concept based in Haggerston, now with branches in Covent Garden and Islington. "It's not just about the chicken – yes, it's mega-crispy and yes, it's super-juicy, but what sets Chick 'n' Sours apart are the garnishes, sides and sauces" – many of them Asian-inspired, such as "the yummy, smashed, spicy, peanuty, cucumber side". / www.chicknsours.co.uk; @chicknsours.

Chilli Cool WC1 £35 4 2 1
15 Leigh St   020 7383 3135   2–1D

"A favourite for authentic spicy Chinese food", this "grungy and basic" student-friendly canteen in Bloomsbury does a wonderful line in lip-tingling Sichuan noodle dishes. The "largely Asian clientele is an effective endorsement of its quality". / WC1H 9EW; www.chillicool.co.uk; 10.15 pm; No Amex.

The Chiltern Firehouse W1 £104 1 1 3
1 Chiltern St   020 7073 7676   2–1A

Five years on from its heyday as London's hottest celeb hangout, this "gorgeous" Marylebone destination is a "contender for the most overpriced in town", and attracts increasingly caustic comments: "how this poseur-filled dump hasn't been found out yet is a complete mystery: with food that's 'all fur coat and no knickers', and service which – if you're not a member of the smart set or the Z-list – is appalling". Some folks still respond to its shiny glamour, though: "the food is tasty and aesthetically pleasing… as are most of your fellow diners. Finish things off in the very sexy bar – if the romance doesn't spark, ditch each other for the beautiful staff…". / W1U 7PA; www.chilternfirehouse.com; 10.30 pm.

China Tang, Dorchester Hotel W1 £103 3 3 4
53 Park Ln   020 7629 9988   3–3A

"Excellent, but expensive" – the late Sir David Tang's stunning take on Art Deco-era Shanghai has always had vertiginous pricing, but its dependable cooking and "buzzy vibe" have silenced its sterner critics over the years, and the worst anyone has to say about it this year is that it's "good but not spectacular". Set in the basement of the Dorchester Hotel and newly refurbished in early 2019, arguably its best feature is its "wonderful cocktail list" and beguiling small bar. / W1K 1QA; www.chinatanglondon.co.uk; @ChinaTangLondon; 11.45 pm.

Chisou £65 4 4 2
22-23 Woodstock Street, W1   020 7629 3931   4–1A
31 Beauchamp Pl, SW3   020 3155 0005   6–1D

"Marvellous, exquisite Japanese food", including "super-fresh fish" and "the best sushi in town that won't break your wallet", is served at this "very professional" Mayfair outfit. Popular with Vogue staffers, who call it the 'Condé Nast canteen', it has a "cosy" offshoot buried in a luxurious corner of Knightsbridge. / www.chisourestaurant.com; 10.30 pm, Sun 9.30 pm.

Chit Chaat Chai SW18 £35 4 4 3
356 Old York Road   020 8480 2364   11–2B

"What a find!" – "superb and authentic Indian street food" developed at a market stall is now found in a permanent home by Wandsworth Town station. "Passionate owner Tania is always there to talk about the menu". / SW18 1SS; chitchaatchai.com; @ChitChaatChai; 10 pm, Sun 9 pm.

Chokhi Dhani London SW11 £58 3 4 3
Unit 2, 2 Riverlight Quay, Nine Elms Lane   020 3795 9000   11–1D

In the "desert" of Vauxhall's riverside developments, this year-old offshoot of one of India's best-known luxury restaurant groups occupies the smartly furnished ground floor of one of the new blocks, and specialises in Rajasthani cuisine. Feedback is still relatively limited, but such as there is says it's been an "excellent arrival". / SW11 8AW; www.chokhidhani.co.uk; @cdgchokhidhani; 22.45pm, Sun 21;45pm.

Chotto Matte W1 £59 4 3 4
11-13 Frith St   020 7042 7171   5–2A

"Exquisite food and cocktails" – "an amazing blend of flavours danced across my tongue!" – and "a great vibe (particularly for late-night dining)" help make this Japanese-Peruvian fusion haunt in Soho a "fun and buzzy" (if "loud", especially when the music's cranked up) destination for a night on the tiles. / W1D 4RB; www.chotto-matte.com; @ChottoMatteLDN; 1 am, Sun 11 pm.

Chriskitch N10 £42 **4** **3** **3**
7a Tetherdown   020 8411 0051   1–1C
"Fabulous, healthy food" ("excellent salads"), delicious brunches,
and "a bread board to die for" are all attractions at this inexpensive, "rather
tiny" neighbourhood fixture in Muswell Hill. "Take-away is a good option
if it's too cold/wet to sit outside". / N10 1ND; www.chriskitch.com;
@chriskitchfood; 6 pm, Sat & Sun 5 pm; L & early evening only; May need
3+ to book.

Christopher's WC2 £86 **2** **2** **3**
18 Wellington St   020 7240 4222   5–3D
This classic American surf 'n' turf restaurant and cocktail bar has a "lovely
atmosphere" thanks to its setting in a very grand townhouse, and has been
a Covent Garden stalwart for almost 30 years. "Perhaps it's showing its age,
but it's still reliable and in a useful location". The food could be better,
although reporters single out the "generally excellent steaks" for praise.
/ WC2E 7DD; www.christophersgrill.com; @christopherswc2; May need 6+ to book.

Chucs £85 **2** **3** **3**
31 Dover St, W1   020 3763 2013   3–3C
97 Old Brompton Road, SW7   020 8037 4525   6–2B **NEW**
226 Westbourne Grove, W11   020 7243 9136   7–1B
Serpentine Sackler Gallery, W2   0207 298 7552   7–2D
Part of the eponymous luxury clotheswear brand – these retro-glam cafés
are mostly located in-store, but the portfolio now also boasts the "beautiful
building by the Serpentine Sackler Gallery" designed by Zaha Hadid.
Perhaps because their price-tag is not exactly 'bargain basement', feedback
is somewhat limited, but there's a fairly clear picture of chic Italian dishes
that, while "good and tasty", can seem "nothing special" given the Monte
Carlo-esque bill. Any such caveats do not seem to be getting in the way
of the chain's ongoing expansion however, most recently into Kensington.
/ www.chucsrestaurants.com; W1 & SW1 11.30 pm, Sun 6 pm; W11 10.30 pm,
W2 8 pm; W2 closed Monday.

Church House SW13
94 Church Road   020 8748 0393   11—1A
Sonny's (RIP) had been part of the Barnes restaurant landscape for over
three decades before it closed in mid 2019. The site is still owned by
Rebecca Mascarenhas and a swift re-launch is already on the cards with this
autumn 2019 newcomer, with two ex-chefs involved who used to work for
her collaborator, Phil Howard. The cuisine will, on initial reports, still, by and
lare, be the modern brasserie fare of its predecessor.

Churchill Arms W8 £39 **3** **2** **5**
119 Kensington Church St   020 7792 1246   7–2B
"Top-value Thai food with personality – love it!". This slightly "bonkers" pub
near Notting Hill Gate looks normal enough, until you discover its "quirky
butterfly conservatory at the rear": "a hustling and bustling" venue serving
"tasty", spicy scoff at prices that are "amazingly low for the area". "Still
a winner" after over thirty years' service: in particular it's "a great choice for
eating with friends". / W8 7LN; www.churchillarmskensington.co.uk;
@ChurchillArmsW8; 10 pm, Sun 9.30 pm.

Chutney Mary SW1 £89 **4** **4** **3**
73 St James's Street   020 7629 6688   3–4D
"Still very much an institution, even though it moved from its original SW10
location": this "buzzy, glitzy high-end Indian" – nowadays in St James's –
delivers a formidable, all-round formula of "delightful" nouvelle Indian
cuisine: "the variety and quality of the menu is truly impressive", backed
up by "a well-matched list of wines and whiskies". Top Top – "sitting in the
bar area is more fun than the main restaurant". / SW1A 1PH;
www.chutneymary.com; @TheChutneyMary.

Chutneys NW1 £21 3 2 2
124 Drummond St   020 7388 0604   9–4C

"Fresh and tasty" veggie fare and an *"amazing lunch buffet"* make this *"ridiculously cheap"* curry house a perennial favourite in Euston Station's *'Little India'*. *"I've been going here for literally decades and have introduced many happy fans to the delights of Chutneys"* – *"the service could be a bit friendlier but when you're getting all you can eat for well under a tenner, who cares?"*. *"The decor of the ground floor has improved over the years, although the basement is less attractive"*. / NW1 2PA; www.chutneyseuston.uk; 11 pm; No Amex; May need 5+ to book.

Ciao Bella WC1 £48 3 4 4
86-90 Lamb's Conduit St   020 7242 4119   2–1D

This *"time-warp classic Italian trattoria"* – a Bloomsbury fixture for more than 35 years – is *"fun, bubbly, and has food as Mama would have made it"* (somewhere between *"delicious"* and *"not bad"*). *"The buzzy atmosphere makes you feel like you've stepped in off the streets of Rome"*, and with its *"1970s food at 1990s prices, the place deserves a medal"* for value. Top Tip – *"charming with young children"*. / WC1N 3LZ; www.ciaobellarestaurant.co.uk; @CiaobellaLondon; 11.30 pm, Sun 10.30 pm.

Cibo W14 £60 4 5 3
3 Russell Gdns   020 7371 6271   8–1D

"Just like being in Italy, with none of the pretensions of so many chef-centric London restaurants" – this *"family-run"* veteran between Olympia and Holland Park is *"amazingly underexposed; you'd probably walk straight by it"*. Regulars swear by its *"excellent staff, comfortable tables and amazing food"*, and it's long been touted by some cognoscenti as *"the best Italian in west London"*. / W14 8EZ; www.ciborestaurant.net; 10.30 pm; closed Sat L & Sun D.

Cigala WC1 £68 2 2 1
54 Lamb's Conduit Street   020 7405 1717   2–1D

Fans warm to the *"reliably, bare-boards, no-fancy-business"* style of this well-regarded Hispanic on an attractive Bloomsbury street, which does a good line in *"authentic tapas"*. But, especially as it's short on creature comforts, the bill does feel *"rather expensive for what it is"*: *"why oh why don't they spend some money on the decor?"*. / WC1N 3LW; www.cigala.co.uk; @cigalalondon; 10.45 pm, Sun 9.45 pm.

Cigalon WC2 £61 4 4 4
115 Chancery Lane   020 7242 8373   2–2D

"Exceptional Provençal cuisine" – *"light and full of fresh flavours"* – ensures that dining is *"always a real pleasure"* here, in what is itself a *"lovely, light and airy"* glass-roofed venue (once an auction room for books) on Chancery Lane, whose *"well-spaced tables"* make it a good choice for a business lunch in legal-land. Part of Pascal Aussignac's Club Gascon group, it has its own cocktail bar, Baranis, downstairs. / WC2A 1PP; www.cigalon.co.uk; @cigalon_london; 10 pm; closed Sat & Sun.

Cinnamon Bazaar WC2 £49 3 3 3
28 Maiden Lane   020 7395 1400   5–4D

This Covent Garden outpost of a grandee of modern Indian cuisine *"means you get the quality of The Cinnamon Club at a more affordable price"* – *"really interesting food"*, *"spiced with expertise"*. There's a particularly useful pre-theatre menu. / WC2E 7NA; www.cinnamon-bazaar.com; @Cinnamon_Bazaar.

The Cinnamon Club SW1 — £92 — 3 2 3
Old Westminster Library, Great Smith St   020 7222 2555   2–4C
"Still a classic" – this "elegant" destination in "Westminster's lovely former library" has long been one of London's most pre-eminent posh Indians; and its "interesting and idiosyncratic" cuisine has made it "something of an institution" (including amongst the politico classes – "being within division bell distance of Parliament, there's a fair chance of spotting a well-known face or two"). Its enjoyment was "tempered by episodes of wobbly service over the last year", however, and those who found the staff "over-stretched" were more likely to judge it "too expensive". / SW1P 3BU; www.cinnamonclub.com; @cinnamonclub; 10.30 pm; closed Sun; No trainers; booking max 14 may apply; SRA-Food Made Good – 2 stars.

Cinnamon Kitchen — £56 — 4 3 3
4 Arches Lane, SW11   02039555480   11–1C
9 Devonshire Sq, EC2   020 7626 5000   10–2D
"Bright, interesting flavours" from an evolved menu that's "delicately prepared" win a thumbs up for Vivek Singh's "well-appointed" duo of modern Indians. The original, inside a large atrium within a City development, benefits from a big 'outside' terrace; its year-old sibling occupies a railway arch within the new Battersea Power Station development. / www.cinnamon-kitchen.com; @CinnamonKitchen.

Circolo Popolare W1 NEW — £46
40 Rathbone Square   5–1A
Hot on the heels of launching smash-hit Gloria, the Big Mamma Group opened this even-more-ambitious follow-up – a larger (280-seat), Sicilian in Fitzrovia – in June 2019. Early press reports say they've absolutely nailed it for a second time, with their trademark maximalist pizzazz, which here incorporates an interior complete with spirit bottles lining the walls, festoons of foliage and twinkly fairy lights; and a pun-tastic menu of pizza by the metre. / W1T 1HX; www.bigmammagroup.com/en/trattorias/circolo-popolare; @bigmammagroup.

City Barge W4 — £51 — 3 3 3
27 Strand-on-the-Green   020 8994 2148   1–3A
"A beautiful situation on the river" in picturesque Strand-on-the-Green is the prime reason to seek out this "friendly local", but its pub grub is consistently well-rated too. In summer there are small terraces with table service to the front and rear of the pub too. / W4 3PH; www.citybargechiswick.com; @citybargew4; 11 pm, Fri & Sat midnight, Sun 10.30 pm.

City Social EC2 — £99 — 3 3 3
Tower 42, 25 Old Broad St   020 7877 7703   10–2C
"Spectacular views" reward a trip to the 24th floor of the City's Tower 42, run since 2014 by Jason Atherton's empire – "an elegant dining room, whose bar is quite sexy at night time with the lights of London on display". Unsurprisingly, it's most recommended as a "reliable option" for business entertaining, a service it carries out with aplomb. A foodie paying their own way, however, might judge the cuisine "OK, but nothing overly exciting". / EC2N 1HQ; www.citysociallondon.com; @CitySocial_T42; 10.30 pm; closed Sat & Sun; booking max 4 may apply.

Clarette W1 — £83 — 3 3 3
44 Blandford St   020 3019 7750   3–1A
These "refitted pub premises" are in their second year as a Marylebone wine bar, brought to us by a part of the family which owns world-famous claret, Château Margaux. Winning solid ratings for its "smart small-plates of French bistro cooking" and "great service" – it's "all very nice, but too expensive" to attract much feedback… unless you're tempted by a glass of 1999 vintage Margaux for £160. / W1U 7HS; www.clarettelondon.com; @ClaretteLondon.

Claridges Foyer & Reading Room W1   3 4 4
49 Brook Street   3–2B

"We've tried other places (including The Ritz) for afternoon tea, but come back here". This "iconic hotel" in the heart of Mayfair combines "art deco elegance with warm scones and piano music", and "because its tea is served in the hotel foyer, there's just the right amount of background activity for a near-perfect, tea-time experience". Also there's a "fabulous breakfast here: ideal for a visiting Aussie or American uncle, with everything from the kippers to the perfect salmon and scrambled egg". / W1K 4HW.

Clarke's W8   £71   4 5 4
124 Kensington Church Street   020 7221 9225   7–2B

"Never failing to excel, even after years and years…" – Sally Clarke's Kensington HQ (opened in 1984) is nowadays a "classic"; and even those who say "it's a bit of a time warp nowadays", concede that her California-inspired cuisine is nigh-on as "modern and fresh" as ever. "The moment you step in, often to be welcomed by Sally herself, you know you are in for a wonderful evening, with imaginative but unpretentious dishes that are impeccably prepared – with great ingredients that are allowed to stand out – while service is always professional and present-without-hovering". The atmosphere here has always been slightly divisive: for a few "dull" or "formal", but to most diners – "with its artwork, soothing colors, and low noise level to allow plenty of engaging conversation" – romantic and "always a delight". / W8 4BH; www.sallyclarke.com; @SallyClarkeLtd; 10 pm; closed Sun; booking max 14 may apply.

The Clifton NW8   £56   3 4 4
96 Clifton Hill   020 7625 5010   9–3A

"It's not only the fact that Edward VII was a regular", which makes this hostelry hidden away in St John's Wood "a great local". It started out as a Victorian hunting lodge where the future king conducted his affair with the actress Lillie Langtry, was a pub, and then – after a period of being vacant – was rescued from the developers to pave the way for its relaunch a couple of years ago. Modern day attractions include a "Sunday roast that's particularly good", while "the new conservatory comes recommended". / NW8 0JT; www.thecliftonnw8.com; @thecliftonnw8.

Clipstone W1   £74   4 4 3
5 Clipstone Street   020 7637 0871   2–1B

"Not at all what you would expect from the outside!" – "fabulous flavours and clever cooking abound" at Will Lander and Daniel Morgenthau's "highly sophisticated" neighbourhood venture, whose understatedly hip premises occupy a deceptively humble-looking corner-site in Fitzrovia. It also features an "exceptional and interesting wine list by glass: I go online after to see what wines I should be buying at home!" / W1W 6BB; www.clipstonerestaurant.co.uk; @clipstonerestaurant; 11 pm.

Clos Maggiore WC2   £83   3 4 5
33 King St   020 7379 9696   5–3C

"I saw a guy go down on bended knee to his girlfriend… she said yes!" This "luxurious and magical" haven – somewhat unexpectedly located "in the heart of Covent Garden" – continues to "live up to its reputation as the most romantic restaurant in London", and "for a meal with that special someone, you won't find much better", especially if you can bag a table (book months in advance) for the "blossom-festooned conservatory" (which some reporters feel is essential to a successful visit; to others it's merely "the icing on the cake"). Unusually for somewhere "oozing romance", standards elsewhere "are not compromised to deliver a memorable experience": "the food might not be the absolute pinnacle of modern British cuisine", but "it's more-than-competent" and "the star gourmet attraction is a wine list of almost biblical proportions". Top Tip – "lunch/pre theatre set menus offer superb value for the excellent quality". / WC2E 8JD; www.closmaggiore.com; @Clos_Maggiore; 11 pm, Sun 10 pm.

The Clove Club EC1 £183 3 3 2

Shoreditch Town Hall, 380 Old St 020 7729 6496 13–1B

In terms of media profile, Daniel Willis, Johnny Smith and chef Isaac McHale's groundbreaking, east London six-year-old is one of the capital's culinary titans: the highest UK restaurant in the famous World's 50-best ranking of global gastronomic champions (one of only two UK names to be thus-recognised). Occupying a neutrally-decorated chamber within Shoreditch's gracious old town hall – with blue-tiled open kitchen on view – the experience features prodigiously-edgy combinations using seasonal British ingredients, and is centred on an extended tasting menu (although there is also a cut-down version available Monday to Thursday, which has a mere six courses; as well another cut-down option at lunch of just four courses). The restaurant also makes a particular feature of thoughtful non-alcoholic and 'ambient tea' drinks pairings to complement its more traditional wine options – an innovation other big names would do well to follow. Does it live up? For many reporters the answer is still yes, with lavish praise for its "lush", "exceptionally creative cuisine", "unusually knowledgeable service" and "remarkable wine". However the "pretentiously unpretentious" interior (no tablecloths of course) lacks charge for somewhere now so famous; and overall the average ratings here are starting to look thoroughly middling in terms of London's other 'heavy hitting' names, by which yardstick its Top 50 placement just doesn't stack up. Flabbergasting pricing is another issue: even fans acknowledge "you need to remortgage your home to go", and 1 in 3 reporters now vote it their most overpriced meal of the year. Oh, and you have to pay in advance... / EC1V 9LT; www.thecloveclub.com; @thecloveclub; 9.30 pm; closed Mon L & Sun; SRA-Food Made Good – 1 stars.

Club Gascon EC1 £107 4 4 3

57 West Smithfield 020 7600 6144 10–2B

"The cuisine of southwest France is constantly re-invented to a superb level" at Pascal Aussignac and Vincent Labyrie's influential establishment by Smithfield Market, which marked its 20th anniversary last year with a major overhaul. "The sumptuous atmosphere" has been retained, and Aussignac "continues to surprise and excite" with a "creative and imaginative menu that changes monthly". / EC1A 9DS; www.clubgascon.com; @club_gascon; 9 pm, Fri & Sat 9.30 pm; closed Sat L & Sun.

The Coach EC1 £60 4 2 3

26-28 Ray Street 020 3954 1595 10–1A

Under chef-director, ex-Racine chef Henry Harris, Harcourt Inns have created a real "neighbourhood asset" with this year-old venture in Clerkenwell, winning a steady stream of satisfied reports of its "very competent", "high-class pub-food": "an interesting menu with unusual items" of a gusty Gallic nature. "Downstairs is more noisy", with a "buzzy" bar at the front, "lovely, glazed-sided restaurant" and a "small terrace garden that's lovely on a sunny day"; upstairs is more elegant and leisurely. / EC1R 3DJ; www.thecoachclerkenwell.co.uk; @thecoachldn.

Coal Office N1 £51 3 4 4

2 Bagley Walk 020 3848 6085 9–3C

"Shame it's impossible to get a table", at Assaf Granit's "happening" ("loud and busy") Israeli newcomer – "possibly now the best restaurant in the new King's Cross quarter", and one of the smash hits of the year. With its "amazing location" – a "very cool", Victorian ex-industrial building, with "funky Tom Dixon decor" ("his designer stuff strewn everywhere") and an "enticing terrace" – it has "an easy casual vibe", boosted by "such happy service". For newbies, "the menu takes a little explanation" and delivers "zingy, appetising, rich" small plates which amaze many diners, although they can also seem "to be trying too hard" and "portions aren't massive". Top Tip – "the bread is outstanding". / N1C 4PQ; coaloffice.com; @coaloffice.

Coal Rooms SE15   £54   4 4 3
11a Station Way   020 7635 6699   1–4D
"A must-visit, right by Peckham station" – whose converted Grade II ticket
office houses this "excellent" two-year-old: a stand-out even by the area's
lofty standards. "Robust, even macho" dishes, from the smoker and robata
grills, are central both to the open kitchen and the menu. Top Tip – "worth
a visit for the WC alone" – beautifully restored, old, Victorian bogs.
/ SE15 4RX; www.coalrooms.com; @coalrooms; 10 pm, Sun 6 pm.

The Coal Shed SE1   £59   3 3 3
One Tower Bridge   020 3384 7272   10–4D
In the shiny new developments south of Tower Bridge, this stylish,
but "down-to-earth" two-year-old (sibling to an original in Brighton) has
a "wide menu" – from "delicious seafood" to mouthwatering steak – but it's
perhaps the "very meaty" dishes that score the highest approval ratings
(charcoal grilled British beef cuts are a mainstay of the menu, and the
Moroccan goat dish, when it's on, is terrific). Top Tip – "perfect before
a show at the new Bridge Theatre" ("I'd go to a performance just as an
excuse to dine at The Coal Shed!") / SE1 2AA; www.coalshed-restaurant.co.uk;
@TheCoalShed1.

CôBa N7   £39   4 3 2
244 York Way   07495 963336   9–2C
"Hard to find but worth the trip": this hard-surfaced pub-conversion –
with plain walls and hanging filament lights – sits in the nondescript wastes
north of King's Cross, not far from Caledonian Road Tube. Why visit?
"A really good variety of Vietnamese dishes" (majoring in BBQ), prepared
by Aussie chef, Damon Bui. / N7 9AG; www.cobarestaurant.co.uk; @cobafood;
10 pm; booking D only.

Cocochan W1   £52   3 2 2
38-40 James St   020 7486 1000   3–1A
Between Selfridges and St Christopher's Place – a "busy and quite noisy"
haunt, where some reporters are very impressed by its Pan-Asian small
plates (including sushi and dim sum dishes), but others feel that they're
"not exciting, but OK". / W1U 1EU; www.cocochan.co.uk; @cocochanlondon;
11pm; Booking max 6 may apply.

Colbert SW1   £74   2 2 4
51 Sloane Sq   020 7730 2804   6–2D
"A slice of Paris in Sloane Square", this hugely popular brasserie rendezvous
is "great for people-watching" and its "atmospheric" faux-period decor
evokes "a gallery of film noir scenes". But while it's incredibly convenient for
those out-and-about in Chelsea, or visiting a production at The Royal Court,
there's something slightly transitory about the experience that makes it the
least engaging of Corbin & King's ventures. Even fans concede its Gallic
brasserie fare is "not exceptional" or that it feels like "a treadmill that
verges on a money-making machine rather than a relaxed venue". Top Tip –
"they do breakfast just right". / SW1W 8AX; www.colbertchelsea.com;
@ColbertChelsea; 11 pm, Fri & Sat 11.30 pm, Sun 10.30 pm.

La Collina NW1   £57   2 3 2
17 Princess Rd   020 7483 0192   9–3B
In a quiet location below Primrose Hill, this little Italian – specialising
in Piedmontese cuisine – has long been a feature of the area, and has built
a very loyal, local following. Reports were a little more hit-and-miss this year
on the food front, but fans say that "the garden on a summer's day more
than makes up for any average dishes". / NW1 8JR;
www.lacollinarestaurant.co.uk; @LacollinaR; 10.15 pm, Sat-Sun 9.15 pm; closed
Mon L; booking max 8 may apply.

The Collins Room SW1 £92 2️⃣3️⃣4️⃣
The Berkeley Hotel, Wilton Place   020 7107 8866   6–1D
"'Pret-a-Portea' remains the most creative afternoon tea, bar none!" and is "always an amazing delight, both for the eyes and the lips" (this year, its beautifully crafted cakes inspired by fashion catwalks came with a Dior tie-in to match the exhibition at the V&A). "Sitting in the light and airy Collins Room is a treat" in itself too, but while for other occasions the food is "always of a high standard" then for a full meal "do not go hungry as portions can be small". / SW1X 7RL; www.the-berkeley.co.uk/restaurants-bars/collins-room; @TheBerkeley; 10.45 pm, Sun 10.15 pm.

Le Colombier SW3 £82 3️⃣4️⃣3️⃣
145 Dovehouse Street   020 7351 1155   6–2C
"A little corner of France in the SWs" – Didier Garnier's "comfortable and old-fashioned French brasserie" on a tucked-away site (with a large outside terrace for the summer) has, for just over two decades, maintained a massively loyal following, particularly amongst "older Chelsea residents", on the strength of its "classic" (if rather "no frills") cuisine; "an excellent wine list with prices that are hard to beat"; and notably "courteous" service. "Tables are packed closed" though, and "it's noisy when busy". / SW3 6LB; www.le-colombier-restaurant.co.uk; 10.30 pm, Sun 10 pm.

Colony Grill Room, Beaumont Hotel W1 £85 2️⃣2️⃣3️⃣
8 Balderton Street, Brown Hart Gardens   020 7499 9499   3–2A
In late 2018, Corbin & King lost the management contract for this luxurious Art Deco hotel near Selfridges (to the Barclay family), including its "exceptional-looking", 1920s NYC-style grill room. However for a certain kind of swish American experience, it still nails it: for example, even a reporter who thinks "it's tailed off a bit since leaving the care of C&K" feels "it's still a must-visit to experience the classic, US-country-club style"; and the "transatlantic, slightly retro cuisine" that goes with that ("very rich – but great if that's to your taste"). On the flip side, a cynical view is that it's at risk of becoming "a theme park for nostalgic Americans longing for the food of their childhood". Top Tip – "a wonderful breakfast" for business or pleasure. / W1K 6TF; www.colonygrillroom.com; @ColonyGrillRoom; midnight, Sun 11 pm.

The Colton Arms W14 £56 2️⃣3️⃣4️⃣
187 Greyhound Road   020 3757 8050   8–2C
Backing onto the rear of Queen's Club in Baron's Court (and with a cute small garden for sunny days) – "a good, standby local pub" given a very stylish revamp a couple of years ago, and serving "a decent array of dishes". "The ambience varies a bit depending on where you are sat in the dining room". / W14 9SD; www.thecoltonarms.co.uk; @thecoltonarms; 10 pm, Sun 8 pm.

Comptoir Gascon EC1 £59 3️⃣2️⃣3️⃣
63 Charterhouse St   020 7608 0851   10–1A
"Excellent duck dishes and super duck-fat chips" capture the flavour of southwest France at this offshoot of nearby Club Gascon in Smithfield. It's a "niche restaurant that sticks to its knitting and does it well", with a "very competitive lunch-time offering providing a good-quality meal at a very nice price". / EC1M 6HJ; www.comptoirgascon.com; @ComptoirGascon; 10 pm, Thu & Fri 10.30 pm; closed Mon & Sun.

Comptoir Libanais £46 2️⃣1️⃣2️⃣
The "consistently tasty food" at these bright and quirky Levantine cafés makes them ideal for a "quick lunch", or "breakfast when you want something more than the usual full English". There are "plenty of options for veggies", although service can be "a little sloppy and chaotic". / www.lecomptoir.co.uk; 10 pm (SW 8 pm), W1C & E20 Sun 8 pm; W12 closed Sun D; no bookings.

Le Comptoir Robuchon W1

6 Clarges Street   awaiting tel

No sooner had Covent Garden's Atelier du Joel Robuchon (RIP) closed its doors following the death of Michelin's favourite chef, than the global empire he founded announced two new ventures to carry forward his name in the capital. This October 2019 opening is the first (the second, Le Deli Robuchon, opens on Piccadilly in November 2019). The focus will be the small plates style of L'Atelier, with a menu in two parts: La Saison (the hint is in the name); and Les Eternels (a list of culinary 'favourite hits').

Con Gusto SE18 £56 3 4 4

No 1 Street   020 8465 7452   12–2D

"In a developing part of Woolwich (an area with lots of blocks of expensive flats going up all along the Thames waterfront, in the grounds of the old Woolwich Arsenal)", this tiny, former guardroom provides a "quirky", pre-Victorian setting ("exposed brick and candle-light") for a meal. "The menu is small (like the place) but tempting – unlike many Italian restaurants where dishes often seem to be an Anglicised fudge, here the food tastes authentic". / SE18 6GH; www.congusto.co.uk.

Il Convivio SW1 £68 3 4 3

143 Ebury St   020 7730 4099   2–4A

This longstanding "local gem" in Belgravia is a "properly Italian restaurant". Currently on great form under chef Cedric Leri, "the food is better than ever, the service ever delightful, the room continues to please" – but "it's rarely full, which is an eternal mystery". / SW1W 9QN; www.etruscarestaurants.com/il-convivio; 10.45 pm; closed Sun.

Coopers Restaurant & Bar WC2 £50 3 4 3

49 Lincoln's Inn Fields   020 7831 6211   2–2D

Stuck looking for a comfortable bite near the LSE? – try this staple of legal-land, typically packed with barristers from Lincoln's Inn. It's unlikely to knock your socks off with culinary fireworks, but regulars say a meal here is "always a pleasure, with a great choice of dishes at good-value prices", and applaud the "professional" staff who "go the extra mile". / WC2A 3PF; www.coopersrestaurant.co.uk; @coopers_bistro; 10.30 pm; closed Sat & Sun; no booking.

Coppa Club Tower Bridge EC3 £45 2 3 5

Three Quays Walk, Lower Thames Street   020 7993 3827   10–3D

"The Christmas igloo during December was one of the nicest experiences ever…" – "the absolutely stunning location on the Thames is perfect for a summers day…" – "you can snuggle up on a sofa in front of the fire during the winter months…"; "the food is a bit so-so, but who cares?": all are comments from fans of this all-day 'club without membership' near Tower Bridge. It's part of a growing chain, with most branches in the Thames Valley, and a (much less interesting) sibling in a bank-conversion looking across the road to St Paul's Cathedral. / EC3R 6AH; www.coppaclub.co.uk; @coppaclub; 11 pm, Sun 10 pm; Booking max 6 may apply.

Coq d'Argent EC2 £80 2 3 4

1 Poultry   020 7395 5000   10–2C

"On a warm summer's day, the roof garden is a secluded and delightful place to escape the pressure of the Square Mile", say fans of D&D London's long-established, 7th-floor perch, just a stone's throw from Bank. Squarely aimed at a "very City clientele", it's a "swanky expense-accounter venue, whose starched napery will not disappoint your visiting client from NYC"; and where a meal can be started with preprandial drinks on the terrace. Fans feel it offers "high quality, well-prepared" French cuisine – the more downbeat version is that it's "pricey for what it provides": either way, you get "a great view!" / EC2R 8EJ; www.coqdargent.co.uk; @coqdargent1; 9.45 pm; closed Sun D; booking max 10 may apply.

Coqfighter W1 NEW £26 5 3 2
75 Beak Street   020 7734 4001   4–2C
"Scrumptious, Korean-style, fried-chicken burgers – so crunchy, and topped
with the most excellent flavour combinations", plus K-wings, bao, and other
finger-lickin' goodies have won a big fanclub for these Aussie-owned pitstops,
which graduated in June 2019 from two Boxpark locations (in Shoreditch
and Croydon) to this new Soho permanent-home, with its mix of communal
and small tables, on, wait for it, Beak Street… / W1F 9SS; www.coqfighter.com.

Cora Pearl WC2 £66 3 2 3
30 Henrietta Street   020 7324 7722   5–3D
"One of the more individual, thoughtful places opening up in Covent
Garden" – this "lively", "very enjoyable little sister of Kitty Fisher" opened
in mid-2018, and inspires many reports of "simple, luxurious food" from
"an incredibly attractive menu" of "delicious, little, sharing bites". "Decent-
without-being-exceptional" is another school of opinion on the cooking,
though, and middling ratings overall take into account seating that's
"so cramped" and service that's "at times, pushy, brisk and hurried". Top
Tip – "I'm not sure what they did to the chips but they transcended any
normal form of potato – order a bowl each as you won't want to share!"
/ WC2E 8NA; www.corapearl.co.uk; @CoraPearlCG.

Corazón W1 £45 3 4 3
29 Poland Street   020 3813 1430   4–1C
Laura Sheffield's "fun, friendly and very good value" Mexican, just off Oxford
Street, is a useful centrally located addition to London's taco scene.
"Interesting veggie options" plus "delicious pulled pork tacos" means
everybody's "pretty happy". / W1F 8QR; www.corazonlondon.co.uk; @corazon_uk.

Core by Clare Smyth W11 £122 5 4 4
92 Kensington Park Rd   020 3937 5086   7–2B
"The third Michelin star must be on its way" say fans of Clare Smyth's
"world class" one-year-old, which – after its "brilliant start" – is much
"better than Restaurant Gordon Ramsay Royal Hospital Road" (her former
gig); and was the most-nominated restaurant in the survey this year for
providing London's top gastronomic experience. Occupying the Notting Hill
venue that some still recall as Leith's (long RIP), she has created a "smart-
but-unintimidating" space, where "superb, friendly, and unpompous staff"
steer a course between "slight informality" (no tablecloths) and being "highly
professional". And "Clare and head chef Johnnie always make time to say
hello". "So much original thought has gone in" to the "masterfully-blended
dishes, showing occasional idiosyncratic touches" to create "precise,
exquisite morsels that look like art on a plate and taste fabulous (if at
a high price tag)". "Words aren't enough to describe the journey your taste
buds go on!". "Unfortunately, however, it has become almost impossible
to book". Top Menu Tip – "I never thought a potato could taste that good!"
/ W11 2PN; www.corebyclaresmyth.com.

Cork & Bottle WC2 £56 2 2 4
44-46 Cranbourn St   020 7734 7807   5–3B
"The wine bar all others aspire to be" (of an old school nature) –
this characterful cellar just off Leicester Square is closing in on its 50th year,
and has seen little change in that time. "The food, while a bit of an eighties
throwback, is perfectly good for soaking up a few glasses" – and "you can't
beat the ham & cheese pie", biggest seller on the menu since 1978. Owner
Will Clayton, who took over from the legendary Don Hewitson, has opened
branches in Bayswater and Hampstead – but it will take them years
to match up to the original. / WC2H 7AN; www.thecorkandbottle.co.uk;
@corkbottle1971; 11.30 pm, Sun 10.30 pm; no booking D.

Corner Room E2 £51 3 2 3

Patriot Sq   020 7871 0461   14–2B

Bethnal Green's old town hall – nowadays a boutique hotel – houses this 30-seater overseen by chef, Simon Shand. Although it lacks the profile it once did, the limited feedback we received this year was all positive: in particular "the fixed price, five-course menu is excellent value for good, modern British cuisine". / E2 9NF; www.townhallhotel.com/cornerroom; @townhallhotel; 9.30 pm, Thu-Sat 10 pm.

Cornerstone E9 £63 5 4 4

3 Prince Edward Road,   14–1C

"In a rather unlikely location, tucked away around the corner from Hackney Wick station" – Tom Brown's stellar yearling is one of the "most impressive" arrivals of the last year or so. His "super-fresh" fish dishes "are inventively conceived and perfectly executed" from an "original menu"; and served in an artfully "plain" and "relaxed" environment, which "brings the area's industrial heritage to the fore, while injecting a hint of Scandi chic". Staff are "very accommodating" too, and – with the open kitchen centre stage – "it's lovely watching the chefs at work". A few reporters consider it "a victim of hype", but, for the overwhelming majority, it's well "worth the expedition". / E9 5LX; cornerstonehackney.com; @Cornerstone_h_w.

Corrigan's Mayfair W1 £108 3 3 3

28 Upper Grosvenor St   020 7499 9943   3–3A

"Classic and club-like (without being oppressive)" – Richard Corrigan's spacious Mayfair HQ, just off Park Lane, offers a traditionally luxurious experience, focused on "unfussy", top-quality British cuisine (from head chef, Aidan McGee). Its ratings looked less secure this year, though, with mounting concerns about its vertiginous pricing – to fans "even if it's expensive, the quality is there", but to foes it now seems "extremely overpriced" to an extent some feel is "ludicrous". Top Tip – "superb value set lunch". / W1K 7EH; www.corrigansmayfair.com; @CorriganMayfair; 10 pm; closed Sat L; Booking max 12 may apply.

Côte £57 2 2 2

"Top choice when meeting up is more important than the food!" – Richard Caring's "brisk" modern brasseries are "a cut-above most other chains" and were once again the survey's most-mentioned national multiple, on the strength of their "very convenient" and often picturesque locations; and an experience generally that's "safe" and affordable (set menus in particular are very "competitively priced"). That said, even many of its legions of fans don't suggest that their performance will set the world on fire: "menus offer a range of formulaic dishes, some more wowing than others", with "basic options such as steak-frites" or burger often touted as the best of the "rather unadventurous" selection. "Service can vary" but usually "problems are swiftly resolved" and staff keep things "speedy" enough. / www.cote.co.uk; 11 pm; closed Sun.

Counter Culture SW4 £47 4 4 2

16 The Pavement   020 8191 7960   11–2D

"Fun, buzzy, hipster, and tiny" – Robin Gill's 16-seater in Clapham (an offshoot of his Dairy, next door) is known for its "novel and ever-changing", small-plates cuisine based around 'pickling, fermenting, curing and bottling the best of the season's produce'. "You don't go for comfort though!", given its bum-numbing stools. It won high ratings this year, but may be about to get even better: star ex-Stem chef Sam Ashton Booth joined in July 2019 and is set to introduce a new menu 'The Allotment', with produce supplied by Bedfordshire-based co-collaborator, Jake 'Wiggo' Ball (who does the growing). / SW4 0HY; www.countercultureclapham.co.uk; @culturesnax; no booking.

The Cow W2 £62 **3 3 4**

89 Westbourne Park Rd   020 7221 0021   7–1B

"A long-time local favourite" celebrating its 25th anniversary this year: Tom Conran's Irish-themed gastroboozer on the Notting Hill-Bayswater border is "always relaxed", with "reliably good food" (both in the bustling downstairs bar, and the cute, cramped first floor). Despite its name, the focus is on seafood (oysters washed down with a pint o' Guinness being the classic choice here). / W2 5QH; www.thecowlondon.co.uk; @TheCowLondon; 11 pm, Sun 10 pm; No Amex.

Coya £81 **4 3 4**

118 Piccadilly, W1   020 7042 7118   3–4B
31-33 Throgmorton St, EC2   020 7042 7118   10–2C

"A real culinary tour of the best of Peru, with mouthwatering ceviche, smoky grilled meats and show-stopping desserts" ("we were blown away by the freshness and amazing flavour combinations"), "… all washed down with a pisco sour or two", helps inspire rave reviews this year for this Latino duo – an "impressive-looking subterranean bar/restaurant in Mayfair", and a similarly "buzzy and relaxed" set-up in the City, tucked away behind the Bank of England. "It's best if someone else is paying" of course, but past flak about whopping prices was absent this year. / www.coyarestaurant.com.

Craft London SE10 £65 **4 4 3**

Peninsula Square   020 8465 5910   12–1D

"You dine very well" from a "really interesting and different menu", hosted by "informative staff", in the restaurant at Stevie Parle's multi-level operation by the O2 Centre. "The bars are pretty good as well" – "brilliant for cocktails, fantastic for people-watching" – and there's a café on the ground floor. / SE10 0SQ; www.craft-london.co.uk; @CraftLDN; 10.30 pm (cafe 6pm); cafe L only; restaurant D only, Sat L & D, closed Mon & Sun.

Crate Brewery and Pizzeria E9 £31 **4 3 4**

7, The White Building, Queens Yard   020 8533 3331   14–1C

In a "lovely spot" across the canal from the Olympic Park (near Hackney Wick station), and with a big waterside terrace, this "very buzzy" and achingly East End microbrewery serves brilliant pizza ("especially if you like them thin-based") and "great own-brewed beers". After a successful CrowdCube fundraiser, the first floor is about to become a venue in itself – and further boost its cutting edge cred – importing zero-waste eco-project Silo (see also) from Brighton. / E9 5EN; www.cratebrewery.com; @cratebrewery; 10 pm, Fri & Sat 11 pm.

Crocker's Folly NW8 £54 **3 3 4**

23-24 Aberdeen Pl   020 7289 9898   9–4A

"Very ornate interiors" at this "fascinating pub" were created thanks to a misguided late-Victorian entrepreneur who thought a major railway terminus would be built in St John's Wood. For the last few years, it's been a new departure for the Maroush group, and – after a poor start dabbling with traditional British cuisine – it's "getting better now that they've returned to their Lebanese roots". Mezze and kebabs in a pub may seem an odd mix and it is "a difficult place to get to", but by all accounts it's worth the effort. / NW8 8JR; www.crockersfolly.com; @crockersfolly.

The Crooked Well SE5 £53 **3 3 3**

16 Grove Ln   020 7252 7798   1–3C

"A great Camberwell local" fitted out with wittier design than you find in your typical greige gastropub; and which "fits the bill for posh pub food… not to mention its cool bar for some pre-dinner gin cocktails". / SE5 8SY; www.thecrookedwell.com; @crookedwell; 10.30 pm; closed Mon L; No Amex; booking max 6 may apply.

The Cross Keys SW3 £59 3 4 4
1 Lawrence Street   020 7351 0686   6–3C

"Eager staff", a proper "local pub atmosphere" and a "great menu" of modern British dishes make this a "real discovery" just a stone's throw from the Thames. The oldest boozer in Chelsea (est. 1708), it has served pints to luminaries including JMW Turner, Dylan Thomas and Bob Marley. / SW3 5NB; www.thecrosskeyschelsea.co.uk; @CrossKeys_PH; 10 pm, Sun 9 pm.

The Crystal Moon Lounge, Corinthia Hotel London SW1 £87 2 4 4
Whitehall Place   020 7321 3150   2–3C

"Sitting under the giant chandelier [careful, it weighs two tons!] eating far too much food is a real treat", when you have afternoon tea in the swish lounge of this luxurious five-star, off Embankment: an occasion for which it's becoming increasingly well-known. It's "a really outstanding offering, served by staff who are clearly versed in the different teas on offer, as well as the delicious sandwiches and cakes". / SW1A 2BD; www.corinthia.com/en/hotels/london/dining/afternoon-tea.

Cub N1 £92 4 4 3
153-155 Hoxton St   020 3693 3202   14–2A

"Just as much a political statement as a meal", this "low-waste, little venue" in Shoreditch is co-owned by Doug McMaster of Brighton's acclaimed zero-waste restaurant Silo, and a similar eco-friendly approach is showcased here. "It serves up a series of challenging plates of principally foraged food from a fixed multi-course menu, alongside cocktails that fall a little outside the usual comfort zone", and wins consistently high ratings (albeit from a relatively small fanclub). See also Silo. / N1 6PJ; www.lyancub.com; @mrlyan; Online only.

The Culpeper E1 £61 3 2 4
40 Commercial St   020 7247 5371   13–2C

"The lovely first-floor dining room is a particular favourite" at this thoughtfully converted Spitalfields gastropub with its own rooftop garden (complete with summer BBQ). "Friendly" and "unpretentious", its cooking pleases all reporters (but misses the raves it once attracted). / E1 6LP; www.theculpeper.com; @TheCulpeper; midnight, Fri & Sat 2 am, Sun 11 pm; SRA-Food Made Good – 3 stars.

Cumberland Arms W14 £56 3 3 3
29 North End Rd   020 7371 6806   8–2D

"Just around the corner from Olympia", it's worth knowing about this well-rated pub, in the not-particularly-auspicious northerly reaches of the North End Road. In the same stable as Earl's Court's excellent Atlas, it delivers "a very enjoyable meal, with a good quality menu and a lovely atmosphere". / W14 8SZ; www.thecumberlandarmspub.co.uk; @CumberlandArms; 10 pm, Sun 9.30 pm.

Curry House Coco Ichibanya WC2 NEW £18
17 Great Newport Street   020 3904 5633   5–3B

Near Leicester Square tube and need a quick bite? – maybe grab a meal at this simple December 2018 newcomer: the first London outpost of Japan's largest (1,000-strong) chain specialising in kare raisu dishes – curry and rice: over 40 different rice toppings are available, including hamburgers, scrambled eggs and fried oysters. / WC2H 7JE; ichibanya.uk.

Cut,
45 Park Lane W1   £122   3 2 2
45 Park Ln   020 7493 4545   3–4A
"I've had better, but if cost is irrelevant…" – this "good but exceedingly pricey" US-style steakhouse in a Park Lane hotel is part of a global brand from celeb chef Wolfgang Puck, the second most famous Austrian-born American in LA. The menu lists 16 steaks, up to a Japanese pure wagyu rib eye from Kyushu at heart-stopping £160. "And did I mention it was expensive? Somehow we racked up a bill of almost £100 for two full English breakfasts with coffee". / W1K 1PN; www.45parklane.com; @45ParkLaneUK; 10.30 pm.

Cut + Grind N1   £35   3 3 3
The Urbanest Building, 25-27 Canal Reach   9–3C
"Some of the juiciest burgers out there" are prepared at this two-year-old King's Cross indie (with outlets at Boxpark Wembley and the Lexington Angel in Islington), which minces its beef onsite every day and offers two veggie versions. / N1C 4DD; www.cutandgrindburgers.com; @cngburgers.

Cyprus Mangal SW1   £40   4 3 2
45 Warwick Way   020 7828 5940   2–4B
"Succulent kebabs, hummus and tabouleh" make this highly rated Turkish-Cypriot grill one of the "best options" in Pimlico – "rapid service without many smiles, and good value". / SW1V 1QS; www.cyprusmangal.co.uk; 10.45 pm, Fri & Sat 11.45 pm.

Da Giua EC1   £56   3 4 2
105 Whitecross Street   020 7374 6713   13–2A
Now over a year old, this newish establishment, between Old Street and Barbican, operates on a site that's seen other ventures come and go, and those who know the area say it's "good to have someone operate something that's working": "a cut-above-the-average, local Italian" at "sensible prices", including "excellent pizza". Top Tip – "a truffle-based menu looked excellent as did the truffle that was brought out for my appreciation when I expressed an interest". / EC1Y 8JH; dagiua.com.

Da Mario SW7   £43   3 3 3
15 Gloucester Rd   020 7584 9078   6–1B
Near the Royal Albert Hall and needing a "reasonably priced" bite? This fun Italian is surprisingly smart given its affordable prices, and its food – majoring in pizza – is consistently well rated. It claims to have been 'Princess Diana's local pizzeria' (and is not shy about promoting the connection via pics on the walls). Top Tip – budget party cave in the cellar. / SW7 4PP; www.damario.co.uk; 11.30 pm.

Da Mario WC2   £53   2 3 3
63 Endell St   020 7240 3632   5–1C
An "old-fashioned, warm and lovely Italian", whose "comforting" 'throwback' style is at odds with its very central Covent Garden location. The family who ran ran it for so many years retired in August 2018, however, and – though the staff remain – some old-timers feel: "since the change of ownership the standard of cooking in this much-loved restaurant seems to have slipped, while the prices have increased. However its proximity to theatres means it is still busy". / WC2H 9AJ; www.da-mario.co.uk; 11.15 pm; closed Sun.

Da Terra,
Town Hall Hotel E2 NEW £32 544
8 Patriot Square 020 7062 2052 14–2B

"A very fine effort by Brazilian chefs with a good team. I hope they succeed!" Paulo Airaudo and Rafael Cagali's ambitious East End newcomer is the latest inhabitant of this space in Bethnal Green's former town hall (which has, over the years, housed Lee Westcott's The Typing Room and Nuno Mendes's Viajante) where a series of wizard small plates (from either an eight-course or eleven-course menu) are delivered, often by the chefs themselves, from the open kitchen. It's yet to generate a huge depth of feedback, but in terms of dazzling ratings it's scored as one of the more interesting arrivals this year; and a very worthy successor to its brilliant predecessors on this site. / E2 9NF; www.daterra.co.uk.

Daddy Bao SW17 £33 433
113 Mitcham Road 020 3601 3232 11–2C
Sibling to Peckham's Mr Bao, this casual, small Tooting yearling similarly specialises in steamed buns and other tasty Taiwanese treats, and wins nothing but very good ratings for its cooking. / SW17 9PE; www.daddybao.com.

Daffodil Mulligan EC1 NEW
70-74 City Road 13–1A
The foodie 'Murphia' is out in force with this late-2019 newcomer, backed by famous chef Richard Corrigan (who first made his name over 20 years ago at a different Mulligan's, then 'of Mayfair'), fellow Irishman John Nugent, and King's Place owner Peter Millican (see Rotunda at King's Place). On the site south of Old Street vacated by Nuala (RIP), we are promised a bar serving proper Irish food, plus regular live music and spoken word gigs. Sláinte. / EC1Y 2BJ; @CorrigansFood.

The Dairy SW4 £53 545
15 The Pavement 020 7622 4165 11–2D
"One of south west London's best restaurants with a great team and food ethos" – Robin Gill's *"very casual and hipster"* haunt provides *"imaginative, skilful small-plate cooking in the heart of Clapham, with good use of seasonal ingredients and information on their sourcing".* A *"trendy and stripped"* space, *"it's a bit long and thin, so some tables feel cramped"*; and *"the menu could be slightly more varied for the regular customer"*; but *"it's still a lovely meal on any occasion!"* / SW4 0HY; www.the-dairy.co.uk; @thedairyclapham; 9.45 pm; closed Mon, Tue L & Sun D.

Dalloway Terrace,
Bloomsbury Hotel WC1 £72 324
16-22 Great Russell St 020 7347 1221 2–1C
With its foliage and fairy lights, it's hard to believe that this hotel terrace (with fully retractable roof) is just two minutes' walk from grungy Centre Point. Feedback is limited, mostly focusing on its afternoon tea possibilities; "great cocktails too in the adjoining Coral room". / WC1B 3NN; www.dallowayterrace.com; @DallowayTerrace; 10.30 pm.

La Dame de Pic London EC3 £120 443
10 Trinity Square 020 7297 3799 10–3D
"A truly world-class representative of London dining" – the Pic family's *"plush"* two-year-old, within a monumental five-star hotel (the Port of London Authority's former HQ), provides a *"stunning-if-pricey"* destination that nowadays ranks in London's culinary top tier; and its heart-of-the-city location by Tower Hill makes it a natural for wining and dining particularly important prospects. The *"calm, white-walled dining room"* provides a *"chic"* and *"beautiful"* setting for a meal, service is *"attentive but un-pushy"*, but its highest rated feature is its *"sensational"*, *"superbly refined"* modern French cuisine. / EC3N 4AJ; ladamedepiclondon.co.uk; @FSTenTrinity; No shorts.

Dandy SE1 NEW
35 Maltby Street   awaiting tel   10–4D
From a shipping container in London Fields to a short-lived restaurant on Newington Green, and now – in the former home of Monmouth Coffee on Maltby Street – this latest, crowdfunded incarnation also has Matt Wells (co-founder of The Dairy) as partner and is slated to open in the second half of 2019. Plans include a bar and ultimately an in-house brewery; on the menu – inventive, seasonal dishes. / SE1 3PA; dandy.restaurant.

Daphne's SW3   £77   2 3 4
112 Draycott Ave   020 7589 4257   6–2C
"So civilised" – this Chelsea stalwart was founded in 1967 by Daphne Rye, the theatrical agent who discovered Richard Burton; and a couple of decades later found fame as Princess Di's favourite haunt. But beyond a local well-heeled crowd its social caché is more limited nowadays, and, despite being part of Richard Caring's Caprice group, it generates only a middling amount of feedback. The Italian cooking is somewhere between dependable and unexciting... especially at the price: "we go for old time's sake, but really the food is average". / SW3 3AE; www.daphnes-restaurant.co.uk; @DaphnesLondon; 11 pm, Sun 10 pm.

Daquise SW7   £56   2 2 2
20 Thurloe St   020 7589 6117   6–2C
"Faded old-world charm and traditional hearty food" ("stuffed cabbage most enjoyable with potato vodka") are the hallmarks of this "historic Polish gem" (est 1947) near South Ken tube, where legendary restaurant critics Jonathan Meades and the late AA Gill used to meet regularly for lunch. Even if dishes can be "stodgy" they are "wonderfully authentic" and in "robust portions", and act as a portal to "the distant past". / SW7 2LT; www.daquise.co.uk; @GesslerDaquise; 11 pm; No Amex.

Darby's SW11 NEW   £74   4 4 4
3 Viaduct Gardens Road, Embassy Gardens   11–1D
Amidst the mushrooming luxury developments of Vauxhall's once-neglected south bank, Robin and Sarah Gill's (The Dairy, Counter Culture, Sorella) biggest venture to-date occupies the ground floor of one such new building, near the new American Embassy. Set around a large central bar with counter – and following an Irish-American theme (incorporating Robin's Irish heritage) – the culinary emphasis is ingredient-led as the website makes clear: '... our single philosophy is: We have a wonderful product, let's try not to feck it up'. It's a comprehensive offering, complete with in-house bakery, large open kitchen with grill, cold storage (showing off steaks and fresh fish), an oyster bar, and a big outside terrace. It opened just as the survey was closing, but early feedback is of food that's "fresh, interesting and delicious" – "the ragu was the best I have eaten anywhere ever!" / SW11 7AY; www.darbys-london.com; @robingillchef.

Darjeeling Express W1   £47   4 3 3
6-8 Kingly Street   020 7287 2828   4–2B
"The small menu really delivers on taste and price" with "some absolutely amazing dishes", at Calcutta-born Asma Khan's former supper club, now in hugely popular, permanent quarters off Carnaby Street. The "friendly" staff, including an all-women kitchen team of self-described 'housewives', ensure there's a real "home-cooked" flavour to the enterprise. / W1B 5PW; www.darjeeling-express.com; @Darjeelingldn; 10 pm, Sun 4 pm.

The Dartmouth Castle W6   £57   3 4 4
26 Glenthorne Rd   020 8748 3614   8–2C
A short stroll from un-lovely Hammersmith Broadway, this atmospheric pub (with outside terrace) surprises with its characterful style and quality cooking. "It's getting busier and busier during the week, but weekends can be surprisingly quiet". / W6 0LS; www.thedartmouthcastle.co.uk; @DartmouthCastle; 9.30 pm, Sun 9 pm; closed Sat L.

Darwin Brasserie EC3   £74   2 2 5

1 Sky Garden Walk   033 3772 0020   10–3D

"Go for the spectacular views alone", "especially at night with the city lights twinkling below", from the "unique perspective" of this all-day brasserie at the top of the Walkie-Talkie tower. "The menu is limited and fairly expensive", but – on most accounts – "the food is surprisingly good" for the location. / EC3M 8AF; skygarden.london/darwin; @SG_Darwin.

Dastaan KT19   £39   5 4 3

447 Kingston Rd   020 8786 8999   1–4A

"Perfectly executed north Indian food" from a pair of former Gymkhana chefs has made this apparently-modest, outer-suburban curry house a site of pilgrimage, despite its "bizarre setting just off the Ewell bypass". "The food is in pretty much perfect inverse correlation to the location", and "sets a new benchmark for Indian food and service" – no wonder it's "booked solid". Top Tip – "the lamb chops alone are worth the Uber". / KT19 0DB; dastaan.co.uk; @Dastaan447; Booking weekdays only.

Davies and Brook,
Claridge's Hotel W1 NEW

49 Brook Street   3–2B

Gordon Ramsay… Simon Rogan… next in the series of celeb-chefs to occupy Claridge's gorgeous Art Deco restaurant is NYC-chef Daniel Humm, of Manhattan's acclaimed Eleven Madison Park. The replacement for Rogan's Fera at Claridges was set to open in summer 2019, but will now do so in the autumn, following Humm's split from his long-term business partner Will Guidara, and the need to buy out his share of the restaurant group behind the opening, 'Make it Nice'. / W1K 4HW; www.claridges.co.uk/restaurants-bars/davies-and-brook.

Daylesford Organic   £60   3 1 2

44b Pimlico Rd, SW1   020 7881 8060   6–2D
6-8 Blandford St, W1   020 3696 6500   2–1A
76-82 Sloane Avenue, SW3   awaiting tel   6–2C
208-212 Westbourne Grove, W11   020 7313 8050   7–1B

Lady Bamford's four organic farm-shop cafés in London make "perfect brunch venues" before stocking up on non-packaged 'zero-waste' goodies from her Cotswolds farm. They're also "nice for people-watching" – although, while the "previously terrible service has improved a lot", "staff are often overwhelmed when things get busy". / www.daylesfordorganic.com; 7 pm - 10 pm, Sun 3 pm - 4 pmGL56 8pm, Sun 4pm, SW3 Mon 7pm, 10pm, Sun 4pm, W11 Mon 7pm, 9.30pm, sun 4pm, SW11 8pm Sun 3pm, W1U Mon 7pm, 9.30 and sun 4pm; W11 no booking L.

Dean Street Townhouse W1   £67   2 3 5

69-71 Dean St   020 7434 1775   4–1D

"Wonderful when it's cold outside – with warm fires burning to make it very welcoming" – and blessed with a nice terrace for summer: this all-day Soho House brasserie (part of their hotel, in the heart of Soho) exudes just the right design pheromones to keep it permanently packed. "Just the job for a power breakfast – it serves decent kippers, cracking kedgeree and a full English that deserves the name". At other times its English comfort food (when did you last see mince and potatoes on a menu?) neither greatly adds nor detracts from the experience. / W1D 3SE; www.deanstreettownhouse.com; @deanstreettownhouse; 11.30 pm, Fri & Sat midnight, Sun 10.30 pm.

Decimo WC1 NEW

The Standard, 10 Argyle St   020 3981 8888   9–3C

Peter Sanchez-Inglesias's famous Bristol restaurant, Casamia, was voted by Harden's reporters the UK's best in last year's survey, and this October 2019 opening on a hip, new hotel rooftop opposite King's Cross will be one of the most closely-watched of late 2019. The venture will offer Spanish and Mexican cuisines in an 114-cover space, whose view takes in the magnificent Gothic rooftops of St Pancras. / WC1H 9JE; www.decimo.london.

Defune W1 £89 4 3 2
34 George St 020 7935 8311 3–1A
"Perfect sushi" and other "top-notch modern Japanese" food has drawn a steady crowd to this "sedate" Marylebone veteran for the last 35 years (it claims to be the 'longest running Japanese restaurant in London'). No-one's ever been that wild about the interior – the focus is very much on the (expensive) food: "you'll leave happy but broke…" / W1U 7DP; www.defune.com; 10.45 pm, Sun 10.15 pm.

Dehesa W1 £58 2 2 3
25 Ganton Street 020 7494 4170 4–2B
Especially "on a rainy night, snuggled up in the window by candlelight", this small modern tapas restaurant off Carnaby Street can still be a valued haunt. But its ratings have dropped sharply in the past two years as the Salt Yard Group changed hands. "The food used to be really delicious: the ideas are still good" – the "brilliant inclusion of Italian elements in the tapas" – but the realisation nowadays can be "mediocre". / W1F 9BP; www.saltyardgroup.co.uk/dehesa; @DehesaSoho; 10.45 pm, Sun 9.45 pm.

Delamina £42 4 4 2
56-58 Marylebone Lane, W1 020 3026 6810 3–1A
151 Commercial Street, E1 020 7078 0770 13–2B
"Part of the new craze for 'modern-Israeli-style' cuisine" – self-taught chef, Limor Chen (with the help of partner Amir) provides "a different take on the ubiquitous Ottolenghi or Palomar approach" at this low-key restaurant near the Wigmore Hall – a kind of "British Middle Eastern food", which "features lots of vegetables, like the spicy okra tempura and charred cauliflower, which are delicious (and I don't normally go for veg'!)". "Nice people run the place" too, which is decked out with the "on-trend, stripped-back, filament-lightbulb look". Its "buzzing and fun" E1 spin-off inspires less feedback, but gets an equally good rep.

The Delaunay WC2 £67 2 4 4
55 Aldwych 020 7499 8558 2–2D
Corbin & King's "grand café", just off Aldwych, is less showy than its Piccadilly stablemate The Wolseley, but nevertheless "a class act", whose "luxurious" decor, "restrained acoustics", well-spaced interior ("the large room never feels packed even when it's full") and "brisk", "very professional" service make it "especially good for business lunches" in 'Midtown'. But it's also "fabulous for breakfast", not to mention "a great option for pre-theatre" and a top choice for afternoon tea ("lovely cakes, scones… good choice of proper loose teas"). "The Mitteleuropean food isn't the most gastronomically exciting, but there's always something on the menu for everyone" (and with "lots of dishes rarely found in London: wild boar sausage, bratwurst, tarte flambé, etc)". Top Tip – "the Delaunay Counter is excellent for coffee". / WC2B 4BB; www.thedelaunay.com; @TheDelaunayRest; midnight, Sun 11 pm.

Delfino W1 £58 3 3 2
121a Mount St 020 7499 1256 3–3B
"Brilliant pizzas" (alongside "typical trattoria dishes") are served at this Mount Street Italian: "good for quick business lunches" and offering notably "great value in the heart of Mayfair". It "could do with some investment in decor and ambience" though. / W1K 3NW; www.finos.co.uk; 10 pm; closed Sun.

Delhi Grill N1 £29 3 3 2
21 Chapel Mkt 020 7278 8100 9–3D
"One of the best simple curry shops in town" – this "friendly" Punjabi 'dhaba' (roadside food stall) in Islington's Chapel Market "has improved if anything over the years and is usually busy these days". Top Tip – "try the railway lamb". / N1 9EZ; www.delhigrill.com; @delhigrill; 10.30 pm; Cash only.

Delicatessen NW3 £66 3️⃣2️⃣2️⃣
46 Rosslyn Hill   020 7700 5511   9–2A

"Possibly the best of the new kosher restaurants beyond Golders Green" –
this Hampstead two-year-old excels (in a barely competitive field,
admittedly) with its *"interesting"*, *"modern Middle Eastern dishes"*
in *"huge portions"* from ex-Ottolenghi chef Or Golan. Service, by contrast,
can seem *"a bit amateur"*. / NW3 1NH; delicatessen.company.

Department of Coffee
and Social Affairs EC1 £14 3️⃣4️⃣3️⃣
14-16 Leather Ln   020 7419 6906   10–2A

"Could this be the best coffee in London?" – this speciality chain has grown
from this Leather Lane site to 15 around the capital in 10 years, and is,
by all accounts, *"exceptional"* – *"definitely worth going out of the way for
a brew"*. *"Staff are friendly"*, and sandwiches, salads and cakes are
prepared fresh every day at a central in-house kitchen and bakery.
/ EC1N 7SU; departmentofcoffee.com; @DeptOfCoffee; 5.30 pm, Sat 4 pm; L only;
No bookings.

Din Tai Fung 3️⃣3️⃣3️⃣
Centre Point, Tottenham Court Road, WC1   awaiting tel   5–1A **NEW**
5-6 Henrietta Street, WC2   5–3D

"Crazily long queues marked the inaugural week" of the UK's first 250-seat
branch in Covent Garden of this legendary Asian soup, dumpling and noodle
chain: established in 1972 in Taipei, and now also set to open a second
branch near Centrepoint. *"For anyone who's been to DTF in the Far East,
the first London one may come across as a slightly unnecessarily puffed-up
version of what is at heart a fantastically efficient and good-value, shopping-
mall brand"*. *"Dumplings, of many and various forms, are uniformly good
(quality-control at this cult brand is notoriously anal)"* and aficionados of the
chain mostly feel *"it lives up to the standards of branches in well-established
locations in Asia"*. But, they also warn that: *"as per my experience
in Singapore etc, they're not about to change your concept of what a good
xiao long bao, etc, can be"*. / www.dintaifung-uk.com.

The Dining Room,
The Goring Hotel SW1 £99 3️⃣5️⃣4️⃣
15 Beeston Pl   020 7396 9000   2–4B

"Still glowing from its Royal Wedding connection" (and nowadays with
a Royal Warrant to show for it) – this once-sleepy, nowadays increasingly
fashionable, traditional British five-star hotel is situated conveniently behind
Buck House. Established in 1910, it is still run by the Goring family,
who have been investing heavily of late, with the creation of Siren (see also)
and the recent relaunch of the hotel's bar. Its *"delightfully old-school"* dining
room is a *"perennial stalwart"*, whose *"quintessentially-British menu"* was
slightly bizarrely starred by Michelin a few years ago. That's not to say that
the cooking is not *"traditional and of high quality"*, but the real reason why
this is the perfect venue for lunching your maiden aunt or *"wowing visiting
prospective clients"* isn't the food, but its *"impeccable"*, *"old-fashioned"*
service and the *"impressive surroundings"* of this *"light, elegant and high-
ceilinged"* chamber (whose *"roomy tables allow for serious business
discussions"*). No surprise that prices are a tad *"steep"*. Top Tip – afternoon
tea in the adjoining lounge can be *"crowded"* but otherwise is as it would
be done by Disney – *"like a fantasy step back in time"* – *"we went wild for
the sandwiches and scones which were offered in abundance!"* / SW1W 0JW;
www.thegoring.com; @TheGoring; 9.30 pm; closed Sat L; No jeans; booking max 8
may apply.

Dinings £79 5 4 2
22 Harcourt St, W1 020 7723 0666 9–4A
Walton House, Walton St, SW3 020 7723 0666 6–2C

"Crazy combinations, truly awesome at times" continue to wow all who taste the "meticulous" sushi and other modernised Japanese dishes at this duo of venues – an "awkward and tired-looking basement" in Marylebone (under chef Tomonari Chiba) and a "much-cooler-than-the-original" setting in Knightsbridge (under chef Masaki Sugisaki). "I've wandered all round the menu with friends, and each bite was terrific! / dinings.co.uk.

Dinner by Heston Blumenthal SW1 £128 2 2 2
Mandarin Oriental, 66 Knightsbridge 020 7201 3833 6–1D

"If you can overlook the stratospheric prices, and don't go often enough to tire of the historical menu" ("we've all heard about the Meat Fruit now, thanks!"), then Heston Blumenthal's Knightsbridge dining room can, say fans, "still deliver stand-out dishes with precise execution, Heston-eque flourishes" and "bold and exciting flavours". Even supporters, though, caution that "you must get someone else to pay" ("even with great cooking, the bill's terrible value") and to its worst critics it's becoming "a horrible and stale experience", especially given an environment that feels ever-more "soulless and hotel-like". / SW1X 7LA; www.dinnerbyheston.com; @dinnerbyheston; 10.30 pm.

Dip & Flip £34 3 2 2
87 Battersea Rise, SW11 no tel 11–2C
115 Tooting High St, SW17 no tel 11–2C
62 The Broadway, SW19 no tel 11–2B

"It's all about the gravy – a game changer!", say fans of this south London burger chain, where beef or lamb, thin-sliced in baps comes with succulent juices for dipping. In August 2019 they announced the closure of the Brixton branch, leaving Battersea, Tooting and Wimbledon. / www.dipandflip.co.uk; @DipFlippo; 10 pm, Thu-Sat 11 pm; SW9 & SW17 booking: 8 min.

Dirty Burger £34 3 3 2
86 The Broadway, SW19 0203 859 1122 11–2B
Arch 54, 6 South Lambeth Rd, SW8 020 7074 1444 2–4D
13 Bethnal Green Rd, E1 020 7749 4525 13–1B

"High-quality burgers" hit the spot at this funky small chain which "does the simple things well". The outlets are "fab for families and kids – there's something for everyone and puddings are a great crowd-pleaser". / www.eatdirtyburger.com; 10 pm-midnight, Fri & Sat 11pm-2 am, Sun 8 pm-11 pm; no bookings.

Dishoom £44 3 4 5
22 Kingly St, W1 020 7420 9322 4–2B
12 Upper St Martins Ln, WC2 020 7420 9320 5–3B
The Barkers Building, Derry Street, W8 awaiting tel 6–1A
Stable St, Granary Sq, N1 020 7420 9321 9–3C
7 Boundary St, E2 020 7420 9324 13–1B

"There aren't many restaurants where I will queue for nearly two hours to get a table but it's worth the wait!" – This "madly popular" Mumbai-inspired chain "has taken London by storm" and is now the capital's most mentioned chain. Even if the heady days of its Covent Garden debut are long gone, criticisms that it's "too popular for its own good" are most notable by their absence; and instead its "a firm favourite" for its massive army of fans who feel "it never fails to impress". The "buzzy, Indian, faux-retro vibe" ("I felt transported to the Parsi eating houses of Bombay in the 1960s") helps set up a "crazy, frenetic atmosphere"; and even if the "noise levels are pretty bad", "somehow it all comes together". It helps that service is "always punctual and friendly" (respect: it's such a busy chain), and the tapas-y food – though no longer as bleeding edge as it once seemed – still feels "vibrant", with a selection of dishes that's "far from run-of-the-mill" ("recommended by all our Indian friends!"), plus "an exceptional list of drinks". Breakfast here is unexpectedly "a true *thing of beauty" too: "so different" in a brilliant way. "You can book during the day, but not at night" – "the wait is tedious, but the buzzer system works well" and cocktails at the bar help blur time. In mid 2019, the chain acquired the former Jamie's Italian site next to its original WC2 branch in order to expand its footprint. Top Tips – "black dahl is still the best" and "the bacon naan – a true thing of beauty – is the greatest restaurant breakfast dish of all time!". / www.dishoom.com; @Dishoom; 11pm, Thu-Sat midnight; breakfast 8, Sat & Sun 9; booking: min 6 after 5.45 pm.*

Diwana Bhel-Poori House NW1 £25 3 2 1
121-123 Drummond St   020 7387 5556   9–4C
Perhaps "the best of the bunch among the Indian restaurants along Drummond Street near Euston" – this "no-frills institution" has served a "varied South Indian vegetarian menu" to a mixed crowd of students and office workers for the best part of 50 years. Its "terrific value" (and BYO policy) means it can be "too crowded for comfort", but while the interior is "sketchy" it's a joy to any style anoraks who want to know what a late 1960s canteen actually looked like. / NW1 2HL; www.diwanabph.com; @DiwanaBhelPoori; 11 pm, Sun 10 pm; No Amex; May need 10+ to book.

Dokke E1 £54 3 4 3
Ivory House, 50 St Katharine's Way   020 7481 3954   10–3D
"Sensational Asian-fusion cooking, with the freshest of ingredients" creates an "exciting" culinary experience at this small waterside café, in St Katharine Docks. "The team is friendly and you can chat to the chef – who is a real artist – as he works in the open plan kitchen area, adjacent to your table". / E1W 1LA; www.dokke.co.uk; @dokkelondon; 10 pm; booking max 10 may apply.

The Don EC4 £67 3 3 3
The Courtyard, 20 St Swithin's Lane   020 7626 2606   10–3C
A "perfect City lunch-spot", handily located just a short cheque-bounce away from the Bank of England, with "plenty of space between tables" and "a cracking wine list". A French menu is "well executed and served" to a very "consistent standard". For the cellar bistro, see Don Bistro & Bar. / EC4N 8AD; www.thedonrestaurant.com; @thedonlondon; 10 pm; closed Sat & Sun; No shorts.

The Don Bistro and Bar EC4 3 3 3
21 St Swithin's Ln   020 7626 2606   10–3C
Down below The Don, this less-formal bistro section occupies a tightly-packed and atmospheric historic cellar, which originally housed Sandeman's port and sherry business. A little cheaper, it's just as business-friendly in its way as up-above, although here the ambience is less formal, and, oh what a shame, no mobile signal... / EC4N 8AD; www.thedonrestaurant.com/bistro; @TheDonLondon; 10 pm; closed Sat & Sun.

Donostia W1 £57 4 4 3
10 Seymour Pl   020 3620 1845   2–2A
This Basque tapas bar near Marble Arch serves "imaginative dishes" including "very tasty pintxos, with some especially good vegetarian options", backed up by a notably "excellent selection of wines". Any negatives are marginal: "tables are a bit small for many tapas", and "it's hard to pace a meal as food can all arrive at once". Named after the Basque for San Sebastian, its sibling Lurra is nearby. / W1H 7ND; www.donostia.co.uk; @DonostiaW1; 11 pm; closed Mon L; booking max 8 may apply.

Dorchester Grill, Dorchester Hotel W1 £105 3 4 4

53 Park Lane   020 7629 8888   3–3A

This "sophisticated and impressive" Mayfair chamber has had its ups and downs in recent times, and despite scoring a respectable level of customer satisfaction in the last couple of years, still comes nowhere near realising its potential as one of the capital's best traditional dining rooms. It's all change at the hotel, though, with the June 2019 appointment of Stefan Trepp as Executive Chef (replacing Henry Brosi who'd been in-post for 20 years); and with the July 2019 hiring of 26-year-old Tom Booton, who shifts over from heading the kitchen at the highly rated Alyn Williams at the Westbury. Can this potentially magnificent dining room now finally regain its place as one of London's foremost hotel venues? / W1K 1QA; www.thedorchester.com; @TheDorchester; 10.15 pm, Sat 10.45 pm, Sun 10.15 pm; No trainers.

Dotori N4 £37 4 3 2

3a Stroud Green Rd   020 7263 3562   9–1D

"Brill sushi and mouth-numbingly spicy Korean hotpots" draw a bustling crowd of overseas students to this "unprepossessing" operation near Finsbury Park tube – once "the best-kept secret in town". But word has spread about the "sensational Korean and Japanese food for £10-£20 a head" – "authentic and in huge portions". Cash only and no booking. / N4 2DQ; www.dotorirestaurant.wix.com/dotorirestaurant; 10.30 pm, Sun 10pm; closed Mon; No credit cards; no booking.

Double Standard WC1 NEW

The Standard, 10 Argyle St   020 3981 8888   9–3C

Part of a trendy, US hotel-chain's summer 2019 opening, opposite King's Cross station – this ground-floor, street-facing 'neighbourhood' bar has Adam Rawson in charge (he will also look after Isla, a garden restaurant). Double Standard promises casual drinking and dining, with draft beers and classic cocktails in a Shawn-Hausman-designed space. See also Decimo and Isla. / WC1H 8EG; www.standardhotels.com/london/features/standard_london_isla.

Dragon Castle SE17 £41 4 3 3

100 Walworth Rd   020 7277 3388   1–3C

"If you want an Asian fix", this huge, "very Cantonese" operation near Elephant & Castle is a "south London legend", with "around 1,000 dishes on the menu" – including "consistently excellent dim sum that's fresh and varied". Low prices make it "most affordable" and help make it "suitable for all kinds of groups: families, friends and greedy gourmets alike". / SE17 1JL; www.dragoncastlelondon.com; @Dragoncastle100; 11 pm, Sun 10 pm.

The Drapers Arms N1 £58 3 3 4

44 Barnsbury Street   020 7619 0348   9–3D

"Fantabulous Sunday roast" heads the "good mix of pub fare and some more lively dishes" at this well-run and "very busy" Islington gastroboozer: one of the best known in that 'hood. It has an "interesting wine list at reasonable prices, too". / N1 1ER; www.thedrapersarms.com; @DrapersArms; 10.30 pm; No Amex.

The Drawing Room at The Dukes Hotel SW1 £73

35 Saint James's Place   020 7318 6574   3–4C

Limited feedback on the eateries of this posh St James's hotel, but its afternoon tea did catch reporters' attention this year. Served in the "beautifully-decorated" drawing room or conservatory, it wins praise for its "very generous portions" and "exceptional service" ("staff treated my young nieces with such kindness, and really catered to their needs in a thoughtful manner"). Out with the girls? – go for the MarTEAni... / SW1A 1NY; www.dukeshotel.com.

Dropshot Coffee SW19
283

281 Wimbledon Park Road   11–2B

"A fantastic, cool, addition to Southfields!" – this neighbourhood corner-café (named for its close proximity to Wimbledon tennis) is serious about its coffee, featuring single-origin house espresso from Brixton roasters Assembly, plus ever-changing guest espresso and filter-coffee options. They do a "great brunch" too. / SW19 6NW; dropshotcoffee.co.uk.

The Drunken Butler EC1   £72   444

20 Rosebery Avenue   020 7101 4020   10–1A

Chef Yuma Hashemi presides over an open kitchen – combining contemporary European small plates with influences from his boyhood in Iran – at this unusual Clerkenwell yearling. In the evenings, you choose from either a short (five-course) tasting menu or a long seven-course one. Sundays are given over to traditional Persian feasting, which fans suggest is the biggest draw here: "a meal to remember, with beautiful flavours and textures"; "tahdig (the caramelised crust at the bottom of a pot of rice) was a thing of utter beauty". / EC1R 4SX; www.thedrunkenbutler.com; @SYumaHashemi; Mon & Tue 2 pm, Wed-Sat 10 pm; Online only.

The Duck & Rice W1   £62   323

90 Berwick St   020 3327 7888   4–2C

This "nice take on typical Chinese dishes", served "tapas-style in a gastropub" on Soho's Berwick Street, is the creation of Asian restaurant maestro Alan Yau. Four years on, however – while it's perfectly decently rated – there is little evidence that he has conjured another winner on the scale of his earlier hits, Wagamama and Hakkasan. / W1F 0QB; www.theduckandrice.com; @theduckandrice; 11 pm, Fri & Sat 11.30 pm, Sun 10 pm.

Duck & Waffle EC2   £86   224

110 Bishopsgate, Heron Tower   020 3640 7310   10–2D

"At midnight, perched high above London in this flashy 40th-floor restaurant, it's thrilling watching the lights of the traffic; and the signature duck & waffle dish with maple syrup was like none we have tasted before" – that's the fanboy view on this luxury diner at the top of the City's Heron Tower, and the fact that it's open 24/7 makes it a big brunch destination. Sceptical diners were more in evidence this year, though, criticising the "stodgy and unbalanced" menu, or "food that's average, but a bill that's WAY above average": "once you take away the hype, that you can eat in the middle of the night and it's up a skyscraper, it's actually nothing special". "Getting a reservation can be difficult, though: book way ahead and eat at a strange hour!" / EC2N 4AY; www.duckandwaffle.com; @DuckandWaffle; open 24 hours.

The Duck Truck E1   £15   533

Lamb Street   07919 160271   13–2B

"Mouthwatering delicious duck" – "not just wraps", but other dishes such as confit duck, pulled duck or duck steaks in a brioche bun – win a massive thumbs-up for this "unusual, quirky and quite unique" street-food star, permanently parked up by Spitalfields Market. "Best chips I've eaten in a very long time… and the duck is pretty good too!" / E1 6EA; www.theducktruck.com; @TheDuckTruck1.

Ducksoup W1   £61   434

41 Dean St   020 7287 4599   5–2A

"So hip, so uncomfortable, so cool it aches" – this funky Soho bar combines natural/biodynamic wines, Italian-North African small plates and sounds on vinyl. For fans, it's a combination that "just makes me happy" – with its "delicious ingredient-led seasonal food, this place just gets better and better". As for the "odd and cloudy" vino – "we were complete natural wine cretins and left knowing ever so slightly more, with a new favourite drink". / W1D 4PY; www.ducksoupsoho.co.uk; @ducksoup; 10.30 pm; closed Sun D; May need 3+ to book.

Duddell's SE1 £87 323
6 St Thomas St   020 3957 9932   10–4C
"Genuine Hong Kong expatriate fare" – "delicious dim sum" and "out-of-this-world Peking duck" – has won a sizeable following for this London offshoot of a top-ranking HK venue. Its ratings slipped a notch this year though, amidst continuing concerns (including amongst fans) that it's rather "pricey"; and also on the basis of the odd meal that was just plain "disappointing". It enjoys the unusual setting of a converted church – St Thomas's, near Borough Market and the Shard: "beautiful" (if a mite "sterile"). / SE1 9RY; www.duddells.co/london; @DuddellsLondon.

The Duke of Richmond Public House & Dining Room E8 £50 323
316 Queensbridge Road   020 7923 3990   14–1A
"A beautiful old boozer on the Dalston/Haggerston border", restored and revamped in mid-2018 as a "cracking local gastropub", with chef Tom Oldroyd (formerly of the Polpo group; see also Oldroyd N1). He has put a traditional French twist on its gastropub fare, helping to win an enthusiastic fanclub, with cod's roe starter, "fab burger" and "top Sunday lunch" singled out for particular praise. "If the place looks familiar, it was previously a seafood restaurant (The Richmond) and before that a cheap 'n' cheerful bistro with weird classical artefacts (LMNT)... and long before that a dodgy boozer". / E8 3NH; www.thedukeofrichmond.com; @dukeofrichmond_.

Duke of Sussex W4 £60 223
75 South Pde   020 8742 8801   8–1A
"A very traditional pub", prominently situated on a corner by Acton Green Common, with a fine old bar, attractive, airy rear dining room and "lovely patio garden, ideal for the summer". Its gastropub cooking includes a number of less usual "Spanish tapas-style plates". While the food can be "tasty and well-presented", ratings suggest it somewhat undershoots its potential. / W4 5LF; www.thedukeofsussex.co.uk; @thedukew4; 10.30 pm, Sun 9.30 pm.

Dum Biryani W1 £55 322
187 Wardour Street   020 3638 0974   3–1D
"Magnificent biryanis" are served in a 'dum' – a heavy pot – at this two-year-old Indian café just south of Oxford Street, the first venture from Dhruv Mittal, who quit his job in the City and retrained as a chef in Mumbai. "All the individual spices, often quite unusual ones, could be identified and appreciated", and there's a "good choice for vegetarians". But the basement setting isn't its strongest point. / W1F 8ZB; dumlondon.com; @dumlondon; 10.30 pm, Sun 10 pm; May need 5+ to book.

The Dusty Knuckle Bakery E8 433
Car Park, Abbot Street   020 3903 7598   14–1A
"A bakery in an old car park in Dalston which gives apprenticeships to troubled 16-25 year olds: delicious seeded sourdoughs and focaccia are both made into the most outrageous and amazing sandwiches". / E8 3DP; www.thedustyknuckle.com; @thedustyknuckle.

Dynamo £45 433
200-204 Putney Bridge Rd, SW15   020 3761 2952   11–2B
16-18 Ritherdon Road, SW17   020 8767 3197   11–2C
"Lovely wood-fired pizzas and imaginative salads" make this "friendly cycle-themed coffee shop" in Putney (and its Balham sibling) a "great place for brunch on the way back from a cycle round Richmond Park". Early rouleurs will find breakfast from 7.30am, and there's "ample bike parking". / www.the-dynamo.co.uk; @WeAreTheDynamo.

The Dysart Petersham TW10 £77 **3 4 4**
135 Petersham Road 020 8940 8005 1–4A

"An excellent setting" is the particular plus of this smart Arts & Crafts pub, near Richmond Park, but its appeal goes well beyond its leaded windows, log fires and flagstone floors. Kenneth Culhane's "innovative" cuisine is "very accomplished" and "often excels", to the point that some cognoscenti consider it deserves much wider culinary recognition. / TW10 7AA; www.thedysartarms.co.uk; @dysartpetersham; Mon - Tue closed, Wed - Sat 9.30 pm, Sun 3.30 pm; closed Sun D.

E Mono NW5 £17 **4 2 1**
285-287 Kentish Town Road 020 7485 9779 9–2B

"Succulent-tasting kebabs" at this "great value", family-run Turkish joint (which adopted its name from the original Victorian signage) were "recommended by Giles Coren" some years ago – and our reporters have consistently backed his judgement: "their success is deserved". / NW5 2JS; emono.co.uk.

E&O £56 **3 3 3**
392 King's Rd, SW3 020 7349 9934 6–3B **NEW**
14 Blenheim Cr, W11 020 7229 5454 7–1A

"Still vibrant and alive after all these years" – Will Ricker's Notting Hill haunt survived its heady A-list celebrity of the early noughties, and even though critics say "you go here to show off your body, or your new friends, to whoever's around", its ethos has actually remained surprisingly un-snooty over the years. Foodwise, it's "no longer breaking new ground with its pan-Asian tastes and mixtures", but remains a "very fun" option for a superior cocktail with some "eclectic", SE Asian fusion bites. In mid-2019, its King's Road sibling, Eight Over Eight – already something of a chip off the old block – was refurbed and relaunched as E&O Chelsea.

The Eagle EC1 £45 **4 3 3**
159 Farringdon Rd 020 7837 1353 10–1A

"This original gastropub still has amazing, genuine food with real flavours". Almost 30 years since its launch near Exmouth Market, it's still a "boisterous and scruffy pub" where "friendly chefs in the open kitchen talk about their food with love – they're keeping it real despite the gentrification and hipsterfication of the entire area". / EC1R 3AL; www.theeaglefarringdon.co.uk; @eaglefarringdon; 10.30 pm; closed Sun D; No Amex; no booking.

Earl Spencer SW18 £51 **3 2 3**
260-262 Merton Rd 020 8870 9244 11–2B

Despite its trafficky Southfields location, this well-known Edwardian roadhouse has an unexpectedly "attractive" interior and is "consistently bang on form", with food that's "a cut-above your usual gastropub"; plus "an excellent range of beers and spirits". / SW18 5JL; www.theearlspencer.com; @TheEarlSpencer; 11 pm; Mon-Thu D only, Fri-Sun open L & D.

EartH Kitchen N16 £26 **3 2 2**
11-17 Stoke Newington Road 020 3873 2345 14–1A

"Try and snag a corner banquette for great E8 people-watching" if you visit this quirky venue – the dining room of a Dalston (technically speaking Shacklewell) events venue where ex-St John chef Chris Gillard delivers some excellent, gutsy dishes. On nights when the venue has a noisy gig though, it can fall down as a foodie experience: "they need to decide if they're a bar and disco, or a restaurant, because diners don't want both at once: the waiters were sidetracked mixing cocktails and the DJ an irritant". / N16 8BH; www.earth-kitchen.co.uk; @EartHKitchenN16.

Eat 17 £50 333

Unit A 77 Fulham Palace Road, W6   020 8521 5279   8–2C
28-30 Orford Rd, E17   020 8521 5279   1–1D
64-66 Brooksbys Walk, E9   020 8986 6242   14–1C

"In the heart of Walthamstow Village", this "great neighbourhood spot" – a Spar supermarket with kitchen attached – wins praise for its "quality" cooking ("the 2019 Harden's description of pub-type grub underplays its standard and originality"). "Very relaxed and welcoming for young children", the venture's best-known innovation is bacon jam, which you can buy by the jar in various flavours. Other branches have opened in Hackney and, most recently, Hammersmith (somewhat better-served areas, so these respective branches are somewhat less of a local lifeline). / www.eat17.co.uk; @eat_17; 9.30 pm, Fri & Sat 10 pm, Sun 8 pm.

Eat Tokyo £32 322

16 Old Compton St, W1   020 7439 9887   5–2A
50 Red Lion St, WC1   020 7242 3490   2–1D
27 Catherine St, WC2   020 3489 1700   5–3D
169 King St, W6   020 8741 7916   8–2B
18 Hillgate St, W8   020 7792 9313   7–2B
14 North End Rd, NW11   020 8209 0079   1–1B
628 Finchley Rd, NW11   020 3609 8886   1–1B

"Genuine", "pleasingly quirky" and "unflashy" – these "humble", extremely popular cafés offer "excellent-value Japanese food" from decent ingredients in "large portions" and are "always full" of "Japanese students and other Asian locals". The "brusque" service is "a little haphazard, as is the seating". / www.eattokyo.co.uk; Mon-Sat 11.30 pm, Sun 10.30 pm; phone bookings only.

Eco SW4 £39 333

162 Clapham High St   020 7978 1108   11–2D

"Classic pizzas, cooked simply and well in a nice, buzzy room" has kept Franco Manca creator, Sami Wasif's Clapham hang-out, in biz for over 25 years: "it's always reliable, and you can nearly always get a table". / SW4 7UG; www.ecorestaurants.com; @ecopizzaLDN; 11 pm, Fri & Sat 11.30 pm.

Edera W11 £64 333

148 Holland Park Ave   020 7221 6090   7–2A

"Lovely… if a little pricey" – this "smart casual" (and business-friendly) Holland Park Italian has survived over a good number of years thanks to its "interesting" Sardinian dishes and an overall feeling of quality: "it doesn't outscore others on specifics, but the whole package works well – professional but not sleek, good but not gastronomic – a favourite". / W11 4UE; www.edera.co.uk; 11 pm, Sun 10 pm.

Eggslut W11 NEW

185 Portobello Road   7–1B

Egg-citing Notting Hill arrival of a California-based chain majoring in… you guessed it… which beamed down from La-La Land into Portobello in late-summer 2019, too late for survey feedback. Signature dish is 'The Slut': a coddled egg on potato puree in a jar, plus sliced baguette. / W11 2ED; www.eggslut.com; @EggSlutLA.

Ekte Nordic Kitchen EC4 £53 322

2-8 Bloomberg Arcade   020 3814 8330   10–3C

"Odd location in the midst of the City for a modern Scandinavian restaurant" – Soren Jessen's (of No.1 Lombard Street) "spacious" yearling in the new Bloomberg HQ has "quality Scandi decor with an open kitchen", but its clean-living associations are perhaps slightly at odds with its site, amongst all the money factories. "The smørrebrød (open sandwiches), particularly the pickled herring, are fantastic and the small but thoughtful wine list and menu are well thought out", but it can "seem quite pricey for what you get". / EC4N 8AR; www.ektelondon.co.uk; @ektelondon.

Electric Diner W11 £51 2️⃣2️⃣**3**
191 Portobello Rd   020 7908 9696   7–1B
For "a perfect end to a Saturday morning on Portobello Road", some still recommend this US-diner-style haunt. But while it's fine if you're a trustafarian working off a hangover, or just posing around Portobello, you wouldn't cross town. / W11 2ED; www.electricdiner.com; @ElectricDiner; 11 pm, Fri & Sat midnight, Sun 10 pm.

Ella Canta W1 £85 **3****3****3**
InterContinental London Park Lane, Park Lane   020 7318 8715   3–4A
"Authentic Mexican street food" stars in the "not-at-all street-food setting" of the Park Lane Intercontinental hotel in this two-year-old from celebrated Mexico City chef Martha Ortiz. The food both "looks and tastes amazing", although – not surprisingly, given the location – it is "expensive for what it is". / W1J 7QY; www.ellacanta.com; @ellacantalondon.

Elliot's Café SE1 £59 **4****4****4**
12 Stoney St   020 7403 7436   10–4C
"The kind of place you could eat at any day of the week" – this open-fronted wine bar and café stalwart looking onto Borough Market wins consistent praise for its "punchy plates", many of them from a wood-fired oven; and "well-priced wine" (with "a good selection by the glass")… so "invent any reason, just go". / SE1 9AD; www.elliotscafe.com; @elliotscafe; 10 pm; closed Sun.

Elystan Street SW3 £88 **5****5****3**
43 Elystan Street   020 7628 5005   6–2C
Phil Howard "is going from strength to strength" at his "vibrant and lively" three-year-old, tucked away in a chichi Chelsea backstreet, where survey ratings scaled new heights this year. Deceptively, the slightly "austere" room "has the feel of a high-quality, neighbourhood local, but standards of food and service are, by contrast, top class". "Phil has gone back to basics" with his culinary approach and his "beautiful, clever dishes are a delight": "really inspired cooking using seasonal ingredients and recipes" with a "light touch" and "superb precision". Famously, he's more 'flexitarian' in approach than when he was at The Square and "while it's not a vegetarian restaurant, it delivers some of the most interesting gastronomic vegetarian dishes ever!" Service is "outstanding" too – "interested, engaged and good communicators". / SW3 3NT; www.elystanstreet.com; @elystanstreet.

Ember Yard W1 £58 **3****3****4**
60 Berwick Street   020 7439 8057   3–1D
Up-and-down reports on this "lovely" Soho haunt, specialising in wood-fired, Mediterranean, grilled dishes – part of Salt Yard Group (all of which was absorbed into the Urban Pubs portfolio in November 2018). Fans applaud the "delicious tapas from this ever-reliable family" but quite a few reports express disappointment: "maybe there's a sense it isn't quite what it was". / W1F 8SU; www.emberyard.co.uk; @emberyard; 11 pm, Sat midnight, Sun 10 pm; booking max 13 may apply.

Emilia's Crafted Pasta £47 **4****4****3**
77 Alie Street, E1   020 3358 0317   13–2C **NEW**
Ivory House, St Katharine Docks, E1   020 7481 2004   10–3D
This two-year old in the picturesque surroundings of St Katharine Docks is "still serving great, home-made pasta". It's had a spin-off nearby in Aldgate since February 2019: "a welcome addition to the original (where you can't always get a table), with the same fab food". / www.emiliaspasta.com; @emiliaspasta.

Emilia W1 NEW £74 443

7 Haunch of Venison Yard   0207 468 5868   3–2B

"Perfect Emilia-Romagna food… and I know because I'm from there!" This *"deeply impressive"* Mayfair newcomer occupies the small-but-stylish space, off the rear of Bonhams auction house (with its own street entrance) that was formerly Bonhams (RIP). Run by the same (non-Italian) team as Clipstone, Portland and the Quality Chop House (Will Lander and Dan Morgenthau), the *"delicate"* cuisine is *"enchanting"*, service is *"classy"* and, at lunch, the upstairs space is *"lovely and light"*. Unsurprisingly though, prices give nothing away. / W1K 5ES; emiliarestaurant.co.uk.

The Empress E9 £50 343

130 Lauriston Rd   020 8533 5123   14–2B

Well-known pub close to Victoria Park, whose gentrification predates much of up-and-coming East London. *"It's what a neighbourhood joint should be about"*, with changing menus providing sufficient interest and variety to keep regulars returning time and again. / E9 7LH; www.empress9.co.uk; @elliottlidstone; 10 pm, Sun 9 pm; closed Mon L; No Amex.

Endo at Rotunda W12 NEW £184 554

White City, 101 Wood Lane   020 3972 9000   1–2B

A *"sensational Japanese sushi experience"*, *"prepared and served by a true entertainer and showman"*, wins near-perfect marks for Endo Kazutoshi's (former sushi chef at Zuma) 16-seat newcomer, in the rotunda atop the former BBC Television Centre in White City – nowadays transformed as a huge, glam apartment complex by Nick Jones of Soho House. The venture invites some comparisons with the early days of Mitsuhiro Araki at The Araki, although here the much glossier setting arguably lives up more to the inevitably stratospheric price tag: *"a highly informative experience of great intimacy: not cheap, but a lot less than a plane ticket to Japan…"*. (On the basis that the comparison with The Araki is warranted, Michelin will likely hand this place two stars in autumn 2019). / W12 7FR; www.endoatrotunda.com.

Eneko Basque Kitchen & Bar WC2 £78 443

1 Aldwych   020 7300 0300   2–2D

"Top-notch Basque food in a great location" in Aldwych has earned much-improved ratings this year for chef Eneko Atxa, whose home restaurant Azurmendi is a regular on 'world's best' lists. It's *"so wonderful to be able to taste some of his adventurous flavours in London"* – *"wasn't sure of the basement setting"* (a recurrent gripe), *"but loved the open kitchen and the food was extraordinary"*. / WC2B 4BZ; www.eneko.london; @OneAldwych; 11 pm, Sun 10 pm.

Enoteca Rosso W8 £60 223

276-280 Kensington High Street   07384 595191   8–1D

"Go for the wine: there's a great selection" focused solely on Italy at this Kensington yearling, with bottles lining many of the walls. Even fans can note that the food (pasta, cheese and meat boards, salads) *"is not as good"*, but it avoids any harsh critiques. Brunch here is also a possibility. / W8 6ND; www.enotecarosso.com.

Enoteca Turi SW1 £83 342

87 Pimlico Road   020 7730 3663   6–2D

"Astonishing Italian wine list: bravo signor Turi!" – Giuseppi and Pamela Turi are *"now firmly ensconced in Pimlico having successfully weathered the transfer"* three years ago from a more neighbourhood-y site near Putney Bridge (which they inhabited for over 20 years) to this much posher postcode; and they have brought with them their *"amazing"* cellar, which is perhaps London's most notable selection of Italian vintages. They have also replicated their *"delightful"* personal touch at this *"comfortable"* new venue, and fans say *"the food has really raised its game since the SW15*

days": "simple dishes, beautifully prepared". Its ratings slipped a fraction this year though, with quite a few gripes that it seems increasingly "pricey". / SW1W 8PH; www.enotecaturi.com; @EnotecaTuri; 10.30 pm, Fri & Sat 11 pm; closed Sun; booking max 8 may apply.

The Enterprise SW3 £65 2 3 4
35 Walton St 020 7584 3148 6–2C
Providing "faithful" service to an expensively dressed clientele in one of Chelsea's prettiest streets – this "lovely local" (too posh really to qualify as a 'gastropub') has an excellent buzz and consistently well-rated food. As always, though, there's the odd grumble here about its price level. / SW3 2HU; www.theenterprise.co.uk; 10.30 pm, Sun 10 pm.

L'Escargot W1 £64 3 2 4
48 Greek Street 020 7439 7474 5–2A
"Beautiful, old-fashioned surroundings" imbue this "classy" Gallic favourite (est 1927) with a "lovely old-school atmosphere", and – if you're looking for a "classic" French meal (Chateaubriand, coq au vin, tournedos Rossini, boeuf bourguignon, profiteroles) in the heart of Soho, it has few rivals nowadays. Its rating slipped a fraction this year, though, on the back of a couple of less wholehearted endorsements: "mainly good, but not as exceptional as your last review implied". / W1D 4EF; www.lescargot.co.uk; @LEscargotSoho; 11.30 pm; closed Sun D.

Est India SE1 £43 3 3 3
73-75 Union Street, Flat Iron Square 020 7407 2004 10–4B
If the food market in Flat Iron Square doesn't take your fancy, remember this consistently good modern basement Indian, serving a wide mix of options, including a number of south Indian dishes like dosas; good with families too. / SE1 1SG; www.estindia.co.uk; @EstIndiaLondon; 11 pm, Sun 10.30 pm.

Estiatorio Milos SW1 £98 3 2 4
1 Regent St 020 7839 2080 4–4D
"The most beautiful fish counter ever" is the dramatic centrepiece of Costas Spiladis's "classy" four-year-old (part of an LA, Miami, etc international group), and – with its "roomy" quarters clad in white marble sourced from mountains outside Athens – it brings a "glammed up Greek atmosphere" to the fringe of St James's. Its fans extol "the best fish in London" and gorgeous seafood that's "second to none", but sceptics caution that "it's priced so that only oligarchs can afford to eat it", and to an extent that can seem "extortionate". Top Tip – by contrast, lunch and pre-theatre deals represent "incredible value". / SW1Y 4NR; www.milos.ca/restaurants/london; @Milos_London; 12.15 am.

Ethos W1 £33 4 2 3
48 Eastcastle St 020 3581 1538 3–1C
"Just wonderful for tasty and healthy food" – a five-year-old vegetarian, "self-service restaurant where you weigh the food you take from the buffet" and pay accordingly, occupying a "clean and modern" unit a short walk from Oxford Circus: "a great concept", where "the food's all delicious". Top Tip – vegan and gluten-free afternoon teas can be hard to find, but are options here. / W1W 8DX; www.ethosfoods.com; @ethosfoods; 10 pm, Sat 9.30 pm, Sun 4 pm; May need 6+ to book.

Evelyn's Table at The Blue Posts W1 £86 4 5 3
28 Rupert Street 07921 336010 4–3D
"So much fun and such a pleasure" – "it's a bit hard to find" (below a cocktail bar, in the cellar of the 275-year-old Blue Posts pub, in Chinatown), but this tiny, year-old sibling to The Palomar and The Barbary is well worth discovering. A "cosy and super-relaxed" 11-seater, with a couple of tiny tables; the food is Italian in inspiration but focused on prime UK ingredients, especially fish brought from Cornwall daily. "The cramped counter gives you a ringside view on some exceptional cooking with a priority on freshness and flavour". / W1D 6DJ; theblueposts.co.uk.

Everest Inn SE3 £36 3 3 3
41 Montpelier Vale   020 8852 7872   1–4D
"Lovely" Nepalese specialities are the menu highlights at this "reliably good local Indian" in Blackheath. Some reporters had the odd issue with the service – "if they could sort that out, this place would be amazing".
/ SE3 0TJ; www.everestinnblackheath.co.uk; 11.30 pm, Fri & Sat midnight.

La Famiglia SW10 £65 2 3 4
7 Langton Street   020 7351 0761   6–3B
Thanks in part to its "beautiful garden", this "very friendly", old-favourite trattoria (est 1966) in a posh and pretty Chelsea sidestreet has attracted more than its fair share of Hollywood A-listers and royalty over the decades, and is particularly popular with the well-heeled locals as a place to bring the little darlings ("as the name says, it is good for families, but it's very busy at weekends"). Opinions split somewhat on how its long service has affected the realisation of its "real Italian cooking": "unchanged for 40 years – just lovely" vies with "hasn't changed in 50 years, very uninspiring".
/ SW10 0JL; www.lafamiglia.co.uk; @lafamiglia_sw10; 11 pm, Sun 9 pm.

Fancy Crab W1 £64 3 3 2
92 Wigmore Street   020 3096 9484   3–1A
"Unbelievably delicious crab" – of the Arctic red king variety, served cold with dipping sauces or baked over charcoal – is presented fast-food-style alongside other seafood and fish at this two-year-old concept in Marylebone. To fans, it's a "great idea" to offer luxury ingredients at such "good value", although limited feedback suggests it's yet fully to win hearts and minds amongst reporters. / W1U 3RD; www.fancycrab.co.uk; @fancycrabuk.

Farang N5 £44 4 4 2
72 Highbury Park   0207 226 1609   9–1D
"Miles more interesting than most Thais" – with food "so hot it makes your eyes water… but in a very good way" – Sebby Holmes's now-permanent Highbury venture (on the old site of San Daniele, RIP) is earning prominence amongst London's new-wave Thais. "Favourable comparisons are made with Som Saa, Kiln and Smoking Goat", approving "zero compromise in the spicing on a short, season-dependent menu". / N5 2XE;
www.faranglondon.co.uk; @farangLDN; 10.30 pm, Sun 5 pm; closed Mon & Sun D; No Amex.

Fare EC1 NEW £57 3 3 4
11 Old Street   0203 034 0736   13–1A
"Chic-looking, but down-to-earth, east London joint" from the folks behind Sager + Wilde, which has opened near Silicon Roundabout on the Clerkenwell/Shoreditch borders. A comprehensive wine list, and "some good coffee" create much of its appeal, and there's also an "unpretentious and not ridiculously overpriced" array of pizzas and "interesting" small plates.
/ EC1V 9HL; farelondon.com; @Farebarcanteen.

Farmacy W2 £63 4 4 3
74 Westbourne Grove   020 7221 0705   7–1B
"Vegan at its best", agree fans of this contemporary Californian-style operation from Camilla Fayed (daughter of the former Harrods owner, Mohamed Al-Fayed). The cooking is "interesting and highly competent", and while "vegan food can often be bland, that's not the case here" – so "if you want your first vegan experience, it's the place to come".
/ W2 5SH; www.farmacylondon.com; @farmacyuk; 11 pm, Sun 7 pm; SRA-Food Made Good – 2 stars.

Farzi Cafe SW1 NEW £53 444
8 Haymarket 0203 981 0090 4–4D
In the heart of the West End, this decidedly glam newcomer scored better
in our survey than the mixed rep it received in press reviews. The
first UK outpost of a 30-strong international chain hailing from India and the
Gulf, its repertoire of tapas-y offerings are very much of the funky, evolved
school of Indian cuisine, and reporters salivate over "an amazing choice
of inventive dishes" that are "far better than you would expect" in this
touristy locale. / SW1Y 4BP; www.farzilondon.com.

Fatt Pundit W1 NEW £55 332
77 Berwick Street 020 7287 7900 4–1C
Hakka (Indo-Chinese cuisine) is centre-stage at this new Soho 60-seater,
where its few early-days reviews are brimming with enthusiasm, particularly
regarding the "excellent" food. You kick off with spicy 'momo' (Tibetan
dumplings) and move onto the interesting selection of mains (dishes
including crab, rabbit, venison…). There's even a "sizzling brownie dessert
to die for". / W1F 8TH; www.fattpundit.co.uk; @FattPundit.

**Fenchurch Restaurant,
Sky Garden EC3** £91 434
20 Fenchurch St 033 3772 0020 10–3D
"It is rare to encounter a five-star ambience, as well as welcoming service,
and a high standard of food, all at once in the City" and, on pretty much all
accounts, there's "no better place if you're looking for an exceptional evening
location" than the 37th floor of the 'Walkie Talkie' ("go for a walk in the
garden... with a drink... take in the amazing view…"). As the survey was
concluding in June 2019, chef Dan Fletcher left for Somerset, and a new
chef, George Farrugia (ex-Bob Bob Ricard) joined this operation run
by caterers 'rhubarb' – hopefully the good all-round performance will survive
the upheaval. / EC3M 3BY; skygarden.london/fenchurch-restaurant; @SG_Fenchurch;
10.15 pm; booking max 7 may apply.

La Ferme £47 333
154 Regent's Park Road, NW1 9–3B
102-104 Farringdon Rd, EC1 020 7837 5293 10–1A
This "excellent local" bistro in Primrose Hill – "there should be one on every
high street" – has a "good buzz" and does "a nice line in deconstructed
versions of French classics". The original La Petite Ferme near Exmouth
Market is a "lovely little" venue "offering brilliant value".

Fez Mangal W11 £28 543
104 Ladbroke Grove 020 7229 3010 7–1A
"Exceptional kebabs; firm, fresh salads; and lovely service in a larger but still
chaotic setting" earn consistent rave reports for this Ladbroke Grove Turk.
"The new Fez Mangal is glitzier without losing its soul" – and it's still
"amazing value", with "wonderful food at typically £15 per head" – helped
by the BYO policy. / W11 1PY; www.fezmangal.com; @FezMangal; 11.30 pm;
No Amex.

Fiddie's Italian Kitchen NW3 £36 332
13 New College Parade 020 7586 5050 9–2A
"Fun and lively, with a management who make you feel extremely welcome"
– this simple, 'Italian kitchen' in Swiss Cottage serves pizza and pasta plus
somewhat more ambitious dishes: it's all "delicious and good value for
money". / NW3 5EP; fiddiesitaliankitchen.com; @FiddiesItalian.

50 Kalò di Ciro Salvo WC2   £33   4 3 2
7 Northumberland Avenue   020 7930 9955   2–3C
*The best pizza in Europe outside of Italy is, according to a recent Top-50,
to be found at this summer 2018 import direct from Napoli – a "huge"
space that's part of a hotel just off Trafalgar Square (but with its own
dedicated entrance). 50 Kalò means 'good dough' in the local Naples dialect
and most reports say it has indeed "captured the essence of good pizza
making": "super light crusts, with amazing charring on the dough, delivering
fantastic textures and taste"; and "varied, high quality toppings" too. Some
reporters feel that to call it the best in London is hype, but all reports agree
this is "simple-but-yummy food that definitely hits the spot". / WC2N 5BY;
www.50kalò.it; no booking.*

Fink's Salt and Sweet N5   £37   3 4 3
70 Mountgrove Road   020 7684 7189   9–1D
*On a Highbury street corner, this coffee shop/deli is the kind of place locals
"love to just drop into, providing there's a free table". "The menu's varied,
whether you're veering towards breakfast or the lunch end of brunch,
the coffee's excellent… and I recently discovered how great their evening
food is, too". / N5 2LT; finks.co.uk; @FinksLondon.*

Fischer's W1   £69   2 2 4
50 Marylebone High Street   020 7466 5501   2–1A
*"Reminiscent of a grand café in turn-of-the-century Vienna" – Corbin
& King's "warm, cosy, and gemütlich" operation has "a Mittel-european vibe
of posh coats, lipstick and gossip", and is just the place to hole up on
a winter's day in particular. Its "broad and comforting menu" of Austro-
Germanic fare does have many fans (who say "the schnitzel is a must-
have"), but can also seem "stodgy and also rather overpriced". Top Tip –
"if you've never had Gröstl for breakfast, go now! Birchermüsli… Kassler
Ham and boiled eggs on proper rye sourdough… herrings and kippers. And
yes, strudel IS an acceptable breakfast food! With Einspanner coffee
(topped with whipped cream), a lovely start to the day. Embrace the
atmosphere… and don't make any plans for lunch!" / W1U 5HN;
www.fischers.co.uk; @FischersLondon; 11 pm, Sun 10 pm.*

Fish Central EC1   £37   3 4 3
149-155 Central St   020 7253 4970   13–1A
*"Dependably good fish" at "outstandingly good value-for-money" prices
is the hallmark of this veteran, family-run, central chippy (est. 1968).
"Been coming here for years and never had a bad dish" – no wonder it's
a "cabbies' haunt". Top Tip – "one of the few post-Barbican event options
on Saturday nights". / EC1V 8AP; www.fishcentral.co.uk; @fishcentral1968;
10.30 pm, Fri 11 pm; closed Sun.*

Fish in a Tie SW11   £36   3 3 3
105 Falcon Rd   020 7924 1913   11–1C
*"A hidden gem of a bistro near Clapham Junction", the focus here is on
Mediterranean food at "exceptional prices", especially if you order from the
set menu options. The name is misleading: it's not a fish restaurant,
although it does serve some seafood dishes. / SW11 2PF; www.fishinatie.com;
midnight, Sun 11 pm.*

Fish Market EC2   £70   2 2 2
16a New Street   020 3503 0790   10–2D
*This seafood specialist in a converted warehouse near Liverpool Street –
part of the D&D London operation – "looks good" and does have fans who
feel it delivers outstanding fish. Ratings were undercut this year, though,
by several moans that it "over-promises and under-delivers". / EC2M 4TR;
www.fishmarket-restaurant.co.uk; @FishMarketNS; 10.30 pm; closed Sun.*

fish! SE1 £63 **4** **2** **2**

Cathedral St 020 7407 3803 10–4C

"A wonderful range of fresh fish is cooked to order" at this "buzzing", glass-fronted venue just by Borough Market. "It gets it right much more often than it gets it wrong" nowadays and is "well worth a visit". / SE1 9AL; www.fishkitchen.co.uk; @fishborough; 11 pm, Sun 10.30 pm.

Fishworks £65 **3** **2** **2**

7-9 Swallow St, W1 020 7734 5813 4–4C
89 Marylebone High St, W1 020 7935 9796 2–1A
2-4 Catherine Street, WC2 020 7240 4999 5–3D **NEW**

"Good fresh fish, simply cooked" is the offer at this trio of seafood bistros (entered via a fishmonger at the front), which are "solid and reliable without being spectacular" – with the bonus, in the case of the Mayfair branch, of finding "really good value so close to Piccadilly". The May 2019 opening of the new Covent Garden venue signals an upswing of a brand that has been in the doldrums since its peak in the late 1990s. / www.fishworks.co.uk; W1B 10.30 pm, Fri & Sat 11 pm; W1U 10.30 pm.

Fiume SW8 £64 **2** **2** **4**

Circus West Village, Sopwith Way 020 3904 9010 11–1C

"The location, near Battersea Power Station, absolutely makes this venue" – a 120-seater run by D&D London, which boasts fine views of the Thames and a big outside terrace. By comparison, "food and service are, well... fine". / SW8 5BN; www.danddlondon.com/restaurant/fiume; @FiumeLondon.

The Five Fields SW3 £112 **5** **5** **4**

8-9 Blacklands Ter 020 7838 1082 6–2D

"More like the Elysian fields!": Taylor Bonnyman's "congenial" but "unpretentious" Chelsea HQ (founded in 2013) doesn't court publicity, but emerged with the survey's highest food rating this year. With its "sophisticated" interior, "spectacular wine list" and "wonderful" service – "impeccably timed, professional, yet warm" – it's long been hailed as an "outstanding all-rounder". But it has hit a particularly impressive and consistent culinary stride in recent times, with not a single negative report received this year (and we received many reports). Head chef, Marguerite Keogh "strives for perfection, and the care and attention to detail of ingredients processed and plated is second to none", delivering "divinely flavoured dishes" in a mould that's "classic in style, but very modern in execution" – "witty and inventive, without being up itself or over-fussy". Much of the produce is sourced from the restaurant's own garden in East Sussex. Choose at lunch or dinner from a prix fixe three-course menu or alternative tasting option. / SW3 2SP; www.fivefieldsrestaurant.com; @The5Fields; 10 pm; D only, closed Mon & Sun.

Five Guys £21 **3** **2** **1**

"When all you want is an old-school burger", these US-based arrivals of recent years really "hit the spot" – you can "build your own", with "tons of accessories"; plus "seriously addictive fries", "thick milkshakes", and "more soda flavours than is reasonable". "The eat-in experience is as depressing as McDonald's", though, in fact perhaps more so – "some branches have a strangely gloomy ambience" – but fans feel that "if you don't mind 1980s-rock, a trip can still be surprisingly fun". / @FiveGuysUK; 10.30 pm, Fri & Sat 11 pm, Sun 10 pm; no bookings.

500 N19 £49 **3** **3** **3**

782 Holloway Rd 020 7272 3406 9–1C

"Lovely, authentic and interesting Italian food" is on the menu at this "great neighbourhood restaurant" near Archway, named after the equally "small and fabulous" Fiat Cinquecento. Founder Mario Magli learned his chops under the late Antonio Carluccio and Gennaro Contaldo, Jamie Oliver's mentor, before setting up in his own right 12 years ago. / N19 3JH; www.500restaurant.co.uk; @500restaurant; 10.30 pm, Sun 9.30 pm; Mon-Thu D only, Fri-Sun open L & D.

500 Degrees SE24 £34 **3** **2** **2**
153a Dulwich Road   020 7274 8200   11–2D
Named for the temperature of its wood-fired oven, this Herne Hill three-year-old delivers "authentic Neapolitan pizza" and not much else, although the "tiramisu is not bad". (Also with branches in Brixton and Crystal Palace.) / SE24; www.500degrees.co; @500degreesuk; 11 pm, Sun 10 pm.

Flank E1 **4** **4** **3**
The Kitchens, Old Spitalfields Market   no tel   13–2C
Thomas Griffiths's stall in Spitalfields Market receives very consistently high ratings from reporters (and he now also has a unit in Market Halls Victoria too). The street-food style fare – brisket sandwich, dumplings, fried-chicken sandwich – belie a sophisticated and sustainable 'modern British, nose-to-tail cooking' approach. / E1 6EW; www.flanklondon.com; @tomgriffchef

Flat Iron £33 **4** **4** **4**
17 Beak St, W1   020 3019 2353   4–2B
17 Henrietta St, WC2   020 3019 4212   5–3C
9 Denmark St, WC2   no tel   5–1A
47-51 Caledonian Rd, N1   9–3D
112-116 Tooley Street, SE1   10–4D **NEW**
88-90 Commercial Street, E1   13–2C **NEW**
77 Curtain Road, EC2   no tel   13–1B
"They put the price up from £10 to £11, but it still can't be faulted!" – for a "a great steak, without any frills" this "always busy, lively and buzzy" chain remains "a winning formula": "it's so nice to have a simple menu choice, and what they do, they do very well"; this includes the very impressively "friendly and professional service-with-a-smile". One catch: "you have to put up with no bookings", so "be prepared to queue". But "if you want a great meal on a budget: go visit!" / www.flatironsteak.co.uk; @flatironsteak; Golbourne 10 pm, Covent Garden 11 pm, other branches 11.30 pm; bookings only in W10.

Flat Three W11 £61 **3** **3** **3**
120-122 Holland Park Ave   020 7792 8987   7–2A
"The kitchen really is doing something different, sending out delicious and original dishes with a mixed Scandinavian and Japanese/Korean heritage" at this "under-the-radar restaurant, hidden away beneath a shop" in Holland Park. All reports suggest it's "definitely worth a visit", but there are caveats: service can be "indifferent" and even fans can find the prices over-egged. / W11 4UA; www.flatthree.london; @infoflat3; 9.30 pm.

Flat White W1 £14 **4** **4** **3**
17 Berwick St   020 7734 0370   4–2D
London's original Flat White was served at this early-wave, Kiwi coffee stop, which first hit Soho's Berwick Street Market in 2005; and its legendary brews and "great staff" have maintained a fair following over the last 15 years. Its brunch-friendly options include pastries, smashed avos on toast and homemade banana bread. / W1F 0PT; www.flatwhitesoho.co.uk; @flatwhitesoho; L only; Cash only; No bookings.

Flesh and Buns £54 **2** **3** **3**
32 Berners Street, W1   020 3019 3492   3–1D **NEW**
Bone Daddies, 41 Earlham Street, WC2   020 7632 9500   5–2C
"A great night out, with fab food and drinks" is the accepted wisdom on Ross Shonhan's rocking izakayas, whose original, Soho-basement location looks set to be eclipsed by its new Fitzrovia sibling – an impressively large (170 covers) space, which adds Peruvian-Nikkei fusion-dishes and an expanded range of smoked meats to its more-established repertoire of Japanese faves (sushi, sashimi, filled steamed buns). It's "amazing food that will leave you feeling VERY FULL". Ratings are dragged down, though, by reporters who find the flavour combinations "odd", or the overall package too expensive. Top Tip – "given that the main menu can be pricey: the set menu before 6pm or tasting menu is by far the best way to go". / www.fleshandbuns.co.

Flor SE1 NEW
1 Bedale Street   020 3319 8144   10–4C

James Lowe and John Ogier – of epic Shoreditch legend Lyle's – plus backers JKS Restaurants launched this all-day bakery and wine bar venture in Borough Market in mid-July, too late for survey feedback. The offering stretches from coffee and croissants in the morning, through small plates at lunch, to a more wine-bar vibe in the evening. Early press reports are predictably adulatory… but they are probably correct. / SE1 9AL; florlondon.com.

Flora Indica SW5   £46   4 4 4
242 Old Brompton Rd   020 7370 4450   6–2A

"Really delicious modern Indian cooking" is making its mark at this two-year-old in Earl's Court, which is further differentiated by its "surprising steampunk decor" – a tribute to the intrepid Scottish botanists who catalogued the flora of the subcontinent in the Victorian era. There's a "good selection of wines by the glass as well as bottle". / SW5 0DE; www.flora-indica.com; @flora_indica; 1 am.

Flotsam and Jetsam SW17   £35   3 3 3
4 Bellevue Parade   020 8672 7639   11–2C

"Go at the right time to avoid all the yummy mummies", to get the best from this "great but often excessively busy neighbourhood brunch spot". "Aussie influence shines through the menu, and is reflected in the quality of coffee served. It has a good little sun-trap for outside seating, and is perfectly located for a post-brunch walk on Wandsworth Common". / SW17 7EQ; www.flotsamandjetsamcafe.co.uk; @_flotsam_jetsam; 5 pm; L only; No bookings.

Flour & Grape SE1   £43   4 3 3
214 Bermondsey St   020 7407 4682   10–4D

"A fantastic, local pasta-and-wine restaurant" (the clue is in the name) on Bermondsey high street, which makes an excellent cheap 'n' cheerful choice. The pasta dishes themselves are "simple", but their realisation is "a cut-above most other pasta restaurants" and when it comes to the vino, there are 25 options by the glass (all Italian). / SE1 3TQ; www.flourandgrape.com; @flourandgrape; 10 pm, Sun 9 pm; closed Mon; booking max 6 may apply.

FM Mangal SE5   £39   3 4 2
54 Camberwell Church St   020 7701 6677   1–3C

Ten-year-old Turkish grill in Camberwell, where the "gracious service" starts with a "free bread and onion appetiser (a real treat)", and carries on with "finely cooked" lamb, meat and vegetables accompanied by "huge fresh salads". It's "a simple proposition, but done well". / SE5 8QZ; midnight; No Amex; no booking.

Foley's W1   £52   4 4 2
23 Foley Street   020 3137 1302   2–1B

"Imaginative and tasty cooking" of a "very high quality", taking its cue from modern pan-Asian cuisines, wins steadily high ratings for chef Mitz Vora (ex-Palomar) at his Fitzrovia three-year-old, and service is generally "fast and friendly" too. Only one negative: the "very tight seating arrangements". / W1W 6DU; www.foleysrestaurant.co.uk; @foleyslondon.

Folie W1 NEW
37 Golden Square   awaiting tel   4–2C

Frenchman Guillaume Depoix has taken over a corner site in Golden Square (previously a PizzaExpress), with a view to opening 'the perfect Soho brasserie' in November 2019 (a brave post-Brexit move, we think). He has extensive front-of-house experience, with four years in London under his belt, plus Alain Ducasse's Plaza Athénée. / W1F 9LB.

Forman's E3 £59 **4** **3** **3**

Stour Rd, Fish Island 020 8525 2365 14–2C

This in-house restaurant of the famous smoked salmon smokery (est. 1905) on the River Lea is a "lovely place to eat the best smoked fish, with a great view" – in fact, two views: from a viewing gallery over the smokery, and across to the Olympic stadium next door. For West Ham fans, it's ideal for a pre-match lunch; for everybody else, "a bit out of the way, but worth the schlep". / E3 2NT; www.formans.co.uk/restaurant; @formanslondon; 9 pm; Closed Mon-Wed, Thu & Fri D only, Sat open L & D, closed Sun D.

Fortnum & Mason, The Diamond Jubilee Tea Salon W1 £78 **3** **4** **4**

181 Piccadilly 020 7734 8040 3–3D

"Amazing, incredible, unlimited everything and WOW!" – for a "quintessential afternoon tea experience", the "elegant, calm and bright" third-floor dining room of The Queen's favourite grocer offers a "fine" (and "extremely filling") experience, encompassing "a tea selection to die for", "wonderfully inventive cakes", and "delicious and plentiful sandwiches and scones". "Yes, it is a bit pricey, but it's an experience to be savoured, and the posh doggie bag they give you means dinner is sorted too…" / W1A 1ER; www.fortnumandmason.com; @Fortnums; 7 pm, Sun 6 pm; L & afternoon tea only; No trainers.

The Fortnum's Bar & Restaurant EC3 NEW£69 **2** **3** **3**

The Royal Exchange 020 7734 8040 10–2C

"Making the best of an amazing space at the Royal Exchange" – Fortnum's have taken over the operation formerly run by D&D London with this luxurious pitstop in the Exchange's magnificent courtyard: not a great place to save money, but "perfect for small plates, plus a glass or two of champers". / EC3V 3LR; www.fortnumandmason.com/restaurants/the-bar-and-restaurant-at-the-royal-exchange; @Fortnums.

45 Jermyn Street SW1 £73 **3** **3** **4**

45 Jermyn Street, St. James's 020 7205 4545 3–3D

"Elegant yet relaxed" – Fortnum & Mason created "a real winner" a couple of years ago with this "beautiful bar/dining room", whose "fabulous cocktails" and "stylish" cuisine make a "smart-but-not-overpowering" replacement for the crusty Edwardian buttery, The Fountain (RIP), which it replaced. Handy for business, it's also a popular early morning choice for a "cosseting and superb breakfast" ("exactly what I need to recover after the overnight from New York!"). Top Menu Tip – Beef Wellington, with the sauce flambéed at the table. / SW1Y 6DN; www.45jermynst.com; @45JermynSt; 11 pm, Sun 10.30 pm; closed Sun D.

40 Maltby Street SE1 £52 **4** **4** **4**

40 Maltby St 020 7237 9247 10–4D

This "natural wine bar with excellent food" has become a "must-eat fixture" for London foodies, where chef Steve Williams produces a daily chalked-up menu of "incredible" small plates, to be consumed in the no-frills surroundings of a Victorian railway arch on the lines into London Bridge station, which houses the Gergovie biodynamic wine import business. There are "interesting gems" on the wine list, "but don't try to navigate on your own – explain to the sommelier what style you're looking for and take the advice". As for the food: "genuinely the most impressive 'sausage roll' I've had in my life – I was truly in heaven, and had to have two". / SE1 3PA; www.40maltbystreet.com; @40maltbystreet; 9.30 pm; closed Mon, Tue, Wed L, Thu L, Sat D & Sun; No Amex; no booking.

Forza Win SE15 £53 **4 4 3**
Unit 4.1, 133 Copeland Rd   020 7732 9012   1–4D
"An unexpected treat despite the location" – a former warehouse at the
back of an industrial building in Peckham – this ex-pop-up Italian serves
"really original food at very good prices", including *"easily some of the
best pasta in London"*. *"You feel the people working here really love what
they do, and it shows in the food – it's seriously happy food"*. / SE15 3SN;
www.forzawin.com; @forzawin.

400 Rabbits £27 **4 3 2**
143 Evelina Road, SE15   020 7732 4115   1–4D
30-32 Westow St, SE19   020 8771 6249   1–4D
521 Norwood Road, SE27   020 8761 0872   **NEW**
"Creative pizzas" on a 'London sourdough' base meet a changing
list of craft beers at this *"vibrant"* southeast London group which has spread
from Crystal Palace to Nunhead and, this year, West Norwood. It's
apparently named after the progeny of a conjugal union between the Aztec
gods of fermenting and brewing. Top Tip – *"if it's on, the octopus special
pizza is incredible"*. / www.400rabbits.co.uk; @4hundredrabbits.

Four Legs at The Compton Arms N1 **NEW**
4 Compton Avenue   020 7354 8473   9–2D
*A new kitchen team have livened up the menu at this Arsenal supporters'
pub, which is said to have inspired George Orwell's fictional, idealised pub
The Moon Under Water. Early press reports are excited about its mix
of pub grub and somewhat fancier fare.* / N1 2XD; www.comptonarms.co.uk.

Four Seasons £49 **4 1 1**
11 Gerrard Street, W1   020 7287 0900   5–3A
12 Gerrard St, W1   020 7494 0870   5–3A
23 Wardour St, W1   020 7287 9995   5–3A
84 Queensway, W2   020 7229 4320   7–2C
"The service is passable and the ambience is poor" at this group
in Chinatown and Bayswater – *"but you only go for one thing: the
barbecued/roast meat"*, especially the *"famous"* and *"perfect Cantonese
roast duck and the char siu pork"*. They might be *"a bit too authentic these
days"*, but they're still *"hard to beat for Chinese food"*.
/ www.fs-restaurants.co.uk; 11pm, Fri & Sat midnight, W2 11.30 pm, Sun 11 pm;
all branches ex W2 closed Sun.

Fox & Grapes SW19 £61 **3 2 4**
9 Camp Rd   020 8619 1300   11–2A
"The best pub on Wimbledon Common", this renovated late-Georgian
boozer serves *"good-quality"* Italian food (alongside English roasts
on Sunday) and is ideal as a reward for a good walk. / SW19 4UN;
www.foxandgrapeswimbledon.co.uk; @thefoxandgrapes; 10 pm, Sun 9.30 pm.

Franco Manca £35 **3 3 2**
*One of the victors in the casual dining downturn: this mushrooming multiple
has become the survey's most-mentioned pizza chain – "it beats
PizzaExpress hands down" nowadays (of which owner David Page was once
CEO) thanks to pizza that's "so much more tasty" than PE's, with "gorgeous
sourdough bases" and "excellent toppings" and "all for a very reasonable
price", so no-one minds the "cheap 'n' cheerful" style of its "loud, very busy
and noisy" branches.* / www.francomanca.co.uk; Mon-Sat 11 pm, Sun 10.30 pm;
no bookings.

Franco's SW1 £63 **3 4 4**

61 Jermyn St 020 7499 2211 3–3C

Classic St James's Italian, whose convivial and civilised quarters amd "totally reliable food" make it "one of the best all-rounders in the area" and, in particular, "a good choice for a business lunch" (or breakfast, which is very good here). It was opened in 1946 by the Wiltons group, and emerged from a major refurb in autumn 2019 with a new bar, refreshed decor and a menu shake-up. "Despite its popularity (and vintage), it retains a freshness both in the food and the service", and while by no means cheap, regulars say "it always delivers". / SW1Y 6LX; www.francoslondon.com; @francoslondon; 10.30 pm; closed Sun.

Frantoio SW10 £70 **3 4 4**

397 King's Rd 020 7352 4146 6–3B

The flamboyant owner, Bucci, creates "a great atmosphere" and helps present a "really good menu for both meat and fish lovers" at this "fun" World's End trattoria. It's a real "favourite" among locals: "I love, love, love this place! Been going for 20 years and it's like walking into a family gathering". / SW10 0LR; www.frantoio.co.uk; 11 pm.

Franzina Trattoria SW9 NEW

395 Coldharbour Lane 07802 473444 11–2D

Chef Pietro Franz has now left Pop Brixton for this simple, stripped-down, forever home where he serves Sicilian small plates and pasta. Little survey feedback so far – more reports please. / SW9 8LQ; franzinatrattoria.com; @franzinabrixton.

Freak Scene W1 £46 **5 4 4**

54 Frith Street 07561 394 497 5–2A

"I approached with trepidation… but everything was delicious!" – this "fun and laid-back", open-kitchen dining experience in Soho delivers a "casual but impressive" meal centred on "surprising-in-a-totally-good-way", Pan-Asian small plates, delivered by "dynamic" staff. A former pop-up – it's the creation of an ex-Nobu team, with Aussie chef Scott Hallsworth and partner Phar Shaweewan. / W1D 4SL; www.freakscene.london; @freakscene.

Frederick's N1 £62 **3 4 5**

106 Camden Passage 020 7359 2888 9–3D

"Tucked away in Camden Passage", this Islington institution is "still going strong after all these years" and remains a real "go-to place for family celebrations" for many north Londoners; as well as "a great place for a romantic dinner". "The ordinary fascia hides a true gem inside", leading onto "a modern, spacious and stylish interior" where the top seats are in the "lovely, light and airy back area". It's not a foodie kind of place, but the cooking is "contemporary and varied (the set menu never disappoints)", and "staff are par excellence, always professional, but fun and cheery". / N1 8EG; www.fredericks.co.uk; @fredericks_n1; 11 pm; closed Sun.

The French House W1 £65 **3 4 5**

49 Dean Street 020 7437 2477 5–3A

"Oozing rustic, Gallic charm of yesteryear" – the "lovely, intimate room" above Soho's famous Francophile watering hole (where de Gaulle is said to have composed his 'À tous les Français' speech during WWII, rallying the French people) oscillates over the years between being a forgotten-about curio, and sporadic partnerships with brilliant chefs (e.g. St John's Fergus Henderson, who started out here) that lead to its re-discovery. The arrival of Neil Borthwick (Mr Angela Hartnett) at the end of last year sees it riding another high – "it's smashing to have this old-favourite reborn under such good hands" – and his "great, old-fashioned, gutsy French menu" ("short, but with dishes which seem dragged from a distant memory") can be "top class", while service is "fabulously friendly" too. A few reporters, though, feels "it doesn't live up to the hype" or that "while great to have it back, it's still a work in progress…" / W1D 5BG; www.frenchhousesoho.com; @FrenchHouseSoho.

Frenchie WC2 £83 **3** 2 2
18 Henrietta Street 020 7836 4422 5–3C

Gregory (nicknamed 'Frenchie' by Jamie Oliver at Fifteen) & Marie Marchand's stylish three-year-old is "a treat, with all its signature dishes imported from their charming Parisian venue of the same name", delivering "beautiful French food", served in a lovely, stylishly-neutral, modern space. Despite the arrival last year of Dale Sutton (the executive head chef of their French operations) however, ratings continue to head south here, and critics feel it's "lost its edge" since its stellar early days. No question, though, it's a "fun" and "useful spot in Covent Garden" that many still extol as the site of their best meal of the year. / WC2E 8QH; www.frenchiecoventgarden.com; @frenchiecoventgarden; 10.30 pm.

The Frog £73 **5** 5 3
35 Southampton Street, WC2 020 7199 8370 5–3D
45-47 Hoxton Square, N1 020 3813 9832 13–1B

"Eating at The Frog is like allowing your palate to go to a firework display" – Adam Handling and his teams create a series of dishes of "always-surprising ingenuity, with quirky presentation and mixture of ingredients" both at his Hoxton Square original and his even-more-successful Covent Garden flagship. Both locations offer a mixture of à la carte and tasting menus – the latter incorporating vegan and vegetarian alternatives as well as beer-matching and wine-matching options. The results inspire massive support,not just for being "a well-devised journey expertly executed", but for food that's "wow, wow, wow beyond delicious!". In keeping with the main man's free-thinking philosophy (and, at E1, a big emphasis on sustainability), his locations have a youthful energy at odds with the fayne dining ethos: an approach that also seems to inspire "impeccable service" from his staff (with a special shout-out to his sommelier – "I've never been disappointed when asking Kelvin for a recommendation!"). Where his taste is a tad more divisive is the ambience – to fans admirably un-stuffy and energetic, but to critics slightly "odd" or "nondescript", and with "loud and dreadful music" in N1. Top Menu Tip – "those cheese doughnuts are the stuff of legend". See also Adam Handling Chelsea. / www.thefrogrestaurant.com; @TheFrogE1.

La Fromagerie £49 **3** 4 3
2-6 Moxon St, W1 020 7935 0341 3–1A
52 Lamb's Conduit St, WC1 0207 242 1044 2–1D
30 Highbury Park, N5 020 7359 7440 9–2D

A "mouthwatering array of wonderful cheeses" – they stock from the UK, Ireland, France and Italy – is the most obvious reason to pay a visit to these cafés-cum-cheese shops. But they also serve excellent snacks and meals throughout the day, making the most of "fresh seasonal ingredients". / www.lafromagerie.co.uk; @LaFromagerieUK.

The Frontline Club W2 £64 2 2 **4**
13 Norfolk Pl 020 7479 8960 7–1D

The ground floor of an international journalists' club, with photo-reportage as wall decoration: this dining room near Paddington Station is particularly worth knowing about as a smartish option in what's still a very thinly provided area. Its modern British cooking is "a little hit and miss", but while it only "sometimes lives up to the space" it seldom goes badly awry. One problem: "with all those photos of heroic war reporting on the wall, one feels a bit of a wimp". / W2 1QJ; www.frontlineclub.com; @frontlineclub; 11 pm; closed Sat L & Sun; booking max 6 may apply.

Fucina W1 NEW £66
26 Paddington Street   020 7058 4444   2–1A
Kurt Zdesar – who has been involved with such illustrious names as Nobu, Hakkasan, Chotto Matte and Ping Pong – and Stefano Stecca (most recently executive chef at Toto's) opened this "spacious" and glamorous-looking Italian newcomer in late-2018 in Marylebone, with a focus on organic ingredients. Early-days feedback was limited, but some "delicious" if pricey food is reported, and the main quibble about the interior is that its moody lighting can leave it "rather dark". / W1U 5QY; fucina.co.uk; @FucinaLondon.

Fugitive Motel E2 NEW
199 Cambridge Heath Road   020 3974 4455   13–1D
A 140-seater 'craft bar and kitchen' near some soon-to-be developed railway arches in hip Bethnal Green that opened in June 2019, too late for any survey feedback. It's open from breakfast on – at lunch and thereafter the main menu offering is pizza. / E2 0EU; fugitivemotel.bar; @fugitive_motel.

Fumo WC2 £52 ❸❸❸
37 St Martin's Lane   020 3778 0430   5–4C
This "fabulous, fun and buzzy" three-year-old next door to the Coliseum, from the national San Carlo group, has won a good following. It specialises in "tasty" cicchetti or Venetian small plates, and provides an "unexpectedly friendly and attractive welcome in the West End": "ideal for a light lunch" and "good for pre-theatre". / WC2N 4JS; www.sancarlofumo.co.uk/fumo-london; @sancarlo_fumo.

Gallery Mess, Saatchi Gallery SW3 £62 ❷❸❸
Duke of Yorks HQ, Kings Road   020 7730 8135   6–2D
A big outside terrace is a key feature of Charles Saatchi's attractive gallery café, which overlooks the green next to Duke of York's Square on the King's Road. Foodwise, it is most recommended for its afternoon tea possibilities, but it's tolerably rated for a light bite at other times too. / SW3 4RY; www.saatchigallery.com/gallerymess; @gallerymess; 11 pm, Sun 7 pm; closed Sun D.

Gallipoli £41 ❷❸❸
102 Upper St, N1   020 7359 0630   9–3D
120 Upper St, N1   020 7226 8099   9–3D
"Tasty, good-value Turkish food" and "a warm welcome" make these "jolly" (lots of "dangly decorations") Ottoman-themed stalwarts just "the sort of bistro you'd be pleased to have near you". / www.cafegallipoli.com; @CafeGallipoli; 11pm - midnight.

Galvin at the Athenaeum W1 £72 ❶❷❷
Athenaeum Hotel, 116 Piccadilly   020 7640 3333   3–4B
Fans of the Galvin Bros' regime at this luxurious five-star hotel near Hyde Park Corner still applaud it as a "solid, nice and efficient" option, whose "good-value set deals" add to its possibilities as a "glam lunch venue". Its ratings took a major hit this year, however, with too many reports of "complete disappointment" and "no generosity over the pricing" – at present it's "really not up to the standards of their other ventures". / W1J 7BJ; www.athenaeumhotel.com; @galvinathenaeum; 10.30 pm.

**Galvin at Windows,
Park Lane London Hilton Hotel W1** £122 3 3 5
22 Park Ln 020 7208 4021 3–4A

"Breathtaking panoramic views over central London" make this "refined",
28th-floor eyrie a natural place for a date or celebration – or "to impress
out-of-towners" – and "sipping a cocktail whilst looking at our great city is a
special experience" (try to secure a window table when you book).
Standards by-and-large avoid the complacency typical of rooms with a view:
service is "professional" and most diners feel the cooking is "wonderful and
beautifully presented". Naturally the experience is fully priced but... Top Tip
– "set lunch is excellent value". / W1K 1BE; www.galvinatwindows.com;
@GalvinatWindows; 10 pm, Thu-Sat 10.30 pm, Sun 3 pm; closed Sat L & Sun D;
No trainers; booking max 5 may apply.

Galvin HOP E1 £70 3 3 3
35 Spital Sq 020 7299 0404 13–2B

This haute-gastropub near Spitalfields Market is next to brothers Chris and
Jeff's deluxe Galvin La Chapelle, and serves "high-quality bistro-style food".
Ratings have improved in the past 12 months as the transition from its
former guise, Café à Vin, has bedded in. / E1 6DY;
www.galvinrestaurants.com/section/62/1/galvinhop; @Galvin_brothers; 10.30 pm,
Sun 9.30 pm; booking max 5 may apply.

Galvin La Chapelle E1 £96 4 4 5
35 Spital Sq 020 7299 0400 13–2B

The "most enchanting setting" – "an out-of-this-world conversion of an old
church" (to be precise, the chapel of a Victorian school) – makes the Galvin
Bros' Spitalfields HQ one of London's most "beautiful" restaurants.
It provides a "special" backdrop "for keen business deals, or to impress your
new love-interest" (and is "a particular attraction for guests from overseas").
There are "high standards across the board", including "fantastic" modern
French cuisine; a "classy wine list"; and "smart, swift, discreet service".
/ E1 6DY; www.galvinlachapelle.com; @galvin_brothers; 10.30 pm, Sun 9.30 pm;
No trainers; booking max 8 may apply.

The Game Bird at The Stafford London SW1£99 3 5 3
16-18 St James's Place 020 7518 1234 3–4C

The "old-world comfort and glamour" of a quiet St James's hotel dining
room provides the setting for "studiedly English food" – "a seasonal mix
of classic and modern dishes" including "excellent roast beef from the trolley
on Sundays". "Exceptionally good service" at "discrete tables which feel very
private" and "a superb wine list" add to its attractions, particularly for
entertaining clients. No surprises, though, that "it's pricey for what you get".
Top Tip – "a preprandial cocktail in the famous American Bar is highly
recommended". / SW1A 1NJ; thestaffordlondon.com/the-game-bird;
@TheGameBirdLON; 10 pm.

Ganapati SE15 £42 4 4 3
38 Holly Grove 020 7277 2928 1–4D

For "ace food" and "an upbeat local boho vibe" – "Ganapati does it every
time". Chef Claire Fisher opened this small Peckham venue 15 years ago
after travelling around South India. "Everything is home-made from the
pickles to the parathas and you can even buy jars of pickle to take home" –
and there's a "fantastic choice for veggies and vegans too". Top Tip – "great
lunchtime thali for £8.50". / SE15 5DF; www.ganapatirestaurant.com; 10.30 pm,
Sun 10 pm; closed Mon; No Amex.

The Garden Cafe at the Garden Museum SE1 £46 3 2 3

5 Lambeth Palace Rd   020 7401 8865   2–4D

"A light and airy space" overlooking a "simply lovely garden" – the pavilion at Lambeth's Garden Museum is an oasis of tranquillity in a grungy part of town. The two-year-old venture operates as a full-on restaurant for lunch and dinner; and its "ambitious, unpredictable, mainly seasonal menu" is "well executed" by chefs Harry Kaufman and George Ryle, who know their chops after stints in St John and Padella respectively. "Service can sometimes make you feel a bit of a nuisance for asking for attention…" / SE1 7LB; www.gardenmuseum.org.uk; @GardenMuseumLDN; 5 pm, Sat 3.30 pm; L only; No Amex; Booking max 12 may apply.

Garden Room WC2 NEW £71 2 2 3

27-31 Charing Cross Road   020 3962 7275   5–4B

"Really lovely views of London" are the reason to discover this new cocktail bar – a roof garden in the West End, on the tenth floor of the Assembly hotel, run by the hip folks from Bourne & Hollingsworth. Feedback, to-date, is limited and cautious though: hit a bum time and there's "zero atmosphere", and the food, though serviceable, "could be so much more than it is". / WC2H 0LS; www.bandhgardenroom.com.

Le Garrick WC2 £55 3 3 4

10-12 Garrick Street   020 7240 7649   5–3C

"A delightful throwback to the French bistros of the 1980s, set over a couple of floors, with tables crammed into nooks and crannies" – this Covent Garden stalwart is "very romantic, with its candles and cosy booths". The "traditional, unpretentious food" is "good value" ("nothing fancy, but consistent") while the "staff are so friendly": if you're in a hurry pre-theatre, "they put you through fast without seeming to hassle you", but "if you have more time they let you linger". / WC2E 9BH; www.legarrick.co.uk; @le_garrick; 10.30 pm, Sun 5pm; closed Sun.

The Garrison SE1 £57 3 3 3

99 Bermondsey Street   020 7089 9355   10–4D

"Pub food at its finest, with some real stand-out dishes" has kept this operation near the antiques market at the forefront since the early days of Bermondsey's booming food scene. "The menu's good, but the specials are worth eating every time". / SE1 3XB; www.thegarrison.co.uk; @TheGarrisonSE1; 10 pm, Fri & Sat 10.30 pm, Sun 9 pm.

The Gate £53 4 2 2

22-24 Seymour Place, W1   020 7724 6656   2–2A
51 Queen Caroline St, W6   020 8748 6932   8–2C
87 Allitsen Road, NW8   020 7833 0401.   9–3A NEW
370 St John St, EC1   020 7278 5483   9–3D

"Standards remain high" at Michael and Adrian Daniel's "veggie stalwart" chain – in particular at the W6 original in a "convivial", offbeat building south of Hammersmith Broadway, which some consider "the best vegetarian in town" thanks to "inventive" food that's "wow-amazing… even for a committed carnivore". Its spring 2019 opening in St John's Wood is also going down well – launching as the second highest scoring member of the group with "a fabulous and very varied selection of vegan and vegetarian food". The W1 operation in Seymour Village and EC1 branch near Sadler's Wells are slightly less highly rated, but the tenor of practically all reports hails "thoughtful and tasty fare, catering to a range of dietary requirements". / thegaterestaurants.com; @GateRestaurant; 10 pm, Sun 9.30 pm NW8 10.15pm, Sun 9.15 pm, W6 Sun 9:15 pm.

Gaucho £80 222

Emerging from a financial rescue package (that has seen the owner of M Restaurants, and former Gaucho CEO, Martin Williams, return to the helm), this moodily decorated Argentinian steakhouse chain still somewhat divides reporters. Prime Latino cuts feature alongside a "well-curated" South American wine list, and even despite its difficulties, detractors don't say the food is dire, merely that the experience can appear "dull" given the "eye-watering bills". Better reports overall, though, do suggest some return to form, with a greater proportion of diners once again inclined to find it "good fun" and "expensive for a reason". Top Tip – look out for their bottomless 'beef & bottle' deals. / www.gauchorestaurants.co.uk; @gauchogroup; 11 pm, Thu-Sat midnight; WC2, EC3V, EC1M closed Sun.

Gauthier Soho W1 £77 443

21 Romilly St   020 7494 3111   5–3A

"Why he has not regained his Michelin star is quite beyond me", say fans of Alexis Gauthier's immensely popular and accomplished venture, which lost its gong in 2012, and which the Tyre Man has pointedly (pointlessly?) ignored ever since. "You have to ring the doorbell to gain entrance" to this quirky old Georgian townhouse in Soho, whose "charming, old-world" dining rooms are on different floors separated by a somewhat "rickety staircase". But whereas its culinary style could once be easily pigeon-holed as "classic" Gallic gluttony – with "exquisite, inventive dishes, beautifully presented" – the main man's banishment of foie gras in 2015, his ongoing conversion to veganism, and his well-known 'Les Plantes' vegan tasting menu (a feature since 2016) is taking the place further and further out of the mainstream. On most accounts results remain utterly "outstanding" whether or not you are a meat eater, but ratings dipped a tad this year on the back of some regulars noting a slight "slip in standards". Sometimes the concern is general ("needs a bit of a revamp"). More often, though, it's linked to the shift away from meat ("getting tired of the vegan 'foie gras' canapés and yearning for the old-style ones"). But, quibbles aside, his achievement in maintaining high standards during such a big shift is impressive, and it will be more so if he fulfills his promise next year and goes entirely vegan. Hats off to AG for "embracing the concept and importance of a plant-based diet and doing wonderful things to vegetables!" / W1D 5AF; www.gauthiersoho.co.uk; @GauthierSoho; 9.30 pm, Fri & Sat 10.30 pm; closed Mon & Sun; booking max 7 may apply.

Le Gavroche W1 £140 454

43 Upper Brook St   020 7408 0881   3–2A

"Elegance... discreet service... classic French cuisine – they never go out of fashion", and nowhere else in London can match Michel Roux Jr's "grande dame of the London restaurant scene" for "perfect, old-school Gallic gastronomy". Founded (on Sloane Street) in 1967 by his father Albert, this famous culinary temple has operated in Mayfair just around the corner from the former US embassy since 1982 and with MasterChef-maestro Michel at the stoves since 1991. Menus (with no prices in the lady's version) are perused in the smallish ground floor lounge, before descending to the "dark and moody basement with its elaborate table ornaments". To a few doubters the style is too "stuffy and formal" (or, alternatively, too dated and 1980s-tastic) – but to most visitors (some of whom are regulars of many decades' standing) the milieu makes it "one of the capital's best dining rooms, setting the perfect scene for any posh liaison"; with "soft furnishings and a layout that means one may hear and converse in quiet and relative privacy; and where it's refreshing to find the standard of dress amongst the patrons still includes a suit and tie". "Attention to detail and personal enjoyment shows in every aspect of the experience: cooking is "superbly judged both in its selection and preparation", and the "wine list is the work of an afternoon – hugely pleasurable to read and to attempt to absorb its width and variety!". "Smooth, unobtrusive service" under maître d' Emmanuel Landré, is "impeccable" – "ideally pitched from when you step through the door to the final farewell"; and Michel (usually in attendance)

"is a charmer as well as a brilliant chef", with "the personal visit from
Le Patron making a special meal very special". The bill? "It's barely
affordable, but worth saving for": "a classic example of the rule, 'you get
what you pay for' and, while expensive, good value for money". Top Tip –
"the renowned set lunch deserves every bit of its reputation": "perhaps the
best value prix fixe deal in town" and "always a top experience". / W1K 7QR;
www.le-gavroche.co.uk; @michelrouxjr; 10 pm; closed Sat L & Sun; Jacket required.

Gazette £53 3 3 3
79 Sherwood Ct, Chatfield Rd, SW11   020 7223 0999   11–1C
147 Upper Richmond Rd, SW15   020 8789 6996   11–2B
This Gallic duo in Clapham and Putney (Balham is now closed, RIP) score
well for "lovely classic French bistro food", "good vibes from friendly staff"
and a "really good value prix fixe lunch". They also run sightseeing meals
on luxury double-decker buses in London and Paris. Top Tip – "seasonal
offerings (e.g. fondue, morilles etc) keep the menu interesting".
/ www.gazettebrasserie.co.uk; 11 pm.

Geales W8 £60 2 2 2
2 Farmer St   020 7727 7528   7–2B
In 1999 the Geale family sold out of this genteel, pre-war (est 1939) fish 'n'
chip restaurant, off Notting Hill Gate, and since 2006 it's been operated
by Concept Venues (with a second branch in Dubai!). Nowadays it lacks the
faithful following of yesteryear, but reports suggest it's still "fine if close by,
if not for a detour". / W8 7SN; www.geales.com; @Geales_London; 10.30 pm,
Sun 10 pm; closed Mon L.

Gem N1 £39 3 3 2
265 Upper St   020 7359 0405   9–2D
"Friendly, with decent nosh" – this Turkish-Kurdish café near Angel "really
is a little gem, with prices that are more than fair for the quality of the
food". The exceptional value for the locations means it "can get very
crowded". / N1 2UQ; www.gemrestaurant.org.uk; @Gem_restaurant; 11 pm,
Sun 10 pm; No Amex.

George in the Strand WC2 £62 3 3 3
213 Strand   020 7353 9638   2–2D
"Surprisingly good food and charming service" make it worth remembering
this historic hostelry (refurbed in recent times), near the Royal Courts
of Justice. You can eat in the ground floor bar, or in the upstairs 'Pig and
Goose' restaurant. / WC2R 1AP; www.georgeinthestrand.com; @thegeorgestrand;
10pm, Fri & Sat 10.30pm, Sun 9pm.

German Gymnasium N1 £72 2 2 4
1 King's Boulevard   020 7287 8000   9–3C
"What a fantastic building!". This D&D London bar/restaurant occupies
a "huge" and "interesting" former Victorian gym – "handily located,
slap bang next to King's Cross" – and despite a tendency to feel
"cavernous" and to become very "loud" ("you can feel a bit like you're
eating in an aircraft hanger") provides a "stunning" location. Its intriguing
focus on German cuisine, and wines in particular, does win it gastronomic
recommendations, but all too often the "stodgy" food "is really nothing
special". Even so, as a watering hole, a business rendezvous, or brunch spot,
it has a big following. / N1C 4BU; www.germangymnasium.com; @TheGermanGym;
11 pm, Sun 9 pm.

Gezellig WC1 NEW £73 4 3 2
Holborn Hall, 193-197 High Holborn   020 3004 0004   5–1D
"You can tell head chef Graham Long trained with Phil Howard", given the
"precise" modern European dishes at this June 2019 newcomer,
in Holborn's old Town Hall (on the fringe of Covent Garden). It opened
just as the survey concluded, but the few initial reports were already wowed
by its 350-bin wine selection. / WC1V 7BD; www.gezellig.co.uk; @gezelligLND.

Giacomo's NW2 £45 3 3 2
428 Finchley Rd 020 7794 3603 1–1B
"Consistently good, basic Italian cooking" has kept this family-run Childs Hill venue busy through two decades. There's *"nothing fancy"* to it beyond a *"warm welcome from happy people"*. / NW2 2HY; www.giacomos.co.uk; 10 pm.

The Gilbert Scott NW1 £73 3 2 4
Euston Rd 020 7278 3888 9–3C
"It's such a wonderful building" – the spectacular neo-Gothic riot of St Pancras Station – and Marcus Wareing's *"fabulously grand"* and *"buzzing"* dining room near the Eurostar platforms *"seduces with its ambience"* (*"it's all rather 'Orient Express'"*). Judged as a foodie destination alone, appreciation of its distinctively traditional, British cuisine is sometimes dogged by gripes about dishes that are *"not up-to-scratch"* (or incidents of *"clunky"* service), but most reports applaud its *"very pleasant"* approach and *"excellent menu that's always evolving, so the food stays interesting"*. / NW1 2AR; www.thegilbertscott.co.uk; @Thegilbertscott; 11 pm, Sun 9 pm; booking max 7 may apply.

Ginger & White Hampstead NW3 £13 3 3 3
4a-5a, Perrins Ct 020 7431 9098 9–2A
Cutely-sited Hampstead café – a chic and highly rated coffee stop (beans care of Square Mile Coffee Roasters) whose all-day breakfasts, toasties and buns are ideal for brunching with beauteous Hampstead types. It no longer has a Belsize Park sibling. / NW3 1QS; www.gingerandwhite.com; L only; No Amex; no booking.

Ginza Onodera SW1 £96 3 3 2
15 Bury St 020 7839 1101 3–3D
Stately Japanese venue – from an international chain based in Tokyo's upmarket Ginza – that's *"de luxe, although not OTT"*; with *"very good food and top-notch service"*. It's not so dissimilar to Matsuri (RIP), the previous occupant of this refurbished (*"not for the better"*) St James's basement, below a department store. / SW1Y 6AL; onodera-group.com/uk; @Onodera_London; 10 pm.

The Glasshouse TW9 £81 4 3 3
14 Station Pde 020 8940 6777 1–3A
"A five-star experience" – this posher-than-usual neighbourhood haunt, by Kew Gardens tube station is *"the lowest profile in the Chez Bruce stable"*. Arguably *"the dining room itself is a little uninspiring, but it has a good atmosphere when it's full"*, and the operation generally shows *"similar care and professionalism"* to its siblings, down to the *"expert cuisine"*; *"well chosen, affordable wine list"*; and *"top cheeseboard"*. After a rocky patch, long term fans feel it's *"sprung back to form"*, but scores have yet to hit their old highs here, and a more representative view is that *"it's not as superlative as it was, but of very high quality nevertheless"*. / TW9 3PZ; www.glasshouserestaurant.co.uk; @The__Glasshouse; 10.30 pm, Sun 10 pm; booking max 8 may apply.

Gloria EC2 NEW £58 3 3 4
54-56 Great Eastern Street 13–1B
"If Wes Anderson did Italian restaurants, they might be something like this"; and this *"very 2019"* Shoreditch newcomer – whose glam, pastiche decor apes a thriving 1960s ristorante – feels *"like popping to the Amalfi Coast for lunch without the air travel!"*. Definitely, it's not one for food purists, who can condemn what they see as *"overhyped, Instagram-led, bog-standard, fake cooking"*. Don't take it too seriously, though, and it's superb *"fun"*, service is *"prompt and smooth-running"*, and the calorie-laden scoff – with echoes of 1970s Britalian – is *"generously portioned"* and *"surprisingly good"*. / EC2A 3QR; www.bigmammagroup.com; @bigmammagroup.

Go-Viet SW7 £57 4 3 2
53 Old Brompton Rd 020 7589 6432 6–2C
"Refined Vietnamese food" – "with clean, fresh flavours" – is showcased at this two-year-old South Ken flagship of former Hakkasan chef Jeff Tan, who also owns Viet Food in Chinatown. Top Tip – "the weekend lunch menu is a steal for the quality". / SW7 3JS; vietnamfood.co.uk/go-viet; @govietnamese; 10 pm, Fri & Sat 10.30 pm.

La Goccia WC2 £58 2 2 4
Floral Court, off Floral Street 020 7305 7676 5–3C
"Outside in the courtyard on a summer's day is a very pleasant experience" at this good-looking, all-day Italian (complete with wood-fired oven) in Covent Garden's recently constructed Floral Court development. No gripes about the food, but it's not especially cheap, and service is "charming" but can be "wayward". / WC2E 9DJ; petershamnurseries.com/dine/la-goccia; @PetershamN .

Goddards At Greenwich SE10 £27 3 4 3
22 King William Walk 020 8305 9612 1–3D
"Crammed with tourists and locals every lunchtime, getting a taste of history", this "genuine and friendly" Greenwich fixture is one of the last purveyors of traditional pie 'n' mash left in London. The "pies haven't changed since 1890" – although they do now offer a veggie version with soya. / SE10 9HU; www.goddardsatgreenwich.co.uk; @GoddardsPieMash; 7.30 pm, Fri & Sat 8 pm; L & early evening only.

Gökyüzü £33 2 2 2
26-27 Grand Pde, Green Lanes, N4 020 8211 8406 1–1C
1 Leisure Way, N12 020 8492 1662 NEW
The Mall, Selborne Road, E17 1–1D
Southend Road, E4 020 8527 4927 14–1C
"Very lively and noisy with families and children" – the "large" Harringay original of this small Turkish group is twenty years old, and remains "understandably popular, given its reasonable prices": "the food is good and plentiful and just keeps coming", and "the grilled meats are just yummy". There are now spin-offs in Chingford, Walthamstow and Finchley. Top Tip – "doggy bags are readily provided". / gokyuzurestaurant.co.uk.

Gold W11 NEW £66
95 Portobello Road 020 3146 0747 7–2B
On the former site of Portobello Gold (RIP), this long-standing Portobello haunt has been utterly revamped by Mahiki-founder Nick House, who has taken its look from grunge to glam. In its new incarnation, there's a garden room (with retractable roof) and a party room on the second floor. Chef Theo Hill used to work at The River Café, while the front of house has worked at various Soho House venues. / W11 2QB; goldnottinghill.com.

Gold Mine W2 £34 4 2 2
102 Queensway 020 7792 8331 7–2C
"The special roasted duck is rightly acclaimed as the best in London" according to fans of this "crowded" Bayswater Cantonese – although its near neighbour the Four Seasons is also a rival for that crown. "Expect long queues", "friendlier service than some of its competitors" and a "slightly chaotic atmosphere". / W2 3RR; 11 pm.

Golden Dragon W1 £44 3 2 2
28-29 Gerrard St 020 7734 1073 5–3A
A "straightforward Chinatown classic": this long-standing, "very authentic" destination provides a "good central location for inexpensive – and always reliable – dim sum" as well as roast meat. / W1 6JW; www.gdlondon.co.uk; 11.30 pm, Fri-Sun midnight.

Golden Hind W1 £36 3|2|2
73 Marylebone Ln   020 7486 3644   2–1A
"Still my favourite fish 'n' chips in Marylebone" – this centenarian
(est. 1914) "ticks all the boxes" and is "fantastic value". The reporter who
complained that "you can no longer bring your own wine" will be pleased
to learn that BYO was restored this summer, with £5 corkage (wine and
cocktails are also on the menu). / W1U 2PN; www.goldenhindrestaurant.com;
10 pm; closed Sat L & Sun.

Good Earth £61 3|3|2
233 Brompton Rd, SW3   020 7584 3658   6–2C
143-145 The Broadway, NW7   020 8959 7011   1–1B
11 Bellevue Rd, SW17   020 8682 9230   11–2C
"A huge cut-above a 'regular' Chinese!" – this "well-run", well-established
family-run chain in Knightsbridge, Balham and Mill Hill (and Esher) offers
an "upmarket" experience that's "always reliable": "not cheap but worth it".
"If feels like a bit of a 1990s throwback and I like it for that!"
/ www.goodearthgroup.co.uk; Mon-Sat 10.45 pm, Sun 10 pm; NW7 11.15 pm,
Sun 10.45 pm, KT10 10.30 pm, Sun 10.15pm.

Goodman £92 4|3|3
24-26 Maddox St, W1   020 7499 3776   3–2C
3 South Quay, E14   020 7531 0300   12–1C
11 Old Jewry, EC2   020 7600 8220   10–2C
"Sustaining their excellent reputation": these NYC-style steakhouses offer
a solid and comfortable, rather than a particularly vibey environment,
but when it comes to the quality of their meat – sourced in the UK, US and
Spain; and dry-aged on-site – they are "second to none"; and the City
branch, in particular, slugs it out with its nearby rival Hawksmoor as a
favourite haunt of carnivorous expense-accounters. "Expensive but always
a treat". / www.goodmanrestaurants.com; 10.30 pm; closed Sun.

Gopal's of Soho W1 £45 3|3|2
12 Bateman St   020 7434 1621   5–2A
"For a cuzza in Soho", this "good Indian in the centre of all the action"
is just the job thanks to its "flavoursome and so tasty" cooking and
"top price/quality ratio". Family run since 1988, its unfashionably traditional
basement setting is also a great antidote when you're sick of being dazzled
by trendy new restaurant design-concepts. / W1D 4AH; www.gopalsofsoho.co.uk;
11.30 pm, Sun 11 pm.

Gordon Ramsay SW3 £160 3|3|2
68-69 Royal Hospital Rd   020 7352 4441   6–3D
"Are people just deducting points because it has Gordon's name?" – that's
the suspicion raised by fans of the world-famous TV-chef, who –
like Michelin – consider his modern French cuisine "simply unbeatable",
and extol his "early-noughties-time-warp-style" Chelsea HQ (currently
presided over by head chef Matt Abé) as "the best in London". The answer
is no! – the problem is the equally sizeable number of diners who feel
"safety first is the word here", and that by the standards of top, world-class
culinary genius it "doesn't really hit the mark": "OK-ish, but too often run-of-
the-mill" or "merely average (except for the price... which is outrageous!)".
/ SW3 4HP; www.gordonramsay.com; @GordonRamsay; 10.15 pm; closed Sat & Sun;
No jeans; booking max 9 may apply.

Gordon's Wine Bar WC2 £39 2 2 5

47 Villiers St   020 7930 1408   5–4D

"An old favourite – but still the best place to meet friends in London" –
this lovingly preserved, 1890s wine bar by Embankment station has a huge
outside terrace and "atmospheric cellars" lit by candles. "This is not about
the food (which is perfectly OK, just very limited) or the grumpy staff –
it's about the wine and the ambience, delivered here in spades".
"How wonderful to take someone who's never been before, to experience
the atmosphere", either as a boozy hideaway in winter, or for a BBQ by the
park in summer. / WC2N 6NE; gordonswinebar.com; @GordonsWineBar; 11 pm,
Sun 10 pm.

Gourmet Burger Kitchen £33 2 2 2

"Hitting the spot when nothing but a burger will do", say devotees of the
original upmarket burger chain that started with a single outlet in 2001.
Losses of £4.6million last year led to the closure of 24 sites around the
country, but the number of reporters complaining of "generally indifferent"
meals is still relatively minor compared to those who still see it as "a safe
bet for the kids" or "sensibly priced and reliable, suggesting it's a franchise
worth saving. / www.gbkinfo.com; most branches close 11 pm, Sun 10.30 pm;
book online.

Goya SW1 £41 3 2 3

34 Lupus St   020 7976 5309   2–4C

"Basic tapas at its best", "decent paella" and a "good selection of wines"
have been the order of the day at this "reasonably priced" Spanish local
in Pimlico for 25 years. "The menu never changes, but the food's always
good". / SW1V 3EB; www.goyarestaurant.co.uk; midnight, Sun 11.30 pm.

Granary Square Brasserie N1 £53 2 1 3

1 Granary Square   020 3940 1000   9–3C

"Very flashy decor" – and (it is claimed) 'the largest al fresco dining terrace
in north London' – help entice diners to this "busy and buzzy" King's Cross
yearling from Richard Caring's Ivy Collection, and sharing all the 'affordable
glam' design ethos of the group. Everyone finds it an agreeably "lively place"
but beyond that views are sharply divided: and whereas fans report
"good quality brasserie food at all times of day", critics dismiss "ordinary"
food and "uninterested service" that's "not up to their pretentions" or the
"ambitious prices". / N1C 4AB; www.granarysquarebrasserie.com; Booking max 12
may apply.

Grand Trunk Road E18 £55 4 3 2

219 High Street   020 8505 1965   1–1D

"An exceptional local" – this Woodford three-year-old (from the ex-manager
and ex-head chef of Mayfair's Tamarind) delivers "a real treat of modern,
well-spiced food", and draws fans from north London to Essex. On the
downside, the "noisy" room "could be more cosy". / E18 2PB;
www.gtrrestaurant.co.uk; @GT_Road; 10.30pm; closed Mon & Sun D.

Granger & Co £51 3 2 3

237-239 Pavilion Rd, SW1   020 3848 1060   6–2D
175 Westbourne Grove, W11   020 7229 9111   7–1B
Stanley Building, St Pancras Sq, N1   020 3058 2567   9–3C
The Buckley Building, 50 Sekforde St, EC1   020 7251 9032   10–1A

"Despite the eternal, off-putting queues, brunching is always such a treat"
at Aussie celeb-chef, Bill Granger's "very buzzy" ("crowded and noisy")
hang-outs. "Old favourite options given a creative spin" feature amidst the
"excellent choice of delicious options" and there's an appealing "freshness"
to the dishes. The Notting Hill original still inspires most feedback, but all
outlets – King's Cross, Clerkenwell and Chelsea – have their followings. For
any occasion other than brunch they provoke less interest. Top Tip –
"OMG, those ricotta pancakes are amazing!" / Mon-Sat 11 pm, Sun 10 pm.

Grays & Feather WC2 NEW   3 4 4
26 Wellington Street   0203 948 4900   5–3D

Promising, if limited, early feedback on this modern 'wine parlour' – recently opened by wine expert Andrew Gray (a merchant with a business at the Southbank Food Market) on a corner-site near Covent Garden (the erstwhile office-space of a Mr Charles Dickens); and with an excellent list of 70 wines: "limited food, but what they do is lovely; tiny space, but it's gorgeous, and well worth a visit, especially as staff are so lovely". / WC2E 7DD; www.graysandfeather.com; @GraysandFeather.

Great Nepalese NW1   £42   3 3 2
48 Eversholt St   020 7388 6737   9–3C

"Delicious and different food and caring hosts who explain its origins" have kept fans loyal to this otherwise nondescript fixture, down the side of Euston Station, for over 50 years. Some of the food is fairly standard north Indian fare – the Nepalese specialities are the way to go. / NW1 1DA; www.great-nepalese.co.uk; 11.30 pm, Sun 10 pm.

The Green Room,
The National Theatre SE1   £48   2 2 2
101 Upper Ground   020 7452 3630   2–3D

For some reporters, the National Theatre's "brisk" in-house diner delivers on the "plain good food near the theatre" you'd hope for, so "it's a shame" that the "food is complacently ordinary" for too many others to make it a reliable recommendation. Top Tip – "best when you can sit in the garden". / SE1 9PP; www.greenroom.london; @greenroomSE1; 10.30 pm, Sun 7 pm.

Greenberry Café NW1   £46   3 3 4
101 Regents Park Road   020 7483 3765   9–2B

"A perfect favourite for brunch" – this "welcoming" café, "quite idyllically located" on Primrose Hill's cute main drag, is not a foodie destination, but a popular all-day hub for breakfast, a bite, or a bun with a brew. "The line outside was a hint that it would deliver… and so it did!" / NW1 8UR; greenberrycafe.co.uk; @Greenberry_Cafe; 10 pm; closed Mon D & Sun D; No Amex.

The Greenhouse W1   £140   3 3 3
27a Hays Mews   020 7499 3331   3–3B

"Down a quiet street in Mayfair", this calm and luxurious temple of gastronomy is a well-known stalwart (est 1977), that's a particular "old-favourite" for those who recall its days under Gary Rhodes. Nowadays part of Marlon Abela's restaurant empire, it has held two Michelin stars since 2014, which were successfully retained by new chef Alex Dilling, who joined in mid 2018. Harden's regulars likewise report a "seamless transition" that's "given a new lease of life" to the kitchen: acclaiming his "thoughtfully sequenced" and "exciting" tasting menus, which manage not to be eclipsed by one of London's most comprehensive wine lists. The experience comes at "hedge fund prices" though, and the continuing ethos of classic gastronomy for its own sake continues to leave some folks with a "stuffy, stilted, and pretentious" impression. "It was bordering on the comical at times – I recall no less than four servers engaged in simultaneously spooning a rather flat Parmesan foam on to our plates with such pomp and ceremony that my guest and I could barely hold back the tears of laughter. I felt like I was misbehaving in church, but this is far from being a sacred place…" / W1J 5NY; www.greenhouserestaurant.co.uk; @greenhouse27a; 10.30 pm; closed Sat L & Sun.

The Greyhound Cafe W1   £61   3 2 3
37 Berners Street   020 3026 3798   3–1D

First European outpost of a Thailand-based chain – a sizeable operation in Fitzrovia that's now in its second year. Some "lovely spicy combinations" help create a "really interesting menu" but views divide a little on the trendily-designed space: "lacking atmosphere" to some but "lovely" and "den-like" to others. / W1T 3LZ; www.greyhoundcafe.uk.

Gridiron,
COMO Metropolitan London W1 NEW   £80

19 Old Park Lane   020 7447 1080   3–4A

Little survey feedback as yet on this late-autumn 2018 opening right on Park Lane – a contemporary 'live fire' steakhouse occupying the space which older hipsters may recall as the Met Bar. The Observer's Jay Rayner felt it was a 'so-nearly-but-not quite' experience, but the team behind it is impressive with Richard H Turner (ex-Hawksmoor) and Colin McSherry (Nuala, Clove Club). / W1K 1LB; www.gridironlondon.com.

Grumbles SW1   £47   3 3 4

35 Churton St   020 7834 0149   2–4B

"Very characterful", ancient bistro, which has been a feature of Pimlico for over 50 years (est 1964). It's treasured by its regulars, who come from near and far, for its rustic style and "top-value" dishes: essentially Anglo/French (moules marinière, escargots in garlic butter, fillet steak, fish 'n' chips, burgers), freshened up with some eclectic international additions over the years (Thai-style duck breast, quinoa and feta salad…). / SW1V 2LT; www.grumblesrestaurant.co.uk; @grumblesbistro; 10.45 pm, Sun 10.30 pm.

Guglee   £38   3 3 2

7 New College Pde, NW3   020 7722 8478   9–2A
279 West End Ln, NW6   020 7317 8555   1–1B

This pair of "quirky", modern curryhouses bowl up "terrific food" including some "great Goan dishes" to happy customers in West Hampstead and Swiss Cottage. They win solid praise even from reporters who generally "don't like the new wave of fancy Indians". / www.guglee.co.uk; 11 pm.

The Guildford Arms SE10   £46   3 4 3

55 Guildford Grove   020 8691 6293   1–3D

"One of the best in the Greenwich area" – this three-storey Georgian tavern has a "beautiful garden" and "sits away from the main drag, so it's not overly packed and touristy". Chef Guy Awford is a well-known name in these parts having cooked at Inside (RIP) for many years, and is credited with some "brilliant cooking" here too. In mid 2019 it closed, to be totally transformed, with re-opening set for September 2019: if they get it half right, this will become Greenwich's No. 1 destination. (Ratings are based on past performance: not yet post-revamp). / SE10 8JY; www.theguildfordarms.co.uk; @GuildfordArms_; 10 pm, Sun 9 pm; closed Mon.

The Guinea Grill W1   £75   3 3 3

30 Bruton Pl   020 7409 1728   3–3B

"Splendid old pub" in a cute Mayfair mews whose adjoining "old school" grill-house – "various small rooms packed with tables" – may be "noisy and less-than-comfortable", but is "an institution" for those fond of a "fabulous steak" or meat pie. "Superb beef and lamb are cooked on the open charcoal grill (you can choose your cut on the way in)" and the meat is of "consummate quality". With its "excellent real ale" it's a "good place for the boys" but its "sky-high prices" can deepen the impression of catering for a "principally male, expense-account clientele". Top Tip – in early 2019, landlord Oison Rogers started opening for breakfast: "full English in meaty portions". / W1J 6NL; www.theguinea.co.uk; @guineagrill; closed Sat L & Sun.

The Gun E14   £67   2 2 4

27 Coldharbour   020 7515 5222   12–1C

"The views alone make it worth a visit" to this Grade II listed Docklands pub operated by Fuller's. Directly opposite The O2, with extensive conservatory and terrace seating, it's a "great little spot on the river", with "upscale food and service". / E14 9NS; www.thegundocklands.com; @thegundocklands; 10 pm, Sun 7 pm.

Gunpowder £48 **4**|**3**|**3**
One Tower Bridge, 4 Crown Square, SE1 awaiting tel 10–4D
11 Whites Row, E1 020 7426 0542 13–2C
"BOOM! Excellent, sometimes-fiery fare" ("they don't hold back on the
spicing") "hits the spot" with "great creative flavours" at this duo of Indian
tapas-style haunts. The "tiny", "so-noisy, full-on and not-so-relaxing" original
sits near Spitalfields, while the "bigger" (but also "buzzing and noisy")
second branch near Tower Bridge is the better-known nowadays, similarly
well-rated and "handy for the Bridge Theatre". Top Menu Tips – "superb
lamb chops and sublime venison doughnuts". / www.gunpowderlondon.com;
@gunpowder_ldn.

Gustoso Ristorante & Enoteca SW1 £48 **3**|**3**|**3**
33 Willow Pl 020 7834 5778 2–4B
"This very decent Italian" is a "hidden gem just a stone's throw from Victoria
Station" – "improbably located in the culinary desert behind Westminster
Cathedral" – with "ever-improving traditional dishes" made from "fresh
ingredients" delivered by "friendly staff" in a "pleasing", relatively modern
setting. / SW1P 1JH; www.ristorantegustoso.co.uk; @GustosoRist; 10.30 pm, Fri &
Sat 11 pm, Sun 9.30 pm.

Gymkhana W1 £77 **5**|**4**|**4**
42 Albemarle St 020 3011 5900 3–3C
"Still at the top of its game" – the Sethi's "posh Indian" in Mayfair is "worth
the hype" and remains the most-mentioned Indian in the survey on account
of "memorable and beautifully flavourful" cuisine delivered by "warm and
friendly staff" in an enveloping, old-colonial-style setting: "get a booth on the
ground floor and prepare to be transported!" Top Menu Tip – "How I love
the tandoori lamb chops. After a marinade in spices, these thick pieces
of meat become so succulent, tender and taste-laden, are magnificently
presented and really delicious on the eager palate!". NB: Just as the survey
closed, in June 2019, a fire gutted the restaurant and according to its
website it remains "closed until further notice". / W1S 4JH;
www.gymkhanalondon.com; @GymkhanaLondon; 10.30 pm; closed Sun.

Haché £42 **3**|**4**|**2**
95-97 High Holborn, WC1 020 7242 4580 2–1D
329-331 Fulham Rd, SW10 020 7823 3515 6–3B
24 Inverness St, NW1 020 7485 9100 9–3B
37 Bedford Hill, SW12 020 8772 9772 11–2C
153 Clapham High St, SW4 020 7738 8760 11–2D
Unit 5 Riverside Walk, KT1 020 8541 5217 NEW
147-149 Curtain Rd, EC2 020 7739 8396 13–1B
"Still some of the best burgers around", say fans of this French group, whose
Gallic je ne sais quoi lends a certain superiority to the offering, while service
is "friendly and speedy". Its seventh outlet opened in Kingston early in 2019,
at a time when rival mid-market operators were struggling.
/ www.hacheburgers.com; 10.30 pm, Fri-Sat 11 pm, Sun 10 pm; WC1 Sat & Sun.

Hai Cenato SW1 £61 **3**|**2**|**2**
2 Sir Simon Milton Square, 150 Victoria St 020 3816 9320 2–4B
"Some of the best pizza in town" – "with really delicious, springy crusts and
interesting flavour combinations" – is the big tick at Jason Atherton's take
on New York Italian dining in Victoria's Nova development. But even some
who say "the food is great" say "it's let down by below-par ambience and
service: one for the lunchtime crowd". / SW1H 0HW; haicenato.co.uk;
@haicenato; 10 pm, Sun 9.30 pm; booking max 6 may apply.

Hakkasan £101 **4 2 3**

17 Bruton St, W1   020 7907 1888   3–2C
8 Hanway Pl, W1   020 7927 7000   5–1A

"Hakkasan has been setting the standard for modern Chinese food in London for ages now", with the nightclubby, "dimly lit" original ("I had difficulty reading the menu and even seeing the food!"), opening "in a tiny, narrow lane with an anonymous entrance" near Tottenham Court Road in 2001; and although both it and its easier-to-find Mayfair spin-off's styling "is a little bling bling" they continue to serve "seriously lovely" food and "refreshing" cocktails. There are drawbacks, which have also changed little over the years: it's "very noisy", staff can seem "bored" or "totally dismissive", and "your wallet will have a hangover in the morning". / www.hakkasan.com; 12.30 am, Sun 11.15 pm; W1 12.30 am, Thu-Sat 12.45 am, Sun midnight; no trainers, no sportswear.

The Halal Guys WC2 NEW £17 **3 3 2**

14-15 Irving Street   020 8706 0307   5–4B

"Finally a US brand that delivers the goods!" This "cheap 'n' cheerful newcomer" – a fast food caff with outside seating just off Leicester Square – is the first UK outpost of a 27-year-old, NYC-brand that started as a hot dog stand, but where now the focus is on halal street food (hot sandwiches, or bowls with meat or falafel), which early reports say is "superb value". The roll-out is already ongoing: a second branch opened in Earl's Court in Summer 2019. / WC2H 7AU; thehalalguys.com; @HalalGuys.

Ham NW6 £57 **3 2 3**

238 West End Lane   020 7813 0168   1–1B

"A brilliant neighbourhood restaurant: actually far better than a typical neighbourhood restaurant!" – so say fans of Matt Osborne's West Hampstead yearling, serving a "changing (if limited)" menu of small-plates. Ratings overall are undercut, though, by those who find its performance "overhyped" or "disappointing after a great start". / NW6 1LG; www.hamwesthampstead.com/ham; @hamwhampstead/.

Ham Yard Restaurant, Ham Yard Hotel W1 £60 **2 3 4**

1 Ham Yd   020 3642 1007   4–3D

Sitting in the cute courtyard of this "immaculately kept" newish hotel, you would never dream you were a two-minute stroll from Piccadilly Circus, and – in colder weather – its "quirky modern/traditional conservatory" is also a lovely destination. In keeping with other Firmdale hotels, the food avoids fireworks, but they have an "excellent-value set lunch and pre-theatre menu", and some would argue it's "the best place in town for afternoon tea – served on quirky china with hand-stitched white table linen and not at all rushed". / W1D 7DT; www.firmdalehotels.com/hotels/london/ham-yard-hotel/ham-yard-bar-restaurant; @Firmdale_Hotels; 11.30 pm, Sun 10.30 pm.

The Hampshire Hog W6 £54 **2 3 3**

227 King Street   020 8748 3391   8–2B

Near Hammersmith's un-lovely town hall, this sizeable 'pub & pantry' has a particularly attractive dining area, looking onto its large garden, and you can also eat in the large bar. Even those who feel "there's not a great menu choice" say a meal here is "an OK experience". / W6 9JT; www.thehampshirehog.com; @TheHampshireHog; 10 pm, Sun 4 pm; closed Sun D.

Hankies £42 **4 2 2**

61 Upper Berkeley Street, W1   020 7958 3222   2–2A NEW
67 Shaftesbury Avenue, W1   020 7871 6021   5–3A

Anirudh Arora's year-old, north Indian, street-food café on the West End's ever-bustling Shaftesbury Avenue also has a new outpost in a smart hotel dining room, near Marble Arch. The duo's title refers to classic Roomali Roti: bread, hand spun into thin sheets, cooked and folded into a 'hankie', and both branches win praise for "great food at a relatively small price".

Hans' Bar & Grill SW1 £71 2 3 3
164 Pavilion Road 020 7730 7000 6–2D
"A good addition to the area, but standards can be a bit rough and ready"
is a balanced view on this "nice, bright venue" in a super-cute enclave off
Sloane Street that's part of nearby luxury boutique hotel, 11 Cadogan
Gardens. On most accounts, its "all-day menu is not too expensive for the
area" making it a versatile choice for a meet-up in Chelsea; but there's the
odd 'off' report of meals "offering a masterclass of how not to do it".
/ SW1X 0AW; www.hansbarandgrill.com; @HansBarGrill; 10.30pm.

The Harcourt W1 £60 3 4 4
32 Harcourt Street 020 3771 8660 7–1D
"Restaurant-quality", "Scandi-influenced", "delicious" food has helped carve
a major reputation for this five-storey gastropub, in "a quiet Marylebone
backwater that's also handy for Paddington". Beautifully decorated: "it's still
just discernibly a pub, but an extremely well presented one". / W1H 4HX;
www.theharcourt.com; @theharcourtldn; 11 pm, Fri & Sat 11.30 pm, Sun 10 pm.

Hard Rock Café 2 3 4
150 Old Park Lane, W1 020 7287 4600 3–4B
Criterion Building, 225 Piccadilly, W1 020 7287 4600 4–4D NEW
Great Cumberland Place, W1 020 7479 5078 2–2A NEW
Since 1971, this age-old rocker has grown from its first site, near Hyde Park
Corner, to 186 globally, and this year saw the group reinvest massively in the
capital, with not just a new hotel (on the site that was once The
Cumberland) by Marble Arch, but also with the July 2019 opening of a
19,000 sq ft, multi-level, new London flagship at Piccadilly Circus. The latter
opening includes a menu shake-up, which introduces an unsuspecting world
to new culinary delights, including the '24-Karat Gold Leaf Steak BurgerTM';
(as well as the retail opportunities of 'the world's largest Rock Shop'"). For
silver-haired reporters (who were alive for the chain's founding) –
a generation by-and-large untroubled by the hipster burger revolution –
the "generously meaty" patties of the original are "still the best", and one
early report on the hotel says its restaurant "really rocks" too…. Even
allowing for cynicism about the effects of nostalgia on the tastebuds,
the brand fares better in the survey than most mass-market offerings.
/ www.hardrockcafe.com/location/london; @HardRockLondon.

Hare & Tortoise £39 3 3 2
11-13 The Brunswick, WC1 020 7278 9799 2–1D
373 Kensington High St, W14 020 7603 8887 8–1D
156 Chiswick High Rd, W4 020 8747 5966 8–2A
38 Haven Grn, W5 020 8810 7066 1–2A
296-298 Upper Richmond Rd, SW15 020 8394 7666 11–2B
90 New Bridge St, EC4 020 7651 0266 10–2A
"Brilliant for a quick pitstop", these Japanese-inspired pan-Asian canteens
consistently churn out "a great selection of fresh and tasty dishes" (sushi,
noodles, laksa,…) at an "impressive speed" – you can watch a "gaggle
of chefs in action with an array of woks". Established in 1996, the group
has lived up to its name, expanding slowly to six sites while its rivals have
proliferated – and, in some cases, crashed and burned.
/ www.hareandtortoise-restaurants.co.uk; 11 pm; EC4 10.30, Fri 11 pm; EC4 closed
Sun; W14 no bookings.

Harlequin SW6 NEW £68 4 4 4
194 Wandsworth Bridge Road 020 7736 7169 11–1B
"An amazing, new, local addition" – James Erasmus (a South African chef
who has graduated from The Ledbury and Harwood Arms stable) is cooking
up a storm in his casual, neighbourhood newcomer, in the depths
of deepest Fulham, presenting a monthly changing seasonal menu, with a
parallel vegetarian option. Someone forgot to tell him that nobody ever
opens a really good restaurant on the Wandsworth Bridge Road! / SW6 2UF;
www.harlequinrestaurant.co.uk.

Harrods Dining Hall SW1 NEW
Harrods, 87-135 Brompton Road   6–1D

The Grade II, 1920s tiled splendour of Harrods Meat & Fish Hall has been revamped and re-imagined as London's poshest food court, with bars dedicated to sushi, pasta, grills (wagyu, rotisserie chicken) and 'Harrods signature fish 'n' chips'. There's also the 26-seat Kama run by Vineet Bhatia, selling 'modernised, regional Indian classics'. The centrepiece is a wine bar, with more than 100 vintages sold by the glass and snacks from Caviar House & Prunier. / SW1X 7XL; www.harrods.com/en-gb/restaurants.

Harry Morgan's NW8   £46   3 3 3
29-31 St John's Wood High St   020 7722 1869   9–3A

"Nobody does better salt beef" than this veteran NYC-style kosher deli: a St John's Wood institution since 1948 that's "packed to heaving on a Saturday". Don't expect innovation – it's a place to "stick to the favourites". / NW8 7NH; www.harryms.co.uk; @morgan_hm; 10 pm.

Harry's Bar W1   £64   2 2 3
30-34 James Street   020 3971 9444   3–1A

Richard Carling's cutely-situated yearling north of Oxford Street – his second 'accessible' version of Mayfair's famous Harry's Bar (which is still very much members only) – hasn't yet hit the same level of satisfaction as its Knightsbridge sibling, Harry's Dolce Vita. But most diners like its "spacious" interior and "good atmosphere", and even those who say the food's "distinctly average" can still feel "it's a useful casual-dining addition". / W1U 1EU; www.harrys-bar.co.uk.

Harry's Dolce Vita SW3   £67   3 3 5
27-31 Basil Street   020 3940 1020   6–1D

Emptied your wallet at Harrods and need to recover over a bowl of pasta and glass of fizz? – Richard Caring's "fun" and "nicely buzzing" Italian brasserie, near the store's rear entrance, can be just the job. Now two years old, its fanbase primarily seems to extend to shoppers and other miscellaneous Knightsbridge types, as it elicits limited survey feedback; but all reports praise its "great consistency in a fun setting with attentive and engaging staff". / SW3 1BB; www.harrysdolcevita.com.

Harwood Arms SW6   £74   4 3 3
Walham Grove   020 7386 1847   6–3A

"Fabulous game" is a highpoint of the "simple food, cooked to perfection" ("mouthwatering meat so tender the knife just fell through it") at this "super-fine" hostelry in the distant backstreets of Fulham – for the second year, the survey's No. 1 gastropub. Full credit goes to head chef Sally Abé for her "top flight" evolution of traditional dishes, but it can't harm to have input from backers who include Brett Graham of The Ledbury, and also the UK's most prominent game chef, Mike Robinson. Aside from the small amount of space dedicated purely to drinking, it feels like an honest-to-goodness, fairly unreformed boozer. Top Menu Tips – "venison scotch egg is to die for, as is the Sunday roast". / SW6 1QP; www.harwoodarms.com; @HarwoodArms; 9.30 pm, Sun 9 pm; closed Mon L; credit card required to book.

Hashi SW20   £44   3 4 2
54 Durham Rd   020 8944 1888   11–2A

A "very good local Japanese": consistently one of the best in the enclave around Raynes Park. Top Menu Tip – notably good sushi. / SW20 0TW; 10.30 pm; closed Mon; No Amex.

Hatched SW11   £71   5 4 2
189 Saint John's Hill   020 7738 0735   11–2C

Shane Marshall's highly accomplished, if spartan Battersea venture (formerly called Darwin) serves "a very small menu of exquisite modern British food" that's well above-par for its anonymous location. "You wouldn't know it was there unless someone told you." / SW11 1TH; www.hatchedsw11.com; @HatchedSW11.

The Havelock Tavern W14 £52 3 2 3
57 Masbro Rd   020 7603 5374   8–1C

"Top local gastropub" in an Olympia backstreet that's *"better run"* nowadays than during its original heyday, and after more than 20 years still *"always delivers"* a *"well thought-out menu"*; and can be surprisingly *"buzzing and hectic"* for such a tranquil location. / W14 0LS; www.havelocktavern.com; @havelocktavern; 10 pm, Sun 9.30 pm.

Hawksmoor £85 4 3 3
5a Air St, W1   020 7406 3980   4–4C
11 Langley St, WC2   020 7420 9390   5–2C
3 Yeoman's Row, SW3   020 7590 9290   6–2C
16 Winchester Walk, SE1   020 7234 9940   10–4C
157 Commercial St, E1   020 7426 4850   13–2B
10-12 Basinghall St, EC2   020 7397 8120   10–2C

Huw Gott and Will Beckett *"do the 'casual excellence' thing very well indeed"* and their still über-fashionable steakhouse chain (founded in 2006) occupies a niche in the hearts of London's fooderati like no other, with its *"distinctly clubby"* (*"big, loud and busy"*) style, its *"to-die-for cocktails"* and its *"top steaks"*: British-bred and *"char-grilled to perfection over wood fires, with deliciously indulgent sides"*. Ratings for such a phenomenon have sometimes seemed middling in comparison to its renown – a reflection of the very full pricing that's always been their policy. That said, despite some accusations that *"it's all gone downhill in recent times"*, its grades actually bounced back significantly this year, and remain in line with its past best. The City branch in particular shines. *"Dark dens and out-of-this-world quality beef are the cornerstones of dealmaking. What deal would not reach a happy ending fuelled by a perfectly cooked rib-eye, grilled bone marrow, and beef dripping fries? Throw in a bottle or two of bordeaux and that IPO is around the corner!"* Top Tips – *"£5 corkage on Monday BYO is an incredible deal"* and starting the day at the Guildhall branch: *"if anyone can do a better breakfast I'd love to try it!"* / www.thehawksmoor.com; 10.30 pm; W1 & WC2 Fri & Sat 11 pm, Sun 9pm-10 pm; EC2 closed Sat & Sun.

Haya W11 NEW
184a Kensington Park Road   7–1B

This September 2019 newcomer on Notting Hill's Kensington Park Road is to be an all-day restaurant riding the current wave of Tel Aviv-inspired diners, featuring healthy sharing-plates. / W11 2ES; haya.london.

Haz £53 2 2 2
9 Cutler St, E1   020 7929 7923   10–2D
14 Finsbury Square, EC2   020 7920 9944   13–2A NEW
34 Foster Ln, EC2   020 7600 4172   10–2B
64 Bishopsgate, EC2   020 7628 4522   10–2D
112 Houndsditch, EC3   020 7623 8180   10–2D
6 Mincing Ln, EC3   020 7929 3173   10–3D

"Straightforward Turkish food at a relatively sensible price (for the Square Mile)" is the simple proposition at this *"useful"* and well-established small chain. They get pretty *"packed and noisy at lunchtime with a boisterous City clientele"*. / www.hazrestaurant.co.uk; 11.30 pm; EC3 closed Sun.

Hélène Darroze,
The Connaught Hotel W1 £155 3 4 4
Carlos Pl   020 3147 7200   3–3B

Hélène Darroze's luxurious Mayfair temple of gastronomy, within Mayfair's most blueblooded hotel, is celebrating its tenth year with a two-month closure, to re-open in September 2019. A revamp is promised, care of French design house, 'Pierre Yovanovitch Architecture d'Intérieur' (whose aesthetic, we are told in the PR, 'focuses on bold re-imaginings of historic spaces, combining the contemporary with luxury materials'). There will also be the addition of a new chef's table and dedicated Armagnac room; plus a new menu 'rooted in Hélène's culinary style, with a larger focus on British producers and suppliers'. The survey consensus on its former incarnation could be summarised as "exceptional cuisine albeit at extortionate prices" to appeal to "a crowd of plutocrats and their lawyers, and very old-money types": we've maintained last year's rating on the conservative assumption that its new incarnation will be a case of 'plus ça change'... / W1K 2AL; www.the-connaught.co.uk; @TheConnaught; 10 pm, Sun 9 pm; closed Mon & Sun; No trainers.

Heliot Steak House WC2 £63 333
Cranbourn Street 020 7769 8844 5–3B
"Exceptional value set deals" (particularly at lunch and pre-theatre) provide reason to discover this unusually situated grill, in the former dress circle of the converted theatre that nowadays houses the UK's largest casino (right by Leicester Square tube) and looks down on the gambling tables below. Casino owner Simon Thomas prides himself on the quality of the steaks and wines on offer, and it shows. / WC2H 7AJ; www.hippodromecasino.com; @HippodromeLDN; midnight, Sat 1 am, Sun 11 pm.

Helix EC3 £82 235
30 St Mary Axe 0330 1070816 10–2D
"The wow factor" of its "remarkable views by day or night" helps make this "fun and busy" space – the top three stories of this landmark City tower (originally restricted to those working in the Gherkin, now open to the public) – a "good choice for a special occasion". The catering has its fans too, although critiques include that it can be "ordinary" or "very expensive". Top Tip – "good set menu". / EC3A 8EP; searcysatthegherkin.co.uk/helix-restaurant; @SearcysGherkin.

Hello Darling SE1 NEW £43 233
131 Waterloo Road 020 7401 9603 10–4A
Limited feedback to-date on this new, 'playful restaurant and botanical bar' next to The Old Vic serving 'killer botanical cocktails' alongside 'eclectic sharing-plates' from Natalie Coleman, winner of MasterChef 2013. One early reporter voiced sentiments similar to the Evening Standard's Fay Maschler: "it's a fun, new opening but with fairly average food". / SE1 8UL; www.hellodarling.london; @HelloDarlingLDN.

Henrietta Bistro WC2 £56 333
Henrietta Street 020 3794 5313 5–3C
Southwestern France and northern Spain are inspiration for the "interesting menu" at this "lovely" yearling bistro in a boutique Covent Garden hotel (which has a "very good bar" too). / WC2E 8NA; www.henriettahotel.com.

Hereford Road W2 £50 443
3 Hereford Rd 020 7727 1144 7–1B
Chef Tom Pemberton's "consistently excellent neighbourhood resto" in Bayswater has a sharp focus on "very good seasonal British produce, very well cooked", and is "a bargain for the quality". "I've been eating here since I gate-crashed the opening in 2007, and I've never been disappointed". / W2 4AB; www.herefordroad.org; @3HerefordRoad; 10.30 pm, Sun 10 pm.

Heritage W1 NEW £75
18 Rupert Street 020 3995 7500 4–3D
This new, Swiss venture landed in Soho in June 2019, too late for any survey feedback. Its aesthetic is a world away from the cod-chalet style of its most obvious, age-old competitor, St Moritz. From fondue, raclette and rösti to barbecuing prime cuts of meat and fresh seafood on table-top charbonnade grills – the (highly priced) Alpine menu designed for sharing is served in a swish, modern setting. / W1D 6DF; www.heritagerestaurant.co.uk.

The Hero of Maida W9 £60 2 2 3
55 Shirland Rd   020 7266 9198   7–1C

Is it the strain of fast expansion at Harcourt Inns? This gentrified Maida Vale boozer, which was one of the group's original properties, opened to great acclaim last year thanks to its "great Henry Harris menu". But reports after a year of operation are mixed. For its supporters, "churning out dishes like sweetbreads, rabbit and brain shows it isn't your average pub", and its "famous Sunday lunch is hard to beat". But a number of former fans scent "a steady descent to mediocrity": they feel staff can appear "unconcerned" or "ditzy", and think the food is "priced as something very special but sub-par". / W9 2JD; theheromaidavale.co.uk; @TheHeroofMaida; 10 pm, Sat & Sun 11 pm.

The Heron W2 £48 4 3 1
1 Norfolk Cr   020 7706 9567   9–4A

The "scruffy basement of a pub" in Bayswater is the setting for what some in the fooderati believe to be "hands-down the best authentic Thai cooking in London" – "food like you'd have in Thailand". Top Tip – "the bbq pork neck is melt-in-your-mouth". / W2 2DN; www.theheronpaddington.com; @theheronpaddington; 11 pm, Sun 10.30 pm; May need + to book.

Hicce N1 £48 2 3 4
Coal Drops Yard   020 3869 8200   9–3C

"In revitalised Coal Drops Yard" – Angela Hartnett protégée Pip Lacey's late-2018 opening is generally credited as "an excellent addition to the new development". But while just about everyone loves its "beautifully designed and buzzy" interior, when it comes to her "interesting dishes, cooked over wood, mainly for sharing", then opinions are more divided. "Some truly unusual combinations" make it a brand-new-favourite for some diners, but even fans sometimes note that "the ratio of tiny portion size to high cost is a problem", and for others the cooking is "just not memorable enough": "confused and far too expensive for what was delivered". Top Tip – it's pronounced 'ee-chay'. / N1C 4AB; www.hicce.co.uk; @hiccelondon.

Hide W1 £143 3 5 4
85 Piccadilly   020 3146 8666   3–4C

"An extraordinary restaurant for an extraordinary occasion!" – Up the "beautiful staircase" accessed through Hide Ground (see also), "no expense has been spared in the creation of this exquisite restaurant", and the "cool" and incredibly spacious first-floor dining room of this Russian-owned yearling provides an impressively luxurious backdrop, "especially if you bag one of the tables facing Green Park". You can choose from either the six-course or nine-course tasting menu, which comes with a vegetarian alternative (and a shorter, "more affordable" option at lunch) and there's the "astonishing complement" of "nearby Hedonism Wines' incomparable 6,000-strong list, as they will run your preferred bottle over if it's not in the restaurant's own cellar". When it comes to Ollie Dabbous's Scandi-inspired cooking, most reporters feel that "thankfully the food lives up to the posh surroundings", delivering "precise, light and intriguing" cuisine that's a "worthy successor to Dabbous". "Impeccable", "helpful" and "charming" service adds further to the mood. "OMG it's oligarch prices" though, leaving doubters – who also feel some plates are a tad "over-engineered" – to conclude that "the biggest impression it leaves is the dent in your wallet!" / W1J 8JB; www.hide.co.uk.

Hide Ground W1 £81 3 4 4
85 Piccadilly 020 3146 8666 3–4C
As a way of dipping your toe into the Hide 'waters', the ground floor of this huge, Russian-backed project near Green Park tube is the safest place to start, offering a selection of menus from early morning onwards, and with a grazing menu, in addition to the ("punishingly expensive") à la carte. As with Above, this likewise is a "beautifully designed and spacious set-up that's good for more than just business but certainly good for a working lunch". Top Tips – "wonderful breakfasts, with a coffee list too" and "lovely afternoon tea watching the world go whilst trying a variety of teas". / W1J.

High Road Brasserie W4 £49 2 3 3
162-166 Chiswick High Rd 020 8742 7474 8–2A
"A suntrap outside and buzzy atmosphere" help make this fashionable Soho House haunt – prominently situated near Turnham Green Terrace – Chiswick's premier brunch spot. Fans say the "food's always good" too, but critics are less convinced ("imagine your worst greasy spoon breakfast, then multiply the bill by five…") / W4 1PR; highroadbrasserie.co.uk; @HRBrasserie; 11 pm, Fri & Sat midnight, Sun 10 pm; booking max 8 may apply.

High Timber EC4 £67 3 3 3
8 High Timber Street 020 7248 1777 10–3B
"Simple, well-prepared steaks" and "an excellent wine list (before you even get to visiting the cellar itself)" are the main treats in store at this South African-owned wine bar. Its "out-of-the-way but still central setting" by the Wobbly Bridge and directly opposite Tate Modern really comes into its own "when you can sit outside in the summer" (otherwise the nearby Thames merely sets the scene as you arrive and depart). / EC4V 3PA; www.hightimber.com; @HTimber; 10 pm; closed Sat & Sun.

Hispania EC3 £68 3 3 3
72-74 Lombard Street 020 7621 0338 10–2C
"In the City but without off-the-chart prices" – this spacious fixture occupies a comfortable, somewhat rustically themed two-floor site, by the Bank of England, and serves "good quality Spanish food". "Good for a business meal", but also relatively "fun". / EC3V 9AY; www.hispanialondon.com; @hispanialondon; 10pm, Mon 9.30 pm; closed Sat & Sun.

Hix W1 £77 1 2 2
66-70 Brewer Street 020 7292 3518 4–3C
"Needing to recover its imagination": Mark Hix needs somehow to reboot his Soho HQ. On the plus side, it's potentially a "lovely" venue – a vaguely Manhattan-esque room, with an attractive cellar cocktail bar – and service is typically "welcoming" (if not always on-the-ball). On the downside, its fish-heavy menu remains far too expensive, and "there seems to be little thought about how to produce something interesting with the ingredients at hand". / W1F 9UP; www.hixrestaurants.co.uk/restaurant/hix-soho; @HixRestaurants; 11.30 pm, Sun 10.30 pm.

Hix Oyster & Chop House EC1 £66 2 2 2
36-37 Greenhill Rents, Cowcross St 020 7017 1930 10–1A
The first of Mark Hix's London ventures – this white-tiles-and-marble chophouse near Smithfield has often somewhat divided reporters. Fans see it as "the go-to place for modern British seasonal classics, from steaks to the fish of the day"; sceptics judge it "very noisy and busy, with average food, and trading on its reputation". / EC1M 6BN; www.hixrestaurants.co.uk/restaurant/hix-oyster-chop-house; @hixchophouse; 11 pm, Sun 9 pm; closed Sat L; No trainers.

Holborn Dining Room WC1   £78   3 2 3

252 High Holborn   020 3747 8633   2–1D

"Savoury pastry heaven" – "outstanding pies, steak puddings and beef Wellington" are the orders of the day at this "fabulous" dining room on the edge of the City, where Chef Calum Franklin oversees a "great menu" also featuring British charcuterie and grills. The setting is "a little hotel-like" but "tables are nicely spaced" helping to make it a big hit with business types. Top Tip – "pick up a takeaway pie from the Pie Room"; and there's "an excellent breakfast, to boot". / WC1V 7EN; www.holborndiningroom.com; @HolbornDining.

Holly Bush NW3   £50   2 2 3

22 Holly Mount   020 7435 2892   9–1A

This "quaint relic from the 18th century" is a Grade II listed tavern on an attractive Georgian side-street in Hampstead. It serves "a fairly restricted menu" of "unmodernised pub food", which can fit the bill for a Sunday roast or simple meal, but critics feel the cooking "really ought to be better". / NW3 6SG; www.hollybushhampstead.co.uk; @thehollybushpub; 10 pm, Sun 9 pm.

Home SW15 SW15   £61   3 3 2

146 Upper Richmond Road   020 8780 0592   11–2B

This yearling all-day brasserie near East Putney tube "has succeeded where several other restaurants have failed", by following a formula of "good food and value for money". "It knocks the socks off the Bill's or Brew and their wannabes". / SW15 2SW; www.homesw15.com; @homesw15.

Homeslice   £38   4 3 3

50 James Street, W1   020 3034 0621   3–1A **NEW**
52 Wells St, W1   020 3151 7488   2–1B
13 Neal's Yd, WC2   020 7836 4604   5–2C
101 Wood Lane White City, W12   020 3034 0381   1–2B
374-378 Old St, EC1   020 3151 1121   13–1B
69-71 Queen Street, EC4   020 3034 0381   10–3C

"Messy... but so tasty!" – the "best pizzas ever" win nothing but rave reviews for these "easygoing and fun" outlets (backed by the late Terry Wogan's sons, Mark and Alan), which were out-scored only by the very narrowest margins by Pizza Pilgrims this year as London's best. "If you like funky topping combos, this is the place for you". NB: Ry Jessup, the Kiwi who originally founded the chain, moved on from the business after the survey closed in summer 2019, but we have maintained the rating. / www.homeslicepizza.co.uk; @homesliceLDN; 11 pm, Sun 10 pm (ex WC2H 10.30 pm); no booking.

Honest Burgers   £29   3 3 3

"A chain that defies the image of chains!" – "by far the tastiest of the 'gourmet' burger groups has yet to succumb to the typical slip-in-quality as it grows", and is nowadays the most-mentioned burger multiple in the survey. It has "taken the mantle from Byron" in recent years, with both a "better, less formulaic approach" and also a "slower and steadier opening programme": a combination that's "maintained the basic fundamentals of a decent, un-mucked-up formula". "Half restaurant/ half fast food in style, there are no starters and only ices for dessert, so you are in and out inside an hour. But, if you are looking for a good quality quick bite, this is the place for you". "It knocks out great-value, no-nonsense burgers, still serves them medium rare in flagrant defiance of food hygiene fascism, does the best veggie burger around (more of a fritter), and now does the famous 'bleeding' vegan burger, oozing beetroot juice for those requiring the illusion of meat with their veg". Other winning features include "addictive rosemary chips", "interesting specials (which vary by branch)" and "great beers on draught" from local breweries. / www.honestburgers.co.uk; @honestburgers; 10 pm-11 pm; SW9 closed Mon D; EC3 closed Sat & Sun; no bookings.

Honey & Co W1 £60 5 3 3
25a Warren St 020 7388 6175 2–1B
"No duds on the fabulous menu" at Sarit Packer and Itamar Sruolovich's "small-but-perfectly-formed" café, near Warren Street tube, where plate-lickingly-yummy Middle Eastern dishes (and you MUST leave space for a cake afterwards) are "made with love and served with a smile". It's "always very busy", though, and you need to shoehorn yourself into some of the seats. / W1T 5JZ; www.honeyandco.co.uk; @Honeyandco; 10.30 pm; closed Sun; No Amex.

Honey & Smoke W1 £59 4 3 2
216 Great Portland Street 020 7388 6175 2–1B
"Plentiful and nourishing Israeli dishes" (with "a delicious mix of spices and textures") win waves of praise for Honey & Co's younger, larger grill-house spin-off, south of Great Portland Street tube. It's "a busy and lively" ("frantic" and "very noisy") venue, popular with large parties, but whose "1970s-style plastic moulded chairs" can seem "strangely utilitarian" (unless you are someone who appreciates "the authenticity of Middle Eastern café culture"). / W1W 5QW; www.honeyandco.co.uk/smoke; @Honeyandco; 11.30 pm; closed Mon & Sun.

Hood SW2 £53 4 3 3
67 Streatham Hill 020 3601 3320 11–2D
"If Streatham Hill can still be called up-and-coming, this local is leading the pack"; a "great casual place with very good food, and a nice range of craft beers, all at a reasonable price". / SW2 4TX; www.hoodrestaurants.com; @HoodStreatham; 11 pm.

Hoppers £48 4 3 3
49 Frith St, W1 no tel 5–2A
77 Wigmore Street, W1 020 3319 8110 3–1A
"Authentic Sri Lankan food (just like my friend's mum used to make)" has won fame for JKS Restaurants's "buzzy" ("not much elbow room at busy times") and "fun", street-food cafés, which – although not quite as "novel" as when they first opened – are still "simply sensational" for most reporters. "Obviously you must have a hopper" (a rice pancake), and also "the curries are delicious, especially the seafood one", as are the "really tasty dosas". And "it's unbelievable that you can have a table filled up with exciting food at less than £30 a head, including drinks!". "While the original location (Soho) is better, it's nice that you can book at St Christopher's Place". / www.hopperslondon.com; @HoppersLondon.

Hot Stuff SW8 £28 3 4 2
19-23 Wilcox Rd 020 7720 1480 11–1D
In the heart of Vauxhall, Raj Dawood's little Indian canteen pre-dates the street food revolution (est 1988), and has a loyal following who award high ratings to its down-to-earth style and zesty scoff. / SW8 2XA; www.welovehotstuff.com; 10 pm; closed Mon; No Amex; No bookings.

House Restaurant, National Theatre SE1 £56 2 3 2
National Theatre, South Bank 020 7452 3600 2–3D
The smartest of the National Theatre's in-house dining rooms has had its high in past years, but is currently "only worth it if you're going to the theatre". The standard of cooking can vary sharply between visits: at best "really excellent and imaginative" but sometimes merely "fine" or "a bit of a production line process". / SE1 9PX; house.nationaltheatre.org.uk; @NT_House; 11 pm; D only (L served on matinee days), closed Sun.

Hubbard & Bell,
Hoxton Hotel WC1 £63 **3 3 3**
199-206 High Holborn 020 7661 3030 2–1D

Actually in Holborn not Hoxton – "an all-pleasing place, with a cool bar area" that's part of the Soho House group, tipped for its "excellent breakfasts" and "simple, classic burgers". / WC1V 7BD; www.hubbardandbell.com; @HubbardandBell; midnight, Sun 11 pm.

Humble Grape £54 **3 4 3**
11-13 Theberton Street, N1 020 3887 9287 9–3D
2 Battersea Rise, SW11 020 3620 2202 11–2C
18-20 Mackenzie Walk, E14 12–1C **NEW**
8 Devonshire Row, EC2 10–2D
1 Saint Bride's Passage, EC4 020 7583 0688 10–2A

"An amazing choice of wines" is served by "lovely staff, who are passionate and knowledgeable about the list" at these "proper wine bars", whose liquid offering is "complemented by a very good food menu" of "well-made" dishes (small plates, plus cheese and charcuterie). The Battersea original is still the branch attracting most feedback, although the chain is spreading eastwards, and its operation in the crypt of St Bride's Church and newer Liverpool Street branch are "very competent": next stop is an opening in Canary Wharf. / www.humblegrape.co.uk; @humblegrape.

Hunan SW1 £95 **4 2 1**
51 Pimlico Rd 020 7730 5712 6–2D

"Be adventurous! There's no menu but Mr Peng selects a fantastic array of dishes for you" at this Pimlico veteran (founded in 1982), which is still often acclaimed as "the best Chinese in London, bar none". "It looks ordinary from the outside (and is nothing special on the crowded inside either!)", but still diners "love the place" and the "entertaining" manner in which Mr P "treats you to a slew of scrumptious Chinese tapas of his choice, with some truly exceptional flavours… until you say you have had enough". "The wine choices are excellent too". All that said though, ratings here took a dip this year, dragged down by a small-but-vocal minority who feel the cooking risks losing some of its edge: "still love it, but the selection can be a little samey, albeit very nicely done". / SW1W 8NE; www.hunanlondon.com; 11 pm; closed Sun.

Hush W1 £91 **2 2 3**
8 Lancashire Ct 020 7659 1500 3–2B

"Elegant without stuffiness", this smooth, "buzzy" bar/brasserie "in a courtyard down a discrete lane" off Bond Street makes "a very nice venue for a business lunch in busy Mayfair". Established 20 years ago (by founders including Geoffrey Moore, Roger's son, and Evgeny Lebedev, owner of the Evening Standard), it clearly knows its market and "offers something for most occasions". / W1S 1EY; www.hush.co.uk; 11 pm; closed Sun; booking max 12 may apply.

Hutong,
The Shard SE1 £106 **2 2 5**
31 St Thomas St 020 3011 1257 10–4C

"Fabulous view" – "fittingly sky-high prices": that's the familiar trade off on the 33rd floor of the Shard, which nobody would deny is "a truly exceptional location", but where other aspects of the experience are sharply divisive. There are those who feel "this is a real luxury treat" and who praise its "high-end Chinese dishes", but a worrying proportion of reports feel the trip is "not really worth the money spent", and dismiss "pretentious" cooking, "but with an extra-big price tag". / SE1 9RY; www.hutong.co.uk; @HutongShard; 10 pm; No shorts.

Ibérica £59 **3** **2** **3**
Zig Zag Building, 70 Victoria St, SW1   020 7636 8650   2–4B
195 Great Portland St, W1   020 7636 8650   2–1B
12 Cabot Sq, E14   020 7636 8650   12–1C
89 Turnmill St, EC1   020 7636 8650   10–1A
From its first branch, on Great Portland Street, which opened in 2007, these "buzzy", "authentic" and relatively stylish Spanish tapas-haunts have grown into a national chain, boosted by their "consistent standards, fair quality and sensible prices" (although "service is a bit uneven"). / 11 pm, SW1 Sun 10.30 pm, E14 Sun 4pm; W1 closed Sun D.

Icco Pizza £18 **4** **2** **1**
46 Goodge St, W1   020 7580 9688   2–1C
21a Camden High Street, NW1   020 7380 0020   9–3B
There are "no frills at all" at this 20-year veteran pizza-joint in Goodge Street, with a branch in Camden Town – "but the fact that you can sit down with a tasty thin-crust pizza in central London for these prices (£3.95 for a Marinara) is well worth the lack of ambience". / www.icco.co.uk; @ICCO_pizza.

Ichi Buns W1 £48 **2** **2** **3**
24 Wardour Street   5–3A
Clubby, three-floor 'Japanese Super Diner' in Chinatown that opened in 2018, with regular DJs on the dim-lit, basement level, and boatloads of retro-Japanese pop-memorabilia throughout. Alongside cocktails it provides burgers, udon and sushi – recommended strongly by some reporters, but "neither here nor there" to others. / W1D 6QJ; www.ichibuns.com; @ichibuns.

Ida W10 £50 **3** **4** **3**
222a Kilburn Lane   020 8969 9853   1–2B
"What a find!" – In a fairly obscure part of town, near the Queen's Park Estate, "a really cosy, neighbourhood Italian, serving a top selection of cheap 'n' cheerful dishes, but also more pricey ones, all freshly made and of great quality" (in particular the hand-rolled pasta). Service from husband-and-wife team Simonetta and Avi "is very professional but lively, and there's a real sense of community at play (e.g. the staff were handing out little pieces of paper with a guest's name on it, asking us to sing along for his birthday!)" / W10 4AT; www.idarestaurant.co.uk; @IdaRestaurant; 11 pm; closed Sat L & Sun; No Amex.

Ikoyi SW1 £106 **4** **2** **2**
1 St James's Market   020 3583 4660   4–4D
"Dazzling reinvention of African classic dishes", featuring "really unique combinations and flavours", has made this much-discussed two-year-old – from Chinese-Canadian chef Jeremy Chan and Nigerian co-founder Iré Hassan-Odukele – one of the most original of recent London openings. It's in the St James's Market development near Piccadilly Circus: an area, in contrast, "stuffed with conformity to the norm", where "the vibes are a bit sterile". In the evening, the main option is a seven-course tasting menu for £75, but an extended version for £100 is also available. / SW1Y 4AH; www.ikoyilondon.com.

Il Guscio N5 £52 **3** **4** **3**
231 Blackstock Road   020 7354 1400   9–1D
This "great little Sardinian restaurant" in Highbury serves up "excellent food (large amounts of it), in a very convivial atmosphere". It's "the perfect local for when we can't face cooking, or want a midweek treat, or are meeting friends, or want a quick pre-dinner drink... in fact, it's good on pretty much any occasion". Kids are welcome, and will love the "amazing pizzas". / N5 2LL; www.ilgusciohighbury.co.uk; 10.30 pm, Fri & Sat 11 pm.

Imperial Treasure SW1 NEW £104 222
9-10 Waterloo Place   020 3011 1328   4–4D
"Everything about this place is wow!… including the breathtaking bill!" –
This extremely swanky, late-2018 newcomer occupies a "beautiful old
banking hall, with butter-soft leather banquettes, and tasteful furniture"
just off Pall Mall. It's the first London branch of a Singaporean chain with
branches throughout mainland China and Hong Kong as well as elsewhere
in Asia. "Don't forget to pre-order your £100 Peking duck with pancakes!",
which has become something of a cause célèbre in (generally unfavourable)
newspaper reviews of its opening, although whether the result
is "magnificent", or "a tasteless rip off" at "obscene prices" is likewise
debated by Harden's reporters. Ultimately ratings here are dragged down
by the vocal minority of critics, but supporters say "you wouldn't complain
about the prices if it were French". / SW1Y 4BE; www.imperialtreasure.com.

India Club,
Strand Continental Hotel WC2 £29 222
143 Strand   020 7836 4880   2–2D
"Step back in time with shades of the 1950s" – "you could imagine Nehru
walking through the door" – at this "atmospheric all-Indian" curry house
on the Strand, close to the Indian High Commission, that was recently saved
from redevelopment. "The food is decent value at a remarkably low price" –
although it's "not really the point". "After lunch in the rather bleak dining
room, coffee in the cocktail bar seems positively luxurious". Top Tip –
BYO from the hotel bar. / WC2R 1JA; www.theindiaclub.co.uk; @hostelstrandcon;
10.50 pm; booking max 6 may apply.

Indian Accent W1 £82 542
16 Albemarle Street   020 7629 9802   3–3C
"From the amuse bouche and blue cheese naan onwards, we were blown
away!" – this "impeccable" Mayfair spin-off from a famous New Delhi
venture is in contention as "the best-of-the-best of London's new wave
of fine dining Indians": "maintaining classic, traditional flavours" but with
"an impressive balance of refinement and power" to create "deliciously
tantalising" dishes. Service is "patient" and "warmly welcoming", while the
interior – though certainly "smart" and "tastefully understated" – can also
seem "very stereotypically Mayfair", or "too businessy". / W1S 4HW;
indianaccent.com/london; @Indian_Accent.

Indian Moment SW11 £41 322
44 Battersea Rise   020 7223 6575 / 020 7223 1818   11–2C
In Clapham's busy 'Nappy Valley', this "great local Indian" earns consistent
ratings for its "well-cooked food" with subtle spicing. Its modern dining room
is far from spacious and can descend into "bedlam in the evenings, when it's
full of screamers… not all of them young!". / SW11 1EE;
www.indianmoment.co.uk; @indianmoment; 11.30 pm, Fri & Sat midnight.

Indian Ocean SW17 £31 343
214 Trinity Rd   020 8672 7740   11–2C
This "old-school Indian" keeps its long-term Wandsworth Common regulars
"very happy" with a "good range of dishes" – not all of them the usual
suspects. Everything is "done perfectly, and it's not too expensive".
/ SW17 7HP; www.indianoceanrestaurant.com; 11.30 pm, Sat 11.45 pm, Sun 11 pm.

Indian Rasoi N2 £37 322
7 Denmark Terrace   020 8883 9093   1–1B
"High-quality, very tasty and authentic dishes" inspired by the Mughal-era
cuisine of northern India make this "cramped" Muswell Hill curry house
"way better than most". / N2 9HG; www.indian-rasoi.co.uk; 10.30 pm; No Amex.

Indian Zing W6 £57 **4 3 2**
236 King St   020 8748 5959   8–2B
The "amazing", "top-quality cuisine" at Manoj Vasaikar's consistently high-rated Ravenscourt Park venue "proves that you don't need to go into central London to get really excellent, authentic Indian food". A long-time favourite – the late Michael Winner was a fan – it serves "Michelin star quality cuisine without the wannabe nonsense" in a tightly packed space. / W6 0RS; www.indian-zing.co.uk; @IndianZing; 11 pm, Sun 10 pm.

Inko Nito W1 £51 **3 3 4**
55 Broadwick Street   4–2B
LA's Art District housed the first branch of this Roka-lite concept (same founder), and this Soho yearling, with its "manifestly cool decor" (from a California design agency) delivers well all-round (even if it's maybe "a little expensive"), especially if you are in the mood for a meal combining "a fun bar ambience" with "simple yet exciting" Korean/Japanese dishes. / W1F 9QS; www.inkonitorestaurant.com/london-soho.

Ippudo £47 **3 3 3**
3 Central Saint Giles Piazza, WC2   020 7240 4469   5–1B **NEW**
31a Villiers Street, WC2   5–4D
1 Crossrail Pl, E14   020 3326 9485   12–1C
"Top ramen with great broth and good combinations", win fans for this genuinely Japanese chain (originating in Fukuoka), which has branches in Holborn, Embankment and Canary Wharf. Ratings, though, fall short of the top heights at the hands of those who feel its food is "not bad, but not memorable". A fourth branch is to open in Fitzrovia in autumn 2019. / www.ippudo.co.uk; @IppudoLondon.

Ishtar W1 £54 **3 3 2**
10-12 Crawford St   020 7224 2446   2–1A
"A finesse not often found in Turkish restaurants" helps set this "comfortable" Marylebone establishment apart: the food is "tasty", with particularly good value set menus, and service "pleasant and friendly". / W1U 6AZ; www.ishtarrestaurant.com; 11.30 pm, Sun 10.30 pm.

Isla WC1 **NEW**
The Standard Hotel, 10 Argyle Street   9–3C
This hip American hotel opened in summer 2019 with several restaurants, including this garden restaurant overseen by Adam Rawson which offers a 'seasonal menu, featuring light proteins and a predominantly natural wine list'. He will also be looking after ground-floor, street-facing 'neighbourhood' bar, Double Standard (see also, and rooftop restaurant Decimo too). / WC1H 8EG; www.standardhotels.com/london/features/standard_london_isla.

Italo SW8 £46 **4 3 4**
13 Bonnington Square   020 7450 3773   11–1D
"Grab a seat outside either at the counter shelf or at one of the tables" of this ten-year-old deli "in an off-the-beaten track, verdant garden square in Vauxhall" for an authentic lunchtime treat from a short Italian menu. In colder weather you eat inside at a few closely-packed tables surrounded by shelves of produce. / SW8 1TE; italodeli.co.uk.

The Ivy WC2 £83 2 2 3
1-5 West St 020 7836 4751 5–3B

"An old favourite, but the diffusion-brand has tarnished its name" – it feels like this Theatreland legend is steadily being sacrificed for the greater good of its growing stable of spin-offs. Many supporters do still feel its "comforting" menu delivers "reliable, traditional British food" in a "classy and buzzy" setting and that the trip is "still worth it (especially if you can get into the adjoining Ivy Club)". But scores here are heading inexorably south across the board, supporting the many former regulars who feel the place "misplaced its soul, serving food that's decidedly average at best" and "lost its caché" to the extent it's "a shadow of its former self". / WC2H 9NQ; www.the-ivy.co.uk; @TheIvyWestSt; 11.30pm, Thu-Sat midnight, Sun 10.30 pm; No shorts; booking max 6 may apply.

The Ivy Café £56 1 1 3
96 Marylebone Ln, W1 020 3301 0400 2–1A
120 St John's Wood High St, NW8 020 3096 9444 9–3A
75 High St, SW19 020 3096 9333 11–2B
9 Hill Street, TW9 020 3146 7733 1–4A

"Trading on The Ivy's name, but nothing like the real thing": outlets of Richard Caring's sub-sub-brand are "squarely bistro in nature" and proving less successful than their brasserie namesakes in capturing diners' affections. True, some do tout them as a "dependable if unexciting" choice, but – lacking the pizzazz which carries the experience at their grander cousins – the focus falls more on the "bland, by-numbers" food and service that's "neither here nor there". Top Tip – "Prefer breakfast to the expensive lunch and dinner options". / 11 pm, Fri & Sat 11.30 pm, Sun 10.30 pm; SW19 11 pm, Sun 10.30 pm; midnight.

The Ivy Grills & Brasseries £60 2 2 4
26-28 Broadwick St, W1 020 3301 1166 4–1C
1 Henrietta St, WC2 020 3301 0200 5–3D
197 King's Rd, SW3 020 3301 0300 6–3C
96 Kensington High St, W8 020 3301 0500 6–1A
One Tower Bridge, 1 Tower Bridge, SE1 020 3146 7722 10–4D
Dashwood House, 69 Old Broad St,, EC2 020 3146 7744 10–2D
50 Canada Square, London, E14 020 3971 7111 **NEW**

"Maybe the brand is a bit stretched", but Richard Caring's bold expansion is paying off by-and-large, certainly in commercial terms, and – though most branches' average food-rating is run-of-the-mill – by the standards of large chains, the group delivers a consistent-enough formula, whereby folks accept predictable nursery fodder in return for a dependable dose of 'affordable glamour'. The "beautiful and festive" Ivy Chelsea Garden (SW3) is the best known in the stable and it's particularly "wonderful if you manage to get a table in their fabulous garden". The "big and buzzy" Ivy Kensington Brasserie (W8) is less highly rated, but nevertheless fills a vital niche in the local market for a comfortable, atmospheric and versatile rendezvous ("its bar is also a fun place for a drink"). The City branches (The Ivy Tower Bridge, The Ivy City Garden EC2) and Canary Wharf outlet (The Ivy in the Park, E14) are the highest rated all-round (perhaps reflecting the ongoing lack of convivial spaces out east). "Awesome views" at Tower Bridge are distinct client-pleasers. Other branches taking above-average flak include The Ivy Soho Brasserie, W1 ("busy mayhem" with "slow and disorganised service") and The Ivy Market Grill, WC2 ("nothing special, rather overpriced, and very busy"). See also Granary Square Brasserie. / ivycollection.com.

Jacob the Angel WC2 £25 3 3 3
16a Neal's Yard no tel 5–2C

"Yummy bakes and great caffeine" help make this tiny coffee house (just 10 covers) in Seven Dials – from the owners of The Palomar – particularly "good for a solo breakfast". / WC2H 9DP; www.jacobtheangel.co.uk; No bookings.

Jaffna House SW17 £26 **3**|**2**|**2**
90 Tooting High St   020 8672 7786   11–2C
"Incredible thalis at awesome prices", inspire a dedicated band of devotees
to the authentic Sri Lankan and South Indian specialities served up in this
"homely dining room": "maybe not the best, but certainly the best-value
lunch in Tooting". / SW17 0RN; Www.jaffnahouse.uk; 11.30 pm.

Jamavar W1 £84 **3**|**3**|**3**
8 Mount Street   020 7499 1800   3–3B
"Boldly flavoured" nouvelle Indian cuisine served in a "dark and clubby",
colonial-theme setting puts Leela Palace's Mayfair two-year-old in London's
premier league, if not perhaps quite at the top of the table: "not as
memorable as some top names, but definitely a favourite". But while it's
"a good attempt at taking Indian cuisine to the next level", it lacks the
stunning verve fans recall from when it first opened: "a fun evening out,
but it will need to do better again to match the best of the best". / W1K 3NF;
www.jamavarrestaurants.com; @JamavarLondon.

Jashan N8 £37 **4**|**4**|**2**
19 Turnpike Ln   020 8340 9880   1–1C
This "old-school curry house in far Turnpike Lane" serves up "wonderful
dishes" from a "menu very different from the norm in suburban Indian
restaurants" (although the atmosphere is "dreary"). Fans say it's "really
fabulous – we go almost every week!". / N8 0EP; www.jashan.co.uk;
@indian_jashan; 10.15 pm, Fri & Sat 10.30 pm; D only; No Amex; May need
6+ to book.

Jean-Georges at The Connaught W1 £114 **2**|**3**|**3**
The Connaught, Carlos Place   020 7107 8861   3–3B
It's as a site for an exceptional afternoon tea – with fusion-flavoured finger
sarnies adding some brio to the traditional experience – or a "chic brunch"
that this posh brasserie, in a conservatory addition to Mayfair's most upper-
crust of hotels, excites enthusiasm. When it comes to star NYC-chef,
Jean Georges Vongerichten's "unusual" main menu – from pizza to caviar
via truffle cheeseburger (and minus the SE Asian notes for which the chef
is most famous) – it can seem like a "stunning and relaxing" experience…
or merely "overpriced", "tired and lacking flavour". / W1K 2AL;
www.the-connaught.co.uk/mayfair-restaurants/jean-georges; @TheConnaught; 11 pm.

Jidori £23 **4**|**3**|**2**
15 Catherine Street, WC2   5–3D
89 Kingsland High St, E8   020 7686 5634   14–1A
"Yakitori heaven" ("everything is so yummy") is to be found at this
minimalist duo, specialising in Japanese skewers, which opened in Covent
Garden in 2018 after a successful first venture in Dalston. The trade-off
is "very simple Muji/utilitarian" decor "but who cares when the food's this
nice". (Versatile Aussie chef Brett Redman is behind it, in partnership with
Natalie Lee-Joe). It also has a karaoke room. / www.jidori.co.uk; @JidoriUK.

Jikoni W1 £75 **3**|**3**|**4**
21 Blandford Street   020 70341988   2–1A
A "delicious and interesting fusion of the familiar and unfamiliar" – and of
chef Ravinder Bhogal's mixed Indian, East African, Middle Eastern and
British heritage – this Marylebone two-year-old is "always delightful".
"A quaint layout with comfy print cushions makes it feel smaller than it is",
while "staff are friendly if perhaps not always expert". / W1U 3DJ;
www.jikonilondon.com; @JikoniLondon.

Jin Kichi NW3 £48 5 4 3
73 Heath St 020 7794 6158 9–1A

"Outstanding" Japanese cooking ("we dream about it!") has made this stalwart "izakaya-style" venue one of Hampstead's best foodie destinations for decades; and it attracts fans from across north London and beyond. "And it's not all about sushi" – yakitori ("grilled delicacies") are also a speciality here, and "the hotpots are brilliant too". "Service is lovely", and the only drawback is its diminutive size – "so get a reservation if you can". Top Tip – "sit by the grill upstairs for the treat of watching the chef at work". / NW3 6UG; www.jinkichi.com; 11 pm, Sun 10 pm; closed Mon L.

Jinjuu W1 £62 4 4 3
16 Kingly St 020 8181 8887 4–2B

This "modern Korean" basement off Carnaby Street does a great line in "delicious but different food" served in "cool surroundings": it "delivers on the staples – fried chicken, dumplings, etc – while more unusual modern interpretations also hit the target", such as "terrific tofu sliders". In June 2019, Korean-American TV chef Judy Joo severed her ties with the venture, but we've maintained the rating for the time being. / W1B 5PS; www.jinjuu.com; @JinjuuSoho; 11.30 pm, Thu-Sat 1 am, Sun 9.30 pm.

Joe Allen WC2 £51 2 2 3
2 Burleigh St 020 7836 0651 5–3D

"Seemingly relocated brick-by-brick, table-by-table" – this "casual and fun" haunt in Covent Garden's (a 1970s spin-off from NYC's famous Theatre District staple) moved a couple of years ago, leaving its original basement home for this new two-level location just a minute's walk away. It's a surprisingly faithful reproduction, and regulars of decades standing feel "it still works and seems unchanged"; and, as a place to refuel before or after a show, it still has a large fanclub, despite a "perennially ordinary" level of cooking…sadly also preserved in the move. Top Menu Tip – "the secret's been out about the off-menu burger for many, many years now", and it's the best bet. / WC2E 7PX; www.joeallen.co.uk; @JoeAllenWC2; 11.30 pm, Fri & Sat 12.30 am, Sun 10 pm.

Joe Public SW4 £18 4 3 2
4 The Pavement 020 7622 4676 11–2D

"Fab pizzas" – "brilliant option of just buying a slice: America meets Clapham!" – have made this tiny outfit in a former public convenience beside Clapham Common a big favourite among locals wanting an ultra-quick bite. "Just love this place – you can eat alone and not feel lonely". / SW4 7AA; www.joepublicpizza.com; @JoepublicSW4; midnight, Sun 11pm; No bookings.

Jolene N16 £61 3 2 3
20 Newington Green 0203 887 2309 1–1C

"This too-kool-for-school hangout in Newington Green" – a yearling bakery/café/restaurant from Primeur and Westerns Laundry founders Jeremie Cometto-Lingenheim and David Gingell – is "full to the rafters with Stokie's coolest hipsters with good reason – the food is spot-on". The vibe, all 'unaltered grains milled onsite', gets up one or two reporters' noses though, who feel "its mincing pomposity makes it the Jacob Rees-Mogg of the Hackney restaurant scene!" / N16 9PU; www.jolene16.com.

Jollibee SW5 £13 1 2 1
180-182 Earls Court Road 020 7244 7444 6–2A

Over 1,000 people queued for its opening, but if you're not Filipino, chances are you won't 'get' this Earl's Court fast-food diner, which has introduced the capital to the delights of authentic 'chickenjoy', yumburger and Jolly Spaghetti (with sweet tomato and hot dog sauce) – "really not special!" / SW5 9QG; www.jollibee.com.ph/international; @Jollibee.

Jones & Sons N16 £52 **3****4****3**
Stamford Works, 3 Gillett Street   020 7241 1211   14–1A
"You can't go far wrong", according to the more-than-local fanclub of this
open-plan venture, hiply located near Dalston Station; and serving
"excellent, modern British food from a frequently changing menu" that's
"good value". Top Tip – bottomless brunch. / N16 8JH;
www.jonesandsonsdalston.com; @JonesSons; 10 pm, Fri & Sat 11 pm, Sun 7 pm;
booking max 7 may apply.

The Jones Family Kitchen SW1 £47 **4****3****3**
7-8 Eccleston Yard   020 7739 1740   2–4B
"The best beef in the area (Belgravia/Pimlico)... nuff said" – this *"shiny"*,
year-old sibling to Shoreditch's Jones Family Project is part of the *"beautiful"*
Eccleston Yards courtyard development: *"a fantastic addition to SW1"* that
doesn't feel at all like somewhere around the corner from Victoria Coach
Station. As well as steak, it features a fairly broad selection of modern British
brasserie fare (including plenty of fish), much of it from the Josper charcoal
oven; plus a decent list of cocktails and wine. Top Tip – for coeliacs there's
a dedicated gluten-free menu. / SW1W 9AZ; www.jonesfamilyproject.co.uk;
@JonesShoreditch .

The Jones Family Project EC2 £58 **3****3****4**
78 Great Eastern Street   020 7739 1740   13–1B
*"Upstairs is 1970s, retro-cocktail fun! – the basement is an atmospheric
restaurant"*, at this Shoreditch venue. *"Outstanding, juicy steak perfectly
cooked (with very good side dishes – the best being the truffled mac 'n'
cheese)"* is the headline feature in culinary terms, but there's a dish to suit
most tastes on the wide-ranging brasserie-style menu. / EC2A 3JL;
www.jonesfamilyproject.co.uk; @JonesShoreditch; 10.30 pm, Sun 6 pm.

José SE1 £53 **5****4****5**
104 Bermondsey St   020 7403 4902   10–4D
"There's no finer tapas outside Spain" than at José Pizarro's *"outstanding,
if authentically tiny"* Bermondsey bar: *"very buzzy and busy, as a tapas bar
should be"* providing *"absolute classic dishes, prepared with attention
to detail and with perfect produce"*. *"It looks chaotic when you turn up and
you have to queue outside with your wine. However the system they have
works because you're soon seated and ready to enjoy some of London's
best tapas"*; *"highly recommended"*. / SE1 3UB; www.josepizarro.com;
@Jose_Pizarro; 10.15 pm, Sun 5.15 pm; closed Sun D; no booking.

José Pizarro EC2 £62 **4****3****2**
Broadgate Circle   020 7256 5333   13–2B
The vibrancy of the star Spanish chef's tapas has always seemed slightly
at odds with the glossy-but-corporate location of this outlet, in the
midst of the City's Broadgate Circle. Even those who don't vibe with the
place, though, acclaim its *"friendly"* style, and the cooking is rated from very
good to exceptional. / EC2M 2QS; www.josepizarro.com/jose-pizarro-broadgate;
@JP_Broadgate; 10.45 pm, Sat 9.45 pm; closed Sun.

Joy King Lau WC2 £43 **3****3****2**
3 Leicester St   020 7437 1132   5–3A
"In a crowded Chinatown field", this three-story Cantonese institution just off
Leicester Square *"is a dependable crowd-pleaser"* with a *"good price-to-
quality ratio"*: *"the queues outside speak for its popularity"*. Highlights from
the *"reliable menu"* include *"fab dim sum every time"*, *"yummy char sui"*
and *"legendary soft shell crab"*, all delivered by staff who *"although rushed
off their feet are generally smiley and friendly"*. Top Tip – *"the ground floor
is a better experience than the higher floors"*. / WC2H 7BL;
www.joykinglau.com; 11.30 pm, Sun 10.30 pm.

Jugemu W1 £43 5️⃣2️⃣3️⃣
3 Winnett St 020 7734 0518 4–2D
"Under the direction of a single, passionate and precise chef"
(Yuya Kikuchi), this brilliantly "authentic" little (about 20 seats) izakaya
in Soho produces some marvels, with dazzling sushi being the top pick
on the menu. Don't go if you're in a hurry. / W1D 6JY; jugemu-uk.crayonsite.com;
@jugemu_uk.

The Jugged Hare EC1 £60 3️⃣2️⃣2️⃣
49 Chiswell Street 020 7614 0134 13–2A
This game-themed gastropub next to the Barbican has a solid following for
its "excellent game and seriously good local produce" from an "interesting
and well-executed menu". Clearly, it's best to come in game season (August-
February), but at other times the kitchen gets by on rare-breed beef,
goat and seafood options, and an "amazing Sunday roast – pricey but
worth it". Arguably, the interior "doesn't lift the spirits, but there's a sheer
lack of decent alternatives around the Barbican". / EC1Y 4SA;
www.thejuggedhare.com; @thejuggedhare; 11 pm, Thu-Sat midnight, Sun 10.30 pm.

Julie's W11 £56
135 Portland Rd 020 7229 8331 7–2A
At last! Since 2015 this Holland Park icon of louche 1970s living –
an intriguing subterranean labyrinth of differently-styled chambers –
has promised that it will reopen, and it finally looks set to happen
in September 2019, in time for its 50th year in business. Its updated looks
are unknown as yet, but they have recruited a good chef in the form of Shay
Cooper, who held a Michelin star at his previous gig, The Goring. / W11 4LW;
www.juliesrestaurant.com; @JuliesW11; 11 pm.

K10 £33 3️⃣2️⃣2️⃣
3 Appold St, EC2 020 7539 9209 13–2B
Minster Ct, Mincing Ln, EC3 020 3019 2510 10–3D
(Takeaway only) 15 Queen Street, EC4 10–2C
(Takeaway only) 78 Fetter Lane, EC4 10–2A
"Good value" sushi, sashimi and other Japanese dishes trundle past your
seat at these two 'kaiten' (conveyor-belt) operations in the City, tempting you
to help yourself. It makes a fun, fast and efficient way to grab lunch. The
chain also has takeaway and delivery options for evenings. / www.k10.com;
Mon-Fri 3 pm; Closed D, closed Sat & Sun; no booking .

Kaffeine £15 3️⃣5️⃣4️⃣
15 Eastcastle St, W1 020 7580 6755 3–1D
66 Great Titchfield St, W1 020 7580 6755 3–1C
This "stylish and serious", coffee-shop operation with two sites in Fitzrovia
is "still one of the best independents in London", 10 years after pioneering
modern Antipodean-style coffee culture in the UK. They serve "brilliant
coffee" (naturally), "a nice range of pastries" and "excellent sandwiches",
and have a "good vibe at both locations". "Only the slightly monastic seating
lets things down" – and there's "not enough" of it! / kaffeine.co.uk/Eastcastle;
@kaffeinelondon; 6 pm, Sun 5 pm; no bookings.

Kahani SW1 £70 5️⃣4️⃣3️⃣
1 Wilbraham Place 020 7730 7634 6–2D
Ex-Tamarind executive chef, Peter Joseph (raised in Tamil Nadu) is cooking
up a storm at his "smart" September-2018 newcomer, "tucked away
behind Cadogan Hall" near Sloane Square. Even a reporter who considers
it "expensive" feels "it's certainly amongst London's Top-5 Indians",
and there's little but high esteem for its "refined", "thoughtfully prepared"
cooking: "distinct and light" dishes featuring "favourite flavours but raised
to a fine dining experience, including a tasting menu option". / SW1X 9AE;
www.kahanirestaurants.com.

Kai Mayfair W1 £127 3 2 2
65 South Audley St   020 7493 8988   3–3A
"If you want Chinese food at its best", numerous reporters award top marks to Bernard Yeoh's luxurious Mayfair fixture, which has held a Michelin star for the last 10 years now, and which is unusual in boasting a heavyweight wine list featuring many of the world's most famous vintages. Even those who say it's "brilliant" acknowledge it's decidedly "not cheap" however. / W1K 2QU; www.kaimayfair.co.uk; @kaimayfair; 10.45 pm, Sun 10.15 pm.

Kaifeng NW4 £71 3 2 2
51 Church Road   020 8203 7888   1–1B
The divide in opinions on this smart, kosher-Chinese stalwart in Hendon has been unvarying since the year dot – to fans it's "the best Chinese food ever eaten" but to critics the most "overpriced". / NW4 4DU; www.kaifeng.co.uk; @KaifengKosher; 10 pm; closed Fri & Sat.

Kaki N1 NEW £48 3 2 1
125 Caledonian Road   020 7278 0004   9–3D
"Superb-if-rustic" Sichuan cuisine – "off-the-wall, especially if you aren't accustomed to it – has won instant acclaim, including amongst newspaper critics, for this newcomer by Regent's Canal: "a weird space that feels like a hastily converted pub" (which it is). Its overall ratings are middling, however, due to those who feel "the food didn't live up to the positive reviews (Coren, Maschler…)", or who "find the flavours a bit one-dimensional". / N1 9RG; www.kakilondon.com.

Kanada-Ya £39 5 3 2
3 Panton St, SW1   020 7930 3511   5–4A
64 St Giles High St, WC2   020 7240 0232   5–1B
35 Upper Street, N1   020 7288 2787   9–3D
"The best ramen in London – such a rich, meaty broth with just the right amount of fatty unctuousness" – is served at this franchise of a Japanese-owned brand, with branches in the West End and now Angel. The "nice, slurpy noodles" are "a firm favourite, great for cold days, hangovers, comfort food", and come with a small selection of side dishes and rice. / www.kanada-ya.com; @KanadaYa_LDN; 10.30 pm, Sun 8.30 pm; WC2 no bookings.

Kanishka W1 NEW 3 3 2
17-19 Maddox Street   020 3978 0978   4–2A
"Off to a great start", with "superb" cuisine, say fans of Atul Kochhar's "upmarket" (and sizeable: 130 covers) new venture on a site that was previously the Mayfair branch of 28:50 (RIP), and which specialises in the "strongly flavoured", relatively undiscovered cuisine of India's north-eastern states (bordering Tibet and China). It's "not cheap" however, and while "some star dishes" are reported "some of the rest are a little more forgettable", while the interior design is "relaxing and warm" to some tastes, but – to others – can appear "cold" or "incoherent". / W1S 2QH; kanishkarestaurant.co.uk; @kanishka_maddox.

Kaosarn £26 4 2 3
110 St Johns Hill, SW11   020 7223 7888   11–2C
181 Tooting High Street, SW17   11–2C
Brixton Village, Coldharbour Ln, SW9   020 7095 8922   11–2D
"Delicious food and incredibly reasonable prices" ensure that this family-run Thai trio in South London (Brixton, Battersea and Tooting) are "hard to beat – especially with BYO". You eat "authentically, but very quickly!" / SW9 10 pm, Sun 9 pm; SW11 closed Mon L; no credit cards; no bookings.

Kappacasein SE16 £9 4 3 2

1 Voyager Industrial Estate 07837 756852 12–2A

Cheese, cheese and more cheese – in toasties, or as raclette – have made Bill Oglethorpe's market stall one of the linchpins of Borough Market. Since 2017, you can also visit their dairy in nearby Bermondsey, although you can only actually eat-in there on Saturday morning and lunchtime. / SE16 4RP; www.kappacasein.com; @kappacasein; 2pm; Sat L only; Cash only; No bookings.

Kashmir SW15 £46 3 3 2

18-20 Lacy Road 07477 533 888 11–2B

Billed as England's only Kashmiri specialist, this Putney three-year-old offers something "genuinely different from the standard Indian fare – and it's "always delicious". Chef Rohit Razdan and his wife Shweta have previously had restaurants in New Delhi and Singapore. / SW15 1NL; www.kashmirrestaurants.co.uk; @KashmirRestUK; 10.30 pm, Fri & Sat 11 pm.

Kaspar's Seafood and Grill, The Savoy Hotel WC2 £92 3 4 4

The Strand 020 7420 2111 5–3D

"The river views are super if you're lucky enough to get a table by the windows", in The Savoy's "plush, calm dining room, at the back of the hotel", which many still recall as The Savoy River Restaurant. Most reports are of fish and seafood "to savour", plus "expert service in beautiful surroundings", although even fans can feel that "it's quite a pricey treat", and some sceptics say that, "while pleasant, standards are not as outstanding as you'd expect from The Savoy". Perhaps its good ratings will improve even further with the July 2019 recruitment of Joost Bijster as head chef. Top Tip – head here for a "perfect breakfast". / WC2R 0ER; www.thesavoylondon.com/restaurant/kaspars-at-the-savoy-restaurant; @TheSavoyLondon; 11 pm.

Kateh W9 £53 4 3 2

5 Warwick Pl 020 7289 3393 9–4A

Cute Little Venice bistro, where "consistently excellent Persian food" is matched with a "fine southern European wine list". "When it's packed with elegant Iranians, you know you're in the right place". / W9 2PX; www.katehrestaurant.co.uk; @RestaurantKateh; 11 pm; closed weekday L.

The Kati Roll Company W1 £22 4 2 2

24 Poland Street 020 7287 4787 4–1C

"You'll be lucky to get a seat at this bustling, Indian street-food outlet" in Soho – London outpost of an NYC-chain with six Manhattan locations. It serves "excellent, wholesome south-Asian-style filled rolls" – "there's a huge variety of rolls to choose from" – and "Bollywood posters and songs make up for what's a very compact space". / W1F 8QL; www.thekatirollcompany.com; @KatiRollCompany.

Kazan £52 3 3 2

77 Wilton Rd, SW1 020 7233 8298 2–4B
93-94 Wilton Rd, SW1 020 7233 7100 2–4B

"Reliably gratifying Turkish food" – "the best in this part of London" – is the calling card for this Pimlico duo, opposite each other close by Victoria Station. Service is "fast", with a "lively cosmopolitan atmosphere". / www.kazan-restaurant.com; 10.15 pm, Sun 9.15 pm.

The Keeper's House, Royal Academy W1 £60 2 2 3

Royal Academy of Arts, Burlington House, 020 7300 5881 3–3D

In the bowels of the RA, this subterranean venue (with bar, garden and dining room) is praised by fans for providing "reliable food in a civilised space". Typically for Peyton & Byrne though, it doesn't impress everyone, with the odd report of some "terrible" dishes. / W1J 0BD; www.royalacademy.org.uk/keepers-house; @TheKeepersHouse; 11.30; closed Sun.

Ken Lo's Memories SW1 £68 3 2 2

65-69 Ebury St 020 7730 7734 2–4B

"Expensive though reliable, like an old friend" – the late Ken Lo's Belgravia operation has won improved marks for its high-quality Oriental cuisine in the past year. Fans say it's "as good as always and good value for the area", taking it as a sign of quality that the clientele is made up of "regulars, not tourists: people are here because of the food". / SW1W 0NZ; www.memoriesofchina.co.uk; 11 pm, Sun 10.30 pm.

Kennington Tandoori SE11 £54 3 4 3

313 Kennington Rd 020 7735 9247 1–3C

Kowsar Hoque's Kennington fixture is "definitely not your regular curry house" – whatever your game. If it's cricket, it's "the only place to enjoy a meal post-Test at The Oval". If politics, it's "famous for its popularity with politicians from all sides: you're quite likely to find Ken Clarke eating alone reading The Economist", while David Cameron had his 'last supper' as PM delivered to Number 10 Downing Street. / SE11 4QE; www.kenningtontandoori.com; @TheKTLondon; No Amex.

The Kensington Wine Rooms W8 £65 2 3 3

127-129 Kensington Church St 020 7727 8142 7–2B

Forty wines by the glass, and 150 by the bottle are the main 'gourmet' attraction at this modern wine bar, near Notting Hill Gate (which, over the years, has added siblings in Fulham and Brackenbury Village). To accompany the liquid refreshment, there's substantial fare like steaks and seared fish, or you can stick to the "great bar platters". / W8 7LP; winerooms.london/kensington; @wine_rooms; 11.30 pm.

Kerbisher & Malt W6 £27 3 2 2

164 Shepherd's Bush Rd 020 3556 0228 8–1C

"I know of no better chippie… apart from the interior", say fans of this ten-year-old venture by Brook Green, whose white-tiled walls and bum-numbing chairs can make it feel "rather Spartan"; and where attractions include ethically sourced fish and home-made curry sauce. As the chain it spawned has shrunk away, though, feedback on this, the original branch, has become much less adulatory, and sceptics feel "it used to be a lot better" and can sometimes be "disappointing" now. / W6 7PB; www.kerbisher.co.uk; @Kerbisher; 10 pm; closed Mon.

Kerridge's Bar & Grill SW1 £92 3 3 4

Whitehall Place 020 7321 3244 2–3C

TV-star Tom Kerridge "has clearly tried to bring a touch of his Marlow pub, The Hand & Flowers to the formal and plush surroundings of the Corinthia" with this much-awaited, late-2018 opening. This massive and potentially "cavernous" chamber has now been successfully cosied-up from its former incarnation as Massimo (RIP), with a big bar area; "clubby" dark decor; and with "rotisseries and meat-maturing cabinets lining one side of the room". "The food, likewise, is a little more hearty and traditional – with a Kerridge twist – than the expected, hotel-fine-dining experience". "Prices, however, remain very much high end", and diners are slightly divided on the overall outcome. A few critics feel the experience "doesn't match the hype", and is "a mismatch of average pub grub with one of London's most exclusive hotels". For a big majority of diners, though, it "fires on all cylinders", combining an "impressive-but-relaxed room" with "suitably professional but informal service" and "interesting and delicious" cooking of a type in line with TK's celebrity persona: "it was probably the most expensive fish 'n' chips I have ever had, but I can't wait to go back!" Top Tip – well spaced tables help make it good for less formal business occasions. / SW1A 2BD; www.kerridgesbarandgrill.co.uk; @kerridgesbandg.

Kiln W1 £35 **5** **4** **4**
58 Brewer Street   no tel   4–3C
"Stonkingly good SE Asian small-plates" – *"spiced to perfection and tasty beyond words"* – are delivered from the *"more-than-interesting menu"* of Ben Chapman's *"brilliant value"* Thai BBQ (sibling to Shoreditch's Smoking Goat): *"it's the kind of punchy and earthy food that you'd normally only encounter in Thailand in non-touristy places"*. *"Thoughtful"* staff help manage the *"tiny"* space – a *"fun"*, *"very, very busy"* and *"crowded"* Soho environment, *"blending in a bit of hipster attitude"*. It's *"hard to get a seat"*, though, and *"there can be some very long waiting times"*. Top Tip – eating perched at the ground floor counter is a good option: it's *"fascinating watching the chefs doing their stuff"*. / W1F 9TL; www.kilnsoho.com.

Kin and Deum SE1 NEW £44 **5** **2** **3**
2 Crucifix Lane   020 7357 7995   10–4D
"Epic Thai cuisine" from *"an interesting and varied"* menu, *"including the old favourites along with some more-innovative choices"* distinguishes this contemporary, white-walled, new pub-conversion near London Bridge, on the site that was formerly Suchard's Freehouse (RIP) but has been transformed into this newcomer by the owner's children. / SE1 3JW; www.kindeum.com; @kin_deum.

Kipferl N1 £46 **3** **2** **3**
20 Camden Passage   020 77041 555   9–3D
A slice of Vienna in Camden Passage that's *"more than a coffee shop"* (with *"terrific brews and cakes"*) but also *"a lovely casual lunch or dinner spot"* with *"great"* Austrian specialities including *"perfect schnitzel"*. A Ladbroke Grove offshoot closed down in early 2019. / N1 8ED; www.kipferl.co.uk; @KipferlCafe; 9.25 pm; closed Mon.

Kiraku W5 £48 **4** **3** **2**
8 Station Pde   020 8992 2848   1–3A
"Basic café serving Ealing's Japanese enclave" (situated near Ealing Common tube): *"sushi is of high quality, service is warm – even if the surroundings are a little plain – and it's very reasonably priced: a winner!"* / W5 3LD; www.kiraku.co.uk; @kirakulondon; 10 pm; closed Mon; No Amex.

Kitchen W8 W8 £72 **4** **4** **3**
11-13 Abingdon Road   020 7937 0120   6–1A
This under-the-radar venture, in a smart row of businesses off Kensington High Street, has supplied *"unexpectedly delicious"* meals to a well-heeled local crowd for 10 years – although the consistently high marks should be no surprise given that it's part-owned by star chef Phil Howard (of Elystan Street and formerly The Square). Atmosphere-wise, it's somewhere between *"quietly sophisticated"* and *"Spartan"*. / W8 6AH; www.kitchenw8.com; @KitchenW8; Mon-Thu 9.30 pm, Fri-Sat 10pm, Sun 9.30 pm.

Kitty Fisher's W1 £79 **3** **3** **3**
10 Shepherd's Market   020 3302 1661   3–4B
Named after an 18th-century courtesan, this *"cosy"* haunt *"has real character"*, while *"the seediness of Mayfair's Shepherd Market at night makes it romantic"*. *"Food and service are delightful and consistent"*, but even so, these days it struggles to live up to the wave of hype generated at its launch, and – judged comparatively – *"it's not as good as when Tomos Parry (now at Brat in Shoreditch) was head chef"*. / W1J 7QF; www.kittyfishers.com; @kittyfishers; 9.30 pm; closed Sun.

Knife SW4 £58 **4 4 3**

160 Clapham Park Road 020 7627 6505 11–2D

"Stonking steaks are the draw" at this small three-year-old, "on a rather bleak stretch of 'Claxton' (CLApham/BriXTON) highway". "The room is pretty basic" (and "intimate to the point of cramped") but fans like its "warm and slightly rustic" charm as enlivened by "the friendliest staff". "Sunday roasts are top notch" too – "you get complimentary mini Yorkshires and gravy to start; and the veg is superb". / SW4 7DE; kniferestaurant.co.uk; @KnifeLondon; 10 pm, Sun 4 pm; closed Mon, Tue & Sun D.

Koji SW6 £89 **3 3 4**

58 New King's Rd 020 7731 2520 11–1B

"The Japanese food prepared in front of you is amazing, the cocktail bar is amazing…" – Pat & Mark Barnett's "lovely Asian-fusion" haunt has unusually glam looks for somewhere near Parsons Green, and is a big local hit for a date or Big Night Out. (Older fans will remember their previous venture, Mao Tai, which they ran on the same site for over two decades). / SW6 4LS; www.koji.restaurant; @koji_restaurant; D only, Sun open L & D.

Kol WC2 NEW

108-110 Seymour Place 2–1A

Due to open in 2020, a Mexican restaurant from Santiago Lastra, who ran Noma's Mexico pop-up back in 2017, and which looks destined to be one of the more talked-about openings of the new year. / WC2B 5DA; kolrestaurant.com.

KoolCha HA9 NEW £44

Boxpark Wembley, Olympic Way 020 3744 4436 1–1A

Rohit Ghai not only opened Chelsea's Kutir this year, but this February 2019 newcomer occupying three units of the Wembley Boxpark (not the loveliest of locations, in the shadow of Wembley Stadium). As yet it's inspired little survey feedback, but if you're a fan of Indian cooking, its wide selection of dishes are said by some social media aficionados to be worth a try. / HA9 0NU; www.koolcha.co.uk.

Koya £36 **4 4 3**

50 Frith St, W1 020 7434 4463 5–2A
Bloomberg Arcade, Queen Victoria Street, EC2 no tel 10–3C

"The #1 Japanese noodles in London" – especially for those who prefer udon, the fat wheat noodles eaten hot or cold that are a healthier alternative to ubiquitous ramen. The 10-year-old Soho original has been joined by a City bar in the Bloomberg Arcade, although an offshoot at Victoria Market Halls closed after only six months this year. Choose the "very interesting specials and consistently good udon – the rice dishes are nice, but not as memorable". Top Tip – "one of the few Japanese restaurants open for breakfast in the West End". / www.koyabar.co.uk; W1 10.30 pm, Sun 10pm; no bookings.

KPH W10 NEW

139 Ladbroke Grove 7–1A

On Ladbroke Grove, this big landmark pub was taken over by Henry Harris and Harcourt Inns, with chef Ruairidh Summers at the stoves, and re-launched in mid-2019, too late for this year's survey feedback. / W10 6HJ; thekph.co.uk.

Kricket W1 £53 444
12 Denman St 020 7734 5612 4–3C
41-43 Atlantic Road, London, SW9 NEW
2 Television Centre, 101 Wood Lane, London, W12 NEW
"So many layers of taste… a throwback to living in India" – their "fantastic take on subcontinental flavours and textures" has helped blaze a trail for Rik Campbell and Will Bowby's street-food brand. Since mid-2015, their "always interesting and very tasty" bites have taken them from a Pop Brixton shipping container to three permanent outlets in Soho, Brixton and White City's TV Centre. "Busy" Soho in particular is "great for counter dining". Top Menu Tips – "spot-on bhel puri", "fab chai, dazzling deep-fried chicken and delicious halwa". / W1D 7HH; www.kricket.co.uk; @kricketlondon; 10 pm.

Kudu SE15 £54 444
119 Queen's Rd 020 3950 0226 1–4D
"Just wow: bags and bags of flavour in every dish" – this "consistently interesting" Peckham two-year-old from chef Patrick Williams and front of house Amy Corbin (daughter of Chris) is hitting an ever-more impressive stride with its "modern and intelligent" South African-influenced cooking, service that's "gracefully informal and knowledgeable" and an interior that's "charming and relaxed, with subdued lighting". It's "generous, too – bread served with whole frying pans full of flavoured butter, for goodness sake!". "A real treat and worth the (in my case) 350-mile round trip", enthused one satisfied reporter. / SE15 2EZ; www.kudu-restaurant.com; @KuduRestaurant.

Kuku Riku NW1 NEW £39
Unit 91 - 92 North Yard, Camden Market 020 3818 7499 9–2B
Rotisserie chicken from the Josper grill is the selling proposition at this new outlet in atmospheric Camden Market, which has room for 70 covers and does takeaway too. / NW1 8AH.

Kulu Kulu W1 £35 321
76 Brewer St 020 7734 7316 4–3C
"Always there to satisfy a Japanese food craving": this conveyor-belt sushi-stalwart in Soho rates well for "fast, good-quality plates" – less so for the "uncomfortable stools and loud music". But nobody is complaining with "fresh hand-made tempura and salmon rolls for £4 – a steal!". It lost its spin-offs this year, though, in Covent Garden and South Kensington. / W1F 9TX; 10 pm; closed Sun; No Amex; no booking.

Kutir SW3 £62 544
10 Lincoln Street 0207 581 1144 6–2D
Rohit Ghai has done it again at his late-2018 newcomer: the latest occupant of the "cosy" and "romantic" (if "on-the-quiet-side") Chelsea townhouse, which for many years was another premier Indian (Rasoi Vineet Bhatia, RIP). Practically all reports are a hymn of praise to his "faultless cooking", which has immediately propelled it into London's very top tier for nouvelle Indian cuisine. / SW3 2TS; kutir.co.uk; @kutirchelsea; No Amex; No shorts; Credit card deposit required to book.

Kym's by Andrew Wong EC4 £52 433
Bloomberg Arcade Queen Victoria Street 020 7220 7088 10–3C
"Very good… but not as good as A Wong" is a common view on Andrew Wong's late-2018 opening in Bloomberg's HQ, which provides "a very different experience and menu from the Pimlico original". Foodwise the emphasis is not on dim sum, but on plates of Cantonese roast meats, and, though "refined" with "lovely clean tastes", results seem "quite pricey". And the interior, though slick, is a trifle "dull" to some tastes. Still, it's "another 'tick' for the City's rise as a dining destination", and the overall verdict is that it's "still well worth a visit". Top Tip – good value 'Sunday roast'. / EC4N 8AR; www.kymsrestaurant.com; @kymsrestaurant.

Kyseri W1 £64 442
64 Grafton Way   2–1B

"Turkish Jim, but not as we know it…" – Selim Kiazim and Laura Christie (who founded Oklava) have another hit on their hands with this *"small and not enormously fancy"* yearling, near Warren Street, whose *"contemporary menu offers a chance to try 'modern' Turkish, Greek and Levantine dishes"*, alongside *"interesting Turkish, Greek, Georgian, etc… wines"*. There are some quibbles over *"prices that pull the ratings down"*, but most reports are of *"stunning food, that's not bad value"*, and of *"very obliging service"* too. Top Menu Tip – *"sublime speciality pasta"*. / W1T 5DN; www.kyseri.co.uk; @Kyseri_ldn.

La Lluna N10 £56 332
462 Muswell Hill Broadway   020 8442 2662   1–1B

Modern Spanish tapas bar that's one of Muswell Hill's brighter culinary sparks, delivering *"enjoyable food, served quickly and efficiently"*. *"Tables are really packed in, intensifying the noise"*, but it's calmer when they open the frontage and terrace in summer. / N10 1BS; ww.lalluna.co.uk; @lallunalondon; 9 pm.

The Ladbroke Arms W11 £61 333
54 Ladbroke Road   020 7727 6648   7–2B

At the posher end of Ladbroke Grove, this smarter-than-usual local is a *"comfortable"* and *"friendly"* spot drawing a crowd of regulars – Jeremy Clarkson among them – as well as tourists. It's *"always a great place to go for Sunday lunch, or indeed any other time"*, to sample the *"small menu of modern British dishes"* – even if some find it hard to accept the *"high prices for what is gastropub food"*. / W11 3NW; www.ladbrokearms.com; @ladbrokearms; 10 pm, Sat 10.30 pm, Sun 9 pm; no booking after 8 pm.

Lady Mildmay N1 £45 333
92 Mildmay Park   020 7241 6238   1–1C

This Victorian-era local on Newington Green relaunched three years ago as a gastropub and has *"maintained its standards"* despite rising popularity – *"long may it stay that way"*. The blackboard menu *"tries hard to cater for all tastes"*… and by all accounts largely succeeds. Craft beers and *"reasonably priced"* wines also go down well. / N1 4PR; www.ladymildmay.com; @theladymildmaypub; 10 pm, Sun 9 pm; May need 6+ to book.

Lagom at Hackney Church Brew Co. E8 NEW £54 433
16 & 17 Bohemia Place   020 8985 3496   14–1B

"Fantastic-quality smoked meat" from Elliot Cunningham's small, to-the-point menu (promising 'a British-Swedish live-fire fusion') is served *"in a beer-hall-style location"* at this heart-of-Hackney brew pub (fka St John at Hackney), which is rated on limited early feedback (all of it very upbeat). It's set in a railway arch (of course it is!), and with a garden for sunny days. / E8; hackneychurchbrew.co.

Lahore Kebab House E1 £34 522
2-10 Umberston St   020 7481 9737   12–1A

"OMG!! Do not judge a book by its cover!" *"The grand-daddy of cheap 'n' cheerful Pakistani kebab joints"* in Whitechapel has been *"an East End staple"* since it opened in 1972. A *"huge, echoey, tiled room, with big screens showing cricket"*, it's *"such amazing value"* and *"so damn consistent, it just keeps getting bigger, busier and better"*. Top Tip – *"step in at the off-licence next door for your booze"*. Top Menu Tips – *"the chops are special"*, and it serves *"the best chicken tikka ever"*. / E1 1PY; www.lahore-kebabhouse.com; @lahorekebabhous; midnight.

Lahpet E1 £51 3 2 3
58 Bethnal Green Road   020 3883 5629   13–1C
"Top Burmese cuisine, with nice modernising touches" has won a fanclub for
this small but growing brand, which as well as operating a 'street food
kitchen' at nearby Spitalfields Market has this year-old, permanent, white-
walled, communal-table canteen. Top Menu Tip – salads, in particular the
tea leaf one. / E1 6JW; www.lahpet.co.uk; @Lahpet.

Laksamania W1 NEW £51 3 2 2
92 Newman Street   020 7637 9888   3–1D
"The best Straits cooking I've found, outside of SE Asia… indeed, having
recently returned from two weeks in Singapore/Malaysia, it actually beats
a lot of the hawker food I had over there!". This new operation just off
Oxford Street "mostly serves laksa" (spicy noodle soup) with "up to ten
different regional variations of the recipe, each one delicious". "Some dishes
are merely good, but the highs really hit the top notes!". "Downstairs
is larger", but more "loud, noisy, and canteeny" than the space above.
/ W1T 3EZ; www.laksamania.co.uk.

Lamberts SW12 £50 4 5 4
2 Station Parade   020 8675 2233   11–2C
"So lucky to have this on my doorstep!" – Joe Lambert's "firm favourite"
near Balham tube has long been the area's top neighbourhood choice
thanks to its "first-rate", "seasonal" cooking; "friendly and informed service";
and an agreeable ambience that's smart enough for a date or special
occasion, but relaxed enough for an evening when you can't be bothered
to cook. Its ratings slipped a tad this year though: not due to any grievous
complaints, but a few more meals were judged "fine-but-nothing-
exceptional". Top Tip – excellent-value early-week menu. / SW12 9AZ;
www.lambertsrestaurant.com; @lamberts_balham; 10 pm, Sun 5 pm; closed
Mon & Sun D; No Amex.

**The Landmark,
Winter Garden NW1** £84 2 3 5
222 Marylebone Rd   020 7631 8000   9–4A
"Among palm trees and exotic flowers", the main event in this spectacular
atrium featuring an eight-storey-high glass roof is the "wonderful afternoon
tea, with homemade cakes and scones"; also popular, though, is the
"excellent Sunday buffet brunch, beautifully cooked and presented,
with unlimited champagne". / NW1 6JQ; www.landmarklondon.co.uk;
@landmarklondon; 10.15 pm; No trainers; booking max 12 may apply.

Langan's Brasserie W1 £72 2 2 4
Stratton Street   020 7491 8822   3–3C
"Determinedly old-school" – this "lively", former A-list brasserie near The
Ritz was opened by the legendary Peter Langan in partnership with Michael
Caine in 1976. To true believers – the firm majority of its clientele –
it's "an institution that always performs" and "great fun for a business meal
in a boisterous setting (even if the bill ends up at more than expected… but
that's life when the wine flows)". Others, though, complain of "classics done
with not quite enough panache or vibrancy", and see it as "an out-of-
towners kind of place harking back to the good old days when Mr L was
about. He isn't and it's a shadow of its former self". / W1J 8LB;
www.langansrestaurants.co.uk; @langanslondon; 11 pm, Fri & Sat 11.30 pm;
closed Sun.

Palm Court,
The Langham W1   £79   **3 3 4**
1c Portland Place   020 7636 1000   2–1B
*They claim they invented afternoon tea, in this "elegant and refined"
chamber, at the heart of the luxurious five-star hotel, opposite Broadcasting
House (so "ideal for BBC expense-accounters"), and which for the big
occasion provides a "beautifully presented, deliciously tasty tea, served
by staff who are efficient, attentive and friendly". Top Tip – also a handy
spot for a stylish pre-theatre bite. / W1B 1JA; www.palm-court.co.uk;
@Langham_London; No trainers.*

Lantana Cafe   £45   **3 3 3**
13-14 Charlotte Pl, W1   020 7323 6601   2–1C
Ground Floor West, 44-46 Southwark St, SE1   020 7403 2633
10–4B
Unit 2, 1 Oliver's Yd, 55 City Rd, EC1   020 7253 5273   13–1A
*With their "chilled ambience and laid-back vibe" this trio of cafés have
championed Aussie-style day-time eating for more than a decade in London.
"Good for breakfast, brunch and lunch", they are "not too overpriced
compared with competitors", and the Shoreditch and London Bridge venues
are open in the evening for drinks and dinner. / lantanacafe.co.uk;
@lantanacafe; EC1 9.30 pm, Sat & Sun 3 pm; W1 3.30 pm, Sat & Sun 5 pm;
W1 no booking Sat & Sun; NW1 closed Sun; W1 no booking Sat & Sun.*

Lao Cafe WC2   £39   **3 2 2**
60 Chandos Place   020 3740 4748   5–4C
*"A funky little joint", off Trafalgar Square and "very convenient for the
Coliseum", which was opened a couple of years ago by one of the founders
of Rosa's Thai; and which specialises in the cuisine of neighbouring Laos.
"Lots of dishes seem novel, it's certainly not like your average Thai, and the
menu includes a selection of bugs! (actually quite tasty!!)". The odd Asian
food connoisseur feels it falls short ("having travelled in Laos, I found
it expensive and rather disappointing") but on most accounts it's "excellent"
for a "cheap 'n' cheerful" bite. / WC2N 4HG; laocafe.co.uk; May need
8+ to book.*

Lardo E8   £55   **3 2 2**
197-201 Richmond Rd   020 8533 8229   14–1B
*This "buzzy", well-known Italian (in the Arthaus building near London Fields)
continues to inspire relatively limited feedback. Pizza is the most popular
option foodwise, and reports say it "ticks all the boxes" for a good time. Its
sibling Lardo Bebe is no more. / E8 3NJ; www.lardo.co.uk; @lardolondon;
10.30 pm, Sun 9.30 pm.*

The Laughing Heart E2   £56   **2 3 3**
277 Hackney Road   020 7686 9535   14–2A
*"Quirky but delightful" Hackney wine bar and merchant, whose funky small-
plates menu is, to its fans, "perfect in every way". "The owner (Charlie
Mellor, ex-Brawn and Elliot's) is a king of the London wine scene, and his
list drifts into natural territory without ever going down the stinky route".
/ E2 8NA; thelaughingheartlondon.com.*

Launceston Place W8   £84   **4 4 4**
1a Launceston Pl   020 7937 6912   6–1B
*"In a quiet residential corner of Kensington", on a picture-book street –
this "lovely and calm" pre-Victorian townhouse (established as a restaurant
in 1985, and owned by D&D Restaurants since 2007) creates a sense
of "privacy" that's particularly "great for a romantic evening". "Over the
years there have been many changes of chef", but since Ben Murphy joined
in early 2017, the food rating here has been "on an upward trajectory" and
his "exciting" cuisine – "fun, whimsical, delicious" – won impressively
consistent praise this year. "Surely a Michelin star is now beckoning for this
young chef"? / W8 5RL; www.launcestonplace-restaurant.co.uk; @LauncestonPlace;
10 pm, Sun 9.30 pm; closed Mon & Tue L.*

Laurent at Cafe Royal W1 £75
Hotel Café Royal, 68 Regent Street   020 7406 3310   4–4C
"Set upstairs in the Café Royal" on its mezzanine level, this glitzy dining space is branded for French chef Laurent Tourondel. After its opening in mid-2018, both Giles Coren of The Times and Jay Rayner of The Guardian lined up to tear the place to shreds ("howling", "shameful pricing",…). Survey feedback regarding its steak and sushi formula is a little thin on which to rate a place of this calibre, but such reports as we have are, by contrast, upbeat: despite the odd warning of "not-so-experienced service" or a "pricey wine list", they suggest it's "very enjoyable". / W1B 4DY; www.hotelcaferoyal.com/laurent-at-cafe-royal; @HotelCafeRoyal.

The Ledbury W11 £150 5 5 4
127 Ledbury Rd   020 7792 9090   7–1B
"Brett Graham never ceases to amaze" at his "simply sensational" Notting Hill fixture, celebrating its 15th year in 2020, and still idolised by its massive fanclub, who feel it stands "head and shoulders above just about any other restaurant in the capital". "Superbly crafted, beautifully balanced modern British dishes are full of wonderful contrasts of tastes and textures, using the freshest seasonal ingredients" (notably, "world-beating game"). But there's a "much more relaxed atmosphere than at most top-end 'Michelin' establishments", with many-a compliment paid to its "easygoing, accommodating and un-fussy" staff; with kudos to sommelier Seamus Williams-Sharkey for his "light touch" and "clever advice introducing you to interesting corners of the world". Decor is sophisticated if low-key, and "while always busy, it's easy to have a conversation". / W11 2AQ; www.theledbury.com; @theledbury; 9.45 pm; closed Mon L & Tue L.

Legare SE1 NEW
Cardamom Building, 31g Shad Thames   12–2A
Jay Patel, previously Barrafina's general manager, and Matt Beardmore, formerly senior sous chef at Trullo, are joining forces to open this 35-cover Italian in Tower Bridge in autumn 2019. / SE1 2YB; legarelondon.com.

Lemonia NW1 £52 1 4 4
89 Regent's Park Rd   020 7586 7454   9–3B
"The miracle is that it doesn't change", say fans of this veteran Primrose Hill taverna: a "big, bustling, cheerful, noisy, Greek family-style restaurant that's been around forever", with particularly "warm" staff of decades' standing, who "don't just tolerate children, they positively welcome them." Never exactly a foodie hotspot, "it's time to revamp the menu…", according to one fan, who then goes on to admit "…but I've been saying that since 1978!" In truth, though, the experience here is finally starting to show its age: there have always been one or two sceptics who "wonder why everyone makes such a fuss about the place", but their number grows more numerous with each passing year. / NW1 8UY; www.lemonia.co.uk; @Lemonia_Greek; 11 pm; closed Sun D; No Amex.

Leroy EC2 £53 3 4 3
18 Phipp Street   0207 739 4443   13–1B
"Perfectly executed classics with a gentle twist" and other small plates with "delicious and inventive combinations" have won foodie renown for this approachable (if "rather cramped") two-year-old: a re-working (and not just of the name) of the same team's original Hackney outfit, Ellory (RIP), occupying a quirky triangular site. Our reporters are a little more circumspect, and unimpressed that the venue sometimes seems to attract "the Michelin-star-chasing crowd… not what you'd want in a neighbourhood Shoreditch restaurant". / EC2A 4NP; www.leroyshoreditch.com; @leroyshoreditch; Credit card deposit required to book.

Levan SE15 £56 | 5 | 5 | 4 |

3-4 Blenheim Grove 020 7732 2256 1–4D

"Fantastic food + great wine list + super-friendly people + brilliant music = cool vibes!" – this new restaurant and wine bar near Peckham Rye station (baby bro' to Salon in Brixton) has cracked the formula for winning fans from SE15 and beyond: a *"casual-yet-special"* operation, it can become *"extremely busy"* and *"crowded"*. Its *"incredible"* small plates are a foil to the *"very good wine list"* and arguably a form of *"wildly indulgent nursery food"*, but are so *"creative and fun"* and with *"flavours that sing!"* / SE15 4QL; levanlondon.co.uk.

The Lido Café, Brockwell Lido SE24 £29 | 3 | 3 | 4 |

Dulwich Rd 020 7737 8183 11–2D

"It's nice to drink coffee in winter watching hardier souls swimming by", as you enjoy an appetising bite at Brixton's marvellously preserved old lido, most often recommended for its blinding brunch. / SE24 0PA; www.thelidocafe.co.uk; @thelidocafe; 4 pm; closed Sun D; No Amex; booking max 8 may apply.

The Light House SW19 £49 | 3 | 3 | 3 |

75-77 Ridgway 020 8944 6338 11–2B

"One of the few, very good restaurants in Wimbledon" – although this *"buzzy"*, 20-year veteran indie has always suffered from being *"very patchy"*, with a *"kitchen that repeatedly underperforms"*. When it's on song though – which is to say pretty often – *"it serves a quality of dishes you would expect in a much more expensive restaurant"*, all *"efficiently and charmingly served"*. / SW19 4ST; www.lighthousewimbledon.com; 10.30 pm; closed Sun D.

The Lighterman N1 £61 | 3 | 2 | 4 |

3 Granary Square 020 3846 3400 9–3C

An *"ideal location overlooking the canal and the King's Square fountains"* means this King's Cross gastroboozer *"books up fast – I'd go again if I could get a table"*. Despite the old-time name, it's a starkly contemporary grey-brick-and-glass building over several floors with a big terrace, which can get *"noisy when it's rammed"*. But reporters say it's *"fun"* and the mod Brit gastro fare earns very solid ratings. / N1C 4BH; www.thelighterman.co.uk; @TheLightermanKX; Mon to Thu: 10.30pm, Fri & Sat: 11pm; Sun: 9.30pm.

Lima Fitzrovia £78 | 3 | 3 | 2 |

31 Rathbone Pl, W1 020 3002 2640 2–1C
14 Garrick St, WC2 020 7240 5778 5–3C

"Fresh, vibrant food" – full of *"interesting, sharp flavours"* – makes this *"relaxed"* Fitzrovia joint and its Covent Garden offspring (*"Floral by Lima"*) *"great places to try out Peruvian cuisine"*. There's a *"diverse range of dishes"*, from *"excellent ceviches to hot main courses"*, although *"portion sizes don't really match the cost"*. / www.limalondongroup.com/fitzrovia; @lima_london; 10.30 pm, Sun 9.30 pm; Mon L closed.

Lina Stores £39 | 4 | 4 | 4 |

51 Greek Street, W1 020 3929 0068 5–2A
20 Stable Street, N1 awaiting tel 9–3C NEW

"A tiny restaurant with a big heart... and wonderful pasta" – the *"transition from great Italian deli to restaurant is a big success"* at this landmark, 75-year-old Soho store, which morphed last year from pure retail to providing an *"excellent, counter-dining experience at moderate prices"* nearby. *"If you love pasta, this is the place to go"* – *"delicately silky, with the most fantastic sauces"* – and it's *"a brilliant stop-off before film, theatre etc"*. It's not going to take 75 years to turn this rip-roaring success into a chain, though: branch no. 2 opens in the second half of 2019 in one of King's Cross's 'heritage buildings' and will be 'an 100-cover outfit decorated in the same pale green-and-white-stripes that diners in Soho have come to know'.

Linden Stores N1 £42 3 3 2
220 Saint Paul's Road 9–2D

Worth remembering near Highbury & Islington tube – a small, white-tiled and brick-lined wine shop and neighbourhood bistro with an "interesting wine selection and nibbles", written up on the blackboard. It's run by Laura Christie (one half of Oklava) and Chris Boustead (erstwhile chef at the Opera Tavern). / N1 2LL; Www.lindenstores.co.uk; @lindenstores; Online only.

Lino EC1 NEW £57 3 4 2
90 Bartholomew Close 020 8016 5199 10–2B

This spring-2019 arrival occupies a "post-industrial space" – part of a converted linoleum factory near Barts – where the focus is on the trendy, modern British food emanating from the open kitchen, prepared by ex-Dairy head chef, Richard Falk. It is "a great newcomer in a barren area", but some mixed reports suggest it still has a way to go before it fully realises its potential (the "food is good without being outstanding…", and the "cavernous space can make conversation difficult…"). / EC1A 7BN; www.linolondon.co.uk.

Lisboa Pâtisserie W10 £10 3 2 3
57 Golborne Rd 020 8968 5242 7–1A

"A little corner of authenticity in an ever-more-gentrified bit of London", this Portuguese café in North Kensington's Golborne Road has been famous for its pastéis de nata for more than 20 years – and, despite increased competition, fans swear they're "still the best custard tarts in town". / W10 5NR; none; 7 pm; L & early evening only; no booking.

Little Bird £60 3 3 4
1 Station Parade, W4 020 3145 0894 1–3A
1 Battersea Rise, SW11 020 7324 7714 11–2C

A "fab menu" of Asian-Med fusion dishes, 'botanical' cocktails and funky interior design add up to a "great little local restaurant" concept from Lorraine Angliss, building her Annie's and Rock & Rose west London group; Little Bird has perched in Chiswick and Battersea. / www.littlebirdrestaurants.com; @LittleBirdW4.

Little Duck The Picklery E8 4 4 3
68 Dalston Lane 020 7249 9177 14–1B

A short stroll from Hackney Downs station, this year-old sibling to Ducksoup operates as a 'fermenting kitchen and eatery' (and you can buy the results by the gram or bottled as part of their The Picklery range). It also operates as a kitchen from breakfast on, serving a short menu, which varies throughout the day (you might have squid risotto, or steak in the evening); and it's later in the day that its "great list of natural wines" comes to the fore. "It feels very relaxed, serves lots of pickled stuff and the food's all good: it's a bit like going around to a friend's house, who's a very good cook and has a lot of very nice wine". / E8 3AH; www.littleduckpicklery.co.uk.

Little Kolkata WC2 £51 4 3 2
51-53 Shelton Street 07712 124868 5–2C

"Easily missed" – "tucked away" in "an unfashionable part of Covent Garden" near Seven Dials – Prabir Kumar Chattopadhyay and Biswajit Deb Das's year-old "little gem" graduated "from a pop-up to provide homecooking in an unpretentious canteen-style outlet". "It showcases a range of interesting regional Indian dishes" including "specialities from Calcutta and Bengal" and fans say it's "a must-visit". Top Tip – "The lunchtime bento box is good value and offers a good choice." / WC2H 9JQ; www.littlekolkata.co.uk; @littlekolkatauk.

Little Taperia SW17 £44 3 3 3

143 Tooting High St   020 8682 3303   11–2C

"Tasty tapas", served in a "slightly odd-shaped room" with a "cheery atmosphere", have created "a Tooting legend in just a few years" at this "excellent" venue dominated by a marble bar. / SW17; www.thelittletaperia.co.uk; @littletaperia; 10 pm, Fri & Sat 11 pm, Sun 9.30 pm; May need 6+ to book.

Llewelyn's SE24 £62 3 2 2

293-295 Railton Rd   020 7733 6676   11–2D

This "all-day neighbourhood restaurant" opened two years ago in an old Victorian dining room opposite Herne Hill station, and quickly established itself as "a top local option" for many reporters; although, because it's "small", it becomes "crowded and noisy" as a result. The "admirably daily-changing menu" has Mediterranean influences and "usually offers interesting dishes" at "good prices" – they would be rated even higher were it not for a few reporters who see them as "decent enough, but nothing special". / SE24 0JP; www.llewelyns-restaurant.co.uk; @llewelynslondon; 9.30 pm; Booking max 8 may apply.

LOBOS Meat & Tapas SE1 £69 4 3 3

14 Borough High St   020 7407 5361   10–4C

"Just incredible! Every mouthful delights the tastebuds" – "punchy, powerful, memorable morsels of real food" – at this meat-centric Borough Market tapas joint, run by "people who seem interested in what they're offering". A "buzzing, little place under a railway arch", it's a "cosy" experience if sometimes a little "rushed and cramped". The Spanish team has a second branch in Soho, likewise praised for "superb tapas, and service with style but not pomp". / SE1 9QG; www.lobostapas.co.uk; @LobosTapas; 11 pm, Sun 10 pm; booking max 8 may apply.

Locanda Locatelli W1 £98 4 4 3

Hyatt Regency, 8 Seymour St   020 7935 9088   2–2A

"A restaurant of the highest calibre, which manages to be elegant and unpretentious at the same time" – Giorgio Locatelli's long-established Italian (which he, and wife Plaxy, opened in 2002) provides "a fantastic experience from start to finish". The hotel environment it sits within can seem "rather sterile", but the division of the moodily-lit dining room "breaks up what could be a large soulless space", and the ambience still feels "buzzing after all these years"; boosted by its "impeccable" and "good-humoured" service. A few diners discern "a lack of wow factor" in the cuisine, but more common is a hymn of praise to "simple ingredients combined and cooked to perfection every time". / W1H 7JZ; www.locandalocatelli.com; 11 pm, Thu-Sat 11.30 pm, Sun 10.15 pm; booking max 8 may apply.

Locket's SW1 NEW

23-27 St James's St   3–4C

The owners of Wilton's and their freshly refurbished Franco's are staying busy by launching a third establishment (bringing their average opening rate up to almost one restaurant a century!) in the now re-named, wackily 1960s former Economist Plaza in St James's; it's to be a casual, all-day cafe and evening wine bar, opening October 2019. / SW1A 1HA; @wiltons1742.

Lockhouse W2 £52 3 3 3

3 Merchant Square   020 7706 4253   7–1D

Canalside in Paddington Basin, and with massive windows providing water views, this large bar/restaurant – occupying the high-ceilinged ground floor of one of the area's blocks – has an attractive, if not super-individual, semi-industrial design. Feedback is limited on its gastropub-ish dishes, but suggests it does what it does well. / W2 1AZ; www.lockhouselondon.co.uk; @Lockhouselondon; 23.30, Sat 5pm.

London Grind SE1 £50 3 4 4

2 London Bridge   020 7378 1928   10–3C

"Good coffee… and the food's OK too" – this Borough Market café remains one of the top caffeine hits in SE1. *"It's great for breakfast"* too. / SE1 9RA; www.londongrind.com; @LondonGrind; 11 pm, Sun 7 pm.

London House SW11 £61 2 2 2

7-9 Battersea Sq   020 7592 8545   11–1C

If this Battersea venue were not owned by Gordon Ramsay, we would probably not trouble to write an entry. Not that this 'neighbourhood bar, garden, and restaurant' is too bad to burn: it just inspires little feedback, all of it humdrum: e.g. *"good everyday food, chips are special, lounge is very relaxing for a drink"*. / SW11 3RA; www.gordonramsayrestaurants.com/london-house; @londonhouse; 11 pm, Sun 9 pm.

London Shell Co. W2 £77 3 3 5

Sheldon Square   07818 666005   7–1C

"A really lovely romantic trip down the canal" on a traditional barge is crowned by four courses of *"delicious fish"*, plus pud – *"great fun!"*. In July 2019 a second floating venue, the Grand Duchess, was added, although it stays permanently at the company mooring by Paddington Station. / W2 6EP; www.londonshellco.com; @LondonShellCo; dinner cruises depart at 7.30 pm; closed Mon, Sun & Sat L.

The Long Bar, The Sanderson W1 £49 2 4 4

50 Berners St   020 7300 1400   3–1D

A *"superb and quirky afternoon tea"* is to be had in the atrium of this boutique hotel north of Oxford Street, with is themed around Alice in Wonderland's Mad Hatter (the 'drink me' potion here, is an invitation to indulge in Champagne!): *"good value for a huge amount of attention to detail – love it!"* / W1T 3NG; www.morganshotelgroup.com/originals/originals-sanderson-london/eat-drink/long-bar.

The Lore of the Land W1 NEW £56 3 3 4

4 Conway Street   020 3927 4480   2–1B

"Distressed in all the right places" – Guy Ritchie and David Beckham have channeled their inner Marie Antoinette at this spring 2019 newcomer – a Fitzrovia boozer transformed into their conception of a perfect country pub, and serving beers from Gritchie (Guy's brewery). *"The food here is so much better than it needs to be, with a short, ideal menu"* of incongruously-polished small plates; and *"with the Sunday menu augmented by a roast"*. *"Attentive staff and a room full of happy punters"* complete the idyll. / W1T 6BB; gritchiepubs.com.

Lorne SW1 £62 5 5 3

76 Wilton Road   020 3327 0210   2–4B

"Lorne has gone from strength to strength since its recovery from its awful flash flood", which closed it for a significant portion of 2018 – *"it's a measure of the warm feelings it generates that just about all staff came back when the restaurant reopened, as did all the regulars who had become loyalists in a relatively short period of time"*. Owned and run by Katie Exton and Peter Hall, it's a *"tranquil space"* with *"no fuss and no pretentiousness"*, but *"unexpectedly good, seasonal food for a street a stone's throw from Victoria, and lined with medium-priced, fast-food restaurants"*. A good chunk of its appeal lies in its *"vast and interesting wine list"* on which *"Katie provides guidance"*. / SW1V 1DE; www.lornerestaurant.co.uk; 9.30 pm; closed Sun.

Louie Louie SE17 £51 3 2 3

347 Walworth Rd   020 7450 3223   1–3C

Bright, white-walled café on a Walworth corner that makes a feature of playing vintage vinyl, and is hailed as a *"fab neighbourhood spot"*, particularly for brunch. Also, *"look out for top-class cooking at pop-up events in the evening"*. / SE17 2AL; louielouie.london; @LouieLouie_Ldn.

Loyal Tavern SE1 NEW
171-173 Bermondsey Street   020 7260 2560   10–4D

Tom Cenci, former executive chef at Duck & Waffle, and Adam White from the Riding House Cafe, opened Loyal Tavern in Bermondsey in late summer 2019. It's on the site of former south east London institution Village East, once a textile factory, making use of British produce to create a 'relaxed neighbourhood environment'. / SE1 3UW; www.loyaltavern.co.uk.

Luca EC1   £88   3 3 4
88 St John St   020 3859 3000   10–1A

"Upscale" two-year-old in Clerkenwell that's an "unassuming-yet-special-feeling" cousin to the famous Clove Club, and whose quirky layout – "lots of different 'zones' in the restaurant, with a cosy bar at the front" and "funky" conservatory to the rear – creates a "delightful" setting for a meal. Its distinguishing culinary feature is the use of British ingredients to produce Italian cooking, alongside an "extremely pleasant Italian-biased wine list", and fans say results are "incredible". "The one gripe: as good as this is, it's pricier than you'd expect". Top Menu Tip – "love the Parmesan fries". / EC1M 4EH; luca.restaurant; @LucaRestaurant.

Luce e Limoni WC1   £63   4 4 3
91-93 Gray's Inn Rd   020 7242 3382   10–1A

"Glory be! A real neighbourhood spot in, of all places, Gray's Inn Road, with proper cooking by proud Sicilians". "It's my favourite family restaurant" – "Fabrizio (Zafarana) is a great host and the food is superb" and "cooked with love". Top Tip – "try the sea urchin ravioli when they have it". / WC1X 8TX; www.luceelimoni.com; @Luce_e_Limoni; 10 pm, Fri & Sat 11 pm.

Luciano's SE12   £54   4 3 2
131 Burnt Ash Rd   020 8852 3186   1–4D

This "great neighbourhood restaurant" in Lee is run by an Anglo-Neapolitan family. Pasta is made on the premises every day, and it has an all-day bar next door. Owner Enzo named it after his father, Luciano Masiello, who played football for Charlton Athletic before going into the catering trade. / SE12; ristorante.lucianoslondon.co.uk; @LucianosLondon; 10.30 pm, Sun 10 pm.

Lucio SW3   £77   3 3 2
257 Fulham Rd   020 7823 3007   6–3B

"It's easy to go too often" to this "friendly" Fulham Road Italian, that has built a strong local following over 15 years. "The menu changes regularly with the seasons" and "portions are generous", but what is "spectacular value" at lunchtime becomes "expensive in the evening for almost the same menu". / SW3 6HY; www.luciorestaurant.com; 10.45 pm.

Lucknow 49 W1 NEW   £57   4 4 3
49 Maddox Street   020 7491 9191   3–2C

Dhruv Mittal (of Dum Biryani House) is behind this Mayfair newcomer, which specialises in Awadhi dishes: the cuisine of Mughal-infuenced Lucknow. Echoing the upbeat reviews it's enjoyed in the press, early-days feedback says it's a winner: "a lovely place, with attentive service, and delicious food". / W1S 2PQ; lucknowldn.com; @Lucknow_Social.

Lucky Cat W1 NEW   £78
10-13 Grosvenor Square   020 7107 0000   3–2A

Gordon Ramsay replaced his ailing, former heavy-hitter 'maze' with this Pan-Asian Mayfair newcomer in the summer of 2019 – his first opening in the capital in the last five years (and most notable for provoking a Twitter-storm of abuse about cultural appropriation seeing as the chap he recruited to head the kitchen is the thoroughly un-Asian, ex-Sexy Fish executive chef, Ben Orpwood). The restaurant, which cost over £5 million to refurbish, aims to emulate 'the drinking dens of Thirties Tokyo and the Far East' (not the first time we've heard that one) but opened too late for survey feedback. / W1K 6JP; www.gordonramsayrestaurants.com/lucky-cat; @LuckyCatGR.

Lupins SE1 £50 4 3 2
66 Union St   020 3908 5888   10–4B
This "wonderful" two-year-old is the brainchild of chefs Lucy Pedder and Natasha Cooke, whose "affordable" modern British small plates are "cooked to a very high standard" – so "full marks to these brave young women". "Handy for Tate Modern" in the Flat Iron complex, Lupins is "small", so remember to book. / SE1 1TD; www.lupinslondon.com; 10.30 pm; closed Mon D & Sun D.

Lupita £44 3 2 2
7 Kensington High Street, W8   020 3696 2930   6–1A
60-62 Commercial Street, Spitalfields, E1   020 3141 6000   13–2C
This "fun Mexican" pair in Kensington and the City fringe serve "super-fresh, close to authentic" food and are "good value". The branch near Embankment station has closed down.

Lure NW5 £44 3 4 3
56 Chetwynd Rd   020 7267 0163   9–1B
"The nicest posh chippy around" – this Dartmouth Park destination draws fans from across north London with its "fancy fish 'n' chips" and "small selection of well-cooked seafood". "It seems to be under new management, so we have to hope it keeps up standards". / NW5 1DJ; www.lurefishkitchen.co.uk; @Lurefishkitchen; 10 pm, Sun 9.30 pm; booking weekends only.

Lurra W1 £66 3 3 4
9 Seymour Place   020 7724 4545   2–2A
"Excellent Basque cooking" and an "interesting wine list" attract high praise for this grill in Seymour Village, near Marble Arch, although the "limited menu" means "the experience is mainly for meat-lovers" – especially the "fantastic Galician steak", much of it using charcoal-grilled cuts from grass-fed cattle reared in Northern Spain. "The lovely almost secret outdoor terrace is a calm oasis in this part of town". Its stablemate, Donostia (see also), is nearby. / W1H 5BA; www.lurra.co.uk; @LurraW1; 10.30 pm, Sun 3.30 pm; closed Mon L & Sun D.

Lutyens Grill, The Ned EC2 £92 3 3 3
27 Poultry   020 3828 2000   10–2C
"A great setting for high-powered, top-quality steak" – "the old bank manager's office" of the former Midland Bank HQ, bang in the middle of the City, has been transformed seamlessly by Soho House into a wood-panelled grill, with such old-world touches as beef Wellington from the trolley at lunch. Initially reserved for the club's members but now open to all-comers, it retains its clubby atmosphere and is (perhaps reassuringly) "very expensive, but worth going, even if just to marvel at the building". A "fun brunch" is a secondary attraction. / EC2R 8AJ; www.thened.com/restaurants/lutyens-grill#; @TheNedLondon.

Lyle's E1 £92 4 3 2
The Tea Building, 56 Shoreditch High Street   020 3011 5911   13–1B
"Notwithstanding the hipster canteen vibe, this is the real thing!". James Lowe's "brilliantly executed", seasonal British small plates – "fresh and light, yet sturdy and filling when required" (and often "using a wood-fired oven to give that extra tang of flavour") – are complemented by "delicious bread" and "a proper list of natural wines", and have rightly won renown for his venerated foodie champion: a light-filled space at the foot of Shoreditch's iconic Tea Building. Its ratings are not quite as beyond-stellar as when the venue first opened, however, and it's no criticism to say that its No. 2 ranking in the UK according to the World's 50 Best has less to do with its "sublime" cooking, and more to do with the in-crowd criteria of the fooderati who vote for it. Top Tip – "the Lyle's Guest Chef Series programme is great". / E1 6JJ; www.lyleslondon.com; @lyleslondon; 10 pm; closed Sat L & Sun.

M Restaurants £79 222

Zig Zag Building, Victoria St, SW1   020 3327 7776   2–4B
Brewery Wharf, Brewery Lane, TW1   020 3327 7776   1–4A
60 Threadneedle Street, EC2   020 3327 7770   10–2C

Martin Williams's glossily-glam steakhouses have a touch of Vegas-glitz to their ritzy design, and particularly win nominations as impressive venues for business, boosted by the range of top-quality meat (the highest grades of USDA, Wagyu and Kobe beef) and an extensive wine selection. Since the top man returned to rescue Gaucho as CEO, however, some reporters feel "it's lost its way since the wonderful early days". / www.mrestaurants.co.uk; @mrestaurants_; midnight; closed Sun.

Ma Goa SW15 £44 343

242-244 Upper Richmond Rd   020 8780 1767   11–2B

This Putney institution "celebrated its 25th anniversary with a great party last summer – they must be getting something right!". Even if "the menu can sometimes be a bit samey", the "authentic Goan/Indian food" is "still exceptional" and the service "so friendly". "I suspect Ma Goa will still be going in 20 years' time". / SW15 6TG; www.magoaputney.co.uk; @magoalondon; 10.30 pm, Fri & Sat 11 pm, Sun 10pm.

Mac & Wild £55 333

65 Great Titchfield St, W1   020 7637 0510   3–1C
9a Devonshire Square, EC2   020 7637 0510   10–2D

"Delicious" Scottish game and shorthorn beef, much of it from owner Andy Waugh's family estate, is showcased at his two venues in Fitzrovia and Liverpool Street. The kitchens "give an interesting modern twist to traditional dishes". / www.macandwild.com; @MacandWild.

Macellaio RC £48 433

6 Store Street, WC1   2–1C
84 Old Brompton Rd, SW7   020 7589 5834   6–2B
Arch 24, 229 Union St, SE1   07467 307682   10–4B
124 Northcote Rd, SW11   020 3848 4800   11–2C
38-40 Exmouth Market, EC1   020 3696 8220   10–1A

"Quality Italian beefsteaks" – most notably from the Piedmontese Fassone breed – are showcased in style at Genovese owner, Roberto Costa's, "unique" steakhouse group, where at each branch you "enter through the butcher's shop" and "you can tell the staff which cut you want". "The well-hung rump steak is absolutely delicious" and "a great selection of Italian wines" helps make it the perfect place to kill off an evening. / www.macellaiorc.com; @macellaiorc; 11 pm.

Machiya SW1 £45 322

5 Panton St   020 7925 0333   5–4A

"Good quality Japanese comfort food" including "proper tonkatsu – rich pork served with cabbage" – is on the menu at this rather "cramped" venue off Leicester Square from the duo behind Kanada-Ya, Aaron Burgess-Smith and Tony Lam. "Also of note is the speakeasy bar in the basement". / SW1Y 4DL; machi-ya.co.uk; @MachiyaLondon; 10.30 pm, Fri & Sat 11 pm, Sun 10 pm.

Madame Pigg E8 NEW £58 344

480 Kingsland Road   07956 925695   14–1A

In oh-so-now Haggerston, this neighbourhood newcomer – from chef Adam Hardiman (ex-St John and The Dartmouth Arms) – opened in November 2018, offering a seasonal, daily-changing menu. It is rated on the limited survey feedback received to date, but all of it is very upbeat, in keeping with newspaper reports and social media buzz about the place. / E8 4AE; www.madamepigg.com.

Made in Italy £46 **4**2**3**
50 James St, W1   020 7224 0182   3–1A
249 King's Rd, SW3   020 7352 1880   6–3C
141 The Broadway, SW19   020 8540 4330   11–2B
"Top pizzas" that "taste as good as they look" are the hallmark of this 30-year Chelsea fixture, now with branches in Wimbledon and Battersea. "I couldn't stop myself from eating every last bit of the dough," reports one happy fan of the pizza, which is served by the metre.
/ www.madeinitalygroup.co.uk; @MADEINITALYgrp; SW3 11.30 pm; W1 11.30 pm, Sun 10.30 pm; SW19 11 pm; SW3 closed Mon .

Maggie Jones's W8 £60 2**3**4
6 Old Court Pl   020 7937 6462   6–1A
"Cosy, fun, old place that has been around for years and years" – a favourite in its time of Princess Margaret, who used to slip away to here from nearby Kensington Palace, and whose alias when booking provides the current restaurant's name. Its rustic, heavily-romantic style isn't dissimilar to its stablemate, La Poule au Pot, and it likewise serves "basic, traditional English dishes" designed to satisfy your hunger at a "decent price" rather than to dazzle your tastebuds. "There's a reasonable wine list too, unless you go for the magnum where they measure with a stick how much of it you've taken from the bottle: amusing to say the least but not their best vintage…" / W8 4PL; www.maggie-jones.co.uk; 11 pm, Sun 10.30 pm.

Maguro W9 £60 **4**32
5 Lanark Pl   020 7289 4353   9–4A
This "spot on" Japanese near Little Venice wins consistent high ratings for its ultra-fresh sushi, sashimi and maki rolls as well as cooked dishes. Do book because it's "small and often overcrowded, but worth it for the food and welcome". / W9 1BT; www.maguro-restaurant.com; 10.30 pm, Sun 10 pm; No Amex.

Maison Bab & Kebab Queen WC2 £120 **543**
4 Mercer Walk   020 7439 9222   5–2C
"Taking the kebab to a whole new level": this sibling to Kingly Court's Le Bab occupies Covent Garden's Mercers Walk development and – in a style reminiscent of Bubbledogs – combines a regular ground floor "cheap 'n' cheerful" diner (serving regular mezze and kebabs – formula price £46), with a much more ambitious basement venue, Kebab Queen (price shown). In the cellar, behind a fake take-away shop-front, is a ten-seater venue where the initial kebab (or rather 'kebabito' as they call it) is merely the first stage of an ambitious £60 six-course tasting experience from chef Manu Canales, served directly onto a heated counter (there's no plates or cutlery). "I was completely cynical about Kebab Queen, but was bowled over by their wickedly tasty and absurdly good-value tasting menu. There's no way on earth they are making money on it?". / WC2; www.eatlebab.com; @eatlebab.

Maison Bertaux W1 £8 **4**4**5**
28 Greek St   020 7437 6007   5–2A
This "eccentric but marvellous treasure" is a Soho landmark and "one of the few remaining original London pâtisseries". "Gateaux to die for" and "wonderful tea and scones" provide a "trip down memory lane" in premises opened by a Parisian exile in 1871 and graced by Karl Marx and Virginia Woolf as well as generations of Soho bohos. / W1D 5DQ; www.maisonbertaux.com; @Maison_Bertaux; 10.15 pm, Sun 8.45 pm.

Malabar W8 £48 3 3 2
27 Uxbridge St 020 7727 8800 7–2B

This "high-quality" Indian has fed happy Notting Hill diners "with some style and on metal platters" for more than 30 years, and – having taken over the premises of an Italian trattoria back in the day – has always had a contemporary look. The odd regular says "is it me, or has this old favourite gotten a bit tired?", but perhaps that's more a comment on how outstanding it once was, as its overall feedback is pretty solid. / W8 7TQ; www.malabar-restaurant.co.uk; 11 pm.

Malabar Junction WC1 £41 3 3 3
107 Gt Russell St 020 7580 5230 2–1C

Keralan specialist in Bloomsbury – an early champion of South Indian cuisine in London – serving "interesting and unusual dishes", and offering "a considerably better choice than the chains". "There's always a smiling welcome and excellent friendly service". / WC1B 3NA; www.malabarjunction.com; 11 pm.

MAM W11 £41 4 4 3
16 All Saints Rd 020 7792 2665 7–1B

"A great addition to the Notting Hill scene", this two-year-old Vietnamese BBQ grill serves a "limited menu which one could eat pretty well every day: fresh, zingy and delicious – what more could you want?". Owner Colin Tu (of the Salvation in Noodles pho joints) serves his mother's recipe for fermented dipping sauce – MAM is pronounced 'mum' in Vietnamese. / W11 1HH; mamlondon.com.

Mamma Dough £43 3 3 3
40 Ladywell Road, SE13 1–4D
179 Queen's Rd, SE15 020 7635 3470 1–4D
76-78 Honor Oak Pk, SE23 020 8699 5196 1–4D
354 Coldharbour Ln, SW9 020 7095 1491 11–2D

"Delicious pizza dough" with top toppings have won a solid following for this "informal" South London group, now reaching as far as Sydenham. Home-made ginger beer and locally brewed craft beer, plus artisan coffee roasted in Shoreditch, complete the deal. / www.mammadough.co.uk; SW9 SE15 and SE26 10.30 pm, SE13, SE23 10pm; phone bookings only.

Mandarin Kitchen W2 £41 4 3 1
14-16 Queensway 020 7727 9012 7–2C

"Better than any lobster noodles in Asia – possibly the best in the world" is the oft-repeated superlative attached to this Queensway temple to "seafood, Chinese style". "Don't go for the ambience", however: "it's noisy and the opposite of stylish" – although it's "a bit smarter than it used to be". / W2 3RX; mandarinkitchen.co.uk; 11.15 pm.

Mangal 1 E8 £29 5 2 2
10 Arcola St 020 7275 8981 14–1A

"Still the best Turkish BBQ in town", say fans of the original Mangal grill that put Dalston on the carnivore's map. "I've been coming here for over 20 years and it's still one of my all-time favourite restaurants. Never fails with great food and excellent service". BYO helps keep the costs down. / E8 2DJ; www.mangal1.com; @Mangalone; midnight, Sat & Sun 1 am; Cash only; No bookings.

Manicomio £76 3 2 3
85 Duke of York Sq, SW3 020 7730 3366 6–2D
6 Gutter Ln, EC2 020 7726 5010 10–2B
It's "always a delight" to visit this sleekly modern Italian duo in Chelsea and the City, which provide an "airy, relaxing escape from the fumes". "Food and service are of a high quality", and "there's been a definite improvement over the last few years". They're "undoubtedly a bit pricey", but "nothing is cheap in these areas". The group has added a third venue, Canto Corvino, in Spitalfields (see also). / www.manicomio.co.uk; SW3 10 pm, Sun 4 pm; EC2 10 pm; EC2 closed Sat & Sun.

Manna NW3 £56 2 2 2
4 Erskine Road 020 7722 8028 9–3B
Now fully vegan, this 1968-vintage Primrose Hill outfit can claim to be Europe's oldest veggie restaurant, and is still co-owned by musician Roger Swallow of the Albion Band, long-time resident in LA. The food has had its ups and downs over the decades and is nowadays mostly (if not uniformly) rated "enjoyable and tasty", even by reporters "neither vegetarian nor vegan". It closed for major refurbishments in summer 2019. / NW3 3AJ; www.mannav.com; @mannacuisine; 10 pm, Sun 7.30 pm; closed Mon.

Manuka Kitchen SW6 £53 3 3 3
510 Fulham Rd 020 7736 7588 6–4A
"Excellent, little rustic-chic local bistro" near Fulham Broadway which is a "lovely spot to eat in at any time but weekend brunch is legendary". The "intriguing menu" has some "delicious, ambitious dishes", and the owner is "delightful and charming". / SW6 5NJ; www.manukakitchen.com; @manukakitchen; 10 pm, Tue-Sat 11 pm, Sun 4 pm; closed Sun D; booking max 8 may apply.

Manzi's (Corbin & King) W1 NEW
1 Bateman's Buildings 5–2A
Due to arrive in mid-2020, an homage to the late, great Manzi's – a once famous fish-icon of the West End – from über-restaurateurs Corbin & King; it's not on the same site (it will be off Soho Square, rather than off Leicester Square as the original was) – but will be a fish-centric offering all the same, and the aim is to be "fun and affordable" like Brasserie Zédel. / W1D 3EN; @corbinandking.

Mao Chow E8 NEW £40
159a Mare Street no tel 14–2B
This mid-2019 newcomer near London Fields is riding just about all of the current food trends: it's a tiny (12 seats), no-booking, vegan, pop-up-turned-permanent BYO in east London – Insta-stardom is next, no doubt. The inventive Chinese-inspired food can also be taken away. / E8 3RH; www.mao-chow.com; No bookings.

Mãos E2 £185 5 5 4
Redchurch Street 02027 88909 13–1C
"Nuno Mendes strikes again, outside the box" at his "informal and wonderful" Shoreditch 16-seater, where a once-daily, three-hour sitting provides a "very intimate" happening, which fans hail as "the top dining experience in town". It is tucked away up a staircase in the 'nurturing' environment of the Blue Mountain School – self-described as 'a progressive vision and a physical place of contemplation' (where one can spend a ton of money on clothes and other artisanal creations). The meal takes place in a bare terracotta chamber at a shared table, and "the opportunity to watch and interact with the chefs makes the experience so much more interesting". "An ever-changing, multi-course tasting menu" is served: "inventive, challenging" and "exciting". It's "a brilliant concept" and one whose scary expense inspires not a single grumble from anyone commenting this year. And – breaking news… – with a recent change of policy, taking pics for your Insta feed is now not only allowed but encouraged. / E2 7DJ; www.maos.dinesuperb.com.

Mar I Terra SE1   £42   2 3 3
14 Gambia St   020 7928 7628   10–4A
This "charming, unpretentious neighbourhood tapas restaurant" in an old
Southwark pub is a "good option near the South Bank and Young Vic
theatre". "The food is reliable if a little old-fashioned" and comes in "proper
portions". The place "can be noisy – the staff, however, are darlings!".
There's "a private room for hire upstairs". / SE1 0XH; www.mariterra.net;
11 pm; closed Sat L & Sun.

Marcella SE8   £45   3 3 3
165a Deptford High Street   020 3903 6561   1–3D
"Smashing it out of the park" – this two-year-old Italian, on Deptford's high
street close to the station, is a prized local in these parts, with first-class
pasta the highlight of a short menu, using British as well as Italian
ingredients. It's the lesser-known sibling to Peckham star, Artusi. / SE8 3NU;
www.marcella.london ; @MarcellaDeptfrd; midnight, Fri & Sat 1 am, Sun 4 pm;
May need 6+ to book.

Marcus,
The Berkeley SW1   £128   3 3 3
Wilton Pl   020 7235 1200   6–1D
"Outstanding in every way", say fans of Marcus Wareing's calm Belgravia
temple of gastronomy: "a big room, where the setting of each table feels
very private", and where the "expertly crafted and seasonal" cuisine (under
chef patrons, Mark and Shauna Froydenlund) is, they feel, "expensive,
but oh-so-worth it". For a large minority, though, its "daft" prices defy
comprehension, and those who remember the era when Marcus himself was
more regularly at the stoves feel that "compared with ten years ago, it's not
a patch on what it was". / SW1X 7RL; www.marcusrestaurant.com;
@marcusbelgravia; 10 pm; closed Sun; No trainers; booking max 6 may apply.

Mare Street Market E8   £55   3 2 5
117 Mare Street   020 3745 2470   14–2B
"A wonderful addition to the area" – a 10,000 square feet market inside
the transformed base of a formerly run-down, Hackney office-block, which
is the brainchild of Marc Francis-Baum (owner of a string of bars and pubs).
With its flowers, vintage design-pieces, artisan coffee, bar, open kitchen and
'dining room' he's channeled hipster design pheromones to maximum
zeitgeisty effect. It's not a majorly foodie hotspot, but "the atmosphere's
buzzing, and the drinks are always flowing. Love it!" / E8 4RU;
www.marestreetmarket.com.

Maremma SW2   NEW   £53
36 Brixton Water Lane   020 3186 4011   11–2D
Brixton locals Alice Staple and Dickie Bielenberg have teamed up with ex-
Bruno Loubet chef Dominique Goltinger to create this little Italian haven.
It opened in early summer 2019, too late for survey feedback, but early
reviews are very upbeat about its honest Tuscan cuisine. / SW2 1PE;
www.maremmarestaurant.com.

Margot WC2   £60   2 4 3
45 Great Queen Street   020 3409 4777   5–2D
"Old-school elegance is mixed with excellent, friendly service" at Paulo
de Tarso & Nicolas Jaouën's "stylish" and "very comfortable" Italian near
the Freemasons' Hall – "one of the better post-Covent Garden options",
and also a useful business venue in WC2 ("an area that isn't too rich
in restaurants of this calibre"). But, while fans still praise its "classic, simple,
well-executed dishes", ratings slid this year amidst some concerns that
it "has suffered from its popularity", producing food that seems
"less enthralling" than it once did: "nice, but nothing special for the price".
/ WC2B 5AA; www.margotrestaurant.com; @MargotLDN.

Market Hall Victoria SW1 NEW £35 4|2|2
Terminus Place 2–4B
Opened in November 2018 on the site that long ago was the nightclub
Pacha, this 400-cover food hall hosts eleven vendors, plus three bars and
a coffee stop. "Variety is the key to its strength" and – as at many similar
venues – "much of the food is better-than-OK but some is not excellent".
A West End branch is opening in late-2019; Fulham was the first, in the
atmospheric former ticketing hall of the tube station. Top Tip – "very family
friendly and you're spoilt for choice". / SW1V 1JR; www.markethalls.co.uk;
@MarketHalls.

The Marksman E2 £62 4|3|3
254 Hackney Road 020 7739 7393 14–2A
"Still just about a pub", this chef-run operation near Columbia Road Market
is "way, way ahead of other gastropubs, and just gets better". It serves
"one of the best and most reliable roasts anywhere" – perfect after a trip
to the flower market on Sunday morning – and "is sublime during the week,
with great cocktails and beer selection". / E2 7SJ;
www.marksmanpublichouse.com; @marksman_pub; 10 pm, Sun 8 pm; closed
weekday L & Sun D.

Maroush £55 3|2|2
I) 21 Edgware Rd, W2 020 7723 0773 7–1D
II) 38 Beauchamp Pl, SW3 020 7581 5434 6–1C
V) 3-4 Vere St, W1 020 7493 5050 3–1B
VI) 68 Edgware Rd, W2 020 7224 9339 7–1D
â˜Gar den') 1 Connaught St, W2 020 7262 0222 7–1D
London's longest-serving Lebanese group has served a "delicious and
generous ensemble of mezze and mains" for almost four decades,
remaining "admirably consistent over the years". There are currently
14 branches under various names (including Ranoush, Beirut Express,
Randa); and at the outlets actually branded as 'Maroush' the "decor is a bit
1980s" especially in the sedate main dining rooms. The better bets are the
"casual" cafés at the original branch and in Beauchamp Place – "for a
quick meal, you can't go wrong", especially from the bargain menu of wraps.
For late-night live music and belly-dancing head to the original Edgware
Road branch. / www.maroush.com; most branches close between 12.30 am-5 am.

Masala Zone £44 3|3|4
"Fresh-tasting food with distinctive flavours" and "unpretentious, tasty thalis"
make this small London group (now in its 20th year) a "go-to chain" for its
fans: "amazing value for such high-quality cuisine". / www.masalazone.com;
@masalazone; 11 pm, Sun 10.30 pm; W1U 9 pm, Sun 4 pm; booking: max 8 online.

Master Wei WC1 NEW £24 4|3|2
13 Cosmo Place 020 7209 6888 2–1D
Down a sidestreet near Russell Square – "a new place opened by the chef
of Arsenal's Xi'an Impression, Wei Guirong, which is slightly more spacious,
but where the menu is almost the same". "It's a simple setting, with the
most amazing Shaanxi food": "great hand-cut noodles" are the headline
option. / WC1N 3AP; masterwei.co.uk.

Masters Super Fish SE1 £28 3|2|1
191 Waterloo Rd 020 7928 6924 10–4A
"The batter's crispy, the chips just right" – plus portions are "generous" –
at this "reliably good" Waterloo chippie, which draws a steady crowd
of locals, passers-by and taxi drivers to be served at its "Formica tables".
/ SE1 8UX; masterssuperfish.com; 10.30 pm; closed Sun; No Amex; no booking, Fri D.

Mathura SW1 NEW
4 Greycoat Place   2–4C
Hot on the heels of Kanishka, Atul Kochhar has announced his next venture to open in autumn 2019, also in collaboration with Tina English. Based in an old fire station building in Victoria, the big (200-cover) operation will, a press release informs us, 'use premium, locally-sourced British produce, while offering unique and unexpected elements which set it apart from his previous restaurants'. / SW1P 1SB; mathura.co.uk.

Matsuba TW9   £45   4 3 2
10 Red Lion St   020 8605 3513   1–4A
"Lovely, tiny Japanese café run by a friendly family" (who are in fact Korean) on the edge of Richmond town-centre's one-way system – "never lets you down" (sushi is the highlight). / TW9 1RW; www.matsuba-restaurant.com; @matsuba; 10.30 pm; closed Sun.

Max's Sandwich Shop N4   £35   5 4 3
19 Crouch Hill   no tel   1–1C
Max Halley's cult Stroud Green café has won renown as an "outstanding, cheap 'n' cheerful" gourmet option, thanks to its wild, wacky and wickedly enjoyable selection of sarnies, each of which amounts to what's effectively a meal between slices of bread (be prepared to get your hands dirty). / N4 4AP; www.maxssandwichshop.com; @lunchluncheon; 11 pm, Fri & Sat midnight, Sun 6 pm; closed Sun D; No Amex; no booking.

maze Grill   £54   2 2 2
10-13 Grosvenor Sq, W1   020 7495 2211   3–2A
11 Park Wk, SW10   020 7255 9299   6–3B
79 Royal Hospital Rd, SW3   020 7352 4448   6–3D
Neighbouring maze has gone, replaced by Lucky Cat, but Gordon Ramsay's hotel grill in Mayfair continues to plough on for the time being. Feedback is negligible compared with its heyday, but its posh grills inspired fewer disappointments this year. It also has a Chelsea spin-off on the site where the f-word chef first made his name, when it was called Aubergine (long RIP), and another on Chelsea's Royal Hospital Road (near the GR mothership): reports similarly are few, with a verdict of tolerable but mixed.

Mazi W8   £65   4 4 3
12-14 Hillgate St   020 7229 3794   7–2B
This "wonderful, buzzy" Greek in Hillgate Village, near Notting Hill Gate, "goes from strength to strength" in its reinterpretation of the traditional taverna as a "modern neighbourhood restaurant". The "fresh, delicious menu is perfect for sharing", but "you need to pick wisely otherwise it's expensive". / W8 7SR; www.mazi.co.uk; @mazinottinghill; 10.30 pm; closed Mon L & Tue L.

MEATLiquor   £38   3 3 3
37-38 Margaret Street, W1   3–1C NEW
6 St Chad's Place, WC1   020 7837 0444   9–3C
17 Queensway, W2   020 7229 0172   7–2C
133b Upper St, N1   020 3711 0104   9–3D
37 Lordship Lane, SE22   020 3066 0008   1–4D
74 Northcote Road, SW11   020 7228 4777   11–2C
"Irreverent pop-art-meets-punk surrounds" are the hallmark of this cult chain, home of the 'Dead Hippie' burger, washed down with 'Grog' ("powerful rum cocktails"), showcased by a new West End flagship just off Oxford Circus. "I thought I might be bored with yet another dirty burger-style place, but these are so good" for "when you need a 'filthy' treat" that's "tasty as hell" (and, moreover, "much better than GBK, Byron and so on"). / meatliquor.com; @MEATLiquor; W1 midnight (Fri & Sat 2 am), N1 11 pm, SE22 midnight, Sun 10.30 pm-11.30 pm; booking: min 6.

MEATmission N1 £34 **3** **3** **4**

14-15 Hoxton Market   020 7739 8212   13–1B

"The messiest, most delicious burgers ever; and a good selection of craft beers as well" – still the deal at this *"hip"* spin-off from the Meatliquor group, which brings the worship of meat to an old Christian missionary building (complete with stained glass windows and illuminated ceiling). / N1 6HG; www.meatmission.com; @MEATmission; 11 pm, Sun 10 pm.

Mediterraneo W11 £67 **3** **2** **3**

37 Kensington Park Rd   020 7792 3131   7–1A

"Always enjoyable" local Italian that's provided consistently well rated meals in Notting Hill for 21 years. Its two siblings, Osteria Basilico and Essenza, are near-neighbours on the same street. / W11 2EU; www.mediterraneo-restaurant.co.uk; 11.30 pm, Sun 10.30 pm; booking max 10 may apply.

Medlar SW10 £75 **4** **4** **3**

438 King's Rd   020 7349 1900   6–3B

"Well worth a visit in this remote corner of Chelsea": this *"outstanding oasis in Worlds End"* has won a big culinary reputation, and chef Joe Mercer-Nairne *"maintains high standards year-in-year-out"*, with a *"classic French approach that's not so over-refined as to suck enjoyment out of it"*. *"Very good ingredients are cooked with great care, love and attention, but not overdone, nor over-fancy"*. Service is of a very *"high class"* too, while the interior is *"sophisticated"* (*"if a little cramped"*). *"It's another surprising omission from the Michelin star list: is it because it's at the wrong end of the King's Road?"* / SW10 0LJ; www.medlarrestaurant.co.uk; @MedlarChelsea; 10.30 pm, sun 9.30pm.

Megan's **2** **3** **4**

571 Kings Rd, SW6   020 7348 7139   6–4A
Unit B, 57-69 Parsons Green Lane, SW6   020 7348 7139   11–1B
27 Circus West Village, SW11   11–1C **NEW**
43 Bedford Hill, SW12   11–2C
86 High Street Wimbledon, SW19   11–2B **NEW**
55-57 The Pavement, SW4   11–2D **NEW**

"Affordable and with a nice vibe" – these good-looking, all-day hang-outs major in brunch, but make reasonably-priced options for a relaxed meal at any time. This year, they added Wimbledon, Battersea Power Station and Clapham branches to the fast-growing stable. / megans.co.uk; @MegansCafes.

Mei Ume EC3 £113 **3** **3** **3**

10 Trinity Square   020 3297 3799   10–3D

Delectable Asian-fusion delicacies – combining dishes of both Chinese and Japanese inspiration – win nothing but bouquets for this palatial dining room in a City five-star hotel, near the Tower of London. On the downside, cynics say *"it feels like a business hotel restaurant"*, and one or two diners *"expected more, considering the big-ticket prices"*. / EC3N 4AJ; www.meiume.com; @meiumelondon; 10 pm.

Melabes W8 **NEW** £49 **3** **2** **2**

221 Kensington High Street   020 7937 3003   6–1A

"Delicious Israeli-tapas and sharing-style plates at very reasonable prices" make it worth discovering this new arrival on Kensington High Street: a two-storey space where the existence of the (larger) upper floor isn't obvious from the street. *"It's rather plain-looking from the outside (and once you're inside too!)"* and *"some soundproofing is called for"*. / W8 6SG; melabes.business.site; @melabes221.

Mele e Pere W1 £54 3 3 3
46 Brewer Street 020 7096 2096 4–3C
"What a great find in Soho!" – "this quirky and funky place offers a nice twist on traditional Italian dishes", and is "so much better than the chains". "Looks tiny from the outside but has this ginormous expanse at basement level", which "can be noisy". "It's not cheap but nor is it outrageously expensive for the area and quality". There's also an on-site aperitivo bar featuring home-made vermouth. / W1F 9TF; www.meleepere.co.uk; @meleEpere; 11 pm, Sun 10 pm.

Menier Chocolate Factory SE1 £55 2 2 3
51-53 Southwark Street 020 7234 9610 10–4B
Stick to the good-value, meal-with-ticket deals at the theatre restaurant of this converted Victorian chocolate factory, whose food is "honest" but rather "hit and miss", hence "not good enough to pay full stand-alone prices" – especially with foodie Borough Market just across the road. / SE1 1RU; www.menierchocolatefactory.com; @MenChocFactory; 11 pm; closed Mon & Sun D.

Meraki W1 £62 4 4 4
80-82 Gt Titchfield St 020 7305 7686 3–1C
"Imaginative Greek dishes with a twist" earn high ratings this year for this two-year-old in Fitzrovia from Arjun and Peter Waney, who seem to have imbued Hellenic cooking with the trademark glamour and excitement they brought to Japanese with Zuma and Roka. The place is "always buzzing and packed", and reporters reckon it's "pricey but worth it" for "the best Greek meal I've ever eaten". / W1W 7QT; www.meraki-restaurant.com; @meraki_lon.

Mercato Metropolitano SE1 £25 4 2 3
42 Newington Causeway 020 7403 0930 1–3C
"Chocca with pop-ups" near Elephant & Castle, this "amazing" 45,000 square foot foodie market is "a great place to hang out and eat" – and is "far less crowded than Borough Market, its neighbour up the road". "The range and quality means you have to return several times to sample everything you want" from 50 different operators including an on-site Bavarian brewer. This 'sustainable community food market' is the brainchild of Andrea Rasca, who runs similar schemes in Milan and Turin. Upcoming developments include markets in Grade I listed St Mark's Church, Mayfair and Ilford's new cultural quarter and an MM Food Factory at the nearby £2.3billion Elephant Park development scheme. The only complaint is that this former paper factory "feels like a barn and can get chilly in winter". / SE1 6DR; www.mercatometropolitano.co.uk; @mercatometropol; 11pm, Sun 9pm.

The Mercer EC2 £61 3 2 2
34 Threadneedle St 020 7628 0001 10–2C
This banking hall conversion just moments from the Bank of England "feels like a gentleman's club" and "has become a City mainstay" for its "good-quality 'school' cooking". "They understand the 'time essence' of the business lunch", so "service comes at a good clip". / EC2R 8AY; www.themercer.co.uk; @TheMercerLondon; 9.30 pm; closed Sat & Sun.

Merchants Tavern EC2 £66 2 2 3
36 Charlotte Road 020 7060 5335 13–1B
Following on from Neil Borthwick's departure a year ago, his wife Angela Hartnett has severed her ties with this large and elegant gastropub-style haunt that she helped create from a converted Shoreditch warehouse. The amount of feedback the place generates has declined dramatically, and the few reports we have are mixed: some say it's still very good all round, but more downbeat commentary says "this used to be very good, but our recent meal was very poor". / EC2A 3PG; www.merchantstavern.co.uk; @merchantstavern; 11 pm, Sun 9 pm.

Le Mercury N1 £33 2️⃣2️⃣3️⃣
140a Upper St   020 7354 4088   9–2D
"Bustling" and "lovely" French-style bistro, which has been an Islington institution for almost 30 years, with its crowd-pleasing formula of a keen set price for each of the three courses (£4.95, £11.95 and £3.95 respectively): the food's not art, but with value like this, nobody cares. / N1 1QY; www.lemercury.co.uk; @le_mercury; midnight, Sun 10 pm; Mon-Thu D only, Fri-Sun open L & D.

Mere W1 £87 4️⃣5️⃣4️⃣
74 Charlotte Street   020 7268 6565   2–1B
"You can tell the moment you walk through the door that the people who own it are involved and want to make their guests' experience enjoyable" – that's the vibe at Monica and David Galetti's "peaceful and delightful" Fitzrovia two-year-old. "You have a relaxing drink at street level in the bar, and then it's down a flight of steps to a chic room flooded in natural light from the street outside". "The heart in the mind-blowing cooking shines through" – in particular the "wonderful, delicate, balanced tasting menu, packed with fresh seasonal ingredients"; and "it's paired with an exceptional wine list". "Staff are outstanding and the chef/patron visiting guests at their tables is a lovely touch". "Must surely get its Michelin star soon?" / W1T 4QH; www.mere-restaurant.com; @mererestaurant; Jacket & tie required.

Meson don Felipe SE1 £54 2️⃣2️⃣3️⃣
53 The Cut   020 7928 3237   10–4A
This "modestly priced" veteran Hispanic opposite the Young Vic is invariably "packed out" from early evening. "It's my default for a quick pre-theatre supper". There's "such a vibe between 7-9pm – nobody's going to write sonnets about the food, but sometimes it's just about the good times". / SE1 8LF; www.mesondonfelipe.com; 10 pm; closed Sun; No Amex.

Meza £33 3️⃣2️⃣2️⃣
34 Trinity Rd, SW17   07722 111299   11–2C
70 Mitcham Rd, SW17   020 8672 2131   11–2C
"Great Lebanese food with lots of delicious veggie options" is what keeps this duo of Tooting/Clapham cafés buzzing. Yes, they're "a bit cramped", but they compensate by being "friendly and fun". / www.mezarestaurant.co.uk; @MezaRestaurants; 11 pm, Fri & Sat 11.30 pm.

La Mia Mamma SW3 £62 3️⃣3️⃣3️⃣
257 King's Road   020 7351 2417   6–3C
An "intriguing concept" – 'A rotation of Mammas' from 20 different Italian regions per year provide the hearty scoff at this welcoming Chelsea yearling, where handmade pasta is something of a feature. By all accounts, the formula works, delivering "interesting dishes not found in your typical Italian restaurant" to a consistently good standard, and – for the 'hood – it's not especially pricey either. / SW3 5EL; www.lamiamamma.co.uk; @LaMiaMamma_.

Michael Nadra £63 4️⃣3️⃣2️⃣
6-8 Elliott Rd, W4   020 8742 0766   8–2A
42 Gloucester Ave, NW1   020 7722 2800   9–3B
"Vibrant", "thoughtful" cuisine is very consistently produced at both Michael Nadra's eponymous restaurants, in Chiswick and Camden Town. Both sites, though, are awkward in their way: the former "is a small space that's a bit of a squeeze" (window tables are best); while the latter, right next to the Regent's Canal, is a little stuck out-on-a-limb, and can seem "a little morgue-like" when it's not busy. Both sites, though, are pepped up by their "friendly" staff. / www.restaurant-michaelnadra.co.uk; @michaelnadra; 10 pm - 10.30 pm, Sun earlier.

Mien Tay £39 **3** 2 2
180 Lavender Hill, SW11 020 7350 0721 11–1C
45 Fulham High St, SW6 11–1B
433 Lordship Lane, London, N22 020 3302 9530
122 Kingsland Rd, E2 020 7729 3074 14–2A
This hard-hitting family-run quartet "kicks the pants off lots of other Vietnamese restaurants", with "food that's hard to beat" at "very reasonable prices" (the late Sunday Times food critic AA Gill raved about their pho and goat with galangal). / mientay.co.uk; @Mien_Tay; 11 pm, Sun 10 pm; E2 Sun 10.30 pm.

Mildreds £47 **3** **3** **3**
45 Lexington St, W1 020 7494 1634 4–2C
200 Pentonville Rd, N1 020 7278 9422 9–3D
9 Jamestown Rd, NW1 020 7482 4200 9–3B
Upper Dalston Sq, E8 020 8017 1815 14–1A
"My partner's a die-hard meat eater, but still thinks this place is the bee's knees!" – this extremely popular vegetarian chain has built on three decades of popularity for the "always-super-busy" (no bookings) Soho original, with branches in Camden Town, Dalston and King's Cross all opened in the last few years. All outlets get a good rep in the survey, with their "great choice" of "very tasty, veggie, comfort food". / @mildredslondon.

Milk SW12 £16 **3** 2 **3**
20 Bedford Hill 020 8772 9085 11–2C
For a top breakfast or brunch, a good number of Balham residents still tip their favourite Antipodean café as the best way to go locally; no bookings, you just rock up (and expect to queue at the weekend). / SW12 9RG; www.milk.london; @milkcoffeeldn; 10 pm; No bookings.

Mimo SE1 NEW £53
1 Cathedral Street 020 3286 7777 10–3C
Jon and Nicole Warren, the husband-and-wife team behind San Sebastian's Mimo (which has branches in Seville, Mallorca and The Algarve) have opened a cookery school, 'experiential dining' and chef's table overlooking Borough Market, with Basque-born Joseba Lasa as chef. You book (for 1-12 guests) for the nightly two-and-a-half-hour 'experience', which incorporates a tasting menu with wines, plus cookery demonstration, around the 'rugged concrete chef's counter'. / SE1 9DE; london.mimofood.com/en; @mimo_food.

**Min Jiang,
The Royal Garden Hotel W8** £87 **3** **3** **5**
2-24 Kensington High St 020 7361 1988 6–1A
"With such delightful views of Kensington Gardens, the food could so easily become secondary", but the impressively glam 8th-floor of the "luxurious" Royal Garden Hotel has long been acknowledged as one of the capital's best destinations thanks to its "consistently excellent" Chinese cuisine ("better than I had in Hong Kong!"). Its ratings came off the boil slightly this year however, amidst some unfamiliar accusations that "it's going downhill and becoming very expensive": "if this is the best Beijing Duck in town, then I'm the Emperor of China!" / W8 4PT; www.minjiang.co.uk; @minjianglondon; 10 pm.

Mint Leaf Lounge EC2 £74 **3** **3** **4**
Angel Ct, Lothbury 020 7600 0992 10–2C
"Light and delicate" Indian-fusion dishes and "nice cocktails" continue to maintain a fanclub for this snazzy-looking haunt, tucked away near the Bank of England. Its Trafalgar Square sibling bit the dust, though, this year (RIP). / EC2R 7HB; www.mintleaflounge.com; @MintLeafLondon; 10.45 pm.

Mirch Masala SW17 £26 4|2|2

213 Upper Tooting Rd 020 8767 8638 11–2D

"A broad range of dishes with distinct sauces at amazing prices" makes this "basic Pakistani place" a standout on Tooting's "curry corridor": "the quality certainly merits the mediocre setting and variable service"; a favourite of Sadiq Khan, it's "often busy and noisy". Top Tips: "nihari – slow-cooked lamb shank – is memorable"; "BYO wine is a plus point, too". / SW17 7TG; www.mirchmasalarestaurant.co.uk; midnight; Cash only; No bookings.

The Modern Pantry EC1 £61 2|2|2

47-48 St Johns Sq 020 7553 9210 10–1A

In June 2019, after ten years, Anna Hansen quit the Clerkenwell haunt she founded with the backing of D&D London, leaving Robert McCleary, who'd cooked with her all that time, at the helm. Known for its eclectic, Kiwi-inspired culinary approach, it's always been a venue that's divided opinion ("others rave, but I'm not sure why"), and we've maintained its existing middle-of-the-road rating for the time being. Most reliably, it's tipped as "a scrumptious brunch place" – "really good food and a light, fresh place to start the day". / EC1V 4JJ; www.themodernpantry.co.uk; @themodernpantry; 10.30 pm, Sun 10 pm.

Moio N16 NEW £53 3|3|3

188 Stoke Newington High Street 020 7923 7119 1–1D

Funky Portuguese- and Scandi-inspired dishes (a 'moio' is an arcane Iberian measure once used in the salt trade with Sweden!) set a culinarily ambitious tone at this early-2019 newcomer, occupying a simple, café-style space on Stokie's main drag. Limited feedback to-date, but all of it upbeat. / N16 7JD; moiorestaurant.com.

Moksha KT3 £35 4|4|3

216 Kingston Road 020 894 92211 1–4A

Out in the boonies of New Malden, first class ratings again – if on slightly limited feedback – for Arjun Singh Rawat and Rajeev Danga's North Indian two-year-old. / KT3 3RJ; www.moksharestaurant.uk; @Mokshanewmalden.

Momo W1 £76 4|3|4

25 Heddon Street 020 7434 4040 4–3B

Old-timers remember when Tom Cruise and Nicole Kidman (still married) chilled in the groove-tastic basement bar at Mourad Mazouz's party-Moroccan after it first opened (in 1997) and – notwithstanding a recent menu revamp and general scrub-up (plus much less snotty service) – it's changed little over the years other than the evaporation of its A-list clientele. In fact, if anything, the "extremely tasty" North African cuisine is higher quality and better value. Top Tip – "love the outdoor garden on a scorching day". / W1B 4BH; www.momoresto.com; @momoresto; 11 pm; credit card required to book.

Mon Plaisir Restaurant WC2 £54 3|3|4

19-21 Monmouth Street 020 7836 7243 5–2B

"For a romantic touch of Paris", this "archetypal" Gallic bistro in Covent Garden (dating from 1946) certainly looks the part – "a warren of rooms", which has seen numerous additions over the years, and where the "delightful" ambience is at its strongest in the oldest section of all. The cuisine is very "traditional" and, according to most diners, "still superb after so many years"; but others are more nuanced in their praise: "it's not the best French food by far, but a visit is like meeting an old friend who's been in your life for decades". Top Tip – "the pre-theatre deal is great value". / WC2H 9DD; www.monplaisir.co.uk; @MonPlaisir4; 10.30 pm; closed Sun.

Mona Lisa SW10 £39 3 3 2
417 King's Rd 020 7376 5447 6–3B
"Very popular workers café by day, rather trendy restaurant by night!" –
this veteran at the 'wrong end' of the King's Road enjoys a *"slick"* double life
as Chelsea's *"fun cheap eat"*. / SW10 0LR; www.mona-lisa.business.site; 11 pm,
Sun 5.30 pm; closed Sun D; No Amex.

Moncks of Dover Street W1 NEW
33 Dover Street 3–3C
An all-day brasserie-concept from luxury Mayfair restaurant Park Chinois:
the 92-cover venue launched in July 2019, with chef Gennaro Vitto, who was
previously a pastry chef at Park Chinois, at the stoves. / W1S 4NF;
www.moncksbrasserie.com.

Monmouth Coffee Company £7 3 5 4
27 Monmouth St, WC2 020 7232 3010 5–2B
2 Park St, SE1 020 7232 3010 10–4C
"There really is only one winner here when it comes to coffee!" – these
caffeine-havens remain the survey's No. 1 coffee company thanks to its
"perfect" brews – from a *"fabulous, rotating and extensive selection
of beans"* – delivered by *"patient and helpful staff"*, who are *"invariably
lovely despite the crazy-massive queues"*. By Borough Market, the *"rustic,
no-frills SE1 branch with its communal heavy wood table"* offers
a *"quintessential London breakfast experience, with a cult following"*
(foodwise, there's bread and jam, plus *"beautifully-sourced pastries"*). The
original WC2 branch is also *"lovely… if you can get a seat"*; and a recent
addition is a Saturday-only branch at Spa Terminus in Bermondsey SE16.
/ www.monmouthcoffee.co.uk; WC2 6:30 pm; SE1 6 pm; SE16 Sat 1.30 pm; closed
Sun; no Amex; no booking.

Monsieur Le Duck EC1 NEW £47 4 3 3
25 Clerkenwell Road 020 7247 2223 10–1A
"Duck in all its variants" (*"cooked in the Gascon style"*) from a *"limited but
brilliant menu"* (duck burger, confit leg, breast) – and *"great frites too"* –
make this street-food brand a *"duck-lover's delight"*. They were a pop-up
until May 2019, when they moved into this permanent Spitalfields home
(the troubled site that saw Workshop and Sarona come and go within
a year). / EC1M 5RN; www.leduck.co.uk.

Morito £45 4 3 3
195 Hackney Road, E2 020 7613 0754 14–2A
32 Exmouth Mkt, EC1 020 7278 7007 10–1A
"Great vibe, great food" – Moro's *"busy"*, *"tightly packed"* spin-off, a few
doors away along Exmouth Market, combines Spanish and North African
tastes into *"terrific"* tapas dishes, served in a *"laid back"* fashion. A second,
slightly larger Morito on Hackney Road, not far from Columbia Road flower
market, wins equally enthusiastic approval. / EC1 10.45 pm, E2 10.30 pm,
Sun 9 pm; EC1 closed Sun D; no bookings.

Moro EC1 £67 3 3 2
34-36 Exmouth Mkt 020 7833 8336 10–1A
"Still going strong twenty years on…", *"still stylish…"*, *"still needing acoustic
engineering…!"* – Samuel & Samantha Clark's *"unflashy"* Exmouth Market
legend has maintained an enormous loyal fanclub over the years. The draw
is its *"consistently excellent cooking, with distinctive Spanish and North
African flavours"* (*"so fresh and vibrant"*); plus *"a great list of sherries and
wines"*, all delivered in a *"relaxed and buzzy"* (*"always noisy"*) setting. But,
for a growing minority of regulars, it's *"not always as good as yesteryear"*:
service *"if well-meaning is sometimes patchy"*; and *"though the old-favourite
dishes are still cracked out with aplomb, they're not as adventurous as they
once seemed"*. Such reservations tend to be quibbles, rather than full-on
complaints, however, and the overall consensus is that it's *"still a real
favourite!"* / EC1R 4QE; www.moro.co.uk; @RestaurantMoro; 10.30 pm; closed
Sun D.

Morso NW8 £60 3 4 3
130 Boundary Road   0207 6247 412   9–3A
"This jewel-like place in a faintly unfashionable corner of St John's Wood exceeds expectations" with "fresh pasta", "friendly service", and "an exciting grappa list", plus "grappa-themed cocktails that really hit the spot". Downsides? "It is very noisy", and "the small-plates format means that bills can add up alarmingly". / NW8 0RH; www.morsolondon.co.uk; @morsolondon.

Mortimer House Kitchen W1 £64 3 3 4
37-41 Mortimer Street   020 7139 4401   3–1C
"Fun" and fashionable newcomer – a glamorous, grown-up, all-day restaurant complete with bar, on the ground floor of 'private workspace and wellbeing destination', Mortimer House in Fitzrovia. Its open kitchen is headed by Antonio 'Lello' Favuzzi (formerly of leading City Italian, L'Anima) who joined as head chef in February 2019. A versatile choice for many occasions, it is particularly tipped for business. Foodwise, one or two reporters consider the Mediterranean-via-the-Middle-East cuisine a little "average", but overall it's consistently decently rated. / W1T 3JH; www.mortimerhouse.com.

Mother SW11 £44 3 3 4
2 Archers Lane, Battersea Power Station   020 7622 4386   11–1C
Still relatively undiscovered by reporters, London's branch of this trendy Copenhagen pizza-stop occupies a moodily and slightly weirdly decorated arch at Battersea Power Station's Circus West Village, complete with tables hewn from big lumps of tree, spaceship lights and candles. On the few reports we received, it's worth a whirl, especially for one of its buffet brunch deals. / SW11 8AB; www.motherrestaurant.co.uk; @mother_ldn.

Mr Bao SE15 £38 5 3 3
293 Rye Ln   020 7635 0325   1–4D
For a "cheap 'n' cheerful" scran-fest, Frank Yeung's small Peckham café comes highly recommended by reporters as distant as Gloucester! It's all about the tasty Taiwanese bao – a total wow! / SE15 4UA; www.mrbao.co.uk; @MrBaoUK; 11 pm.

Mr Chow SW1 £88 2 1 2
151 Knightsbridge   020 7589 7347   6–1D
The very acme of dining glamour when it opened in 1968 – Sir Terence Conran once hailed it as a breakthrough in restaurant design – this expensive Chinese stalwart in Knightsbridge is now showing its age. "I used to love this place but the food is now old-fashioned and hasn't kept up with the times" is the politest of this year's feedback. Other reporters are blunter: "remarkable it continues to have any customers…" / SW1X 7PA; www.mrchow.com; @mrchow; midnight; closed Mon L.

Munal Tandoori SW15 £28 4 4 2
393 Upper Richmond Road, Putney   020 8876 3083   11–2A
"Massive portions of happiness" describes the "fabulous Indian/Nepalese food in generous-sized dishes" at this stalwart local: on the South Circular at Putney now for 30 years. / SW15 5QL; Www.munaltandori.co.uk; @munalrestaurant.

Murano W1 £99 **4 5 3**

20-22 Queen St   020 7495 1127   3–3B

With its "understated" style, Angela Hartnett's "elegant-but-relaxed" HQ manages to be one of the most personal of the "luxury" central London restaurants run by a big name, particularly one in Mayfair. Under head chef, Oscar Holgado, the accomplished modern cuisine "with an Italian twist" is "first class", as is the wine list: incredibly consistent and, "if not cheap, not wildly expensive". But it's the "professional service with a smile" that sets the seal on the experience: "warm, welcoming, and less pushy than at some other top destinations". "I'd just returned from Rome and was worried I'd be disappointed, but in fact it topped things off with a level of refined luxury I enjoyed very much". / W1J 5PP; www.muranolondon.com; @muranolondon; 11 pm; closed Sun.

Myrtle SW10 NEW **4 3 3**

1a Langton Street   020 7352 2411   6–3B

"Brilliantly executed, Irish-inspired food (we particularly enjoyed the black pudding – made from beef, not pork – in a potato roll; and the beef fillet with boxty)" wins high praise from early-days reporters on chef Anna Haugh's May 2019 opening, near World's End in Chelsea (named for her hero – Ballymaloe chef, Myrtle Allen – and aiming to offer 'modern European cooking with an Irish influence, using the finest Irish produce'). It's a "cosy and welcoming" space too: "part of a small, Chelsea townhouse, so quite tightly packed, with steep stairs to the upper level or down to the toilets". / SW10 0JL; www.myrtlerestaurant.com; @myrtlerest.

Nanashi EC2 £63 **3 2 2**

14 Rivington St   020 7686 0010   13–1B

"Super sushi and some decent hot plates too" win enthusiastic but limited feedback for this "pleasant if rather cramped" Japanese two-year-old in Shoreditch. / EC2A 3DU; www.nanashi.co.uk; Tue - Wed 10 pm, Thur - Sat 11 pm.

Nandine SE5 NEW **4 5 3**

45 Camberwell Church Street   1–3C

"A marvellous alternative to generic Middle East cuisine" – this family business has graduated from Peckham Levels (where they still trade) to this new café in Camberwell, where they offer "a Kurdish take on classic Middle Eastern dishes: well spiced, utterly fresh and served with a warmth worth mentioning because it's so uncommon...". A rave August 2019 review from Jay Rayner has propelled it to becoming a fooderati talking point. / SE5 8TR; @NandineUK.

The Narrow E14 £62 **1 2 3**

44 Narrow St   020 7592 7950   12–1B

"Always disappointing for the food, but the view saves it" sums up the general attitude toward Gordo's Limehouse pub, which despite its celeb chef ownership has never reliably cut it gastronomically. The "standard brasserie fare" is "average" at the very best – it "could and should be so much better". / E14 8DP; www.gordonramsayrestaurants.com/the-narrow; @thenarrow; 10.30 pm, Sun 8 pm.

Native SE1 £57 **3 3 2**

32 Southwark Street   07943 934 375   10–4C

"Refreshingly innovative dishes" which "bring out the best in British ingredients" – including squirrel meat, left-overs and peelings under a strict 'zero waste' regime – "create a truly unique dining experience" at Ivan Tisdall-Downes and Imogen Davis's new and bigger venue near Borough Market, where they moved last year from their cramped Neal's Yard original. "Hidden away" behind a curtain, "the joint seems more East End than South Bank", but its "funky interior makes for a fun night out". Marks would have been higher without a significant minority who were "disappointed" by various aspects of the new venture. / SE1 1TU; www.eatnative.co.uk; @eatnativeuk.

Naughty Piglets SW2 £57 **5** **5** **3**

28 Brixton Water Ln 020 7274 7796 11–2D

Joe and Margaux Sharratt's "distressed-chic Brixton/Brockwell Park fixture" continues to win "top marks" for its French-inspired "small-plates at reasonable prices" ("if I lived next door I'd get rid of my kitchen!"). The "friendly, chatty and informal staff" and "South London style" also go down well, although the occasional reporter is "not so sure about the natural wines". The same team has opened a sister venue at Andrew Lloyd Webber's The Other Palace theatre in Victoria (see also). / SW2 1PE; www.naughtypiglets.co.uk; 10 pm, Sun 3 pm.

Nautilus NW6 £38 **4** **4** **1**

27-29 Fortune Green Rd 020 7435 2532 1–1B

"Delicious fresh fish", "battered or crumbed in matzo meal", and "friendly" service make this classic West Hampstead chippy stand out from the crowd. Even regulars who've "been coming for years" point out that "the restaurant could do with a makeover"… but we've been saying that for nearly three decades now, so are not exactly holding our breath! / NW6 1DU; 10 pm; closed Sun; No Amex.

Needoo E1 £26 **4** **3** **2**

87 New Rd 020 7247 0648 13–2D

Whitechapel Punjabi BYO that's a real match for its better-known Pakistani competitors in the East End due to its "grilled meats at bargain prices" and other "fantastic, freshly made dishes" from the sub-continent. / E1 1HH; www.needoogrill.co.uk; @NeedooGrill; 11.30 pm.

Neptune, Kimpton Fitzroy London WC1 £86 **2** **2** **2**

8 Russell Square 020 7520 1806 2–1D

"Stylish, grand-hotel decor" creates an "impressive" backdrop to a meal in the year-old incarnation of this dining room within a huge Victorian pile (fka Hotel Russell) on Russell Square. Its brasserie-style cooking is decently rated but can seem "very pricey". / WC1B 5BE; neptune.london; @Principal_Hotel.

Next Door SE22 £45 **4** **3** **2**

151 Lordship Lane 020 3659 1413 1–4D

"A welcome addition to East Dulwich" and "really worth the trip" – "super-fresh fish (from the namesake Moxon's fishmonger next door)" helps this year-old venture "punch above its weight". "The whole roast fish to share is a real delight, but there are also lots of tasty small plates, which are equally satisfying". "You must book, and try and go there early, as it's small, and the best dishes don't last very long". "Not a cheap meal" especially as the "simple premises are somewhat cramped", but "well worth the money as it's so good". "Outside tables during good weather are at a premium". / SE22 8HX; www.moxonsnextdoor.com.

Niche EC1 £56 **3** **3** **2**

197-199 Rosebery Avenue 020 7837 5048 9–3D

'Gluten free but you wouldn't know it!' is the motto at this modern bistro "very handy for the Sadlers Wells theatre": "a charming and slightly eclectic restaurant with enthusiastic staff" and "a varied menu to suit all tastes". "My gluten-free friend was delighted to find he could eat anything on the menu, and happily tucked into pie and mash, saying that you wouldn't know it was gluten-free (a point echoed by the non-gluten-free among us)". / EC1R 4TJ; www.nichefoodanddrink.com; @Nichefoodbdrink ; 9.45 pm, Fri & Sat 10.15 pm, Sun 3.30 pm.

The Ninth London W1 £78 5 4 3

22 Charlotte Street   020 3019 0880   2–1C

"Mouth-watering food" – *"French-style with a difference"* – wows almost all visitors at Jun Tanaka's *"informal fine-dining"* joint in Fitzrovia. *"The food is taken seriously but the atmosphere is grounded and relaxed"* – *"when I want a solid and thoughtful meal, I go here"*. Better still, it's *"a bit of a bargain for the quality"*, and there's *"huge value in the wine list for a Michelin restaurant"*. / W1T 2NB; www.theninthlondon.com; @theninthlondon; 10 pm, Thu-Sat 10.30 pm; closed Sun.

No. 5 Social W1 NEW £79

5 Pollen Street   020 7870 3730   3–2C

The mid-2019 relaunch of Little Social (RIP) over the road from the Pollen Street mothership sees it re-invented but still under the aegis of the Jason Atherton empire; this Mayfair 60-seater now sports a softer, more classically luxurious style than its siblings. It's to be a new showcase for chef Kostas Papathanasiou – whose CV incorporates The Fat Duck and The Ledbury – with a focus on seasonal, British cuisine. Top Tip – the prix fixe menu is a good deal for the area: £19.50 for 2 courses or £24.50 for 3 courses. / W1S 1NE; www.no5social.com; @no5social.

No. Fifty Cheyne SW3 NEW £81 3 4 4

50 Cheyne Walk   020 7376 8787   6–3C

"Extremely well-appointed, and featuring an open grill" – this Chelsea newcomer, picturesquely located right by the river near Albert Bridge, bears many of the hallmarks of its elegant predecessor on the site, the Cheyne Walk Brasserie, which has undergone a complete rebuild under the watchful eye of Sally Greene (Director of The Old Vic and proprietor of Ronnie Scott's). Chef Iain Smith (formerly head chef at Social Eating House) provides the eats for the 70-seat restaurant. Top Tip – the cocktail bar and drawing room upstairs, is a particularly fab space with brilliant views. / SW3 5LR; www.fiftycheyne.com; @50Cheyne.

Noble Rot WC1 £58 3 4 4

51 Lamb's Conduit St   020 7242 8963   2–1D

"Allied to the magazine of the same name", Mark Andrew and Daniel Keeling's Bloomsbury three-year-old took over the *"lovely"*, if *"slightly cramped"* premises that were previously the marvellously old-school wine bar Vats (RIP). It has a *"brilliantly curated"* wine list *"featuring something for everyone: from small, natural and biodynamic producers using grapes you've never heard of (from areas you didn't even know produced wine), to the grand marques of the first growth Bordeaux. There is something for everyone and the staff are ridiculously knowledgeable and keen to help guide you through as much or as little as you want"*. The *"simple"* fare that accompanies it is better-than-incidental too (*"sometimes outstanding"*), and prepared with *"an assured touch"*. *"It's not a place for loony foodies of the Instagram persuasion, thank God. Just really good fun!"* And *"all without it being daylight robbery"* too. / WC1N 3NB; www.noblerot.co.uk; @noblerotbar; 10 pm.

Nobu,
Metropolitan Hotel W1 £100 3 2 2

19 Old Park Ln   020 7447 4747   3–4A

"It no longer pulls the A-list celebs, it's no longer difficult to get a table – but the food is still exceptional" at the Japanese-South American fusion chain's original London flagship. It can be *"hit or miss"*, though – *"some days it's the real Nobu with the exquisitely prepared black cod signature dish, but at times it seems the chef has forgotten the recipe"*. More than 20 years after its arrival in the UK, the global brand is still expanding, with a second hotel scheduled to open in the West End in early 2020. / W1K 1LB; www.noburestaurants.com; @NobuOldParkLane; 10.15 pm, Fri & Sat 11 pm, Sun 10 pm.

Nobu Berkeley W1 £104 322

15 Berkeley St   020 7290 9222   3–3C

"Fab but SO expensive"; the Mayfair branch of Matsuhisha Nobu's luxury, Japanese-Latino fusion brand still pleases with its "absolutely incredible food ("stunning black cod") – it even converted my non-sushi-eating husband to sushi". It's no longer a celeb-magnet nowadays however, and every year, a huge proportion of reporters complain how painfully "overpriced" it is, especially given its 'meh' decor and iffy service. / W1J 8DY; www.noburestaurants.com; @NobuBerkeleyST; 11 pm, Thu-Sat midnight, Sun 9.45 pm; closed Sun L.

Nobu Shoreditch EC2 £110 222

10-50 Willow St   020 3818 3790   13–1B

In the basement of this very boutiquey, year-old Shoreditch hotel – London's first from the global Japanese-American chain – the big, airy dining room opens onto a small sunken garden. To fans, its sleek styling, wizard sushi and "perfect cocktails" make it "pricey but worth it for a special blow-out". To sceptics, though, it's all a bit 'vieux chapeau': "for what it is – an old formula with nothing innovative – it's overpriced; and you can have much better Japanese elsewhere at a fraction of the bill". / EC2A 4BH; www.nobuhotelshoreditch.com; @NobuShoreditch.

Noizé W1 £79 454

39 Whitfield St   020 7323 1310   2–1C

Mathieu Germond, former manager of Pied à Terre, "has worked his considerable magic here", and has created an "amazing wine list" with "very fair mark-ups" at his "very charming" Fitzrovia yearling (on the former site of Dabbous, RIP) – "go for his suggestions" from the "wide and interesting range, many by the glass". Ed Dutton's "delightful" French cuisine is "excellent too", showing "genuine, old-school skill", while the "tasteful decoration, with lots of natural light" and "spot-on" service ("personable" – "there when you need them and non-intrusive") "make it an ideal spot for an informal business lunch, as well as more serious entertaining". / W1T 2SF; www.noize-restaurant.co.uk; @NoizeRestaurant.

Noor Jahan £47 343

2a Bina Gdns, SW5   020 7373 6522   6–2B
26 Sussex Pl, W2   020 7402 2332   7–1D

"Reliably upmarket curry house" on the Earl's Court-South Ken border – a true veteran (est. 1964) whose loyal, well-heeled clientele rate its "consistency" and comforting atmosphere. Given its posh neighbourhood, it's attracted its share of slebs, with Brangelina, Gwyneth and Robbie spotted over the years. The Bayswater offshoot is similar, but less fashionably located. / W2 11.30 pm, Sun 11 pm; SW5 11.30 pm.

Nopi W1 £76 432

21-22 Warwick St   020 7494 9584   4–3B

"A wonderful treasure-house of Middle Eastern dishes" – "absolutely fabulous sharing-plates", of which the vegetarian ones "would sway even a committed carnivore with their culinary magic" – inspire many rave reviews of Yotam Ottolenghi's Soho flagship; and its "unusual wines" are also "very acceptable". "Downstairs, by the busy and interesting open kitchen, there are communal tables; the ground floor is more fashionable (busier and noisier) and, unlike at his main chain, you can book". It's no huge bargain though: "the small plates are as tasty as the cookbooks suggest but portions seem in inverse proportion to the price!" / W1B 5NE; ottolenghi.co.uk/nopi; @ottolenghi; 10.30 pm, Sun 4 pm; closed Sun D.

Nordic Bakery W1 £13 **3**22

14a Golden Sq   020 3230 1077   4–3C

"Nordic sarnies and cinnamon buns are as good as ever, along with the coffee", at this Scandi fixture in Soho. "Pity about the other sites", which closed down a couple of years ago and are "greatly missed – but at least the Golden Square original is still there". / W1F 9JG; www.nordicbakery.com; 8 pm, Sat & Sun 7 pm; L & early evening only; No Amex; no booking.

The Norfolk Arms WC1 £56 **3**33

28 Leigh St   020 7388 3937   9–4C

"Great, good-value tapas" is a slightly surprising find at this classic London pub, "hiding" in sidestreet near King's Cross: "a real revelation in an area not noted for good places to eat". / WC1H 9EP; www.norfolkarms.co.uk; 11pm, Sun 10.30 pm; No Amex.

Norma W1 NEW

8 Charlotte Street   2–1C

Following the success of The Game Bird, the team from The Stafford London took the bold step of opening this independent non-hotel restaurant, in a Fitzrovia townhouse, in September 2019. The cooking, overseen by the Salt Yard's ex-culinary director, Ben Tish, is 'inspired by the culture of Sicily, with particular emphasis on the Moorish influences on the island's cuisine'; a crudo (raw) bar is also a feature. / W1T 2LS; thestaffordlondon.com/norma-london; @Norma_ldn.

North China W3 £47 **4**33

305 Uxbridge Rd   020 8992 9183   8–1A

Though its fans would differ, this "utterly reliable", "family-run" stalwart (est 1976) is by no means "the best Chinese restaurant in London" or England! It is, however, an unusually high quality operation to find deep in the 'burbs of Acton and has a much wider following than you would expect of somewhere in this location. "The food is fresh and full of flavour" and service under owner/manager Lawrence Lou is very professional and warm. / W3 9QU; www.northchina.co.uk; 11 pm, Fri & Sat 11.30 pm.

North Sea Fish WC1 £47 **3**4**2**

7-8 Leigh St   020 7387 5892   9–4C

"The real deal!" This "popular" Bloomsbury chippy – "run by the same family for more than 40 years" – is one of the best in town, certainly of those within striking distance of the West End. "The choice is always good, and simply grilled is a fantastic option", or fried in matzo meal; and you can round off with "excellent English puddings and custard". It's a good idea to book. / WC1H 9EW; www.northseafishrestaurant.co.uk; @TheNorthSeaFish; 10 pm, Sun 9.30 pm; closed Sun D; No Amex.

The Northall, Corinthia Hotel WC2 £101 **3**2**3**

10a Northumberland Ave   020 7321 3100   2–3C

"Fine if you're staying in the hotel, but not a destination restaurant", is a common verdict on this "elegant" chamber, which is currently most often tipped by non-residents as a "perfect business lunch venue": "comfortable, with good food, and you're always well looked-after". It's an impression the management of this beautiful five-star hotel, near the Embankment, is keen to change, however, and the arrival of André Garrett at the stoves from Cliveden in late-2018 was a statement of intent to zhoosh things up, as they have done with Kerridge's (see also). Since André's arrival its food rating is, in fact, little-changed (good but unmemorable), but perhaps that's all about to change: in a June 2019 interview with trade website 'Big Hospitality', he promises 'something big' including a name change, refurb, and a new dedicated restaurant entrance. / WC2N 5AE; www.thenorthall.co.uk; @CorinthiaLondon; 10.45 pm.

Northbank EC4 £58 223
One Paul's Walk   020 7329 9299   10–3B

You can't argue with the location of this bar/café, right by the Wobbly Bridge, looking over to Tate Modern, and with an outside terrace in summer. It inspired limited and mixed feedback this year: fans applaud its seasonal modern British cooking and tip it as a business option, but one or two others feel "it's overpriced, with poor service, and only exists due to its view of the Thames". / EC4V 3QH; www.northbankrestaurant.co.uk; @NorthbankLondon; 10 pm; closed Sun.

Novikov (Asian restaurant) W1 £105 324
50a Berkeley St   020 7399 4330   3–3C

"A playground for oligarchs" – Arkady Novikov's infamously glam, Eurotrash-magnet remains one of Mayfair's most happening scenes, luring the fast crowd with its mix of light Asian bites, sushi, grills and noodles. It's not exactly somewhere to go if you're counting the pennies, but, actually, "dim sum at lunch is excellent and very reasonably priced". / W1J 8HA; www.novikovrestaurant.co.uk; @NovikovLondon; 11.15 pm; No trainers.

Novikov (Italian restaurant) W1 £109 222
50a Berkeley St   020 7399 4330   3–3C

Wreathed in the über-Eurotrashy environs and telephone-number prices of Russian restaurateur Arkady Novikov's well-known, Mayfair glamour-magnet, it's hard to form a totally balanced judgement on its Italian dining room. It's fabulously "overpriced" of course, but most diners do actually feel the "classic Italian cuisine" is "proper" and "delicious". / W1J 8HA; www.novikovrestaurant.co.uk; @NovikovLondon; 11.45 pm.

Nuovi Sapori SW6 £48 333
295 New King's Rd   020 7736 3363   11–1B

"Honest food", "delightful service" and an upbeat atmosphere again win praise for this well-established, neighbourhood trattoria, near Parsons Green; it's good with kids too. / SW6 4RE; www.nuovisaporilondon.co.uk; 11 pm; closed Sun; booking max 6 may apply.

Nusr-Et Steakhouse SW1
The Park Tower Knightsbridge, 101 Knightsbridge   6–1D

First announced in July 2017, this December 2019 opening on Knightsbridge from social media sensation, Nusret Gökçe is The Park Tower hotel's answer to breathing life into the deathly dull-looking space that was for many years One-O-One (RIP). Now it's to be Salt Bae's latest branch in a steak chain that nowadays spans the globe. / SW1X 7RN; www.nusr-et.com.tr/en/home.aspx.

Nutbourne SW11 £59 223
29 Ransomes Dock, 35-37 Parkgate Rd   020 7350 0555   6–4C

"Quirky and relaxed" Battersea venue, on the waterside site long occupied by Ransome's Dock (RIP), which is run the Gladwin brothers using the same farm-to-fork formula as at their other ventures (see Rabbit and The Shed). "Great wines" from the eponymous family vineyard in Sussex are a plus, but the modern British cooking is "inconsistent", with "some hits and some misses"… but rather too many "misses". / SW11 4NP; www.nutbourne-restaurant.com; @NutbourneSW11.

Nutshell WC2 NEW
30 Saint Martin's Lane   5–4C

Modern Iranian cuisine is served at this August 2019 newcomer in Covent Garden, which opened too late for any survey feedback. Former head chef of The Palomar, Jeremy Borrow, will oversee the kitchen of this 85-seater, split over two floors and – as at his former gaff – featuring counter-style seating with an open kitchen. (The idea was trialled last year as a pop-up, by a different chef, Leonardo Pereira.) / WC2N 4EJ; nutshelllondon.co.uk; @NutshellLondon.

O'ver £52 **4** **3** **3**

St. James's Market, SW1   020 7930 9664   4–4D **NEW**
44-46 Southwark Street, SE1   020 7378 9933   10–4B

"Out-of-this-world pizza" – using seawater in the dough, and whose
"toppings are inventive without being bizarre" – again inspires high praise
for this "piece of Napoli in London", "on a busy street that's a little out
of the way", but "not far from Borough Market". In the evening it can
be "crowded and very noisy", but staff are "always very welcoming". As of
June 2019, it has a new heart-of-the-West End sibling, in the St James's
Market development. / www.overuk.com.

Oak £60 **3** **3** **4**

243 Goldhawk Rd, W12   020 8741 7700   8–1B
137 Westbourne Park Rd, W2   020 7221 3355   7–1B
39 Parkgate Road, SW11   020 7924 3999   6–4C **NEW**

"Tasty pizzas" top the bill at these "good-looking gastropub" conversions
in Notting Hill and Shepherd's Bush, with the "excellent new addition" of a
"stylish bistro" in a "stunning, huge space" on the river at Battersea. "Pizzas
and starters outshine main courses, but overall very pleasant and relaxing".
/ W12 10.30pm, Fri & Sat 11 pm Sun 9.30pm; W2 10.30pm, Fri & Sat 11 pm,
Sun 10 pm.

Oblix SE1 £105 **2** **2** **4**

Level 32, The Shard, 31 St. Thomas Street   020 7268 6700   10–4C

"The view is spectacular" from the 32nd floor of the Shard, so "why not put
the £35 it would cost to go to the viewing deck towards a meal here", in the
brasserie from Rainer Becker of Zuma and Roka. "The meal is ridiculously
overpriced", of course, but "the atmosphere feels special" and – though the
food is not without its detractors – a relatively high proportion of diners here
feel "it matches the panorama". You can choose between the West section
for a restaurant-style meal or the East bar with food. / SE1 9RY;
www.oblixrestaurant.com; @OblixRestaurant; 11 pm; booking max 6 may apply.

Odette's NW1 £62 **4** **4** **3**

130 Regents Park Road   020 7586 8569   9–3B

This "smart" Primrose Hill veteran of 40-odd years is "a most likeable place
enhanced by the patina of time, and combined with inventive high-end
cooking" from chef Bryn Williams, who has owned it for the past decade.
It's "always a treat" to taste the "beautiful ingredients", which include
produce from the Williams family farm in Wales; although the patron's tilt
towards a Welsh and Irish heritage means it's "tempting here to overdo the
carbs, cream and calories: Irish soda bread, cheesy choux nibbles, creamy
tarts and caramel-sauced soufflés to name but a few…" / NW1 8XL;
www.odettesprimrosehill.com; @Odettes_rest; 10 pm, Sat 10.30 pm, Sun 9.30 pm;
closed Mon; No Amex.

Ognisko Restaurant SW7 £54 **3** **4** **5**

55 Prince's Gate, Exhibition Road   020 7589 0101   6–1C

"What a wonderful oasis of calm in the hustle of London's museum area" –
this "elegant dining room of a Polish emigrés' club" (open to the general
public) has a "wonderful 19th-century vibe" and is a "civilised and reliable"
setting that's both "cosy in winter" and with a particularly "beautiful terrace
for summer". Its "authentic traditional Polish fare" is "charmingly served"
in "huge portions" with lashings of vodka and some interesting wines.
/ SW7 2PG; www.ogniskorestaurant.co.uk; @OgniskoRest; 11.15 pm, Sun 10.30 pm;
closed Mon L; No trainers.

Oka £48 4 3 2
Kingly Court, 1 Kingly Court, W1   020 7734 3556   4–2B
251 King's Road, SW3   020 7349 8725   6–3C
71 Regents Park Rd, NW1   020 7483 2072   9–3B
88 Church Road, SW13   020 8741 8577   11–1A NEW
*"Punching above their weight in terms of flavour and presentation" –
this "buzzy" quartet of "medium-priced" Japanese/Asian fusion "pit-stops"
are "fab little places" for a high-quality refuelling (the new Barnes site
is "perfect before a film at the Olympic across the road").
/ www.okarestaurant.co.uk; 10.30 pm.*

Oklava EC2 £57 4 4 3
74 Luke St   020 7729 3032   13–1B
*"Outstanding Turkish and Cypriot cuisine" – with an original, light spin that
can come as a "real surprise" – wins plaudits for this Shoreditch venue.
"Sitting at the counter watching the food being prepared is eye-opening;
and owners (Selin Kiazim and Laura Christie) obviously love what they do".
"It's not strictly vegetarian, but has many options if you are". / EC2A 4PY;
www.oklava.co.uk; @Oklava_ldn; 10.30 pm, Sun 4 pm; booking max 6 may apply.*

Oldroyd N1 £56 4 3 2
344 Upper St   020 8617 9010   9–3D
*"Tiny, really tiny!" – Tom Oldroyd's converted Islington house is "either
intimate or cramped... it's hard to decide", but "even though the space
is confined, it has character" ("upstairs is slightly better"), plus it's staffed
with "nice people". The draw is the "simple and well-prepared food", which
is "really tasty and interesting": in the space, "how they do it is a mystery!"
/ N1 0PD; www.oldroydlondon.com; @oldroydlondon; 10.30 pm, Fri 11 pm,
Sun 9.30 pm; Booking max 4 may apply.*

Oliveto SW1 £60 4 3 2
49 Elizabeth Street   020 7730 0074   2–4A
*"Loud without being unpleasant", this "cheerful and buzzy" Sardinian has
been a Belgravia stalwart for many years – "my son spent his formative
years coming back to this place because of the huge and excellent pizzas"
(and the repertoire also includes pasta and salads). Older regulars are more
enamoured of the "interesting Italian/Sardinian wine list". / SW1W 9PP;
www.olivorestaurants.com/oliveto; @OlivoGroup; 10.30 pm, Sun 10 pm.*

Olivo SW1 £74 3 3 2
21 Eccleston Street   020 7730 2505   2–4B
*"An old haunt of style and enjoyment" – this Sardinian was the original
in Mauro Sanna's upmarket Belgravia group – "an absolute banker for
consistency". "The freshness of the cooking and the delightfully different
wines" make it a "great lunch venue", although – this being SW1 –
it's "now outrageously priced". / SW1W 9LX; www.olivorestaurants.com;
@OlivoGroup; 10.30 pm; closed Sat L & Sun L.*

Olivocarne SW1 £80 3 2 2
61 Elizabeth St   020 7730 7997   2–4A
*"Excellent meat" puts the 'carne' into this accomplished Belgravian – part of
Mauro Sanna's group of upmarket Sardinian locals – which shares the
"original" cooking and "special and varied wines" of its siblings. Its austere
but zany minimalist decor lacks charge but is certainly 'different'.
/ SW1W 9PP; www.olivorestaurants.com; 11 pm, Sun 10.30 pm.*

Olivomare SW1 £79 3 3 2
10 Lower Belgrave St   020 7730 9022   2–4B
*"Always a-buzz with locals", this "buoyant" Sardinian seafood
specialist in Belgravia is "a bit steep in its prices at £60-£70 a head, but the
freshness and range of fish make it worthwhile". It was the third to open
in the Olivo group owned by Mauro Sana, who seemingly "personally knows
more than 70% of his clientele". / SW1W 0LJ; www.olivorestaurants.com;
@OlivoGroup; 11 pm, Sun 10.30 pm; booking max 10 may apply.*

Olley's SE24 £39 3 3 2
65-69 Norwood Rd 020 8671 8259 11–2D
"Generous portions of consistently excellent fish 'n' chips" have made Harry Niazi's "friendly" rustic chippie a fixture opposite Brockwell Park since 1987. It inspired the odd 'off' report this year, though: "supposedly the best chippy in the area, but we found it a huge let-down". / SE24 9AA; www.olleys.info; 10 pm, Sun 9.30 pm; No Amex.

Olympic, Olympic Studios SW13 £52 2 2 3
117-123 Church Road 020 8912 5170 11–1A
The all-day brasserie at the legendary recording studios-turned-indie-cinema and members' club is "popular with Barnes residents" after a "pre-film snack". Reporters agree that "breakfast and brunch – especially at one of the outside tables under the cherry trees – are good"; lunch and dinner less so: "the cuisine is over-ambitious and not well-realised". / SW13 9HL; www.olympiccinema.co.uk; @Olympic_Cinema; 11 pm, Fri & Sat midnight, Sun 10 pm.

Olympus Fish N3 £37 3 3 2
140-144 Ballards Ln 020 8371 8666 1–1B
"Fish 'n' chips as it's meant to be" – "non-greasy, tasty and in good portions" – makes this chippy a "great local" for Finchley. It's Turkish-run, which gives the option to "try fish from the charcoal grill". There's still the odd glitchy report, but one regular says that "after an off-patch recently, it's back on form", as it enters its 20th year in business. / N3 2PA; www.olympusrestaurant.co.uk; @Olympus_London; 11 pm.

On The Bab £36 3 3 2
36 Wellington St, WC2 020 7240 8825 5–3D
305 Old St, EC1 020 7683 0501 13–1B
9 Ludgate Broadway, EC4 020 7248 8777 10–2A
"A good stab at proper Korean food" – these "nicely buzzing", K-pop styled pit-stops are "not subtle" but score points for their punchily flavoured bites (the fried chicken is the fave rave), served "cheaply and quickly". / onthebab.co.uk; @onthebab; EC1 & WC2 10.30 pm, Sun 10 pm; W1 & EC4 4 pm; EC4 closed Sat & Sun; W1 closed Sun; no bookings.

108 Garage W10 £79 4 3 2
108 Golborne Rd 020 8969 3769 7–1A
The "fantastic experience" of eating at this highly original and "exciting" venue – a former car repair shop off Portobello Market featuring "industrial stripped-down walls" – has been restored with the return to the kitchen of Chris Denney, "a really inventive chef", following the loss of sibling-venture Southam Street. It's "uber trendy, but the food is of exceptional quality". / W10 5PS; www.108garage.com.

104 Restaurant W2 NEW £87 4 3 3
104a Chepstow Road 020 3417 4744 7–1B
"So glad to have 104 back on the map", say fans of this tiny 14-seater on the fringe of Notting Hill – formerly Marianne's (RIP) and now re-launched without fanfare by chef Richard Wilkins and front-of-house Matt Hough: the former of whom had worked here with Marianne Lumb before she moved onto pastures new. Early feedback on this "very pretty room" ("romantic", but "be prepared to overhear everyone else's conversation") does include the odd caveat ("excellent quality overall, but some dishes seemed overly simple; and some of the accompanying sauces had gone wrong – the lemon sabayon with the asparagus just tasted of synthetic gloop"). For the most part, however, the picture is of rave reviews for "stunning and very high quality dishes at a reasonable price for such great produce". / W2 5QS; www.104restaurant.com.

101 Thai Kitchen W6   £38   5 2 2
352 King St   020 8746 6888   8–2B
*"Phenomenally authentic", family-run Thai caff near Stamford Brook,
on busy King Street, that's become a cult destination amongst Asian food
cognoscenti for its Isaan dishes from the country's northeast, supplemented
by southern seafood by 'Auntie Bee'; the food "feels like the real McCoy –
and is quite challenging as a result". The place is "filled with Thai expats –
what more do you need to say? Oh, it's cheap as chips". / W6 0RX; 10.30 pm,
Fri & Sat 11 pm; No Amex.*

1 Lombard Street EC3   £86   2 2 2
1 Lombard St   020 7929 6611   10–3C
*"Such a classic City venue" – former banker, Soren Jessen's smooth
operation in a converted banking hall near Bank station has traded off
Square Mile expense accounts for 20 years. If nobody thrills to the cuisine,
nor do they tend to have very harsh words for it – "whenever I'm looking for
dinner with a nice wine, I head to 1 Lombard Street where I won't
be disappointed". There's a "great atmosphere at breakfast time", too.
/ EC3V 9AA; www.1lombardstreet.com; @1LombardStreet; 10 pm; closed Sat & Sun;
booking max 10 may apply.*

Onima W1 NEW   £86   3 3 4
1-3 Avery Row   020 7078 9747   3–2B
*Swish, Greek-owned, late-2018 newcomer, which occupies two floors of a
five-storey Mayfair townhouse (the remainder being dedicated to a bar, club,
roof terrace, etc) which aims to 'brings the spirit of Mykonos to London'
on a site that once housed the HQ of Cartier's watch-making empire. Ex-
Novikov chef, Sicilian Carmelo Carnevale, oversees a Mediterranean/Asian
mash-up of a menu, which earned solid ratings in early feedback, alongside
perhaps predictable concerns about the slightly scary pricing. / W1K 4AJ;
www.onimarestaurant.com.*

Les 110 de Taillevent W1   £83   2 3 3
16 Cavendish Square   020 3141 6016   3–1B
*"You will never get bored, although you might get drunk!" at this London
scion of Paris's famous Taillevent group, where "you can try 110 different
types of superb wine by the glass". Set in "an attractive former private
banking hall" – on the opposite side of Cavendish Square from the back
of Oxford Street's John Lewis – its "staff are extremely well-drilled and make
everything effortless and smooth". However, "the total cost of a meal takes
it out of brasserie territory", while the "seasonal French cuisine", though
"enjoyable", doesn't always seem in keeping with the level of ambition that
the final bill might imply. / W1G 9DD; www.les-110-taillevent-london.com;
@110London; 10.30 pm; closed Sat L & Sun.*

OOTY W1 NEW   £75   5 4 3
66 Baker Street   020 3727 5014   2–1A
*"Gorgeous, perfect, elegant" Indian cuisine from former Rasoi chef,
Manmeet Singh Bali, wins very high food-ratings for this Marylebone
newcomer. It's on the site that was formerly well known as Galvin Bistrot
de Luxe (RIP), which has been given a "beautiful", unusually tasteful
makeover; "impeccable" service adds to the very civilised, if slightly
"low key" tone. Fingers crossed word gets out fully, though: "it was a bit
empty when we went which made it a bit of a barn: with a few more people
it could have been fantastic". / W1U 7DJ; www.ooty.co.uk; @ootylondon.*

Opera Tavern WC2   £59   4 4 3
23 Catherine Street   020 7836 3680   5–3D
"Not really a pub any more, though it certainly used to be" – this well-known tapas bar near Covent Garden operates on two atmospheric, if noisy, floors, and is a "go-to for pre-theatre dining, with superb small plates at a relatively reasonable cost for the location". "The little morsels of Spanish and Italian deliciousness haven't faltered since the Salt Yard chain was taken over" (in late-2018). In late summer 2019 it emerged from a major revamp. / WC2B 5JS; www.saltyardgroup.co.uk/opera-tavern; @saltyardgroup; 11.15 pm, Sun 9.45 pm.

Opso W1   £59   3 3 3
10 Paddington St   020 7487 5088   2–1A
A modern take on Greek cuisine in Marylebone hailed for its "authentic food and lively atmosphere (crowded and noisy inside but good outside on a fine day)". Other plus points include "friendly, helpful service" and "a nice selection of Greek wines" – in fact, there's "little to complain about, except perhaps the pricing". A more casual street-food offshoot, Pittabun, opened off Carnaby Street last year. / W1U 5QL; www.opso.co.uk; @OPSO_london; 10:30pm, Sun 10 pm; closed Sun D.

The Orange SW1   £65   3 2 3
37 Pimlico Rd   020 7881 9844   6–2D
This spruced-up gastro-boozer in an attractive square on the Pimlico-Chelsea border makes for a "fun dining experience with all the benefits of a pub". The cooking is "better than expected", with the "reliable pizzas a safe bet". / SW1W 8NE; www.theorange.co.uk; @theorangesw1; 10 pm, Sun 9.30 pm.

Orange Pekoe SW13   £36   3 3 4
3 White Hart Ln   020 8876 6070   11–1A
"A vast choice of great teas, coffees, cakes and sandwiches, plus daily specials" attract hordes of visitors to this "very popular" tea shop near the river in chichi Barnes. If you want to sit down for a proper afternoon tea, you'd be wise to book. / SW13 0PX; www.orangepekoeteas.com; @OrangePekoeTeas; 5 pm; L only.

Orasay W11 NEW   £59   4 4 4
31 Kensington Park Road   020 7043 1400   7–1A
As "a welcome arrival in the area", Jackson Boxer's "friendly and unpretentious" new venture (which oldies will think of as opposite the long-RIP 192) commands a lot of support from Notting Hill locals, and it's drawing a "fun crowd", including a few famous faces. The cuisine focuses on the Hebridean islands where Boxer spent childhood summers: to fans, results are "superb", but one or two reporters feel "good ingredients are fussily assembled" to create dishes that are merely "good but not amazing". / W11 2EU; orasay.london; @Jackson_Boxer.

Ormer Mayfair, Flemings Mayfair Hotel W1   £100   4 4 2
7-12 Half Moon Street   020 7016 5601   3–4B
"A delight!" – Shaun Rankin's "exceptional" and "beautifully presented" cuisine at this posh, Mayfair hotel dining room wins acclaim from all reporters this year: "not sure why it doesn't have a stronger following – highly under-rated". He made his name on Jersey – an 'ormer' is a Channel Islands gastropod – before shifting to the capital in 2016. "It's a beautiful interior, but the basement setting can make it a bit gloomy for lunch". / W1J 7BH; www.ormermayfair.com; @ormermayfair; No shorts.

Oro Di Napoli W5 £35 **4**|**4**|**3**
6 The Quadrant, Little Ealing Lane   020 3632 5580   1–3A

"There's no better pizza in London" ("twenty or so combinations of toppings or you can make your own as you wish"), say fans of this "humming" South Ealing spot, where "the kitchen is visible (almost indivisible) from the small and intimate dining area" presided over by "smiling, passionate staff". It's thriving in an area thick with the smoke of Neapolitan wood-fired ovens – nearby Santa Maria is another claimant as 'London's best'. / W5 4EE; www.lorodinapoli.co.uk; 11 pm.

Orrery W1 £89 **3**|**3**|**3**
55 Marylebone High St   020 7616 8000   2–1A

Opened by Sir Terence Conran in 1997 (on the first floor, above the eponymous Conran Shop) – this "calm and well-run", light-filled Marylebone fixture remains one of the most consistent performers in the D&D London stable. Igor Tymchyshyn has been at the stoves since 2008 (and became 'chef-patron' in 2016), and his "top quality" and "well-presented" modern cuisine is served by "accommodating and unfussy" staff in a stylish setting: a narrowly-proportioned room, with great views of the adjacent church. Top Tip – "the 'secret' rooftop terrace is a joy on a summer's evening". / W1U 5RB; www.orrery-restaurant.co.uk; @The_Orrery; 10 pm, Fri & Sat 10.30 pm; booking max 8 may apply.

Oscar Wilde Lounge at Cafe Royal W1 £82 **3**|**4**|**5**
68 Regent St   020 7406 3333   4–4C

"One of the most magical afternoon tea locations" – "overseas guests are particularly impressed by the sumptuous surroundings" of this "OTT" rococo chamber (the original Café Royal Grill Room, dating back to 1865), which comes "with loads of mirrors and gold leaf" and flamboyant murals. "Don't go just for the room", though – "staff are great (making you feel special without being too pompous), while the sandwiches are varied and plentiful", pastries are "featherlight" and there are a variety of options for tea itself. / W1B; www.hotelcaferoyal.com/oscarwildebar; @HotelCafeRoyal; 6 pm; L & afternoon tea only.

Oslo Court NW8 £66 **3**|**5**|**4**
Charlbert Street   020 7722 8795   9–3A

"Like going on a 1970s cruise without leaving the shore" – this "crazy-but-fun throwback" at the foot of a Regent's Park apartment-block is certainly "one of a kind", and always "leaves you smiling". "Faultless and charming" staff of decades' standing bantering with silver-haired regulars of a not-dissimilar vintage create an atmosphere that's "half restaurant – half theatre": "there are always generations of families celebrating a birthday" and "the hubbub can be deafening, with cakes arriving at regular intervals". The "absurdly retro menu" (crudités, melba toast, steak Diane…) is seemingly unchanged from when the place opened, and delivers "overwhelming helpings of well-cooked classic dishes, washed down with very sensibly priced wine". "The renowned dessert waiter with his trolley is still there, but of late, no longer always does the same performance at the end of the meal, whereby he tells you what you want without you asking, and says 'mama saved the last piece for you!'" / NW8 7EN; www.oslocourtrestaurant.co.uk; 11 pm; closed Sun; No jeans.

Osteria,
Barbican Centre EC2   £58   3 3 2

Level 2 Silk Street   020 7588 3008   10–1B

"I am truly surprised at the low ratings this has received in Harden's!" – Searcy's seem to have pulled their socks up at their Italian brasserie and cocktail bar, which sits in the beating heart of the Barbican arts centre (making it a natural pre-theatre option), and which by day enjoys "excellent views" over the centre's lake and St Giles Cripplegate church. Some diners do still say its overall performance is "no better than adequate", but more fans this year lauded its "excellent food from a regularly changing menu". / EC2Y 8DS; osterialondon.co.uk; @searcyslondon; 10.30 pm, Sat 11.30 pm; closed Sun.

Osteria Antica Bologna SW11   £50   3 2 2

23 Northcote Rd   020 7978 4771   11–2C

"For a 'local Italian' it's hard to beat" this "consistently good" trat that celebrates three decades on Clapham's foodie Northcote Road this year. "It looks and feels like an authentic taverna in Northern Italy" – "there's nothing flash and no emphasis on fancy tableware or presentation, but I've had better food here than at fancier places in town". It's "a bit dark inside", though, "so better for lunch than dinner". Top Menu Tip – "wild boar ragu". / SW11 1NG; www.osteria.co.uk; @OsteriaAntica; 10.30 pm, Sun 10 pm.

Osteria Basilico W11   £63   4 3 2

29 Kensington Park Rd   020 7727 9957   7–1A

"Simple, honest Italian fare done well" – with "fresh ingredients and great service" – is a combination that has served Notting Hill well for almost 30 years at this local trattoria: the senior in a group of three siblings in the same street (see also Mediterraneo and Essenza). / W11 2EU; www.osteriabasilico.co.uk; 11.30 pm, Sun 10.30 pm; no booking, Sat L.

Osteria Dell'Angolo SW1   £64   3 3 2

47 Marsham St   020 3268 1077   2–4C

"Ignore the lobbyists feeding MPs and enjoy this for what it is" – a smart, traditionally decorated corner-spot that's one of the only restaurants in Westminster worth going to eat in! "Italian through and through", it features "many regional dishes" and "unusual takes on traditional pasta and main courses (including crab, rabbit and quail)"; plus an interesting, all-Italian wine list. / SW1P 3DR; www.osteriadellangolo.co.uk; @Osteria_Angolo; 10 pm; closed Sat L & Sun.

Osteria Tufo N4   £52   4 3 2

67 Fonthill Rd   020 7272 2911   9–1D

This "Italian gem" in Finsbury Park has locals purring with its "wonderful homemade pasta" and "brilliant service from Paola and her team" – "we were a fussy group aged 7 to 75 and the staff catered for our every desire". Yes, there's "a singing waiter", but "it's not cringe-worthy, he's really good!". / N4 3HZ; www.osteriatufo.co.uk; @osteriatufo; 10.30 pm, Sun 9.30 pm; closed Mon & Sun L; No Amex.

The Other Naughty Piglet SW1   £50   4 3 2

12 Palace Street   020 7592 0322   2–4B

In a masterstroke of casting, Andrew Lloyd Webber recruited Brixton's Naughty Piglets team to run the restaurant at his new Other Palace Theatre in Victoria, bringing their "dependably delightful" cuisine to this "almost secret location tucked away by Buckingham Palace". / SW1E 5JA; www.theothernaughtypiglet.co.uk; booking max 10 may apply.

Otto's WC1 £73 **4 4 3**

182 Gray's Inn Road 020 7713 0107 2–1D

"A joyous celebration of how restaurants used to be and how they should be"; "eccentric Otto" is "a breath of fresh French air", and his "gift of showmanship", "traditional service" and "classic Gallic cuisine" – all in a "pleasant and old-fashioned", if slightly "faded", dining room in out-of-the-way Bloomsbury – is part of a nowadays "unique" approach that most diners feel is "always a wow". "Otto's duck and lobster à la presse is superlative" (he's recently added pigeon too), "the steak tartare is London's best" and such culinary throwbacks form part of a "magnificent", unreformed, old-school menu. Caveats? – some of the food is "devastatingly cream-rich – not all modern eaters could manage it" – and "though it's all very likeable, watch out as the bill stacks up quickly". "But it's one-of-a-kind". / WC1X 8EW; www.ottos-restaurant.com; @ottosrestaurant; 9.30 pm; closed Mon, Sat L & Sun.

Ottolenghi £58 **3 2 2**

13 Motcomb St, SW1 020 7823 2707 6–1D
63 Ledbury Rd, W11 020 7727 1121 7–1B
287 Upper St, N1 020 7288 1454 9–2D
50 Artillery Pas, E1 020 7247 1999 10–2D

"A feast for the eyes and always fresh, delicious" and full of "interesting flavour" – the "unusual salads" and habit-forming cakes at Yotam Ottolenghi's starkly decorated café chain: an ongoing success-story particularly beloved of brunching yummy-mums and Guardian-reading types ("is this a restaurant or a cult?… some of the clientele on my trip seemed beyond parody"). "It's only the food that makes it worth it" though – branches are "super-busy and never enjoyable" – and, given the prices, a visit can "feel like daylight robbery". / www.ottolenghi.co.uk; N1 10.30 pm, Sun 7 pm; W11 & SW1 8 pm, Sat 7 pm, Sun 6 pm; E1 10.30 pm, Sun 6 pm; W11 & SW1 no booking.

Oxo Tower, Restaurant SE1 £100 **1 1 1**

Barge House St 020 7803 3888 10–3A

"Tried it again… still disappointing" – this notorious South Bank rooftop has been our No. 1 top dud for about as long as we can remember. "Yes, the views are fine, but – with its quite insipid cooking and no glamour whatsoever" – the experience here is "just dull and mediocre". At some level, "you've got to congratulate them for still getting patrons for such overpriced rubbish!" / SE1 9PH; www.harveynichols.com/restaurant/the-oxo-tower; @OxoTowerWharf; 11 pm, Sun 10 pm; booking max 8 may apply.

Oxo Tower, Brasserie SE1 £75 **1 1 3**

Barge House St 020 7803 3888 10–3A

"Why can't they get it right?" in the cheaper section of this South Bank landmark. "The view is superb, the setting is relaxing… if only the food lived up to it". / SE1 9PH; www.harveynichols.com/restaurants/oxo-tower-london; @oxo_tower; 11 pm, Sun 10 pm; May need 2+ to book.

The Oystermen Seafood Kitchen & Bar WC2 £63 **4 3 3**

32 Henrietta St 020 7240 4417 5–3D

"You'll expect to look out the window at the beach and waves… yet it's Covent Garden out there!". This "fun and casual" two-year-old perhaps "feels different since they grew" (into the next door premises) in the autumn of 2018. "But you still eat cheek-by-jowl with neighbouring tables" in a "hustling-and-bustling" setting, and most reports still feel it's "just as good in its expanded space". Amongst the selection of "cracking" fish and seafood, "the oysters are a joy", "the crab's a wow"; and it's all "amazing value". "Likeable staff", too. / WC2E 8NA; oystermen.co.uk; @theoystermen.

Ozone Coffee Roasters EC2 £44 3 3 4
11 Leonard Street   020 7490 1039   13–1A
"Damn fine coffee! Nuff said!" – "complex and expertly made" – is the
focus at this "super-cool spot" in Shoreditch (the offshoot of an NZ original).
The beans are "roasted downstairs" with wonderful aromas floating up from
the big machines in the basement, while upstairs a "funky crowd enjoy food
and drinks" from the "best breakfast" to late-night cocktails. A second
London branch is scheduled to open in Bethnal Green in late-2019.
/ EC2A 4AQ; ozonecoffee.co.uk; @Ozonecoffeeuk; 9 pm, Sat & Sun 4.30 pm
; May need 8+ to book.

P Franco E5 £48 4 2 3
107 Lower Clapton Road   020 8533 4660   14–1B
No Eater newsletter is complete without paradisical claims for this – still the
online fooderati's favourite bottle shop – in gentrifying Clapton: a "funky"
and "buzzy", if "very crowded" little space where "sensational wines"
(of the 'natural' variety) are accompanied by "amazing" and "eclectic" small
plates from an ever-changing roster of chefs: all eaten at a communal
central table. / E5 0NP; www.pfranco.co.uk; Thu-Sat 10 pm, Sun 9 pm; closed
Mon-Wed, Thu-Sat D only, Sun L & D; No Amex; No bookings.

Pachamama 2 2 3
18 Thayer Street, W1   020 7935 9393   3–1A
Great Eastern Street, EC2   13–1B NEW
"Big, punchy flavours" come through from the "varied" menu at these
"lively" ("we could barely hear one another above the din") Peruvians,
in Marylebone and – since November 2018 – now also in Shoreditch
(Pachamama East).

Padella SE1 £28 5 4 3
6 Southwark St   no tel   10–4C
"Bellissimo!" – Tim Siadatan and Jordan Frieda's Borough Market three-
year-old remains one of the capital's best options on a budget. The formula
is simple: "no reservations, no frills": just "superlative, freshly made pasta"
from a "compact and great value menu". "Arrive ultra-early to dodge the
worst of the perma-queues", although "the line moves relatively quickly,
and their beeper system means you can go for a drink and come back
to get your table". In September 2019, they announced a second branch
is top open on Phipp Street in Shoreditch in early 2020. / SE1 1TQ;
www.padella.co; @padella_pasta; 10 pm, Sun 5 pm; no booking.

Paladar SE1 £59 4 3 3
4-5 London Road   020 7186 5555   10–4A
"A great find in the wasteland around Elephant & Castle, where everything
is South American, from ingredients, such as plantain and cassava, to the
wine list and the lively clientele". A bar/restaurant (with walled garden for
warmer days), it's "a great introduction to Latino food": "typical dishes such
as ceviche and braised black beef are produced to a higher standard than
just about anywhere else in London". Top Tip – all dishes are gluten-free,
with a range of veggie and vegan options. / SE1 6JZ; www.paladarlondon.com;
@paladarlondon.

Palatino EC1 £60 4 3 2
71 Central Street   020 3481 5300   10–1B
Chef Stevie Parle's two-year-old pasta specialist is a real "crowd-pleaser",
with "consistently interesting, extremely tasty" Roman-inspired dishes
emerging from its "impressively visible kitchen". It's part of a "warehouse-
style" Clerkenwell work-space, but "when busy you forget the office
atmosphere which can otherwise be a little cold". Top Tip – "cacio e pepe
is to die for". / EC1V 8AB; palatino.london; @PalatinoLondon; 10 pm; closed Sun.

The Palomar W1 £64 **4** **3** **4**
34 Rupert Street 020 7439 8777 4–3D
"Deafening and crowded, but that's all part of the fun" – Tel Aviv comes
to Theatreland at this "interesting haven", on the fringe of Chinatown.
"If you like atmosphere, too much noise, and somewhere right in the heart
of things, it hits the bullseye"; and "sitting at the bar, bantering with the
chefs and soaking up the superb playlist help make this a truly memorable
occasion". The "stunning and stunningly different", "Israeli-influenced" small
plates are "simply scrumptious" too, even if "prices are high for such
a quick turnover of covers". / W1D 6DN; www.thepalomar.co.uk; @palomarsoho;
11 pm, Sun 9 pm; closed Sun L.

Pappa Ciccia £37 **3** **3** **2**
105 Munster Rd, SW6 020 7384 1884 11–1B
41 Fulham High St, SW6 020 7736 0900 11–1B
96 Lower Richmond Rd, SW15 020 8785 7349
"The best pizza in the area" – "thin, very tasty" and in "large" portions –
wins fans for this "friendly" family-owned trio that has built a solid following
in Fulham and Putney over two decades. SW15 is primarily take-out and
delivery (but has some outside seating). / www.pappaciccia.com; SW6 5RQ
11 pm, Sat & Sun 11.30 pm; SW6 3JJ 11 pm.

Paradise W1 NEW
61 Rupert Street 4–2D
Replacing Soho's Spuntino (RIP) – a Sri Lankan 30-seater from a team who
have been popping up around London recently, so it will have a ready-made
fanclub when it opens in October 2019. The refurb is being done by the
designer behind Kiln and Smoking Goat, who is aiming to keep the site's
stripped-back aesthetic, but with a new 'warm-yet-raw' look. / W1D 7PW.

Paradise by Way of Kensal Green W10 £55 **2** **2** **5**
19 Kilburn Lane 020 8969 0098 1–2B
For a chilled Sunday roast, vibey night out, date, birthday party, funeral
wake – whatever – it's still worth considering this vast Kensal Green tavern,
with seemingly endless bars, dance-floors, party rooms, and terraces, plus its
gorgeous dining room and garden. The days when it was in the vanguard
of London's gastropub scene are long gone, but it's still a magnet for chilled
Notting Hillbillies who've strayed north; and still serves dependable grub.
/ W10 4AE; www.theparadise.co.uk; @weloveparadise; 10.30 pm, Fri & Sat 11 pm,
Sun 9 pm; closed weekday L; No Amex.

Paradise Hampstead NW3 £41 **4** **5** **4**
49 South End Rd 020 7794 6314 9–2A
"Lovely neighbourhood Indian" near Hampstead Heath that's deservedly
popular for its "tasty food from an interesting menu" and "reasonable
prices". Now run by the second generation of the founder's family,
who provide "exceptionally friendly service", its only drawback is that
it "can be difficult to get a table". / NW3 2QB; www.paradisehampstead.co.uk;
10.45 pm.

El Parador NW1 £41 **3** **3** **3**
245 Eversholt St 020 7387 2789 9–3C
Veteran, family-run tapas bar, near Mornington Crescent, which garners
consistent high praise for "home cooking of the kind you rarely find these
days". What's more, there's a "pleasant garden for outdoor eating in fine
weather". / NW1 1BA; www.elparadorlondon.com; 11 pm, Fri & Sat 11.30 pm,
Sun 9.30 pm; closed Sat L & Sun L; No Amex.

Paranhodu SE14 £23 **3** **4** **2**
125 Lewisham Way 020 3573 8175 1–4D
Down near Goldsmiths in need of a decent scoff? Don't forget this "good,
independent Korean" – a five-year-old café offering "a solid representation
of all the classics: nice banchan, satisfying dolsot bibimbap and kimchi tofu
stews etc". / SE14 6QJ.

Park Chinois W1　　　　　　　£136　　2 2 3
17 Berkeley St　020 3327 8888　3–3C
There's no denying the "seductive" pull of this opulent venture (founded in 2015 by Alan Yau and nowadays owned by an anonymous Turkish family) which brings a slice of 1920s Shanghai decadence to Mayfair. But while fans "love the dim sum selection and vibes on a busy night", saying it "ticks all the boxes", its "off-the-scale prices" inspire outrage amongst many reporters, and raise a suspicion that beneath the glamorous veneer, "it's just a bog standard Chinese". / W1S 4NF; www.parkchinois.com; @ParkChinois; 11 pm, Sun 10.15 pm; No jeans.

Park Terrace Restaurant,
Royal Garden Hotel W8　　　　£62　　2 3 3
2-24 Kensington High St　020 7361 0602　6–1A
With its "beautiful views over Kensington Gardens", this "quiet and comfortable" hotel restaurant makes a useful venue for lunch or afternoon tea. "The service is a perfect blend of efficiency and friendliness", while the Sunday roast – sirloin of Buccleuch beef, carved from the trolley – is "delicious". / W8 4PT; www.parkterracerestaurant.co.uk; 10:30.

Parlour Kensal NW10　　　　　£50　　3 4 4
5 Regent St　020 8969 2184　1–2B
This "super gastropub" on Kensal Rise has a "creative, ever-changing and good-value menu" that starts with a "fantastic breakfast". The "always incredible welcome" ensures a "perfect chilled time". / NW10 5LG; www.parlourkensal.com; @ParlourUK; 10 pm; closed Mon.

Parrillan N1 NEW　　　　　　　£66　　3 4 4
Coal Drops Yard　020 7018 3339　9–3C
"An experience as well as amazing food!" – the Hart Bros' spring 2019 newcomer, in Coal Drops Yard, occupies a big, glam terrace, overlooking Regent's Canal: "it's outside only, partially protected from the rain, but with no protection from any wind". Each table has its own DIY tabletop mini-grill (the eponymous 'parrillan'): "you grill your own partially-prepared vegetables, meats and fish"; and there's also a selection of 'para picar' (Spanish nibbles). All early feedback says the formula stacks up well, but one or two diners feel the bill ends up a tad pricey. / N1C 4AB; barrafina.co.uk; @ParrillanLondon.

Parsons WC2　　　　　　　　　£65　　4 3 2
39 Endell Street　020 3422 0221　5–2C
"It's the fresh fish that brings you" to this "tiny, tiny space" in Covent Garden (sibling to 10 Cases, just across the road) – a "crowded, congested and stripped-down room" that's almost "more of a seafood bar than a restaurant as you perch on stools". "There's a small menu, with a few specials painted on the walls showing the catch of the day", "all cooked to perfection behind the counter and served as soon as it's ready". "Ideal for pre-theatre, but it doesn't encourage lingering". / WC2H 9BA; www.parsonslondon.co.uk.

Passione e Tradizione N15　　£39　　3 2 2
451 West Green Road　020 8245 9491　1–1C
"A top local" – this small, basic-looking two-year-old between Wood Green and Tottenham is worth remembering for its "great pizzas along with superb pastas". / N15 3PL; spinach.london; 11 pm.

Passyunk Avenue W1 NEW £47 4 4 3
80 Cleveland Street   020 3960 2251   2–1B

"Pure fast food evil (in the best kind of way)" – this retro newcomer in the shadow of the BT tower is named for the home of the Philly cheesesteak, which it serves with "great authenticity (as validated by my colleague from Philadelphia)", alongside "the best buffalo wings in London (and maybe outside of Pennsylvania)", plus other classics from Rocky Balboa's hometown like "wiz cheese and bacon tater tots". "Friendly staff" complete its down-to-earth vibe; there's also a branch in Westfield Stratford. / W1T 6NE; www.passyunk.co.uk; @passyunkavenue.

Pasta Remoli £40 3 3 3
Dickens Yard, 16a New Broadway, W5   020 8840 2687   1–3A NEW
7 Clifton Terrace, N4   020 7263 2948   9–1D
Westfield Stratford City, E20   020 8555 9149   14–1D NEW

From its Finsbury Park base (next to the Park Theatre), this "cheerful" group of "good neighbourhood pasta-stops" has expanded to Ealing this year, with a Wembley branch coming soon (there's also an outlet in Westfield Stratford); all deliver "well-cooked", affordable pasta. / www.pastaremoli.co.uk; @PastaRemoli.

Pastaio W1 £45 3 3 2
19 Ganton Street   4–2B

"Amazing fresh pasta that's great value for central London" has carved a strong following for Stevie Parle's "loud" and buzzy Kingly Court operation for a "swift", "cheap 'n' cheerful" bite. / W1F 7BU; www.pastaio.london; @pastaiolondon.

Pasticceria Marchesi 1824 W1 NEW
117 Mount Street   020 8075 5380   3–3B

For a posh bun, it's hard to upstage this new Milanese import: a fashionista favourite for its superlative cakes and also serving some more substantial dishes (such as risotti) alongside cocktails and wine. Too limited feedback for a rating as yet, but all of it enthusiastic. / W1K 2AL; www.pasticceriamarchesi.com.

El Pastór SE1 £43 4 3 4
7a Stoney Street   no tel   10–4C

"Some of the better tacos in London" have made the Hart Bros' "very crowded" taqueria one of the hits of Borough Market. "Really delicious, interesting flavours – you just want to try them all" – especially if "you love really hot, spicy Mexican food". The Harts have followed up with Casa Pastór at King's Cross (see also), Tortilleria at nearby Maltby Street, and most recently Pastorcito in the new Arcade Food Theatre at Centre Point. / SE1 9AA; www.tacoselpastor.co.uk; @Tacos_El_Pastor; 11 pm; No bookings.

Patara £62 3 4 3
15 Greek St, W1   020 7437 1071   5–2A
7 Maddox St, W1   020 7499 6008   4–2A
181 Fulham Rd, SW3   020 7351 5692   6–2C
9 Beauchamp Pl, SW3   020 7581 8820   6–1C
82 Hampstead High St, NW3   020 7431 5902   9–2A
18 High St, SW19   020 3931 6157   11–2B

"Andy Murray is a regular visitor (to the Wimbledon branch), and with good reason", report fans of this "upmarket" group. Like Sir Andy, "great service" is a particular strength, while "the food is pretty authentic" too. Now an international operation, the first of its six London venues opened in 1990. / www.pataralondon.com; @PataraLondon; 10.30 pm, Thu-Sat 11 pm.

Paternoster Chop House EC4 £61 2 2 2
I Warwick Court 020 7029 9400 10–2B
*This business-friendly venue overlooking St Paul's Cathedral is part of the
D&D London operation and offers "pretty good steaks" cooked over
charcoal, although the "ridiculous prices" are likely to deter all but expense
account diners (and maybe also TV fans, as the show First Dates has been
filmed here for the past six years). / EC4M 7DX;
www.paternosterchophouse.co.uk; @paternoster1; 10.30 pm; closed Sat & Sun D;
booking max 12 may apply.*

Patogh W1 £18 4 3 2
8 Crawford Pl 020 7262 4015 7–1D
*"Don't let the shabby interior put you off" – this "wonderful, simple Iranian
café" off Edgware Road serves "excellent and authentic Persian dishes"
including "superb lamb". "I love this place" – "small, squashed and full
of character", it all but defines "cheap 'n' cheerful" ("and BYOB").
/ W1H 5NE; www.patoghlondon.com; 11 pm; Cash only.*

Patri 3 4 3
139 Northfield Avenue, W13 020 3981 3388 1–3A NEW
103 Hammersmith Grove, W6 020 8741 1088 8–1C NEW
*"Love this new Indian street-food joint" – a neighbourhood cantina
in Hammersmith not dissimilar to its predecessor (Chai Naasto), refurbed,
formatted and renamed by the same owners to become this current
incarnation. It serves a "good selection of veg and non-veg options",
and some dishes are "fantastic". There's also a branch in Northfields.*

Patty and Bun £29 4 3 3
18 Old Compton St, W1 020 7287 1818 5–2A
54 James St, W1 020 7487 3188 3–1A
14 Pembridge Rd, W11 020 7229 2228 7–2B
19 Borough High Street, SE1 10–4C
36 Redchurch Street, E2 020 7613 3335 13–1C
2 Arthaus Building, 205 Richmond Road, E8 020 8525 8250 14–1B
22-23 Liverpool St, EC2 020 7621 1331 10–2D
Swingers Crazy Golf, Saint Mary Axe, EC3 020 3846 3222 10–2D
*There's "clear blue water between Patty & Bun and other wannabe mass
burger offerings" – the only drawback is "you have to queue all the time".
Having started out as a pop-up, the small chain has grown to eight
branches and two spin-offs: Smash Patty and Jefferies, a chicken specialist.
The core of the offer is "burgers dripping in all the good stuff, loud tunes,
friendly vibes and lots of napkins". Top Tip – the "legendary lamb burger
always makes me smile". / www.pattyandbun.co.uk; @pattyandbunjoe;
10 pm-11.30 pm, Sun 9 pm-10pm.*

Pavilion Cafe & Bakery E9 £10 4 2 4
Victoria Park, Old Ford Road 020 8980 0030 14–2C
*"Sambar curry is super, and a great way to start the day!" at this brunch
favourite – a quaint-looking, domed café by the water in Victoria Park,
where Sri Lankan options feature alongside full English and vegan
breakfasts; there's offshoots in Colombia Road and Broadway Market.
/ E9 7DE; www.pavilionbakery.com; @pavilionbakery; 3 pm; L only; No Amex;
No bookings.*

The Pear Tree W6 £42 3 4 4
14 Margravine Rd 020 7381 1787 8–2C
*Entering this "quiet neighbourhood pub" in a backstreet behind Charing
Cross Hospital is "like stepping back in time" into a "piece of living history"
– dating from 1824, it has kept an unspoilt vintage interior and wood fires.
The "good food at reasonable prices" manages to be both traditional
(beef & kidney suet pudding) and modern (with a vegan menu). / W6 8HJ;
www.thepeartreefulham.com; 9.30 pm, Fri-Sun 9 pm; Mon-Thu D only, Fri-Sun open
L & D.*

Pearl Liang W2 £53 **4** **2** **2**
8 Sheldon Square 020 7289 7000 7–1C
"Consistently excellent dim sum" – "very good for the price" as well – is the menu highlight at this "go-to" Cantonese destination in Paddington Basin. Despite its smart modern fit-out, however, the basement location can appear "noisy" and "soulless". / W2 6EZ; www.pearlliang.co.uk; @PearlLiangUK; 11 pm.

Peckham Bazaar SE15 £56 **3** **3** **3**
119 Consort Rd 020 7732 2525 1–4D
"All the dishes deliver bags of flavour and something different to the usual" at this "really interesting Balkan restaurant", "well off-the-beaten-path (even by Peckham standards)". Much is cooked on a charcoal grill so "there's a happy smoky vibe to the place", although it's "always busy" and "can feel cramped". / SE15 3RU; www.peckhambazaar.com; @PeckhamBazaar; 10 pm, Sun 8 pm; closed Mon, Tue-Fri D only, Sat & Sun open L & D; No Amex.

Peckham Levels SE15 £17
95a Rye Lane none 1–4D
"Tasty street-food vendors, a good pint and a great atmosphere" (plus, for families, "plenty of space for kids to scoot around") win a thumbs-up for this vibey project, converted from seven levels of an underutilised multi-storey car park. Levels five and six are the heart of the action foodwise: residents include Nandine (offshoot of a Kurdish café in Camberwell), Other Side Fried (chicken burgers) and Hao Hao chi (handmade regional Chinese street food). / SE15 4TG; www.peckhamlevels.org; @peckhamlevels.

Peg E9 NEW **4** **3** **3**
120 Morning Lane 020 3441 8765 14–1B
In early summer 2019 (just as our survey was getting underway), some of the backers behind P Franco and Bright opened this: another painfully hip, East End natural wine bar (on the former site of Hackney's now-defunct Legs – geddit?). This time Australian chef Byron Fini is at the stoves cooking up a small menu of light, "Japanese-izakaya-style" bar snacks – including ferments and pickles, and majoring in grilled skewers (lots of them chicken-related) – which are served in a bright, stylishly-neutral, small space that's very 'now' (communal seating, tabletops made from recycled yoghurt pots, vinyl soundtrack, etc). Foodwise, the odd disappointment is noted ("if you want Japanese, go to a Japanese restaurant") but most reports are in line with the rhapsodic write-ups it's received in the press, rating the dishes very good to exceptional. / E9 6LH; www.peglondon.co.uk; No bookings.

E Pellicci E2 £25 **3** **5** **5**
332 Bethnal Green Rd 020 7739 4873 13–1D
"You don't come here for the food: the welcome and the banter are the main attraction!", say fans of the Nevio family's "buzzy" (but hipster-free) Bethnal Green greasy spoon, which is a top choice for a "simple breakfast". Architecture anoraks will also want to examine its (listed) Art Deco interior (often used as a location for TV). / E2 0AG; epellicci.has.restaurant; 4 pm; L only, closed Sun; Cash only; No bookings.

Pentolina W14 £57 **4** **5** **3**
71 Blythe Rd 020 3010 0091 8–1C
This "hidden gem near Brook Green", with "authentic and imaginative home-made Italian food", is an "absolute favourite neighbourhood restaurant". "The lovely couple who own it" – chef Michele and front-of-house Heidi – "are so friendly and passionate about their cuisine", while "standards are constantly improving" – especially "now that they change the menu regularly". / W14 0HP; www.pentolinarestaurant.co.uk; 10 pm; closed Mon & Sun; No Amex.

Perilla N16 £62 **4 4 3**

1-3 Green Lanes   0207 359 0779   1–1C

"Intelligent, creative, modern British food from chef Ben Marks" is attracting widespread foodie attention at his "hip" two-year-old, whose huge picture windows overlook Newington Green. Still in his twenties, the Noma graduate wins praise for his "really great cooking and innovative thinking" – "you can really feel the kitchen's sense of excitement at diners enjoying their delicious food", and it's "very rare to get a chef of this quality in the kitchen every night". / N16 9BS; www.perilladining.co.uk; @perilladining; 10.30 pm, Sun 8.30 pm.

The Petersham WC2 £91 **2 1 4**

Floral Court, off Floral St   020 7305 7676   5–3C

"Like being in the country, but without leaving London": this year-old 'lifestyle destination' in a new Covent Garden development – spun out from the Richmond garden centre's famous shabby-chic restaurant – comprises a shop, florist, deli, cicchetti (Italian small plates) bar and a main restaurant. It's a lavish investment from the Boglione family, with a "beautiful atmosphere", but the food is "only just about good enough for the prices", while the "disorganised and chaotic service requires some serious work". Still, for a romantic lunch on a summer's day in the centre of town, its flower-filled courtyard is hard to beat. / WC2E 9DJ; petershamnurseries.com; @PetershamN; midnight.

Petersham Nurseries Cafe TW10 £80 **2 2 5**

Church Lane (signposted 'St Peter's Church'), off Petersham Road
020 8940 5230   1–4A

"The setting is just 'wow' on a sunny day" – "a secret paradise among the plants and bushes in a greenhouse" – "but the food is such a disappointment" ("seemingly great ingredients but very mediocre cooking") nowadays at this venue near Richmond Park that became famous under former chef Skye Gyngell a decade ago. It now has a smart offshoot in Covent Garden, but there's "something missing" at the original – not to speak of "the inadequate facilities, which leave you queueing outdoors for the toilet... in January!". / TW10 7AB; www.petershamnurseries.com; 2 pm, Sat & Sun 3.30 pm; L only, closed Mon; SRA-Food Made Good – 3 stars.

Le Petit Citron W6 NEW £48 **3 2 3**

98-100 Shepherds Bush Road   020 3019 1175   8–1C

"To the Brook Green site of Mustard (RIP) and before that Café Rouge (longer RIP) comes this attractive and inexpensive new French bistro". "Not much has changed since its predecessor" (same owners, who also own Covent Garden's Joe Allen) – "the food's decent" and comes at "very reasonable prices". / W6 7PD; lepetitcitron.co.uk; @lepetitcitronw6.

Petit Ma Cuisine TW9 £52 **3 3 3**

8 Station Approach   020 8332 1923   1–3A

This "simple, cosy French bistro" from Central Casting – gingham tablecloths, Impressionist posters, menu of Gallic classics – is a "reliable" hit with both Kew locals and visitors to the nearby botanical gardens. Top Tip – "great value set lunch" ("busy when we went on a Monday lunchtime!") / TW9 3QB; www.macuisinebistrot.co.uk; 10 pm, Fri & Sat 10.30 pm; No Amex.

Petit Pois Bistro N1 £58 **4 3 3**

9 Hoxton Square   020 7613 3689   13–1B

"Delicious French food in a small space" is the prospect of this "so, so good" Gallic bistro on Hoxton Square (with a small outside terrace). Top Menu Tip – "the chocolate mousse really is to die for!" / N1 6NU; www.petitpoisbistro.com; @petitpoisbistro; 10.30 pm, Sun 9 pm.

The Petite Coree NW6   £45   4 3 2
98 West End Lane   020 7624 9209   1–1B
Not far from West Hampstead station, this well-established, modern bistro
serves "small but delicious portions" of distinctive, "Asian-French fusion
cuisine": no doubt a legacy of chef-owner Jae's stints working for Nobu and
Hélène Darroze at the Connaught. The "limited ambience" may represent
a "missed opportunity" for cooking of this style and quality – the vibe
is "nice local" rather than "romantic" – but it's a "hidden gem" worth
discovering. / NW6 2LU; www.thepetitecoree.com; @thepetitecoree; 9.30 pm;
booking max 6 may apply.

La Petite Maison W1   £114   4 3 4
54 Brook's Mews   020 7495 4774   3–2B
"Beautiful, light, fresh sharing plates" bring a taste of Mediterranean
sunshine to a glam Mayfair crowd at this spin-out of a famous Côte d'Azur
haunt – "not the usual cream and butter of French cooking,
but delectable!". Although, just as in the South of France, the arrival of the
bill can induce a mild seizure. Chef Raphael Duntoye has tweaked the
original formula here for the London market – "it's nothing like the Nice
original" – which he has since exported to the Middle East, Miami and
most recently Hong Kong. / W1K 4EG; www.lpmlondon.co.uk; @lpmlondon;
10.45 pm, Sun 9.45 pm.

Pétrus SW1   £115   3 4 3
1 Kinnerton St   020 7592 1609   6–1D
"An impressive wine vault in the middle of the dining room" provides
a talking-point at Gordon Ramsay's "beautiful" and "romantic" (luxuriously
anodyne) Belgravian, whose capacious wine list is one of its defining
features. Russell Bateman joined as chef in mid-2018, and, according
to most reports, his "fabulous" modern cuisine "ticks every box"
to contribute to a "fabulous all-round experience". Ratings slid here a bit this
year, though, due to concerns about value: "it's good, but so painful on the
wallet". / SW1X 8EA; www.gordonramsayrestaurants.com; @petrus; 10 pm; closed
Sun; No trainers.

Pham Sushi EC1   £42   4 3 3
159 Whitecross St   020 7251 6336   13–2A
"Surprisingly great sushi" – among "the best in London" – is to be found
at this "modest Japanese" near the Barbican. "I lived in Japan for 10 years,
so I know good sushi when I have it". / EC1Y 8JL; www.phamsushi.com;
@phamsushi; 10 pm; closed Sat L & Sun.

Phat Phuc SW3   £30   3 3 2
Chelsea Courtyard, 151 Sydney Street   020 7351 3843   6–3C
"Delicious Vietnamese street food" – almost certainly "the best" in this part
of London – is found at this Chelsea noodle bar apparently meaning "happy
Buddha". The "scrumptious prawn laksa" is technically a Singaporean dish,
but who gives a ph**? / SW3 6NT; www.phatphucnoodlebar.co.uk;
@Phat_PhucNoodle.

Pho   £37   3 3 2
"Fresh soup noodle with an authentic, tasty tang, straight from the streets
of Hanoi" continues to win fans for these "pleasant" street-food pitstops,
which provide "very enjoyable, cheap and healthy", "Viet-style" bites.
/ www.phocafe.co.uk; 10 pm-11pm, Sun 6.30 pm-10 pm; EC1 closed Sat & Sun;
no booking.

Phoenix Palace NW1   £63   3 2 2
5-9 Glentworth St   020 7486 3515   2–1A
This "huge, traditional Chinese banqueting hall" – a rather 1970s space
near Baker Street tube – can be "a revelation" to newbies. "It does all the
typical Cantonese dishes" from a menu boasting more than 300 dishes,
and is particularly well-known for its "wonderful dim sum". "The service
runs like clockwork... as it has to". / NW1 5PG; www.phoenixpalace.co.uk;
11.30 pm, Sun 10.30 pm.

Pick & Cheese WC2 NEW

KERB Seven Dial Market   5–2C

One of the first concessions to be announced for the new Seven Dials Market from KERB (opened in late Summer 2019), is a cheese conveyor belt (yes, you read that right!) restaurant, from the owners of Camden's Cheese Bar. Twenty-five British cheeses will be delivered by the 40-metre conveyor belt. / WC2H 9HD; www.sevendialsmarket.com.

Pidgin E8   £78   5 3 2

52 Wilton Way   020 7254 8311   14–1B

"I don't know how they do it, but every week there is a new, exciting and delicious menu that never seems to be repeated" at this genius foodie-mecca in Hackney, which has rightly won renown on account of its "uniquely delicious, complex-without-being-baroque" cuisine. "It has a Michelin star and, after a few mouthfuls, it's clear to see why: the food is always innovative, mixing bold ranges of flavour and ingredients, focused on seasonal produce, all served up with a 'too-cool-for-skool' vibe", by staff who "move around the incredibly-tightly-packed dining room with a balletic poise". "The wine list is short but excellently curated", but the major win is the value: "in Mayfair it would cost double". On the downside, one or two regulars feel that the food has been "more hit-and-miss" in recent times, and the self-consciousness of the enterprise is a big turn-off for some folks: "a mixture of over-earnest staff intoning the menu without smiles, and sombre presentation of food as something sacred left us underwhelmed, on both visits". "I think I prefer food to be more unobtrusive, so you can spend the evening enjoying it alongside friends and conversation, rather than having each dish explained and having to come up with the requisite 'ooh, that sounds lovely, thank you' with every course..." / E8 1BG; www.pidginlondon.com; @PidginLondon; 11 pm; closed Mon & Tue, Wed & Thu D only, Fri-Sun L & D.

Piebury Corner   £20   3 2 2

3 Caledonian Rd, N1   020 7700 5441   9–3C

209-211 Holloway Rd, N7   020 7700 5441   9–2D

"Prime pies" named after legendary Gunners are available at the Holloway shop on Arsenal match days and full-time at the King's Cross venue. Their quality makes for "a pleasant surprise – with vegetarian options no afterthought", and there's also Scotch eggs, craft beers and cider. / N7 9.30 pm, Sun 5pm, N1 10 pm, Thu-Sat 11 pm, Sun 8 pm; N7 closed Mon-Wed ; no bookings.

Pied à Terre W1   £104   4 4 4

34 Charlotte St   020 7636 1178   2–1C

David Moore's illustrious Fitzrovian "continues to shine" under the tenure of head chef Asimakis Chaniotis, and this "elegant" townhouse remains one of London's foremost temples of gastronomy. "Letting Chef Chaniotis take you through an evening with a great custom tasting menu is second to none" – "he really is a master of meat, but they have great vegetarian and vegan tasting menus too", and "there's always something new and exciting" to sample. "An impressive wine list and a great sommelier's intelligent recommendations" complete the formula. The proportions of the building are not expansive, but tables are "well-spaced" and the overall experience is an "intimate" one. / W1T 2NH; www.pied-a-terre.co.uk; @PiedaTerreUK; 10.45 pm; closed Sat L & Sun; May need 12+ to book.

Pig & Butcher N1   £54   3 4 3

80 Liverpool Road   020 7226 8304   9–3D

Craft ales and on-site butchered meat combine at this "great local pub" in Islington – where the "hearty fare" is (perhaps unsurprisingly) "great for meat-lovers". It's "buzzy and busy", so "expect to queue" at prime times. / N1 0QD; www.thepigandbutcher.co.uk; @pigandbutcher; 10 pm, Sun 9 pm; Mon-Thu D only, Fri-Sun open L & D.

Pique Nique SE1   £60   3 2 3
32 Tanner Street   020 7403 9549   10–4D
"Sister restaurant of nearby Casse Croute that occupies a funny, mock-Tudor building (built as a shelter) on the borders of Tanner Street Park, complete with bar and open kitchen. The traditional Gallic cuisine – though good – lacks the all-round excellence of its sibling: service, though "friendly", is "a bit more sloppy"; and the environment is "cosy but a little less so". / SE1 3LD; pique-nique.co.uk; @piquenique32.

El Pirata W1   £49   2 3 3
5-6 Down St   020 7491 3810   3–4B
"Fast, furious" – and offering resoundingly "good value for Mayfair" – this "cheap 'n' cheerful" bar is "brilliant for a quick lunch at just over a tenner including beer", or for an early evening booze up. It serves "proper tapas" which are "OK", but it's not a foodie destination, it's a "fun" one. / W1J 7AQ; www.elpirata.co.uk; @elpirataw1; 11.30 pm; closed Sat L & Sun.

Pisqu W1   £60   3 3 2
23 Rathbone Place   020 7436 6123   5–1A
"Very refined food from the Amazon, full of flavour" has established this Fitzrovia two-year-old as "possibly one of the best Peruvian restaurants in London". "Often overlooked by people passing in favour of better-known Lima on the same street", it's "very different, and good value for money too". / W1T 1HZ; www.pisqulondon.com; @PisquLondon.

Pizarro SE1   £61   4 3 3
194 Bermondsey St   020 7256 5333   10–4D
Lacking the pizzazz of José P's nearby tapas-bar sibling, which is one block away, his somewhat bigger contemporary Spanish restaurant never inflames quite as much passion as its little sister. It still achieves very good ratings, though, for its "really interesting food" and "attractively priced wine list". / SE1 3TQ; josepizarro.com/pizarro-restaurant-bermondsey; @Jose_Pizarro; 10.45 pm, Sun 9.45 pm.

Pizza da Valter SW17   £45   3 2 2
7 Bellevue Road   020 8355 7032   11–2C
Solidly rated, wood-fired pizza is the staple at this spot, on foodie Bellevue Parade, overlooking Wandsworth Common, but "the dishes beyond the pizza are also very good". There's also a branch at Fulham Broadway (which doesn't inspire feedback in the survey). / SW17 7EG; Www.pizzadavalter.co.uk; @pizzadavalteruk.

Pizza East   £58   3 2 4
310 Portobello Rd, W10   020 8969 4500   7–1A
79 Highgate Rd, NW5   020 3310 2000   9–1B
56 Shoreditch High St, E1   020 7729 1888   13–1B
"Big and still with a great buzz" – these "vibey", industrial-style haunts, owned by the Soho House group, have won an impressive following with their "inventive pizzas" (lots of them meaty), grungy-cool styling and staff who – despite a fair dose of hipster cred – maintain a welcoming attitude. Its ratings came off the boil a little this year, though, and the odd reporter feels their performance is seeming more "tired". / www.pizzaeast.com; @PizzaEast; E1 11pm, Thu midnight, Fri & Sat 1am, NW5 9.30 pm, Fri & Sat 11.30 pm, Sun 10.30 pm, W10 10 pm, Thu-Sat 11pm, Sun 10.30 pm.

Pizza Metro SW11   £47   4 3 3
64 Battersea Rise   020 7228 3812   11–2C
"A long-time favourite", "always full of chatter and laughter", this Battersea pizzeria was the first in town to serve by the metre (or round, if you prefer) in 1993. "Both pizzazz and pizza that are long and good". / SW11 1EQ; www.pizzametropizza.com; @pizzametropizza; 11 pm, Fri & Sat midnight; No Amex.

Pizza Pilgrims £41 **4** **3** **3**
102 Berwick St, W1   0778 066 7258   4–2D
11-12 Dean St, W1   020 7287 8964   4–1D
Kingly Ct, Carnaby St, W1   020 7287 2200   4–2B
23 Garrick Street, WC2   020 3019 1881   5–3C
12 Hertsmere Rd, E14   020 3019 8020   12–1C
136 Shoreditch High St, E1   020 3019 7620   13–1B
15 Exmouth Mkt, EC1   020 7287 8964   10–1A
Swingers Crazy Golf, Saint Mary Axe, EC3   no tel   10–2D
"So delicious and affordable every time!" – the Elliot brothers' "speedy and
cheerful" small chain put in a stellar performance this year as London's top
pizza multiple, pipping rival Homeslice by tiny decimals. "You can see the
dough being made on entering: everything is very fresh, and you get crisp,
thin pizzas with quality toppings". / pizzapilgrims.co.uk; @pizzapilgrims;
10.30pm, Sun 9.30 pm; WC2 11 pm, Sun 10 pm; Dean St: no booking.

PizzaExpress £50 **2** **2** **2**
Entering its 55th year, the granddaddy of all UK pizza chains has "survived
the passing of time". These past five years have not been vintage ones for
the brand, however – since its takeover by Hony Capital in 2014, "the whole
experience seems a bit more soulless" and, after a continual slide, its ratings
have bottomed out somewhere between "just so average" and "all-in-all not
bad". As "a good introduction for kids to eating out" however, it still enjoys
massive support thanks to its "kind and supportive service given to frazzled
grandparents and over-excited grandsons". Some wider hope comes from
the recently "much-improved" Oxford Circus branch which is the prototype
of a promising new look ("newly revamped with a central bar feature,
at which you can eat if you prefer, plus draught Peroni and a better menu
has brought some desperately-needed vigour back to this tired chain").
"Only a few more hundred branches to refurb now..." / www.pizzaexpress.co.uk;
11.30 pm - midnight; most City branches closed all or part of weekend; no booking
at most branches.

Pizzeria Pappagone N4 £38 **3** **3** **3**
131 Stroud Green Rd   020 7263 2114   9–1D
"Such a fun neighbourhood pizzeria" – this "friendly", if hectic, indie has
been a Finsbury Park fixture for 21 years. They do "very competent pasta",
too, and are kid-friendly to the extent of producing "pizza dough dinosaurs".
/ N4 3PX; www.pizzeriapappagone.co.uk; @pizza_pappagone; midnight.

Pizzicotto W8 £55 **4** **5** **3**
267 Kensington High Street   020 7602 6777   8–1D
"Skip the ubiquitous PizzaExpress locations and head to this family-run
sister to Il Portico" ("owned by the same family"), a few doors down,
and opposite Kensington's new Design Museum. The pizzas (featuring
"activated charcoal bases") are "miles better than the usual", and they also
offer "freshly made pasta and traditional entrees". Top Tip – "go for the
incredibly simple Sicilian deep-fried pizza dough with salt on – then ask why
there aren't east London hipsters selling these!". / W8 6NA;
www.pizzicotto.co.uk; @pizzicottow8; 10.30 pm, Sun 9.30 pm.

Plaquemine Lock N1 £47 **2** **4** **3**
139 Graham St   020 7688 1488   9–3D
This tribute to the cuisine of Louisiana in a converted Islington canal-side
boozer is "fun and different" – and possibly "the best way to try Creole and
Cajun food without having to brave Homeland Security". Two years on from
opening, though, it hasn't fully lived up to the expectations raised by founder
Jacob Kenedy, known for his brilliant Bocca di Lupo. "The best dishes are
fabulous, but genuine Southern food seems to mean a lot is fried". / N1 8LB;
plaqlock.com.

Les Platanes W1 NEW £63
26-28 Bruton Place   020 7629 5613   3–2B

In a Mayfair townhouse that was formerly the short-lived Babel House (RIP), this 'contemporary bistro de luxe' features a southern French menu from chef Thierry Laborde, and opened in mid-2019, too late for any survey feedback. In his early review, The Evening Standard's David Sexton focused on its handsome design, variably realised and expensive cuisine, impressive wine list and bargain set lunch (£25 with wine). / W1J 6NG; lesplatanes.co.uk.

Plateau E14 £64   3 3 3
4th Floor, Canada Sq   020 7715 7100   12–1C

Atop Canada Place, opposite One Canada Square tower, this D&D London operation is well-known to denizens of Canary Wharf as one of its top expense-account destinations, thanks not least to its stunning views across the development. Those not slaving in the local money mills are less inclined to make the trip (except perhaps for brunch), but Jeremy Trehout's modern European cuisine is consistently well-rated this year. Top Tip – the adjoining grill is cheaper than the main restaurant. / E14 5ER; www.plateau-restaurant.co.uk; @plateaulondon; 10.30 pm; closed Sat L & Sun.

Plot SW17 £42   4 3 3
Unit 70-72 Broadway Market   020 8767 2639   11–2C

High marks again for this brave hipster outpost occupying one of the stalls in Tooting's covered market, and where funky, seasonal, British small plates are served at the counter. Some diners found themselves "questioning some of the combinations", but most judged results "very good". / SW17 0RL; plotkitchen.com; @plot_kitchen.

The Plough SW14 £45   2 2 4
42 Christ Church Rd   020 8876 7833   11–2A

Close to leafy Richmond Park, this 18th-century inn is a "lovely local boozer", with a "nice, quaint inside" for the winter months, and a "restful outside terrace that makes a perfect setting for a drink outdoors". Service is "very friendly" too, so it's a shame they don't make a bit more of an effort on the mostly enjoyable pub grub: "they don't aim for fancy, difficult dishes, but basic execution can disappoint". / SW14; www.theplough.com; 9.30 pm, Fri & Sat 10 pm, Sun 9 pm.

Plum + Spilt Milk,
Great Northern Hotel N1 £74   2 3 3
King's Cross St Pancras Station, Pancras Road   020 3388 0818   9–3C

This "beautiful" first-floor dining room is part of the restored Great Northern Hotel at King's Cross (the name derives from the Flying Scotsman's colours). By the standards of railway-related restaurants, it's a distinct cut above, with a "good-value set lunch" and "some nice options on the menu". Fair to say, though, that the cuisine is generally overshadowed by the "elegant decor", but that helps make it "a good spot for a business lunch". / N1C 4TB; plumandspiltmilk.com; @PlumSpiltMilk; 11 pm, Sun 10 pm.

Pollen Street Social W1 £113   3 3 3
8-10 Pollen St   020 7290 7600   3–2C

"If I want a guest to feel special, this is where I always choose to go!" – Jason Atherton's "first class" Mayfair HQ is "a great all-rounder with a very nice, light touch to its approach": most particularly its "clever and immaculately presented food" served "with flair", but also its relaxed-yet-upscale ambience. "It's not cheap but – to quote another famous brand – quality is remembered long after the price is forgotten". "Amazing cocktails" too. / W1S 1NQ; www.pollenstreetsocial.com; @PollenStSocial; 10.30 pm; closed Sun; booking max 7 may apply.

Polpo £51 1 2 2

41 Beak St, W1   020 7734 4479   4–2B
6 Maiden Ln, WC2   020 7836 8448   5–3D
Duke Of York Sq, SW3   020 7730 8900   6–2D
126-128 Notting Hill Gate, W11   020 7229 3283   7–2B
2-3 Cowcross St, EC1   020 7250 0034   10–1A

Now ten years old, Russell Norman and Richard Beatty's Venetian/Mediterranean chain faces the well-publicised challenge of a March CVA (Company Voluntary Agreement), amidst a drip-feed of branch closures. Fans do still applaud its "very convivial and fun" formula, but even they often feel it's "somewhat lost its way", with staff who can seem "overwhelmed" and serving Venetian small plates that are often "no better than fine", and at worst "uncared for" or "very mediocre". / www.polpo.co.uk; 10 pm-11 pm; W11 closed Sun & Mon, EC1M closed Sun; no bookings.

Pomona's W2 £57 3 4 4

47 Hereford Road   020 7229 1503   7–1B

"Love the garden and the creative spin they put on classic brunch dishes" – hitherto the main reasons to seek out this bright Notting Hill pub conversion. With the arrival of Ruth Hansom in April 2019, however, the menu has taken on a more serious, and British-sourced, slant – very early reports are upbeat: "exquisite cooking from a fabulous new female chef". / W2 5AH; www.pomonas.co.uk; @PomonasLondon; 10 pm, Fri & Sat 10.30 pm, Sun 9 pm.

Le Pont de la Tour SE1 £77 2 2 3

36d Shad Thames   020 7403 8403   10–4D

It can be "very special, particularly on a sunny day", at this well-known D&D London stalwart, thanks to its "lovely situation" (complete with large terrace) by the Thames near Tower Bridge; and it remains "a firm favourite" for a few folk, including for a date. Its famous heyday, when the Blairs and the Clintons supped on salmon and Bollinger at the height of Cool Britannia is well gone now, though, and – remarkably for what was once the City's top expense-accounter destination – of the relatively limited feedback this place now inspires, none of it plugs its suitability as a business rendezvous. The straightforward French-ified menu, likewise, elicits muted enthusiasm, although its heavyweight wine list still rates mention... as do the prices. / SE1 2YE; www.lepontdelatour.co.uk; @lepontdelatour; 10.30 pm, Sun 9.30 pm; No trainers.

Popeseye W14 £64 4 3 2

108 Blythe Rd   020 7610 4578   8–1C

"Grotty-looking, but serving top steak!" – that's been the trade-off for over two decades at this "intimate and special", but simultaneously "fairly basic" little quirk of a bistro, in the backstreets near Olympia. "If you like good steak then this is as good a place to start as any: its excellent meat, cooked perfectly, takes some beating", and is supplemented by an intriguing wine selection of well-chosen bin ends. The N19 branch is no more. / W14 0HD; www.popeseye.com; 10.30 pm; D only, closed Sun; Cash only.

Popolo EC2 £52 5 4 3

26 Rivington Street   020 7729 4299   13–1B

"An amazing experience at a price that doesn't hurt your wallet" – Jonathan Lawson's "superb Italian food with Spanish and Moorish influences, and including brilliant pasta (just as good as at The River Café!)" is well-worth the trip to Shoreditch to discover his brilliantly casual and laid back little hole-in-the-wall, with counter seating at the open kitchen downstairs, and a small upstairs dining room. / EC2A 3DU; popoloshoreditch.com; @popolo_EC2; no booking.

Poppies £48 **3 3 3**

59 Old Compton St, W1   020 7482 2977   4–2D
30 Hawley Cr, NW1   020 7267 0440   9–2B
6-8 Hanbury St, E1   020 7247 0892   13–2C

Fish trade veteran Pat 'Pops' Newland started out cutting up newspapers to wrap portions at the age of 11, and has kitted out his three tourist-friendly chippies (in Soho, Spitalfields and Camden Town) in 1950s memorabilia to commemorate the era. The "no-frills" fish he serves is "excellent" and "consistently fresh" – but even fans can find it "overpriced by a long way". / 11 pm, Fri & Sat 11.30 pm, Sun 10.30 pm.

Poppy's **3 2 4**

129-131 Brackenbury Road, W6   020 8741 4928   8–1C **NEW**
30 Greyhound Road, W6   8–2C
78 Glenthorne Road, W6   020 8748 2351   8–2C

"A really quirky taste in decor" is working out well for this little group of Thai cafés in W6. From its tiny first branch (Poppy's I) on a traficky bit of Hammersmith's one-way system, it's progressed via a branch off the Fulham Palace Road (Poppy's II) to occupy the well-known former site of The Brackenbury, RIP (Poppy's III). Nowadays, the latter is hidden behind a terrace of foliage and packed with stuffed animals, mirrors and chandeliers. Notwithstanding a rather functional level of service, its low prices for tasty scoff and BYO policy are packing 'em in.

Il Portico W8 £62 **3 5 4**

277 Kensington High St   020 7602 6262   8–1D

This "proper, family-run Italian trattoria" in Kensington pre-dates the new Design Museum on the other side of the road by decades, and exudes "cosy", "olde world charm". That it's "family-owned and family-friendly" is key to its longevity, and has made it a "go-to restaurant" for its many long-term regulars. But "after decades, the business has passed down a generation, and young and old alike agree it's brought an improvement, with an approach that's more energetic". Its strengths are "a charming atmosphere", "authentic Emilia-Romana cuisine, instead of the usual floods of red sauce" and the "unfailing and unflappable care of owner James Chiavarini and his well-trained staff". / W8 6NA; www.ilportico.co.uk; 11 pm; closed Sun.

Portland W1 £80 **4 4 2**

113 Great Portland Street   020 7436 3261   2–1B

"Always on form, always interesting" – Will Lander and Daniel Morgenthau's acclaimed Fitzrovian has won a serious culinary reputation over the years, with both an à la carte and tasting menu available lunch and dinner. Fans say its interior is "lovely and modern", but – despite its "charming" service – the set-up can also seem a little too no-nonsense; the focus is very much on the modern European cuisine – "every dish is a success". / W1W 6QQ; www.portlandrestaurant.co.uk; @portland113; 9.45 pm; closed Sun.

Portobello Ristorante Pizzeria W11 £54 **3 3 3**

7 Ladbroke Road   020 7221 1373   7–2B

Just off Notting Hill Gate, this "splendid staple" wins solid marks for "great pizza, pasta and more" – including a decent array of fish showcased in a chiller-cabinet. "Authentically Italian in its chaos and delicious food", it's also "fun and child-friendly". The best seats are outside on the glorious terrace in summer (which is also very effectively covered in winter and bad weather). / W11 3PA; www.portobellolondon.co.uk; 10 pm, Fri & Sat 11 pm, Sun 10 pm.

The Portrait,
National Portrait Gallery WC2 £74 ②③④
St Martin's Place 020 7306 0055 5–4B

"Cracking views over the rooftops of Trafalgar Square and beyond from a sun-drenched room" earn the NPG's top-floor dining room decent ratings as a venue for brunch, lunch or afternoon tea, or for an "early supper before the opera at the Coliseum". The food is "quite adequate" although "not spectacular". (There's also a Spartan café in the basement). / WC2H 0HE; www.npg.org.uk/visit/shop-eat-drink/restaurant.php; @NPGLondon; 8.30 pm; Sun-Wed closed D.

Le Pot de Terre N8 NEW ③②③
34 High Street 020 8340 0099 1–1C

"A Caribbean edge" adds an "interesting twist" to the fundamentally European menu at this late-2019 newcomer, which opened without fanfare in the heart of Hornsey. "The chef has little support so expect a relaxed service!" / N8 7NX; lepotdeterre.co.uk.

Potli W6 £44 ④④③
319-321 King St 020 8741 4328 8–2B

"Exceptionally flavoured, and unusual, 'street-food' dishes" – "the spicing makes them stand out" – have earned consistently high marks for this "inventive" Indian for much of the decade. It compares well with the better-known Indian Zing just a few steps closer to Ravenscourt Park tube station, and is "well worth a try". / W6 9NH; www.potli.co.uk; @Potlirestaurant; 10.15 pm, Fri & Sat 10:30 pm, Sun 10 pm.

La Poule au Pot SW1 £61 ③③⑤
231 Ebury St 020 7730 7763 6–2D

"Get snuggly" at this "engaging if somewhat faded", "typically Gallic" 1960s-"throwback" in Pimlico, whose "dark", candle-lit interior and "cosy tables hidden away in nooks and crannies" make it "one of the most romantic restaurants of all time" (it's Londoners' No. 2 for romance in the survey this year). Foodwise, "there's no nonsense, no surprises" – just "very traditional French classics" that are "still passable" ("cuisine grand mére" – think calf's liver, coq au vin, cassoulet), served by "the most colourful French waiters". Top Tip – "idyllic terrace for long lunches and dinner al fresco": "you could imagine yourself in a little French marketplace having a simple bistro-style lunch". / SW1W 8UT; www.pouleaupot.co.uk; 10 pm; No trainers.

Prawn on the Lawn N1 £62 ④③②
292-294 St Paul's Rd 020 3302 8668 9–2D

"Fish at its best: fresh, dressed and novel – seared, crispy and spiced; or as a mountain of fruits de mer au naturel" is the reason this "fabulous", "almost caff-like" local on Highbury Corner (which doubles as a fishmonger) is "always very busy". It's "a rarity in London", and "every bit as good as its Cornish cousin" in Padstow. One caveat: it's "far too tiny and cramped and always needs to be booked days ahead – wish they would expand". / N1 2LY; prawnonthelawn.com; @PrawnOnTheLawn; 11 pm; closed Mon & Sun; No Amex.

Primeur N5 £51 ③③③
116 Petherton Rd 020 7226 5271 1–1C

A 1920s former car garage provides an "unusual" setting for this Stoke Newington fringe haunt, whose "look and feel (with most people at communal tables, or on counters with stools) works well", despite it being "crammed" and with "a high noise-level". There's quite a "traditional", 'bistronomy-style' menu, from which everything's "well-cooked", and there's an "interesting" list of wines (low intervention, naturellement). / N5 2RT; www.primeurN5.co.uk; @Primeurs1; 10.30 pm, Sun 5 pm; closed Mon, Tue L, Wed L, Thu L & Sun D; booking max 7 may apply.

The Princess Victoria W12 £50 ❸❸❸
217 Uxbridge Road 020 8749 4466 8–1B

This "old Victorian gin palace" "must be one of the best pubs in the Bush", so for locals it has been "wonderful to see the Vic resurrect itself from the ashes of oblivion" (after a short period of closure last year).
"The atmosphere is warm and friendly and the food is quite delicious" – "proper restaurant quality"; "they've recently added a pizza oven, and even the pizzas are a substantial cut above what you might expect". / W12 9DH; www.princessvictoria.co.uk; @threecheerspubs; 10pm, Sun 9pm.

Princi W1 £37 ❸❷❸
135 Wardour St 020 7478 8888 4–1D

This "stylish and modern" Soho outpost of Rocco Princi's self-service Milanese bakery is "always buzzing" with a crowd chasing its "delicious breakfasts", "great sandwiches" and "incredible cakes"; there are "creative salads and pizzas", too (the latter are particularly good). / W1F 0UT; www.princi.com; @princi_london; 11 pm, Sun 10 pm; no booking.

Prix Fixe W1 £48 ❸❷❷
39 Dean St 020 7734 5976 5–2A

"Unostentatious and slightly lacking in character", this "basic, cheap 'n' cheerful French-style bistro" (sibling to Pierre Victoire) offers "good, honest cooking and excellent value" in the heart of the West End – "more enjoyable, with better food, than many a swankier venue". / W1D 4PU; www.prixfixe.net; 11.30 pm.

The Promenade at The Dorchester W1 £133 ❷❹❹
The Dorchester Hotel, 53 Park Lane 020 7629 8888 3–3A

"Impeccable in every way: from the quietly unintrusive pianist in the background, to the service…" – this plush Mayfair hotel lounge is an orgy of opulent soft furnishings with a spoiling afternoon tea to match (plus other luxury bites from breakfast on); "not cheap", say fans, "but actually worth every penny". / W1K 1QA; www.dorchestercollection.com/en/london/the-dorchester/restaurant-bars/afternoon-tea; @TheDorchester; 10.30 pm; No shorts.

Provender E11 £41 ❸❸❸
17 High St 020 8530 3050 1–1D

A "happy choice for dinner" in Wanstead – this "busy", neighbourhood bistro from veteran restaurateur Max Renzland inspired the odd gripe this year, but most reports say it's "a safe bet" for traditional Gallic fare. / E11 2AA; www.provenderlondon.co.uk; @ProvenderBistro; 10 pm, Fri & Sat 10.30 pm, Sun 9 pm; booking max 10 may apply.

Prufrock Coffee EC1 £13 ❸❸❷
23-25 Leather Ln 020 7242 0467 10–2A

Celebrating its 10th year, this City-fringe café near Hatton Garden takes its caffeine seriously, running its own barista training schemes and taking supplies from Square Mile Roasters and various guest roasters from all over Europe. Good light bites at lunch, too. / EC1N 7TE; www.prufrockcoffee.com; @PrufrockCoffee; L only; No Amex.

Pucci Mayfair W1 NEW £64 ❸❸❸
39 Maddox Street 020 3887 4363 3–2C

Fans of the long-gone Pucci Pizza on the King's Road will be glad to know that it's back (if with a few tweaks). Pucci's son Rufus Albanese has revived the brand in Mayfair, serving thin-crust pizzas made to the family recipe as well as mezze: "great fun and great pizza". / W1S 1FX; puccimayfair.com; @PucciMayfair.

The Punchbowl W1 £60 **3** **3** **4**

41 Farm St 020 7493 6841 3–3A

Approaching its 300th birthday, this Mayfair pub is more stylish than most in the West End, partly due to its history of celebrity ownership (it was part of Madonna and Guy Ritchie's divorce settlement, with Ritchie getting The Queen of Pop's share when they split). Foodwise, it's also been a decent bet in recent times (although it did receive one 'off' report from a former fan this year). / W1J 5RP; www.punchbowllondon.com; @ThePunchBowlLDN; 11 pm, Sun 10.30 pm; closed Sun D.

Punjab WC2 £42 **3** **4** **3**

80 Neal St 020 7836 9787 5–2C

Many Londoners have tried this very traditional, north Indian veteran on the fringe of Covent Garden (founded in 1946, and now in the 4th generation of family ownership) at some time or another, but it lacks a regular local following due to its touristy location. It wins consistent praise, however – including for its support of the armed forces (10% discount to those who've served). / WC2H 9PA; www.punjab.co.uk; 11 pm, Sun 10 pm; booking max 8 may apply.

Pure Indian Cooking SW6 £51 **3** **4** **2**

67 Fulham High Street 020 7736 2521 11–1B

This "real local gem" north of Putney Bridge serves "delicious and unusual Indian food" – and is "refreshingly free from the usual clichés". Owner Shilpa Dandekar is a "great and innovative chef" – she trained at the Taj Group and worked under Raymond Blanc – and her cooking is "beautifully presented". Only the "rather ordinary room" gets brickbats – "more prestigious surroundings required!". / SW6 3JJ; www.pureindiancooking.com; @PureCooking.

Purezza NW1 £45 **4** **3** **3**

43 Parkway 0203 884 0078 9–3B

"Truly amazing tastes recommended for both vegans and non-vegans!" help win high scores for this year-old, Camden Town offshoot of the UK's first vegan pizzeria (which first hit Brighton in 2015). Bases include sourdough, hemp and gluten-free options: "it's the best pizza I've had in a very long time!". Top Tip – kids under 10 get a free pizza when eating with their parents. / NW1 7PN; www.purezza.co.uk; @purezza; Booking max 6 may apply.

Quaglino's SW1 £76 **2** **3** **5**

16 Bury St 020 7930 6767 3–3D

D&D London's "fabulous, shimmering dining room from the Jazz Age" – which, in fact, owes much of its glam looks to Sir Terence Conran's 1993 revamp of this massive, subterranean, 1920s ballroom in St James's – is unusual amongst high-end venues nowadays in making "fantastic entertainment" and live music a regular feature of its ritzy offering. After many years on the skids, its standards of service and posh-brasserie fare have been somewhat on the mend in recent times, and – though ratings are still in middling territory – all feedback this year was upbeat. Top Tip "Sunday brunch is worth the trip". / SW1Y 6AJ; www.quaglinos-restaurant.co.uk; @quaglinos; 10.30 pm, Fri & Sat 11 pm; closed Sun; No trainers.

The Quality Chop House EC1 £71 **4** **4** **4**

94 Farringdon Rd 020 7278 1452 10–1A

"You either love or hate the iconic and original (and cramped and uncomfortable) Victorian booths, which are part of the charm of this Clerkenwell institution" (est 1869) , "which has not been a 'Progressive Working Class' establishment for a very long time, no matter what it says on the ancient, etched-glass windows!". Relaunched in the early 1990s in the first stages of Britain's latter-day food revival, it's been run since 2012 by Will Lander and Daniel Morgenthau and its ratings are going from strength to strength on the back of its "honest, modern-ish take on hearty traditional dishes" ("perfect for meat eaters – huge steaks") and "unusual

and interesting wines". They run a deli and wine shop next door too, 'Quality Wines' which is currently a voguish haunt in its own right, with chef Nick Bramham producing a small menu of trendy small plates. / EC1R 3EA; thequalitychophouse.com; @QualityChop; 10.30 pm; closed Sun.

Quartieri NW6 £44 433
300 Kilburn High Road 020 7625 8822 1–2B
"The tastiest Neapolitan pizza, with lots of delicious toppings", wins fans for this "great neighbourhood joint" in Kilburn – thanks to its combination of "fail-proof classic choices and exciting, delightful specials" delivered by "service with a smile", it's "always filled with Italians". Top Tip – "straccetti – deep-fried pizza dough with hazelnut chocolate for dessert – is out of this world!". / NW6 2DB; www.quartieri.co.uk; @quartierilondon; 11 pm.

Le Querce SE23 £47 433
66-68 Brockley Rise 020 8690 3761 1–4D
"Distinctly regional" Sardinian cooking – "above average and at reasonable prices" – has earned a strong following for this "very good family-run trattoria" from chef Antonello Serra in Brockley Rise. Look out for "great home-made bread and specials", along with "their own ice creams and sorbets in dozens of intriguing mixtures like strawberry and pepper"; "interesting wine list" too. / SE23 1LN; www.lequerce.co.uk; @lequercerest; 9.30 pm, Sun 8.15 pm; closed Mon & Tue L.

Quilon SW1 £71 552
41 Buckingham Gate 020 7821 1899 2–4B
"Consistently excellent" Keralan cuisine – "beautifully presented and served" – from chef Sriram Aylur ensures this 20-year-old, from the luxury Taj Group, remains at the summit of modern Indian gastronomy in the capital. Despite the swish hotel decor, though, it's a decidedly low-key institution – if it wasn't for such "friendly and thoughtful staff" the ambience could become stifling and leaden here. A short walk from Buckingham Palace, it's close enough to Parliament to have its own division bell to summon MPs for a vote. Top Tip – "set lunch is tremendous value". / SW1E 6AF; www.quilon.co.uk; @thequilon; 11 pm, Sun 10.30 pm; SRA-Food Made Good – 2 stars.

Quirinale SW1 £68 343
North Ct, 1 Gt Peter St 020 7222 7080 2–4C
"One of the finest Italian restaurants in London" for almost two decades, this is "near the Palace of Westminster, so frequented by MPs, journalists and lobbyists – but don't let that put you off". This clientele might explain why "tables are the right distance apart" in the "low-ceilinged basement". Top Tip – "go in truffle season – divine". / SW1P 3LL; www.quirinale.co.uk; @quirinaleresto; 10.30 pm; closed Sat & Sun.

Quo Vadis W1 £61 335
26-29 Dean St 020 7437 9585 4–1D
"It feels small now that Barrafina has taken up half of the original space" following a re-jig a year ago, but the Hart Bros' "gorgeous" landmark (est 1926) remains a "discrete", "comfortable" and "fun" oasis from the bustle of Soho. Chef Jeremy Lee's seasonal menu "is frequently refreshed with innovative dishes" and, at its best, delivers "unusual but superb" riffs on British cuisine, alongside a list of "interesting wines" and "fine cocktails". Top Tip – "a bangin' place for a traditional breakfast in classy surroundings". / W1D 3LL; www.quovadissoho.co.uk; @QuoVadisSoho; 11 pm; closed Sun.

Rabbit SW3   £56   3 2 3
172 King's Rd 020 3750 0172 6–3C
"Truly delicious tapas" showcasing *"great farm-sourced food"*,
with *"some robust, well-judged flavours"* win ongoing appreciation for the
Gladwin brothers' five-year-old King's Road operation. There's also
a *"cool vibe"* to the *"quirkily decorated room – loved it!"*. / SW3 4UP;
www.rabbit-restaurant.com; @RabbitResto; midnight, Mon 11 pm, Sun 6 pm; closed
Mon L & Sun D.

Rabot 1745 SE1   £64   2 3 2
2-4 Bedale St 020 7378 8226 10–4C
*"A chocolate-themed restaurant is a good idea in principle, but some dishes
work better than others"* is the general verdict on this Borough Market
outlet of a St Lucia plantation owned by Hotel Chocolat, which *"uses cocoa
in every dish"*. *"Chocolate mac 'n' cheese"*, anyone? What does work is the
"fantastic hot chocolate", and the café/bar has a *"fun atmosphere"* in the
evening, while *"the breakfast menu is really tasty, too"*. / SE1 9AL;
www.rabot1745.com; @rabot1745; 9.30 pm; closed Mon & Sun.

Radici N1   £68   2 2 2
30 Almeida St 020 7354 4777 9–3D
It's a *"spacious, modern and stylish"* venue – on the site of Islington's
Almeida (RIP) – but owners D&D London and respected chef Francesco
Mazzei *"really ought to up their game"* here: it *"beats a pizza chain"*,
but should deliver much more. As it is, being *"convenient for the Almeida
Theatre"* is one of the best things that reporters have to say about it:
"without this neighbour they probably wouldn't survive". / N1 1AD;
www.radici.uk; @radici_n1.

Ragam W1   £35   4 4 2
57 Cleveland St 020 7636 9098 2–1B
"Unpretentious but brilliant" Keralan veteran near the Telecom Tower, which
offers some of the *"best-value curry in London"*. It's *"still rough as anything
in terms of the building but the food consistently nails it"* – including some
"proper veggie choices". Top Tip – *"the dosas at Ragam are the best I've
found in London"*. / W1T 4JN; www.ragamindian.co.uk; 11 pm.

Rail House Café SW1   £66   2 2 2
Sir Simon Milton Sq 020 3906 7950 2–4B
*"Having read some mixed reviews, we were pleasantly surprised on a recent
visit"* – the Riding House Café group's *"eclectically decorated"*, year-old unit
in Victoria's Nova development again inspires somewhat up-and-down
reports, but most are positive regarding its *"friendly"* staff and *"well-
presented and tasty"* food, tipping it for a breakfast or coffee and a snack;
outside seating in summer is a bonus. / SW1H 0HW; www.railhouse.cafe;
@railhouse_cafe.

Rambla W1   £56   3 3 2
64 Dean Street 020 7734 8428 5–2A
"A good find for tapas" in *"the heart of Soho"* – this *"good-value Spanish"*
two-year-old is *"ideal for a pre-theatre meal"* or a *"casual meet-up, rather
than somewhere for a relaxed evening"*. Barcelona-born chef Victor Garvey
has opened and closed a quick succession of ventures – Encant, Sibarita
and Barullo, the latter of which only lasted two months earlier this year –
with Bar Jaleo scheduled to launch in late 2019. / W1D 4QG;
www.ramblalondon.com; @ramblasoho.

Randall & Aubin W1 £61 4 3 5

14-16 Brewer St   020 7287 4447   4–2D

"No-fuss", "fresh seafood done really well" combines with a "fun" and
"buzzy" ("riotous" even!) ambience, at this Soho landmark – formerly
a butcher (est 1911) that morphed into a restaurant 25 years ago. "It's still
excellent after all these years, like meeting an old friend – we love it".
"Go for the specials, they're always worth trying". / W1F 0SG;
www.randallandaubin.com; @randallandaubin; 11 pm, Fri & Sat 11.30 pm,
Sun 9.30 pm; booking L only.

Raoul's Café W9 £42 3 2 4

13 Clifton Rd   020 7289 7313   9–4A

This "really good all-rounder" near Little Venice has long been a "very nice
option for brunch/lunch" with "still some of the best eggs Benedict
in London after so many years". "The ambience is much better since it's
usually a little quieter nowadays". / W9 1SZ; www.raoulsgourmet.com; 10.15 pm;
no booking L.

Rasa £37 3 4 2

6 Dering St, W1   020 7629 1346   3–2B
(Travancore) 56 Stoke Newington Ch St, N16   020 7249 1340   1–1C
55 Stoke Newington Church St, N16   020 7249 0344   1–1C

Fans of the "unbeatable, unpretentious, delicious Keralan cuisine" at the
three Rasas say it's "not your standard Indian fare" – "the spicing is second
to none, giving a unique, delicate and surprising balance of flavours". They
also say that the Stokie original, "established over 20 years ago", is "still the
best veggie curry in north London" (with meat an option at its younger
Travancore spin-off across the road); and that its popular Oxford Circus
offshoot is a handy – and good-value – option in the West End. All locations,
though, suffer accusations that they are "not as good as they were", and –
though solid – ratings in each case no longer 'smash the ball out of the
park' as once they did. / www.rasarestaurants.com; N16 & Travancore N16
10.45 pm, Fri & Sat 11.30 pm, W1 11 pm, Sun 9 pm.

Ravi Shankar NW1 £32 3 2 2

132-135 Drummond St   020 7388 6458   9–4C

A "long-term favourite" in Euston station's Little India, this is "the place
to come for your masala dosa fix: there's lots to choose from, they're big,
really really tasty, and amazingly cheap". "The weekend buffet has to be the
best deal in town – you can gorge yourself on delicious vegetarian food and
still get change from a tenner". / NW1 2HL; www.ravishankarbhelpoori.com;
10.30 pm.

Red Farm WC2 £56 3 2 3

9 Russell Street   0203 883 9093   5–3D

"Killer dim sum combinations make for an experience not to forget" at this
three-storey canteen-style import from NYC in Covent Garden, famous
on Instagram for its prawn dish that looks like the ghosts in Pac-Man. Even
some fans, though, query "why is it so expensive? The food's great and fun
and adventurous, but simply too pricey!" / WC2B 5HZ; redfarmldn.com.

The Red Lion & Sun N6 £58 3 3 3

25 North Road   020 8340 1780   9–1B

"Lovely on all levels" – this cosy gastropub in a leafy corner of Highgate
is not the largest, but has earned a solid reputation for its "yummy food".
Well-behaved dogs and children are welcome, too. / N6;
www.theredlionandsun.com; @redlionandsun; 10 pm.

Red Rooster EC2 £68 2️⃣2️⃣**3**

45 Curtain Road 020 3146 4545 13–1B

The hugely hyped offshoot of a famous Harlem NYC soulfood kitchen, from Ethiopian-Swedish celebrity chef, Marcus Samuelsson has failed to catch fire in Shoreditch. Some reporters like it – "a foodie dream" – but too many find it a "deep disappointment" (although "Sunday lunch is worth a visit for the live entertainment"). / EC2A 4PJ; www.thecurtain.com; @RoosterHarlem; midnight, Wed 1 am, Thu-Sat 2 am, Sun 5 pm; closed Sun D.

Regency Cafe SW1 £16 **3**️⃣**3**️⃣**5**

17-19 Regency Street 020 7821 6596 2–4C

"One of the few completely authentic greasy spoons in central London" now – this "unchanging" veteran in a Westminster side street won the Harden's Award for Best Breakfast last year: "for the full English, it's tops" and "well worth queuing for". Opened in 1946, the original Austerity Era interior makes it sought-out as a location for films (Brighton Rock, Layer Cake), and the "old school caff" atmosphere is rounded off by "the lady behind the counter who bellows when your order's ready" – "being there always lifts the spirits". / SW1P 4BY; regencycafe.co.uk.

Le Relais de Venise L'Entrecôte £48 **3**️⃣**3**️⃣**3**

120 Marylebone Ln, W1 020 7486 0878 2–1A

50 Dean St, W1 020 3475 4202 5–3A

5 Throgmorton St, EC2 020 7638 6325 10–2C

"Bish, bash, bosh… great steak!" – "amazing result!". "You know what you're going to get", and "what you're given is very good" at this Gallic steakhouse chain which "does what it says on the tin" – a "no-decision" menu of steak-frites, served with the chain's trademark 'secret sauce', plus seconds if you're still hungry (followed by a variety of puddings). "They're busy, so be prepared to queue, and to vacate your table as soon as you've finished." / www.relaisdevenise.com; 10 pm - 11 pm; EC2 closed Sat & Sun; no booking except in Soho.

Reubens W1

79 Baker St 020 7486 0035 2–1A

What a difference three months can make! In August 2019, a quarter of a year after the closure of this well-known, 46-year-old, kosher deli in Marylebone (due to family bereavement) came news that it was to re-open after a big refurb, courtesy of restaurateur Lee Landau. It will still be the same format – deli on the ground floor, a restaurant in the basement. Let's hope the new era will herald better cooking! / W1U 6RG; www.reubensrestaurant.co.uk; 10 pm; closed Fri D & Sat; No Amex.

The Rex Whistler Restaurant, Tate Britain SW1 £71 **3**️⃣**3**️⃣**5**

Millbank 020 7887 8825 2–4C

"Why go? The exceptional wines and the magnificent Whistler mural" provide most of the answer at the Tate's "delightful" dining "oasis": an "unexpected treat" by the standards of gallery venues, dating from 1927. It is true that its British cuisine "doesn't match the liquid refreshment", but it is generally "inviting"; and "the range and depth of wines on offer is reason alone to go", providing "some gems and at fair prices" ("wine is purchased and laid down, more like a St James's Club than a commercial restaurant"). "Satiated by stylish cooking and sensational wines – what better way to kick off a trip around the galleries upstairs…" / SW1P 4RG; www.tate.org.uk/visit/tate-britain/rex-whistler-restaurant; Booking lunch only.

Rhythm & Brews W4　　　　3 4 5
22 Walpole Gardens　020 7998 3873　8–2A
"A lovely, local independent coffee shop" on the distant borders of Chiswick and Gunnersbury combining *"laid-back music on vinyl (some of which you can buy)"* and a *"cosy"* vibe with *"great pastries"* and other simple fare, plus some fine brews (using Union coffee). / W4 4HA; rhythmandbrews.co.uk; @InfoBrews.

The Rib Man E1　　　　£12　　5 3–
Brick Lane, Brick Lane Market　no tel　13–2C
"Unbelievably good ribs and pulled pork" continue to win top marks for street-food legend Mark Gevaux – even though he *"concentrates more on his outrageously hot Holy F**k chilli sauce these days"*. *"The meat is melt-in-the-mouth, superbly cooked and exceptional value"* – it's *"a pain that you have to wake up early-ish on a Sunday"* to scoff a portion on Brick Lane, but the only other option is outside the Boleyn Tavern before West Ham home games. / E1 6HR; www.theribman.co.uk; @theribman; No bookings.

Rib Room,
Jumeirah Carlton Tower Hotel SW1　£100　3 2 3
Cadogan Pl　020 7858 7250　6–1D
Smart and luxurious dining room, off the lobby of a super-swanky five-star hotel bordering Sloane Street, whose focus on traditional meat dishes has been (somewhat) diluted over the years, with the introduction of a wider menu. Even so it's the *"melting rib-eye"* and other cuts which inspire most praise here, which is most popular as a business haunt: *"relaxed, and ideal for talking the deal"*. / SW1X 9PY; www.theribroom.co.uk; @RibRoomSW1; 9.30 pm, Sat 10 pm.

Riccardo's SW3　　　　£51　　3 2 2
126 Fulham Rd　020 7370 6656　6–3B
This *"great neighbourhood favourite"* on a Chelsea corner wins solid marks for its *"genuine Italian food"*, *"with Riccardo himself ensuring you're well looked after"*. It's *"cheap 'n' cheerful"* with a *"lovely informal environment"* – *"perfect for family Sunday lunch with dog under the table and children throwing pasta over each other"*. / SW3 6HU; www.riccardos.it; @ricardoslondon; 11.30 pm, Sun 10.30 pm.

Rick Stein SW14　　　　£66　　3 3 4
Tideway Yard, 125 Mortlake High St　020 8878 9462　11–1A
"The food may not live up to the hype, but it's still good, and the overall atmosphere is great", at the Stein empire's two-year-old, near Barnes Bridge. Who knows? If it wasn't named for TV-star Rick, its *"decent-but-not-extraordinary fish, simply cooked"* might seem more impressive, and might not seem *"a little overpriced for what it is"*. But, just as was the case when this site was previously the Depot (RIP) *"what makes the restaurant is the fabulous Thames view"*. / SW14 8SN; www.rickstein.com/eat-with-us/barnes; @SteinBarnes; 9.30 pm.

Riding House Café W1　　　　£59　　2 3 3
43-51 Great Titchfield St　020 7927 0840　3–1C
For *"a social start to the day"* or to kill off *"a boozy afternoon"*, many recommend this all-day bar/brasserie just north of Oxford Street in Fitzrovia, whose vibey looks and *"great brunch menu"* have earned it a big fanclub. At other times, some reckon *"the food is underwhelming"* – a view possibly shared by the management, who shut up shop for ten days in August 2019 to give the interior and general offer a 'facelift'. It now boasts a new long bar and five-course tasting menu. / W1W 7PQ; www.ridinghousecafe.co.uk; 10.30 pm, Fri & Sat 11 pm, Sun 9.30 pm.

The Rising Sun NW7 £63 **3** **3** **3**
137 Marsh Ln 020 8959 1357 1–1B
This "picturesque", 17th-century pub (Grade II listed) in Mill Hill attracts
a solid following for its "quality British/Italian grub with exceptional service
from ever-cheerful brothers Luca and Matteo (Delnevo)". "So different from
the chains", it's "reasonably priced" and "there's always a great pasta dish
on the menu". / NW7 4EY; www.therisingsunmillhill.com; @therisingsunpub; 10 pm,
Fri & Sat 11 pm, Sun 8.30 pm; closed Mon L.

Ristorante Frescobaldi W1 £84 **3** **3** **2**
15 New Burlington Pl 020 3693 3435 4–2A
"Beautiful cooking and a stunning room" set the scene at this "quiet Mayfair
Italian, perfect for business". The heavyweight wine list reflects its ownership
by a Tuscan banking and wine dynasty stretching back 30 generations.
"Why isn't this restaurant more popular?" – perhaps because: "it's better
if you're not paying for yourself – it's pricey!". / W1S 5HX;
www.frescobaldirestaurants.com; @frescobaldi_LDN; 11 pm.

The Ritz W1 £129 **3** **4** **5**
150 Piccadilly 020 7493 8181 3–4C
"For a very special occasion, there is nowhere better" than this "beyond-
compare" Louis XVI chamber, widely acclaimed as "the most beautiful
dining room in London": "it will not only rekindle the romance in your
marriage, it's also great for impressing on business". "Not to be totally
outdone by the surroundings, staff are friendly and unpretentious, and the
classic cuisine under head chef John Williams is measured and precise
(if not exactly cheap… but it's not supposed to be!)". Top Tip – "a lovely
fancy place for an epic breakfast"; also "the dinner dance is special and
great value". / W1J 9BR; www.theritzlondon.com; @theritzlondon; 10 pm; Jacket &
tie required; SRA-Food Made Good – 2 stars.

The Ritz, Palm Court W1 £114 **3** **4** **5**
150 Piccadilly 020 7493 8181 3–4C
"The gold standard" for afternoon tea – this "exquisite room" ("a unique
feature of the experience") "is a well-known institution for a reason!".
"I've been to more afternoon teas than I can count, and the majority are
trying to emulate the Ritz experience". "Book ahead (months ahead, it is
notoriously difficult to get a table!) and accept that it's expensive and that
it has a dress code. But it's well worth it. A fantastic treat with flawless
service and a wonderful, refined, atmosphere. British culture at its best!"
/ W1J 9BR; www.theritzlondon.com; @theritzlondon; Jacket & tie required.

Riva SW13 £65 **4** **4** **1**
169 Church Rd 020 8748 0434 11–1A
Loyal regulars (who include numerous fooderati celebs) totally 'get' Andreas
Riva's "understated" stalwart, in a row of Barnes shopfronts: a celebrated
(to those in-the-know) favourite, where "professional and accomplished
staff" deliver "simple", "seasonal and classic" northern Italian dishes, which
are "perfectly prepared" and "exquisite tasting": they say it's "an authentic
experience, without any airs". Even fans admit the interior is "squashed"
and "dowdy", however, and that prices are very "hefty". / SW13 9HR;
10.30 pm, Sun 9 pm; closed Sat L.

The River Café W6 £104 **3** **3** **3**
Thames Wharf, Rainville Rd 020 7386 4200 8–2C
Ruth Rogers' "thrilling" canteen, in an "out-of-the-way" Hammersmith
backstreet (originally founded to serve husband, Richard's, architectural
practice) has won global renown on the back of "perfectly seasoned" Italian
dishes "of such bare simplicity the quality of the phenomenal ingredients
truly sing". "On a hot day, there's no better spot in London" than its
"delightful" outside terrace near the Thames; and in cooler weather,
its "faithfully preserved 1990s-chic" interior, though "tightly packed", mostly
gets the thumbs-up too – "bathed in light at lunch, or with a certain buzzing

energy in the evening". It's the "ferocious prices", though, which bitterly divide reporters, and which yet again win it No. 1 billing in our list of Most Overpriced restaurants. To its more ardent fans, the situation is clearcut: "forget the haters" – "if you think it's overpriced, you simply don't understand food!" Very many other diners, however, are badly torn: "I know, I know, I know: it's an institution, a pioneer, an icon! And I value it hugely for its contribution to the London scene. The room is still one of my favourites. The food is delectable. But let's be honest: we have many excellent Mediterranean restaurants all across town nowadays, and a grilled piece of fish, a slice of lemon tart, and a glass of Vermentino isn't really worth half-a-week's wages!!" / W6 9HA; www.rivercafe.co.uk; @RiverCafeLondon; 9 pm, Sat 9.15 pm; closed Sun D.

Rivington Grill SE10 £60 2️⃣2️⃣2️⃣
178 Greenwich High Rd 020 8293 9270 1–3D
A "usually reliable choice in Greenwich" (where there is little by way of competition) – this Caprice Group venue is the sole surviving offshoot of Mark Hix's original Shoreditch grill, which closed in 2017. But while it's generally "acceptable", the harsh would say that equally there's "nothing noteworthy" either. / SE10 8NN; www.rivingtongreenwich.co.uk; 11 pm, Sun 10 pm; closed Mon, Tue L & Wed L.

Roast £71 3️⃣2️⃣4️⃣
Great Portland Street, W1 020 3006 6111 3–1C NEW
Stoney St, SE1 0845 034 7300 10–4C
"Nice views of Borough Market, if you get a window seat" ("watch out for the trains on the adjoining viaduct that appear to be coming towards you") add to the considerable appeal of this "light and airy dining space" (which atmospherically incorporates a converted glazed portico, originally part of the Royal Opera House). Specialising in British cuisine – particularly roast meats – most reports say the food is "brilliant", but there remains a sceptical view that it's "less-than-good home cooking". Top Menu Tip – breakfast and brunch have long been a very reliable experience here. / www.roast-restaurant.com; @RoastRestaurant.

Robata W1 NEW £46
56 Old Compton Street 020 7287 5766 5–3A
Izakaya-style Soho newcomer, which opened in Spring 2019, making a feature of the robata skewers for which it is named, and whose other attractions include bao buns, sushi and cocktails. It opened too late to inspire much in the way of survey feedback, but the general social media buzz about the place is upbeat. / W1D 4UE; www.robata.co.uk.

Rocca Di Papa £41 3️⃣3️⃣4️⃣
73 Old Brompton Rd, SW7 020 7225 3413 6–2B
75-79 Dulwich Village, SE21 020 8299 6333 1–4D
"There's a friendly buzz" at this pair of "good-value neighbourhood Italians" in South Kensington and Dulwich Village, which are handy for most occasions: "reliable for an informal business lunch", but equally "very child-friendly" and "perfect for a family meal with half portions of everything for kids". On top of that, the "food is actually not bad at all – better pizzas than the chains and decent enough fresh pasta". / www.roccarestaurants.com; SW7 11.30 pm; SE21 11 pm.

Rochelle Canteen E2   £64   3 3 3
16 Playground Gardens   020 7729 5677   13–1C
Margot Henderson (wife of St John's Fergus) and Melanie Arnold's
"charming" converted school bike shed near Spitalfields elicits lyrical praise
from fans of their "great" British cooking – even if some reporters flinch
at the "exorbitant wine list". Ratings have rebounded after last year's dip,
possibly caused by the pair's takeover of the ICA's catering. "My last meal
would be Rochelle Canteen's mince on dripping toast with horseradish and
watercress, and a magnificent bottle of wine". Top Tip – "pleasant garden
in good weather". / E2 7ES; www.arnoldandhenderson.com; 4.30 pm, Thu-Sat 9 pm;
L only, Thu-Sat L & D.

Rochelle Canteen at the ICA SW1   £50   4 4 2
The Mall   020 7930 8619   2–3C
"Margot and Melanie, we love you and your earthbound but fine cooking:
gutsy, simple and defiantly based on flavour!". This "bright, if utilitarian,
space looking out onto The Mall" is a takeover of a longstanding arts centre
café, near Admiralty Arch; a year-old spin-off from Melanie Arnold and
Margot Henderson's quirky Spitalfields original: "the seasonal-and-often-
unusual ingredients married to straightforward, accurate cooking have
transferred successfully from the hipsterland of the East End". "Wines are
also good and unusual" (although one or two reporters consider them
"toppy pricewise for this kind of set-up"). / SW1Y 5AH;
www.ica.art/rochelle-canteen; 11 pm.

Roe SW9 NEW   £54
Unit S38 Pop Brixton   07535 269098   11–1D
Occupying one of Pop Brixton's shipping containers (and with a little terrace,
too), Irish chef Simon Whiteside (from Hook in Camden) is serving up fish
and seafood cuisine with inspiration from his homeland. Feedback is too thin
for a rating but praises its "beautiful, very fresh fish", suggesting it's worth
a visit. / SW9 8PQ; www.roebrixton.com; @roebrixton.

Roganic W1   £93   5 4 2
5-7 Blandford St   020 337 06260   2–1A
"The closest you can get to L'Enclume without travelling to the lakes" –
Simon Rogan delivers "stunning concoctions (your imagination can really run
riot)" at his year-old Fitzrovian, which offers either a seven-course or ten-
course evening tasting menu (or, at lunchtime, a three-course option).
"Although not as glitzy as his stint at Fera at Claridges, the food
is just as good." But "if the cuisine is undoubtedly Michelin-quality, the venue
is less so" – the former premises of L'Autre Pied, which remain "rather
bland" and "cramped". Top Tip – "the utterly divine Tunworth cheese (cake)
and caviar dessert (which sounds wrong, but which actually works").
/ W1U 3DB; www.simonrogan.co.uk; @roganic; 9.15 pm; closed Mon & Sun.

Roka   £81   5 4 4
30 North Audley St, W1   020 7305 5644   3–2A
37 Charlotte St, W1   020 7580 6464   2–1C
Aldwych House, 71-91 Aldwych, WC2   020 7294 7636   2–2D
Unit 4, Park Pavilion, 40 Canada Sq, E14   020 7636 5228   12–1C
"I've never had a bad meal at Roka, and I've eaten there many,
many times" – Arjun Waney and Rainer Becker's small modern Japanese
group delivers an "exceptional", "all-round" package of clean-tasting fusion
food served in stylish and "buzzy" contemporary surroundings. Dishes are
"beautifully presented but also amazingly well-flavoured" – be it "fantastic
black cod", "fabulous sushi" or grilled tapas-y bites from the robata grill. Top
Tip – in E14, the "weekend brunch menu is splendid value for money:
especially the children's menu". / www.rokarestaurant.com; 11.30 pm,
Sun 10.30 pm; E14 11pm, Sun 8.30 pm; WC2 11 pm, Sun 8 pm; booking: max 5
online.

Romulo Café W8 £62 **3** **4** **3**

343 Kensington High Street   020 3141 6390   8–1D

"Beating Jollibee if you want to try decent, quality Filipino food" –
this London outlet of a Philippines-based chain (owned by the grandchildren
of a famous general) operates on a different level than its fast-food rival
in nearby Earl's Court (see also Jollibee). Offering "very fresh" and
interesting dishes (for newbies, "there's a strong whiff of Thai cuisine"),
"enthusiasm is key, and the food is presented with great bravura".
/ W8 6NW; www.romulocafe.co.uk; @romulolondon; 10 pm.

Rosa's £42 **3** 2 2

The "lovely Thai food" at these reliable cafés is "impressively authentic given
that they are a chain" – "excellent value" and "fast", if occasionally let
down by "iffy service". Founded in 2008 by Saiphin and Alex Moore,
who inherited the name of their first East End site, the group has
15 branches in London and expanded to Liverpool and Leeds this year
following the sale of a majority stake to US investors. The couple also have
two spin-offs, Lao Café in Covent Garden and the new Chinese noodle bar
Hoh Sek in St Katharine Docks. / rosasthaicafe.com; @RosasThaiCafe; 10 -
10.30 pm; E15 9 pm, Sat 10 pm, Sun 6 pm; E1, SW1 & SW9 6+ to book, W1 4+
to book.

The Rosendale SE21 £50 **3** **3** **3**

65 Rosendale Rd   020 8761 9008   1–4D

This "lovely, relaxed" Victorian coaching inn in West Dulwich is "great with
the kids – and the dog!". The food is simple but consistent – "never had
a bad meal there". / SE21 8EZ; www.therosendale.co.uk; @threecheerspubs;
10 pm, Sat 9.30 pm, Sun 9 pm; No Amex.

Rossopomodoro £49 2 2 2

John Lewis, 300 Oxford St, W1   020 7495 8409   3–1B
50-52 Monmouth St, WC2   020 7240 9095   5–3B
214 Fulham Rd, SW10   020 7352 7677   6–3B
1 Rufus St, N1   020 7739 1899   13–1B
10 Jamestown Rd, NW1   020 7424 9900   9–3B
46 Garrett Ln, SW18   020 8877 9903   11–2B

"Neapolitan influences are evident in the choice of ingredients, and the
wood-burning oven makes for good, chewy, charred crusts, unlike most high-
street pizzas" – so say fans of this global chain, whose HQ is indeed
in Naples. Not everyone is impressed, though, and ratings are dragged down
by those who feel it's merely an "everyday" choice: "OK for a bog-standard
group, but not great". / www.rossopomodoro.co.uk; 11 pm, Fri & Sat 11.30 pm,
Sun 10 pm.

Roti Chai W1 £46 **4** **3** **3**

3 Portman Mews South   020 7408 0101   3–1A

Inspired by street and railway station snacks on the subcontinent, this "large
modern Indian", a short stroll from Selfridges, has built a big fanclub thanks
to its "marvellous" and "authentic" bites that are "full of interesting
flavours". But while reporters agree on the high quality of the food, they are
divided about where is best to sit – is it the "good-value" upstairs café,
or "classy" basement restaurant? / W1H 6AY; www.rotichai.com; @rotichai;
10.30 pm; booking D only.

Roti King NW1 £28 **5** 2 1

40 Doric Way   020 7387 2518   9–3C

"Worth the queue and the terrible decor" – this "crowded" basement dive
near Euston has been around in various locations for yonks, but, with the
rise of street food as a genre, has become more 'discovered' in recent times.
"Exciting roti" ("with mutton curry, is ridiculously good") that are "cheap
and authentically delicious" are the pay-off for braving its decidedly "down-
to-earth" quarters. / NW1 1LH; rotiking.info; No bookings.

Rotunda Bar & Restaurant, Kings Place N1   £56   3 3 4

90 York Way   020 7014 2840   9–3C

A "great setting" next to the Regent's Canal, with a large and attractive terrace that comes into its own during the summer months, isn't the only feature that raises this bar/dining room to being a destination rather than merely an arts-centre amenity – "its farm-to-plate ethos is something special" too, with a dedicated Northumberland farm providing all beef and lamb (hung onsite in their own hanging room, and with an in-house butcher). A recent refurb has added an open kitchen and large meat-aging cabinets on view. / N1 9AG; www.rotundabarandrestaurant.co.uk; @rotundalondon; 10.30 pm, Sun 6.30 pm; closed Sun.

Roux at Parliament Square, RICS SW1   £95   4 4 3

12 Great George St   020 7334 3737   2–3C

"Never had a bad meal, and the food can be outstanding" – this Roux-branded operation near Parliament Square offers accomplished cuisine overseen by Steve Groves (winner of MasterChef: The Professionals in 2009) in an "impressive" (if, by the nature of the building, slightly institutional) setting. It's typically "backed up by well-judged, discreet service" (although one or two meals were "slow" here this year). Top Tip – "the excellent and well-priced set lunch menu is a bargain for the area". / SW1P 3AD; www.rouxatparliamentsquare.co.uk; @RouxAPS; 9 pm; closed Sat & Sun; No trainers.

Roux at the Landau, The Langham W1   £93   4 5 4

1c Portland Pl   020 7965 0165   2–1B

"Smooth-running and elegant" – the recently-adopted, more modern and svelte style of operation (no tablecloths, and a new central bar for counter-style dining) is suiting this Roux-branded dining room: part of a luxurious five-star hotel, opposite Broadcasting House. Despite the harder-edged look, the ambience remains "delightful" and the cuisine is "first class", with the option of eating à la carte, or from the six-course tasting menu. "Spot-on service", in particular, featured in numerous reports this year. / W1B 1JA; www.rouxatthelandau.com; @Langham_London; 10.30 pm; closed Sat L & Sun; No trainers.

ROVI W1   £65   5 4 4

59-65 Wells Street   020 3963 8270   3–1D

"An impressive step-up for Ottolenghi, and with all the elements that make his food unique": Yotam Ottolenghi's "just brilliant", veg-centric yearling in Fitzrovia provides "some of the most innovative food in town" – "very clever" and "exciting" sharing-plates with "intense flavours" and "exceptional presentation" – and "even though there's meat on the menu, it could turn the most ardent carnivore vegetarian!". With service that's "exemplary" and "committed" and "a really delightful atmosphere (buzzing but not noisy) it's all-in-all a memorable experience". / W1A 3AE; www.ottolenghi.co.uk/rovi; @rovi_restaurant.

Rowley's SW1   £80   2 2 3

113 Jermyn St   020 7930 2707   4–4D

"Very English steak and chips" – this classic St James's outfit from the 1970s (occupying Wall's sausages' early-Victorian premises) is, say fans, "one of those places you need to visit" thanks to its "amazing Chateaubriand" and the entrecôte steak, served on a table burner with the signature "delicious Roquefort butter sauce and unlimited fries – what more could one ask for?". Ratings, however, seldom hit the heights here: especially given the 'Welcome to Tourist London' prices, it can seem "disappointing". / SW1Y 6HJ; www.rowleys.co.uk; @Rowleys_steak; 10.30 pm.

Royal China £52 **3 1 2**
24-26 Baker St, W1   020 7487 4688   2–1A
805 Fulham Rd, SW6   020 7731 0081   11–1B
13 Queensway, W2   020 7221 2535   7–2C
30 Westferry Circus, E14   020 7719 0888   12–1B

"As far as dim sum goes – the go-to place" – these famous Cantonese fixtures are "not unlike ones you could find in Hong Kong". "No-one comes for the cuddly service" ("don't expect any smiles from the staff"), nor the ambience ("proper Chinese chaos") of the group's 1980s-tastic black-and-gold lacquered branches, but they "predictably deliver good food every time you visit" in the manner of an "industrial assembly-line"; and "kids love it". / www.royalchinagroup.co.uk; 11 pm, Sun 10 pm; W1 Fri & Sat 11.30 pm.

Royal China Club W1 £70 **4 3 3**
38-42 Baker St   020 7486 3898   2–1A

Some of the "best Chinese food in London" is on the menu at the Marylebone flagship of the Royal China group, including "fine quality" Cantonese classics and dim sum. It's certainly "not cheap", but a four-month refurb last year seems to have addressed the concerns expressed by reporters in previous years: marks for service and ambience are both up in the latest survey. / W1U 7AJ; www.royalchinagroup.co.uk; @RoyalChinaGroup; 11 pm, Sun 10.30 pm; booking weekdays only.

Rucoletta EC2 £49 **4 2 2**
6 Foster Lane   020 7600 7776   10–2B

"Excellent, simple Italian food for a good price" is a rarity in the City, so it's well worth knowing about this no-nonsense trattoria near St Paul's: "it's cramped, but your wallet feels OK!" / EC2V 6HH; www.rucoletta.co.uk; @RucolettaLondon; 9.30 pm, Thu & Fri 10 pm; closed Sat D & Sun; No Amex.

Rules WC2 £77 **3 3 5**
35 Maiden Ln   020 7836 5314   5–3D

"If one wants to wow a visitor to London" then this superbly atmospheric Covent Garden "old timer" – the capital's oldest restaurant to operate continuously on the same site (since 1798) – is just the ticket. The "amazing", "traditional" panelled interior is "very impressive"; and although the "classic British cooking" (rib of beef, game in season, steak 'n' kidney) is decidedly "not cheap" and doesn't please everyone, it mostly makes a decent fist of flying the native culinary flag. Given its prime location, it can inevitably be "overrun with tourists" at times, but it's still a big hit with many locals too. / WC2E 7LB; www.rules.co.uk; @RulesRestaurant; 11.45 pm, Sun 10.45 pm; No shorts.

Ruya W1 £94 **3 3 3**
30 Upper Grosvenor Street   020 3848 6710   3–3A

"Absolutely delicious, fine-dining Turkish-inspired cuisine (another sharing plate concept)" is to be found at this big, fancy-schmancy Park Lane yearling: part of a Dubai-based restaurant empire. "It is, shall we say, a little bit toppy" when it comes to the prices (oh boy, it is), but all reports agree this is "great, great food". / W1K 7PH; ruyalondon.com.

Sabor W1 £63 **5 4 4**
35 Heddon St   020 3319 8130   4–3A

"Just thinking about it is making my mouth water!" – Nieves Barragan and José Etura's "bustling, casual and friendly" two-year-old, tucked off Regent Street, is establishing itself as one of the West End's brightest stars: "a guaranteed first-class food experience with a lot of fun thrown in". "The downstairs bar serves modern tapas, including the beloved carabineros and croquetas. Upstairs at the communal tables, you'll feast on traditional dishes like suckling pig, cooked in an Asador (wood-fired oven)". Both locations score a big thumbs up: "not cheap, but what an utter treat to have well-executed, passionate, uncomplicated cooking of Spanish classics in the middle of London". / W1B 4BP; www.saborrestaurants.co.uk; @sabor_ldn.

Le Sacré-Coeur N1   £47   3 2 3
18 Theberton St   020 7354 2618   9–3D
*Searching for that classic, "romantic", "cheap 'n' cheerful" bistro of legend?
Try this "relatively inexpensive French local" off Islington's Upper Street:
"the food's very good considering the price, and portions are generous".
/ N1 0QX; www.lesacrecoeur.co.uk; @LeSacreCoeurUK; 11 pm, Fri & Sat 11.30 pm,
Sun 10.30 pm.*

Sacro Cuore   £39   4 3 2
10 Crouch End Hill, N8   020 8348 8487   1–1C
45 Chamberlayne Rd, NW10   020 8960 8558   1–2B
*"Real-deal, crisp bases – like in Italy"; this Kensal Rise and Crouch End duo
cook some of "the best Neapolitan pizzas in town", and they're "excellent
value". Top Tip – "the Nutella pizza (for dessert) is a must-try".
/ www.sacrocuore.co.uk; @SacroCuorePizza.*

Sagar   £35   3 3 2
17a Percy St, W1   020 7631 3319   3–1D
31 Catherine St, WC2   020 7836 6377   5–3D
157 King St, W6   020 8741 8563   8–2C
*This long-running South Indian trio (with an outpost in Harrow) offers
a "great selection of really tasty vegetarian and vegan dishes" that can
accommodate specific diets such as 'no onions'. They're "cheap 'n' cheerful
but the food is so good" ("seriously, the breads, curries and their lentil pizza
thingy is so delish!!!"). / www.sagarveg.co.uk; 10 pm - 11 pm.*

Saigon Saigon W6   £36   3 2 3
313-317 King St   020 8748 6887   8–2B
*"Reliable and always packed" – this good-value Vietnamese is a stalwart
of Hammersmith's restaurant row. Its ratings this year were not on a high,
with the odd gripe that it's "not as good as it used to be",
but most reporters continue to recommend the place. / W6 9NH;
www.saigon-saigon.co.uk; @saigonsaigonuk; 10.30 pm, Fri & Sun 11 pm.*

St John Bread & Wine E1   £66   3 2 3
94-96 Commercial St   020 7251 0848   13–2C
*Home of "possibly the best bacon sandwich in London amongst all the
faddishness and superficiality of modern Spitalfields" – this "carnivore
heaven" is "more accessible and less full-on than the original (and still best)
St John", but still serves "excellent nose-to-tail food" from
breakfast to dinner. Its white-walled, canteen-like quarters are echoey and
not especially comfortable, but somehow avoid seeming as grimly utilitarian
as they otherwise might. Top Tip – the baking is gorgeous: "an Eccles cake
here will offer all the benefits of a warm hug". / E1 6LZ;
www.stjohngroup.uk.com/spitalfields; @sjrestaurant; 10.30 pm, Mon 8 pm.*

St John Smithfield EC1   £68   5 4 3
26 St John St   020 7251 0848   10–1B
*"The original nose-to-tail flag-bearer, and still a joy!" – Trevor Gulliver and
Fergus Henderson's "stark" ex-smokehouse in Smithfield has won fame with
"top quality, distinctive British cuisine" ("using unusual cuts", most famously
offal), and "although they might have started the trend, they still lead from
the front with exciting, innovative and surprisingly delicious food". It's
"honest, skilful cooking that puts the produce front and centre"
on "an uncompromising and sometimes challenging menu"; and the
"hearty-yet-nuanced" results are a case of "simple things done well"…
"perfect". With its brutally "simple and stylish", "whitewash-walled" interior
("deafeningly loud" at times) and "relaxed but attentive service", it remains
"a must-go" ("what a place to take visitors to show off London's restaurant
scene"). Top Tip – "Eccles Cake with Lancashire Cheese is outstanding".
/ EC1M 4AY; stjohnrestaurant.com; @SJRestaurant; 11 pm, Sun 4 pm; closed
Sat L & Sun D.*

St Johns N19 £56 3️⃣2️⃣3️⃣
91 Junction Rd 020 7272 1587 9–1C

Handsome Archway tavern that's "hard to beat when on form" and is one of north London's best-known gastropubs, accommodating a large volume of diners throughout, and in the large ex-ballroom space at the rear of the pub. It appeared "more variable this year" in general however; in particular the fact that it can be "extremely noisy when full" bothered more reporters, detracting from what's otherwise a characteristic experience. Top Tip – "quieter in the bar", where you can eat a tidy range of tapas. / N19 5QU; www.stjohnstavern.com; @stjohnstavern; 10 pm, Tue-Sat 11 pm, Sun 9 pm; Mon-Thu D only, Fri-Sun open L & D; No Amex; booking max 12 may apply.

St Moritz W1 £57 3️⃣4️⃣4️⃣
161 Wardour Street 020 7734 3324 4–1C

"Part time-travel, part being transported to actual Switzerland", this chalet-style Soho veteran (est. 1974) is a perennial hit for its "authentic" Alpine cuisine. "What could be more romantic than sharing a bubbling pot of melted cheese in a cosy Swiss chalet?" / W1F 8WJ; www.stmoritz-restaurant.co.uk; 11.30 pm, Sun 10.30 pm.

Sakagura W1 £67 3️⃣3️⃣2️⃣
8 Heddon Street 020 3405 7230 4–3B

This upmarket steak and sake bar is a co-production from the people behind the Araki and Japan Centre, and offers a "wide range and good choice of Japanese food" – "some dishes are more flavoursome than others" but all are "well executed"; and there's "an amazing choice of sake". / W1B 4BU; www.sakaguralondon.com; @sakaguraldn; 10.30 pm, Thu-Sat 11.30 pm, Sun 10 pm.

Sake No Hana SW1 £82 4️⃣3️⃣3️⃣
23 St James's St 020 7925 8988 3–4D

"Beautiful food in a stunning location" – a Modernist building next to The Economist in St James's – again wins high ratings for this long-running Japanese outfit in the Hakkasan Group. It's never really made its mark, however, and continues to inspire limited feedback, but such as there is brims with enthusiasm nowadays for the "always-great meals". And if you support sustainability, you'll want to know that Sake No Hana is, as of September 2019, the first restaurant in the UK to sell fully farmed Bluefin tuna rather than the endangered variety. / SW1A 1HA; www.sakenohana.com; @sakenohanalondon; 11 pm, Fri & Sat 11.30 pm; closed Sun.

Sakonis £29 3️⃣2️⃣1️⃣
127-129 Ealing Rd, HA0 020 8903 9601 1–1A
330 Uxbridge Road, HA5 020 8903 9601 1–1A

Stalwart Indian veggie in Wembley, which has developed over 35 years from a family fruit 'n' veg stall to a full-fledged restaurant (with branches in Hounslow and Hatch End). There's a "really good variety of cuisine, with Indo-Chinese on the side", with "something to suit everyone… except carnivores". Opinions differ on whether the buffet option or main menu is the best way to go: either way it's cheap as chips.

Salaam Namaste WC1 £47 3️⃣3️⃣2️⃣
68 Millman Street 020 7405 3697 2–1D

"The tastes of freshly ground spices" infuse the interesting modern regional cuisine at chef-patron Sabbir Karim's affordably priced Bloomsbury Indian, close to Russell Square tube. "Boy, does it get busy – and I can see why!". / WC1N 3EF; www.salaam-namaste.co.uk; @SalaamNamasteUK; 11.30 pm, Sun 11 pm.

Sale e Pepe SW1 £67 343
9-15 Pavilion Road 020 7235 0098 6–1D
"Unchanged for donkey's years!" – a "noisy and crowded", old-school trattoria, near the rear entrance to Harrods, whose "at times flamboyant service" provides a heartily "friendly welcome", plus traditional Italian cuisine, which loyal regulars declare "always reliable". / SW1X 0HD; www.saleepepe.co.uk; @salepepe_it.

Salloos SW1 £67 323
62-64 Kinnerton St 020 7235 4444 6–1D
Posh Pakistani, hidden away in a Belgravia mews townhouse for more than 40 years: some may find it "stuffy", while others praise the "great ambience". It's certainly "not the cheapest", but it's survived on its "stalwart, authentic, fantastic food" (particularly lamb chops). / SW1X 8ER; www.salloos.co.uk; 11 pm; closed Sun; May need 5+ to book.

Salon Brixton SW9 £56 443
18 Market Row 020 7501 9152 11–2D
"Ambitious modern British cuisine" – an "interesting" menu of "trendy but unfussy dishes that are well-prepared" – plus a good list of natural wines win consistent high praise for Nicholas Balfe's "buzzy spot in Brixton market", although "it can get a bit manic". The team has opened a second venue, Levan in Peckham (see also). / SW9 8LD; www.salonbrixton.co.uk; @Salon_Brixton; 10 pm.

Le Salon Privé TW1 £48 333
43 Crown Rd 020 8892 0602 1–4A
"Excellent French food prepared by an Italian chef" – Gianluca di Monaco, who trained under the great Pierre Koffmann – wins solid ratings for this "very pretty" St Margaret's bistro. Its prix-fixe menu offers "excellent value and choices", ensuring it is "always busy". Top Tip – "good venue before the rugby at nearby Twickenham". / TW1 3EJ; lesalonprive.net; @lesalon_tweet; 10.30 pm.

Salt Yard W1 £54 443
54 Goodge St 020 7637 0657 2–1B
This pioneer of Spanish and Italian small-plates dining near Goodge Street station is "still going strong after so many years for a very good reason" – "interesting and yummy dishes plus good wine". Ratings have remained solid since the whole group (including siblings Dehesa, Opera Tavern and Ember Yard) was taken over late last year by Urban Pubs & Bars from Simon Mullins and Sanja Moy, who opened Salt Yard in 2005. There's even been a "big improvement in the ambience of the basement". Top Menu Tip – "deep fried courgette flowers with honey: the cheesy goodness within marries perfectly with the honey sweetness drizzled over… just wow!" / W1T 4NA; www.saltyard.co.uk; @SaltYardGroup; 10.45 pm, Sun 9.45 pm; ; booking max 8 may apply.

Salut N1 £71 433
412 Essex Road 020 3441 8808 9–3D
Tiny Canonbury fixture, with "a small but perfectly formed menu" of ambitious modern European dishes, prepared in an open kitchen – "wonderful, well-flavoured, light cooking", from "the amazing roast potatoes to the soups and everything in between". / N1 3PJ; www.salut-london.co.uk; @Salut_London; 11 pm, Sun 10 pm.

Sam's Riverside W6
Riverside Studios, 101 Queen Caroline Street 8–2C
Facing the Thames with views of (currently closed and hence very tranquil) Hammersmith Bridge, this October 2019 opening provides an all-day, 90-cover brasserie locals hope will prove a long-needed cheaper alternative to another river café five minutes walk away. It's the brainchild of Sam Harrison, who for years ran long-RIP Chiswick favourite, Sam's Brasserie. / W6 9BN; samsriverside.co.uk; @samsriversideW6.

Sambal Shiok N7 NEW £38 3 3 1
171 Holloway Road 020 7619 9888 9–2D

"Fantastic new arrival in N7" – Mandy Yin's "always crowded, really buzzy" laksa bar (her progression from street-food markets) has ridden a wave of good reviews; fans say, "if you like laksa, chilli and spice, you won't find anywhere better for this type of money". That's the majority view anyway, although there is a minority who feel "it's not worth the time queueing", citing "hype" and clumsy cooking ("either they changed chef, or they're too busy"). There's also some disagreement over the booking slots policy: supporters say "the 90 minute time allocated for the meal is plenty because the service is so fast", but others feel "very rushed given the fixed arrival and departure points". / N7 8LX; www.sambalshiok.co.uk; @SambalShiok; Mon closed; Tue - Sat 9.30 pm; Sun closed.

San Carlo SW1 £66 3 4 4
2 Regent Street Saint James's 020 3778 0768 4–4D

'Affordable glam' is a defining feature of the national San Carlo group, and its large St James's yearling on the lower half of Regent Street carries the classy, comfortable design of its nationwide siblings. "Efficient staff" and "excellent food" complete an all-round good-quality package. / SW1Y 4AU; sancarlo.co.uk/restaurants/san-carlo-london; @SanCarlo_Group.

San Carlo Cicchetti £56 3 3 4
215 Piccadilly, W1 020 7494 9435 4–4C
30 Wellington St, WC2 020 7240 6339 5–3D

"Don't be fooled by its prominent location, just off Piccadilly Circus, that it's just one for the tourists" – this "bustling, noisy and so-atmospheric" Venetian brasserie (which also has a similar sibling, more tucked away in Covent Garden) "looks like a tourist trap, but offers an authentic culinary experience" with its "delicious small plates" (cicchetti) – "a format that caters to all appetites", all at "reasonable prices". Staff are "enthusiastic and professional" and "feed off the buzz of the place", which "feels smart, even if tables are very close together". / www.sancarlocicchetti.co.uk; @SanCarlo_Group; W1 11.30 pm; WC2 midnight; M1 11 pm, Sun 10 pm.

San Pietro W8 £50 3 2 2
7 Stratford Road 020 7938 1805 6–1A

"Expertly prepared fresh fish" ("magnificent scallops, large and with the coral attached: so rare!") makes it worth truffling out this "slightly expensive but useful local" – the Italian successor to the quiet Kensington site that was for aeons Chez Patrick (RIP), and which nowadays is in a more stylish guise, with the main dining room upstairs, and a counter downstairs. / W8 6RF; www.san-pietro.co.uk.

The Sands End SW6 £51 3 3 4
135 Stephendale Road 020 7731 7823 11–1B

This unobtrusive-looking gastroboozer in a Fulham backstreet came to prominence for its highly-rated grub and off-duty visits from Prince Harry, a pal of the former owner. It changed hands last year and Harry got hitched, so he's not expected back, but marks have held up for what is still a "great local" – "not so cheap but definitely cheerful". / SW6 2PR; www.thesandsend.co.uk; @thesandsend; 10 pm, Sun 9 pm.

Santa Maria £42 **4** **3** **3**
160 New Cavendish St, W1   2–1B
15 St Mary's Rd, W5   020 8579 1462   1–3A
92-94 Waterford Road, SW6   020 7384 2844   6–4A
"Consistently fantastic pizza, with interesting toppings and a nicely textured base" have created a major buzz around this independent Neapolitan trio, which started out in Ealing before opening off Fulham Broadway and in Fitzrovia. It's still the W5 original that incites most fuss – "a small cafe/bistro, it's always crowded you can end up sitting in a rather tight, alley-like room" although in recent times they've also colonised the Red Lion next door so you can "set yourself down at the pub and tuck in with more space and vibe". / www.santamariapizzeria.com; @SantaMariaPizza.

Santa Maria del Sur SW8 £54 **3** **4** **3**
129 Queenstown Rd   020 7622 2088   11–1C
Since 2006, this out-of-the-way Argentinian has won a strong Battersea following, particularly with its selection of succulent steaks (flown in from Latin America) and "lovely" staff. If you have veggie friends, don't despair: they do now have the odd vegan option. / SW8 3RH; www.santamariadelsur.co.uk; @StaMariadelSur; 10 pm.

Santini SW1 £80 **2** **3** **3**
29 Ebury St   020 7730 4094   2–4B
There's "still a sense of occasion when you dine" at this "very smart and fashionable" Belgravia Italian, which remains in the same family after 35 years and is nowadays run by Laura, daughter of founder Gino. It's "very business-y" though, and having hosted Frank Sinatra and the Clintons back in the day, it's fair to say it is "past its glory years". / SW1W 0NZ; www.santini-restaurant.com; @santinirest; 10.45 pm.

Santo Remedio SE1 £63 **3** **3** **3**
152 Tooley Street   020 7403 3021   10–4D
This "authentic, up-beat" cantina "lifts the reputation of Mexican cuisine in London" with its "delicious food" and colourful atmosphere. Founders Edson Diaz-Fuentes (ex-Wahaca) and his wife Natalie brought it to Bermondsey via pop-ups, supper clubs and a short-lived Shoreditch venture. A minority of reporters complain of "inconsistency", with dishes veering between "excellent" and "flavourless". / SE1 2TU; www.santoremedio.co.uk; @santoremediouk; 10 pm, Sat 11 pm.

Santore EC1 £52 **3** **2** **2**
59-61 Exmouth Mkt   020 7812 1488   10–1A
"Cheerful local Italian" in Exmouth Market that excels in the "delivery of classic dishes by staff who clearly enjoy working here and interacting with customers" – "it's always good to hear Italian spoken in the background". / EC1R 4QL; www.santorerestaurant.london; @Santore_london; 11 pm.

Sanxia Renjia £38 **3** **2** **2**
29 Goodge Street, W1   020 7636 5886   2–1B
36 Deptford Broadway, SE8   020 8692 9633   1–3D
"Great food at a good price" continues to win acclaim for the Deptford branch of this Sichuanese duo, whose chilli-hot and numbing cuisine makes it one of SE8's brighter culinary sparks. No feedback this year on its less noteworthy Goodge Street branch.

Sapori Sardi SW6 £57 **3** **3** **2**
786 Fulham Rd   020 7731 0755   11–1B
Limited but all-round positive feedback again on this family-run Sardinian – one of the few bright culinary sparks in the area near the western end of the Fulham Road. / SW6 5SL; @Saporisardi; 10.30 pm; No Amex.

Saravanaa Bhavan HA0 £42 `4` `3` `2`
531-533 High Rd   020 8900 8526   1–1A
The Wembley branch of an international South Indian veggie chain, which has eight venues in Greater London, serves, according to fans, "the best tiffins (light day-time meals) ever". Fascinating fact: P Rajagopal, the 'dosa king' who founded the group in 1981, died of heart failure in June at the age of 71, one week into a life sentence for the murder of an employee whose wife he wanted to marry. / HA0 2DJ; www.saravanbhavanlondon.com; Mon - Thurs 10.30pm, Fri-Sun 11pm.

Sardine N1 £59 `4` `3` `3`
15 Micawber Street   020 7490 0144   13–1A
"Intriguing southern French-inspired food", "simply cooked from fresh ingredients", is the draw at former Rotorino chef Alex Jackson's three-year-old in "an off-the-beaten-track area" near Silicon Roundabout. "Stripped-down décor" and "great natural and low-intervention wines" help set the "very casual" tone. / N1 7TB; www.sardine.london; @sardinelondon; 10 pm.

Sartoria W1 £77 `3` `3` `3`
20 Savile Row   020 7534 7000   4–3A
This "formal" Mayfair Italian is "one of the best D&D London venues", in a "beautiful, discreet and spacious setting", with "expert service" and an "excellent kitchen" nowadays directed by ex-L'Anima chef Francesco Mazzei. All this comes at a price, of course, so while the formula might "work well for business-lunchers", it can appear "expensive" to other diners. / W1S 3PR; www.sartoria-restaurant.co.uk; @SartoriaRest; 10.45 pm; closed Sat L & Sun.

The Savannah NW1 £54
81-103 Euston Street   020 7691 8588   9–4C
Limited-but-upbeat feedback on this new hotel dining room: "an oasis of calm near Euston station (an area short of nice places to eat!)". Ethical sourcing and African influences in dishes – as well as Asian ones – help take it slightly out of the mainstream, and one or two early reports say it's "a hidden gem". / NW1 2EZ; www.thesavannah.co.uk; @TheSavannahLDN; 10 pm.

Savoir Faire WC1 £47 `3` `4` `3`
42 New Oxford St   020 7436 0707   5–1C
"Images redolent of 'Le Gai Paris' (the naked bottoms went perfectly with my slow roasted pork belly!)" grace the muralled walls of this "friendly and efficient" Gallic corner bistro, near the British Museum: "a reliable and enjoyable choice", serving affordable classic French dishes. / WC1A 1EP; www.savoir.co.uk; 10 pm.

The Savoy Hotel, Savoy Grill WC2 £105 `2` `3` `3`
Strand   020 7592 1600   5–3D
"One of London's iconic dining rooms": this panelled chamber – just off the foyer of The Strand's famous Art Deco landmark – still exudes "old-school elegance", and, even if it's not quite the pre-eminent power dining scene that it was in Thatcher's day, it's still popular with expense-accounters, who particularly appreciate its "comprehensive wine list". Under the stewardship of the Gordon Ramsay group, its "classic (old-fashioned even) menu" is "pricey but fabulous" to fans, but a wider view is that it's "moderately average and not cheap": "nothing wrong but no sparkle". / WC2R 0EU; www.gordonramsayrestaurants.com; @savoygrill; 11 pm, Sun 10.30 pm.

The Savoy Hotel, Thames Foyer WC2 £97 2 3 4

The Savoy, The Strand 020 7420 2111 5–3D

For a "lovely afternoon tea" and "a truly elegant experience" there's much to recommend the light-filled foyer of this posh hotel lounge (set beneath a glass dome). "The price is eye-watering but seconds are regularly provided, so it's actually good value for the amazing experience". Breakfast here is also "a gorgeous start to the day". / WC2R 0ER; www.fairmont.com/savoy-london; @TheSavoyLondon; 11 pm.

Scalini SW3 £88 2 3 3

1-3 Walton St 020 7225 2301 6–2C

"The diner is transported straight back to the 1960s, not least because of the breadsticks and very old-fashioned service" at this traditional Italian, close to Harrods. "No doubt because of the location, it's not exactly a bargain" – the "pricey food, although good, does not quite live up to expectations" – but it's popular (opening a branch in Dubai last year), and "when busy, it's pretty much shoulder-to-shoulder". / SW3 2JD; www.scalinilondon.co.uk; 11 pm; No shorts.

Scott's W1 £86 4 4 4

20 Mount St 020 7495 7309 3–3A

"Pure glamour" attaches to Richard Caring "really classy" and "sophisticated" Mayfair A-lister – 007's favourite lunch spot – which is "an ideal place to go celeb spotting… if you're into that kind of thing". Culinarily speaking, it's famous for its "spanking fresh" fish and seafood (and vies with its stablemate J Sheekey as the capital's top venue for such specialities) although it also offers "enough meat choices to keep the carnivores happy". In terms of style, it's "smart" and quite "formal", which – together with its "silky smooth service" and "well-spaced tables" – makes it an "impressive" choice for entertaining and "clients love it" (although, by the same token, "the room can be overrun with business suits", especially at lunch, robbing it of some of its habitual sparkle). Top Tip – "the terrace tables are great, weather permitting!" / W1K 2HE; www.scotts-restaurant.com; 10.30 pm, Sun 10 pm; booking max 6 may apply.

Scully SW1 £62 5 4 3

St James's Market 020 3911 6840 4–4D

"Mind-blowing food" that's "hard to classify" – "a true pot pourri of tastes from around the world using a cascade of daringly combined ingredients to create a theatrical experience for the eyes, and a surprising explosion for the taste buds" – is carving ever-wider culinary renown for Ramael Scully's "exceptionally interesting" two-year-old in St James's Market, whose kitchen is "really pushing the boundaries". The room is "classy" too, and staff are "so extremely knowledgeable and helpful". "The only downside is a crowd that's a bit St James'y". Top Tip – "sit at the counter, where talking to the chefs is a bonus". / SW1Y 4QU; www.scullyrestaurant.com; @scully_ldn.

Sea Containers, Mondrian London SE1 £71 2 3 3

20 Upper Ground 020 3747 1000 10–3A

Views of the Thames and a chic interior combine to create a lovely setting for this well-groomed South Bank destination: on the ground floor of a swish hotel near Blackfriars Bridge. It escaped the harsh criticisms of past years in the most recent survey feedback: in particular its "super buffet brunch" with bottomless Prosecco is a top feature. / SE1 9PD; www.seacontainerslondon.com; @SeaContainers_; 11 pm.

Sea Garden & Grill SW17 £46 4|4|4
29 Tooting High Street   020 8682 2995   11–2C
Helping make Tooting's Broadway Market a foodie destination, this "very affordable" two-year-old seafood specialist wins praise for its "fabulous food, great service and big smiles". The "really inventive" approach extends to drinks, which include an "amazing gin cocktail" flavoured with oysters. Antiques trade veteran Jimmy Luttman is an "excellent" host. / SW17 0RJ; www.seagardenandgrill.co.uk; @theseagardenuk .

The Sea, The Sea SW3 NEW £64 4|4|4
174 Pavilion Road   020 7824 8090   6–2D
"Fish shop by day and seafood restaurant by night", this "cutely-situated", mid-2019 newcomer, in an über-chichi enclave off Sloane Street, comes from the same stable as Bonnie Gull, and has won instant acclaim as a "great entrant to the London seafood scene". "Minimalist decor" sets a tone where the focus is on pristine ingredients zhooshed up with a bit of culinary magic by chef Leandro Carreria: beautiful, if "very expensive". You can also eat there at lunch, but with "no mains, desserts or coffee". / SW3 2TJ; www.theseathesea.net.

Seabird SE1 NEW
The Hoxton, 40 Blackfriars Road   020 7903 3000   10–4A
The 14th floor rooftop of the new Hoxton hotel – this time confusingly located in Southwark, despite the name – is home to a fish and seafood restaurant from the team behind Brooklyn's Maison Premiere. It opened in September 2019, with a raw bar, a wide range of oysters – and 'the fresh flavours of southern Europe'. Oh, and great views. / SE1 8NY; thehoxton.com/london/southwark/hotels.

Seafresh SW1 £51 3|2|2
80-81 Wilton Rd   020 7828 0747   2–4B
Marios Leonidou runs this well-established Pimlico veteran, originally founded by his dad, and celebrating 55 years in 2020. For a (slightly) posher-than-usual fish 'n' chip experience, it's something of a classic choice, and the menu runs far beyond cod to scallops, oak-smoked salmon and Dover sole. / SW1V 1DL; www.seafresh-dining.com; @SeafreshLondon; 10.30 pm; closed Sun.

Searcys St Pancras Grand NW1 £59 1|2|3
The Concourse   020 7870 9900   9–3C
"If one arrives early for the train to Paris", this "beautiful, grand space in an historic setting" is, say fans, "not a bad place to while away the time". But a large majority of reporters agree, "it could and should be better" – "I was hoping for the sort of vibe experienced at Grand Central Station in New York but it didn't have the same panache" and "the food can be a let-down for the price". / NW1 2QP; www.searcys.co.uk; @SearcyStPancras; 10.30 pm, Sun 8 pm.

The Sea Shell NW1 £51 3|2|2
49 Lisson Grove   020 7224 9000   9–4A
"Great traditional fish and chips" – "still done very well" – have made this chippy a "cabbies' favourite" for decades. Strangely, though, for an institution tracing its origins back almost a century, the interior of its Lisson Grove premises is dull and "without atmosphere". / NW1 6UH; www.seashellrestaurant.co.uk; @SeashellRestaur; 10.30 pm; closed Sun.

Season Kitchen N4 £50 3|3|2
53 Stroud Green Rd   020 7263 5500   9–1D
"Off the beaten track" in Finsbury Park, this "great-value" little spot, named for its seasonal approach to cooking, is one of the best options in these parts: from a short and very to-the-point menu, results are uniformly well rated. / N4 3EF; www.seasonkitchen.co.uk; @seasonkitchen; 10.30 pm, Sun 8 pm; D only.

FSA RATINGS: FROM 1 POOR — 5 EXCEPTIONAL

Sen Viet WC1 £29 3 4 2
119 King's Cross Road 020 7278 2881 9–3D
"Not the most attractive area" – the traffic arteries south of King's Cross
station – "but the food in this outwardly fairly nondescript-looking restaurant
is fabulous", and this makes a very handy and good value Vietnamese
refuelling spot. / WC1X 9NH; senviet.uk.

Señor Ceviche W1 £51 3 3 2
Kingly Ct 020 7842 8540 4–2B
18 Charlotte St, W1 020 7842 8540 NEW
This "buzzy Peruvian in Kingly Court" provides consistently "good, super-
tasty food and a warm ambience". A second branch has followed
in Charlotte Street. / W1B 5PW; www.senor-ceviche.com; @SenorCevicheLDN;
11.30 pm, Sat midnight, Sun 10.30 pm; booking max 6 may apply.

Sette SW1 NEW £92
Bulgari Hotel, 4 Knightsbridge Green 020 7151 1025 6–1D
The replacement for Alain Ducasse's Bulgari (RIP) – the first London sibling
to famous NYC restaurant Scarpetta opened in Knightsbridge's Bulgari Hotel
in June 2019, serving Italian classics. The seventh location for the group,
this one is named Sette for "lucky number seven", apparently. It opened too
late for survey feedback, but received a major panning from Sunday Times
critic, Marina O'Loughlin for pasta "sauced in the American rather than
Italian way: drowned rather than dressed…" / SW1X 7QL;
www.settelondon.co.uk.

Seven Park Place SW1 £111 4 4 3
7-8 Park Pl 020 7316 1620 3–4C
"Consistently lovely food" over the past 10 years has earned an ecstatic,
if limited, foodie following for low-key chef William Drabble, who "remains
a hit in the kitchen rather than on the TV screen". The "cosy" and
"romantic" dining room of this hideaway luxury hotel in St James's also
benefits from "cute, quirky decor and friendly, helpful staff". / SW1A 1LS;
www.stjameshotelandclub.com; @SevenParkPlace; 10 pm; closed Mon & Sun;
No trainers.

7 Saints W11 £56 4 4 4
7 All Saints Road 020 7460 8566 7–1B
On the site that was Ripe Tomato (RIP), John Gummer's (former maître d' at
The Wolseley) popular yearling is praised as "a neighbourhood spot that has
it all": a "monthly changing", "short-but-impossible-to-choose-from menu"
and an ambience "like going to a friend's house and being left to do what
you want in the privacy of your own table". / W11 1HA; 7saints.co.uk.

Sexy Fish W1 £100 1 2 2
1-4 Berkeley Sq 020 3764 2000 3–3B
"Let your friends know you've been, and they'll ask about the clientele
before wanting to know about the food…" – Richard Caring's notorious, LA-
style, bling-fest in Mayfair (which reportedly cost £15m to fit out)
is most "definitely a place for those eager to see and be seen". Fans also
believe its luxurious menu of Asian-inspired fish and seafood (heavy on funky
sushi, tempura, and gyoza) is plain "awesome" too. But to a large
proportion of reporters, it's "awful – just awful" – exacting "extortionate"
prices to deliver "some weird-and-not-always-felicitous flavour combinations"
to "a horrific stew of Mayfair types". / W1J 6BR; www.sexyfish.com;
@sexyfishlondon; 11 pm, Sun 10.30 pm; booking max 6 may apply.

Shackfuyu W1 £46 4 3 3
14a, Old Compton St   020 3019 3492   5–2A
"Some amazingly tasty dishes" – of a funky, western-influenced Japanese
genre – again earn high ratings for this "really delightful" Soho outfit
(the brainchild of Australian chef, Ross Shonhan, creator of the Bone
Daddies group). "It may not quite count as cheap 'n' cheerful, but the
tasting menu is a bargain for £30" – in fact, it may be a better choice than
going off-piste, where "the bills rack up quickly". Top Tip – "deliciously
indulgent green tea ice cream dessert". / W1D 4TJ;
www.bonedaddies.com/restaurant/shackfuyu; @shackfuyu; 11 pm, Mon & Tue 10 pm,
Sun 9 pm; no booking.

Shahi Pakwaan N2 £32 4 4 3
25 Aylmer ParadeAylmer Road   020 834 11111   1–1B
This "fabulous" two-year-old Indian in East Finchley punches well above its
weight with "top-class, authentic food" based on the royal cuisine
of Hyderabad. Its reputation for "high-quality cooking" is attracting attention
from beyond the immediate locality, despite the "obscure location" in a
converted shop – and there's "easy parking". / N2 0PE;
www.shahipakwaan.co.uk.

Shake Shack £30 3 2 2
Nova, 172 Victoria St, SW1   01923 555188   2–4B
80 New Oxford St, WC1   01925 555171   5–1B
24 The Market, WC2   020 3598 1360   5–3D
Boxpark Wembley, Olympic Way, HA9   1–1A
The Street, Westfield Stratford, E20   01923 555167   14–1D
45 Cannon Street, EC4   10–3B
In less than 20 years, Danny Meyer has transformed his New York City hot-
dog cart into a global fast-food brand giant with eight outlets in London –
including a Covent Garden flagship that was revamped earlier this year.
Ratings remain remarkably solid for "a chain that does what it's supposed
to do". / WC2 & E14 11 pm, Sun 9 pm-10.30 pm; E20 9.30 pm, Fri & Sat 11 pm;
no bookings.

Shampers W1 £47 3 4 4
4 Kingly St   020 7437 1692   4–2B
"With lashings of individuality", this unreconstructed Soho wine bar from
1977 stands out for its "old-fashioned style and service" – "the owner,
Simon, and his crew simply deliver!" – and "is still going strong with
a traditional menu" of "classic French bistro food" (gravadlax, calf's liver,
steak…). There's also a "most interesting wine list that has great depth
at good prices, rather than too many wines at very high prices". It can,
though, "become a little overcrowded (due to its seeming popularity with the
Chartered Surveyors' Tribe)". / W1B 5PE; www.shampers.net; @shampers_soho;
11 pm; closed Sun; No bookings.

Shanghai Modern WC2 NEW 3 2 2
Central Cross, 12 Newport Place   020 7734 6137   5–3B
In Chinatown's shiny, new, Central Cross development, this "functional but
bright and clean" 150-seater opened in spring 2019, and early days
feedback says it's a good, modern addition to the area. "My wife and I know
Shanghai food from both Hong Kong and Shanghai – this is good,
with generous portions at good-value prices". "Staff, despite being rushed off
their feet, were pleasant and helpful, though few spoke English". / WC2H 7JP.

The Shed W8 £54 3 3 3
122 Palace Gardens Ter   020 7229 4024   7–2B

"Lovely food and a great casual atmosphere" draw a buzzy crowd to this quirky, small Notting Hill site (which old-timers recall as The Ark). It was the first of the Gladwin bros' shabby-chic venues in London (see also Rabbit and Nutbourne) and their Sussex-farm-to-metropolitan-fork concept provides an "interesting English variation on the tapas theme"; on the downside, some find the rustic furniture "very uncomfortable". / W8 4RT; www.theshed-restaurant.com; @theshed_resto; 11 pm; closed Mon L & Sun.

J Sheekey WC2 £81 4 4 4
28-34 St Martin's Ct   020 7240 2565   5–3B

"Unfailing, first class, and in the heart of Theatreland" – Richard Caring's "wonderfully old-school" icon (est. 1896) has long been the survey's No. 1 most talked-about destination as well as its top choice for fish and seafood. Tucked away, down an alley just off St Martin's Lane, you navigate your way in past a uniformed doorman. The tantalisingly-translucent frontage only gives hints of the "classic" interior beyond with its "feeling of bygone glamour": a series of "compact" panelled rooms , which "feature wood, brass, glass, and vintage photos of stage stars", all presided over by "very professional" staff. The effect is "intimate" ("albeit a bit cramped") and the atmosphere is "always buzzing" (if, occasionally, "to the wrong side of hectic"). The "traditional", "comfort-fish" cuisine is "not inventive nor innovative", "but always of the highest quality". "New ingredients like harissa enliven an otherwise static menu, but if the formula works, why change it?" "The fish pie and and seafood platter remain classics", while "Dover sole is served in umpteen different ways with on/off menu options". Despite expansion (with the addition of the neighbouring Atlantic Bar), "it has maintained remarkable standards for years and years". / WC2N 4AL; www.j-sheekey.co.uk; @JSheekeyRest; 11.30 pm, Sun 10 pm; booking max 6 may apply.

J Sheekey Atlantic Bar WC2 £74 3 3 4
28-34 St Martin's Ct   020 7240 2565   5–3B

"So cool eating at the bar" – this "enjoyably bustling" spin-off from the neighbouring Theatreland classic has "very good, 1930s-style decor" (even though it was only created about 10 years ago). Compared with the main restaurant it's "perhaps a bit more about the ambience versus the food" here, and – "with the menu opting for the small-plates approach – costs can mount up". But, results are "predictably good", and the operation's "slick" style and "flexible" format suits it to many different occasions: it's particularly "great for lunch sitting at the bar, or an early pre-theatre dinner at one of the tables". / WC2N 4AL; www.j-sheekey.co.uk; @JSheekeyRest; 11.30 pm, Sun 10.30 pm; booking max 3 may apply.

Shikumen, Dorsett Hotel W12 £57 4 2 2
58 Shepherd's Bush Grn   020 8749 9978   8–1C

"Excellent upmarket Chinese food" and "great dim sum" may seem out of place on grungy Shepherd's Bush Green, but this joint "can claim to be one of London's top Oriental restaurants – it's where I take my Singaporean friends when they visit". The venue – a plush modern hotel, part of a Hong Kong-owned group – makes for a rather "cold ambience" by some standards, but there are no complaints about the scran. / W12 5AA; www.shikumen.co.uk; @ShikumenUK; 10.30 pm, Sun 10 pm.

Shilpa W6 £36 5 3 1
206 King St   020 8741 3127   8–2B

In an anonymous-looking Hammsersmith parade of shops, this Keralan café is a particularly notable "hidden gem" – "when it comes to authentic, deft, southern Indian cooking for a minimal bill, Shilpa sure hits the spot" and is "unbelievable value". A word of caution: "it's anything but an exciting place": it's all about the "genuine cooking". / W6 0RA; www.shilparestaurant.co.uk; 11 pm, Thu-Sat midnight.

Shoryu Ramen £49 **3** 2 2
9 Regent St, SW1   no tel   4–4D
3 Denman St, W1   no tel   4–3C
5 Kingly Ct, W1   no tel   4–2B
84 New Oxford Street, WC1   5–1B
35 Great Queen Street, WC2   5–1D
45 Great Eastern Street, EC2   13–1B
Broadgate Circle, EC2   no tel   13–2B
"Hard-to-beat ramen" – "the tonkotsu pork broth has amazing depth
of flavour" – make Japan Centre owner Tak Tokumine's "relatively
authentic" West End duo (in Soho's Kingly Court and on Regent Street)
"preferred noodle-stops in a very competitive market". / 11 pm-midnight,
Sun 9.30 pm-10 pm; E14 9 pm, Sun 6 pm; no booking (except Kingly Ct).

The Sichuan EC1 £49 **3** 3 2
14 City Road   020 7588 5489   13–2A
"Delicious dumplings" and other "fine" dishes from southwestern China
make this nondescript looking three-year-old "a real find on the western
edge of the City, near Bunhill Fields". "I even ate their tofu with great
enjoyment, which was a revelation". / EC1Y 2AA; www.thesichuan.co.uk; 11 pm.

Sichuan Folk E1 £45 **4** 2 2
32 Hanbury St   020 7247 4735   13–2C
The "strongly authentic Sichuan food" at this "fairly basic" Brick Lane venue
"may not be the best in London, but nonetheless offers a properly 'ma la'
(numbingly spicy) experience". It's particularly "good value for lunch".
/ E1 6QR; www.sichuan-folk.co.uk; 10.30 pm; No Amex.

Signor Sassi SW1 £65 **3** 3 3
14 Knightsbridge Green   020 7584 2277   6–1D
"Always a treat", this old-school trattoria near Harrods is "just the place for
traditional Italian hospitality". Launched 35 years ago, it is now part of the
upmarket San Carlo group and has branched out in recent years into the
Middle East. / SW1X 7QL; www.signorsassi.co.uk; @SignorSassi; 11.30 pm.

Silk Road SE5 £23 **5** 2 2
49 Camberwell Church St   020 7703 4832   1–3C
"Xinjiang/Uighur flavours that make few excuses for local palates",
with "big portions and small prices" have combined to win a cult following
for this outpost of north west China in deepest Camberwell. Expect "great
food in a basic setting" along with "a wait – it gets seriously busy". Top Tip
– hand-made noodles and "lamb fat skewers are divine". / SE5 8TR;
10.30 pm; closed Sat L & Sun L; Cash only; No bookings.

Silo E9 NEW
The White Building, Unit 7 Queens Yard, White Post Lane   14–1C
Due to land in October, Brighton's zero-waste restaurant Silo is coming
to London after a half-million-pound crowdfund by chef Doug McMaster.
With a similar eco-gourmet formula to the original, it's going to occupy the
first floor of Crate, Hackney Wick's grungily-groovy pizza-and-microbrewery
haunt, near the Olympic Park. / E9 5EN; silolondon.com; @SiloBrighton.

Simpson's in the Strand WC2 £82 2 2 3
100 Strand 020 7420 2111 5–3D

"Quintessentially British cuisine in very generous portions" is the raison d'être of this historic, panelled dining room, which has its bicentenary in sight; and where "a recent revamp seems to have done some good – it's still old-fashioned, but in a good way". But when it comes to the quality of the cooking, it's still not a safe bet – there are regulars who feel "its roast beef and Yorkshire pudding never disappoints", but there remains a sizeable contingent, who rate the beef "below average" and the accompanying veg "school dinner standard" – "such a shame for a wonderful old establishment". Top Tip – a Full English here is a good way to start the day. / WC2R 0EW; www.simpsonsinthestrand.co.uk; @simpsons1828; No trainers.

Simpson's Tavern EC3 £45 3 3 4
38 1/2 Ball Ct, Cornhill 020 7626 9985 10–2C

"Like stepping back in time" – this "prehistoric eatery in the City" (est 1757) has "an incredible atmosphere" and is "old-fashioned in a way we can rejoice in". The Dickensian menu of "traditional English" chops and roasts, steak 'n' kidney pies and 'stewed cheese' wins solid ratings this year – and is "not for those with a small appetite". Top Tip – "this ancient spot dishes up a top Full English". / EC3V 9DR; www.simpsonstavern.co.uk; @SimpsonsTavern; 3.30 pm; L only, closed Sat & Sun.

Sinabro SW11 £69 3 3 3
28 Battersea Rise 020 3302 3120 11–2C

"You need to sit at the bar to watch the cooking and food preparation" according to fans of this 20-seater in Battersea, that fans say is "delightful in every way" not least its "super quality" modern British cuisine, available either à la carte, or from the five-course tasting menu. / SW11 1EE; www.sinabro.co.uk; @SinabroLondon; 10 pm, Fri & Sat 10.30 pm.

Singapore Garden NW6 £50 4 4 2
83a Fairfax Rd 020 7624 8233 9–2A

"Consistently excellent food with friendly service" – all "at reasonable prices" – ensures that this cramped, pan-Asian veteran, tucked away in a parade of shops near Swiss Cottage, is "always busy". Giles Coren of The Times claims to have eaten here more than a thousand times, drawn back by the Malaysian and Singaporean specialties. / NW6 4DY; www.singaporegarden.co.uk; @SingaporeGarden.

Singburi Royal Thai Café E11 £23 4 3 3
593 Leytonstone High Rd 020 8281 4801 1–1D

As accolades go, the 'best restaurant in Leytonstone' is a bit of a two-edged sword, but this small Thai local is worth remembering for its "cheap 'n' cheerful" chow; and you can BYO. / E11 4PA; @SingburiThaiCaf; 10.30 pm; D only; Cash only.

Siren SW1 NEW £106
15 Beeston Place 020 7769 4485 2–4B

Occupying a newly-built pavilion designed by Russell Sage Studios, in the lush garden of the ever-more 'with it' Goring Hotel, this collaboration with über-chef Nathan Outlaw, opened in June 2019, focused on showcasing the Cornish fish and seafood for which Outlaw is famous. Its arrival was too late for survey feedback, but an early review from the Evening Standard's Fay Maschler was most unimpressed. Others, since, have been kinder. / SW1W 0JW; www.thegoring.com/food-drink/siren; @TheGoring.

Six Portland Road W11 £63 **4 4 3**
6 Portland Road 020 7229 3130 7–2A
"Understated Holland Park local" worth discovering on account of its
"consistently delicious and always changing British food" – an "inventive
menu providing enough diversity to make it a place to return to on a regular
basis". It's "cosy" too, with "charming, quirky service" and an "excellent,
interesting and different wine list"; in short, a "perfect neighbourhood
bistro". / W11 4LA; www.sixportlandroad.com; @SixPortlandRoad; 10 pm; closed
Mon & Sun D.

Sketch,
Lecture Room at Library W1 £151 **3 3 4**
9 Conduit St 020 7659 4500 4–2A
Up the sweeping staircase of this vast Mayfair palace, this "spectacular,
grand, imposing and romantic" dining room certainly looks the part for
a fairytale date (hint: "it might be a bit OTT for some tastes"). Star chef
Pierre Gagnaire's "creative" and complex menu features some "really quirky
and delicious touches" and for most reporters "its two Michelin stars are
well-deserved". Even some fans, though, feel the wine list in particular
is "stupidly overpriced" and there is a school of thought that, although
"the tasting menu is all very nice, dishes don't really hang together too well";
or that you plain just "shouldn't waste your money here". "A selfie in the
crystal-lined loos is a must though". / W1S 2XG; www.sketch.uk.com;
@sketchlondon; 10.30 pm; closed Mon, Sat L & Sun; No trainers; Booking max 6 may
apply.

Sketch,
Gallery W1 £90 **1 2 3**
9 Conduit St 020 7659 4500 4–2A
Part of Mourad Mazouz's lavish Mayfair palazzo, this OTT favourite
(the 'cheap' dining option here – see also Sketch, Lecture Room) is a
perennial hit with a Zoolander-esque crowd keener on looking 'really, really,
really ridiculously good looking' than on the eclectic cuisine, which is very
expensive, and can seem like a case of "Emperor's new clothes". Who cares
though? – with David Shrigley's pinker-than-pink design-scheme it's
"an Instagrammer's dream", and who doesn't want to have paid
at least one visit to the egg-shaped loos? / W1S 2XG; www.sketch.uk.com;
@sketchlondon.

Skewd Kitchen EN4 £47 **4 3 3**
12 Cockfosters Parade 020 8449 7771 1–1C
This "fun, friendly and welcoming Turk" at the northern end of the Piccadilly
line in Cockfosters is reinventing the Anatolian grill 'with attitude'. It's a big
hit with locals, who say "they're always updating their menu with fantastic
specials". / EN4 0BX; www.skewdkitchen.com; @SkewdKitchen; 11 pm.

Skylon,
South Bank Centre SE1 £73 **2 3 4**
Belvedere Rd 020 7654 7800 2–3D
"Still one of the best views in London" – this vast chamber was built, back in
this South Bank arts centre's, 1950s, Festival-of-Britain prime,
as 'The People's Palace' and it remains "a great-looking venue with
an enviable location overlooking the Thames" through gigantic picture
windows. All reporters would agree that it's a "brilliant spot for watching the
world and river go by, and the cocktails are great", but too many find the
cooking either "expensive" or "disappointing", or both. Top Tip – "worth
visiting for the 'Saxy Saturday Brunch' featuring a nice but limited set menu
but also bottomless Prosecco which helps draw in a crowd". / SE1 8XX;
www.skylon-restaurant.co.uk; @skylonsouthbank; closed Sun D; No trainers.

Sloane Street Deli SW1 NEW
162 Sloane Street   6–2D
With views of Cadogan Place Gardens, this new Caprice Holdings sibling adjacent to the Cadogan Hotel is in the same mould as Richard Caring's now-defunct Mount Street Deli, and opened in mid-2019. Initially opening is till late-afternoon, but ultimately a wine bar style operation is planned in the evenings. / SW1X 9BS.

Smith & Wollensky WC2   £103   2 3 2
The Adelphi Building, 1-11 John Adam St   020 7321 6007   5–4D
NYC's famous, steakhouse chain opened this über-swanky offshoot three years ago at the foot of the Adelphi Building, just off The Strand, but it's never made waves this side of 'The Pond', written off from day one by the cognoscenti due to its "outrageous prices": a complaint that persists in a significant number of reports to this day. But its "amazing steaks" – the best USDA dry-aged cuts, and prime meat from the British Isles too – also help win it good-to-outstanding ratings in practically all feedback; and, especially if you have company plastic to burn, it can cater well for a business occasion in particular. / WC2N 6HT; www.smithandwollensky.co.uk; @sandwollenskyuk; 10.30 pm, Fri & Sat 11 pm; No trainers.

Smith's Wapping E1   £71   4 4 5
22 Wapping High St   020 7488 3456   12–1A
"Panoramas over the Thames" and "an excellent view of Tower Bridge" provide extra incentive to discover this popular fish brasserie, at the foot of a Wapping development (sibling to a long-standing original, in Ongar). It offers a "well-put-together" all-round experience, incorporating "professional" service that "goes the extra mile", with "well-cooked and presented" fish and seafood. / E1W 1NJ; www.smithsrestaurants.com; @smithswapping; lunch last orders 2.30pm, sunday 3.30pm. Dinner mo; closed Sun D; No trainers.

Smiths of Smithfield, Top Floor EC1   £77   3 2 4
67-77 Charterhouse St   020 7251 7950   10–1A
A "lovely location" with "great views" across the meat market to the City is reason enough to visit this top-floor venue, with a menu that focuses unsurprisingly on red meat. There's a "good atmosphere, with tables not too close together", which makes it a top choice for City-fringe business lunches. The "fixed-price steak and Malbec is great value for money". / EC1M 6HJ; www.smithsofsmithfield.co.uk; @thisissmiths; 10.45 pm; closed Sat L & Sun; booking max 10 may apply.

Smoke & Salt SW9   £46   5 4 3
53 Brixton Station Rd   07421 327 556   11–1D
"It's a slightly mad room in a shipping container" – well, that's Pop Brixton for you – but this "relaxed and friendly" 20-seater offers "the epitome of modern dining" with its "super-tasty and interesting" dishes: 'on-trend small plates created using British ingredients and the ancient techniques of smoking, curing and preserving'. / SW9 8PQ; www.smokeandsalt.com; @SmokeandSaltLDN; 10 pm Sun 6 pm; May need 4+ to book.

Smokehouse Islington N1   £57   3 3 3
63-69 Canonbury Rd   020 7354 1144   9–2D
This "very busy (booking is essential)" gastropub in Canonbury is "great for roast meat" – but the starters and desserts also win plaudits, and "there are so many beers on tap (20) to work your way through". "Terrific quick meal before a gig, and I didn't even get to try their signature smoked meat!". / N1 2RG; www.smokehouseislington.co.uk; @smokehouseN1; 10 pm, Sun 9 pm; closed weekday L.

Smokestak E1 £50 5 3 3
35 Sclater Street   020 3873 1733   13–1C
*Some of "the best smoked meat in London" (including "excellent brisket")
is prepared on the charcoal in front of you, alongside "some fantastic sides"
at David Carter's rugged, southern US-style grill-house, just off Brick Lane.
Just one complaint: "the room is nice, but smokey". / E1 6LB;
www.smokestak.co.uk; @smokestakUK.*

Smoking Goat E1 £51 5 4 4
64 Shoreditch High Street   no tel   13–1B
*"Better Thai food than Thailand!" – Ben Chapman's hip Shoreditch BBQ
goes from strength to strength, with its "perfect and spicy" dishes; and a
"slightly haphazard, rock 'n' roll atmosphere when it's busy" (i.e. mostly).
"It's a perfect place to celebrate with friends, as the food's handy for
sharing, staff are super friendly and there are great local craft beers
on tap". Top Menu Tip – "Sometimes the chilli can be a bit heavy handed,
but those crunchy, fish sauce chicken wings are like catnip: utterly addictive".
/ E1 6JJ; www.smokinggoatsoho.com; @SmokingGoatBar.*

Smokoloko E1 5 3 –
Old Spitalfields Market, Bethnal Green Road   07508 675363   13–2B
*It's a dead cinch to spot Cleo Vizioli's street market stall at Spitalfields
Market: it's the one with the old train locomotive! This is the only permanent
site, although there are three other locos in the pipeline to serve events and
markets around town. The USP is its "amazing smoked meats": "there's
always a queue, but the meat-loaded rolls are divine". / E1 6GY; smokoloko.uk;
@smokolokoBBQ.*

Snackbar E8 NEW
Farm:Shop, 20 Dalston Lane   14–1A
*'Pickled' author Freddie Janssen launched a Kickstarter campaign for this
new, August 2019 venture in hip Dalston – an all-day café sitting alongside
a co-working space and urban farm, and delivering a funky-sounding menu
which reads like a 'pick 'n' mix' of global inspiration. / E8 3AZ;
snackbarlondon.com.*

Snaps & Rye W10 £59 4 4 3
93 Golborne Rd   020 8964 3004   7–1A
*"Simple Scandi café" and take-away in North Kensington, at the north end of
Portobello market, owned by husband-and-wife team, Kell and Jacqueline
Skott, that wins rave reviews from its local fanclub for its straightforwardly
delicious, Danish-infuenced dishes. Breakfast and brunch are a big deal here
with smørrebrød (open sarnies), kedgeree and other light bites: in the
evenings they serve a limited, somewhat more substantial menu (meatballs,
pan-fried fish, sharing-plates…) / W10 5NL; www.snapsandrye.com;
@snapsandrye; 10 pm; L only, Fri open L & D, closed Mon.*

Snooty Fox N5 £41 3 2 3
75 Grosvenor Avenue   9–2D
*Jolly Canonbury boozer decorated with pictures of 60s icons. There's also
a jukebox – so it "can get very noisy". On the menu: "honest pub grub",
including "the best burgers" and spit-roast chicken. / N5 2NN;
www.snootyfoxlondon.co.uk; @Snootyfoxlondon.*

Soane's Kitchen W5 NEW £47 2 2 3
Pitzhanger Manor, Walpole Park   020 8579 2685   1–3A
*"A lovely room and outside garden area" – "great on a sunny day" – makes
this "a brilliant addition to the west London scene": the new café in the
garden adjacent to Pitzhanger Manor (owned, in days past, by the renowned
architect Sir John Soane). But while there's a "good-value set menu" and
an à la carte with something for everyone ("covering
veggie/vegan/flexi/typical diets"), some dishes are "expensive and poor".
/ W5 5EQ; soaneskitchen.co.uk.*

Social Eating House W1   £80   2 2 4
58-59 Poland St   020 7993 3251   4–1C
Ratings dropped for the second year running at Jason Atherton's casual Soho venture, amid gripes from reporters confused by the "pub setting with proper restaurant prices" or having to "wade through four menus". Some say the food is still "consistently brilliant". Others were "left wondering what all the hype is for" – "dishes lacked any wow factor" and are "certainly not worth the high price tag". / W1F 7NR; www.socialeatinghouse.com; @socialeathouse; 2.45pm;10.45 pm; closed Sun.

Soif SW11   £59   3 3 3
27 Battersea Rise   020 7223 1112   11–2C
"Easy-yet-delicious French bistro" option, offering the combination of gutsy Gallic small plates and an interesting wine list that's become the hallmark of outlets run by natural and organic wine pioneer Les Caves de Pyrène. / SW11 1HG; www.soif.co; @Soif_SW11; 10 pm, Sun 4 pm; closed Mon L & Sun D.

Som Saa E1   £52   3 2 3
43a Commercial St   020 7324 7790   13–2C
"Possibly the most authentic Thai cooking in town" ("fresh", "fragrant" and focused on fiery, north-eastern-Thai cuisine), plus some "delicious cocktails" have carved a major culinary reputation for this trendy three-year-old, in a converted factory south of Spitalfields Market. Its ratings were dragged down this year though by a few less rapturous reports: "perfectly good, but not the outstanding blow-out we expected from some reviews". / E1 6BD; www.somsaa.com; @somsaa_london; 11.30 pm, Sat midnight, Sun 10.30 pm.

Sông Quê E2   £39   3 3 2
134 Kingsland Rd   020 7613 3222   14–2A
"Very basic", but zippy, Vietnamese chow ("soft shell crab, YOM!") has made this busy dive one of the better known in Shoreditch's 'Little Vietnam' on the Kingsland Road. "Sometimes service is a little bit attitude-y, but you're not going for that; and it's crowded, but the food's the focus". / E2 8DY; www.songque.co.uk; 11 pm, Sun 10.30 pm; No Amex.

Sophie's Steakhouse   £62   2 2 3
42-44 Great Windmill St, W1   awaiting tel   4–3D
311-313 Fulham Rd, SW10   020 7352 0088   6–3B
"Decent burgers and reliable steaks" are highlights of the menu at this pair of "family- and group-friendly" steakhouses in the Fulham Road and Soho – useful ports of call before a match at Stamford Bridge or a night out in the West End. Overall, the level culinary performance is rated somewhere between "solid" and "pretty average". / www.sophiessteakhouse.com; SW10 11pm, Fri & Sat midnight, Sun-Mon 10 pm, W1D 11 pm, Fri & Sat midnight, Sun 10 pm; no booking.

Sorella SW4   £55   4 3 4
148 Clapham Manor Street   020 7720 4662   11–1D
"A great local addition that's worth travelling to": Robin Gill's small, neighbourhood two-year-old, near his Clapham HQ, The Dairy, takes its inspiration from the Amalfi coast, and its traditionally presented Italian dishes (cicchetti, antipasti, primi, secondi and dolci) are consistently "wonderful"; and it's "good fun" too. / SW4 6BX; www.sorellarestaurant.co.uk; @SorellaClapham.

Soutine NW8 £59 | 3 | 3 | 4 |
60 St John's Wood High Street   020 3926 8448   9–3A

*"It's early days, but all the signs are good for Corbin & King's new venture"
in St John's Wood (on the site of a defunct branch of Carluccio's) – "a big hit
in an area where, surprisingly, there are few really good places to eat"
(and "streets-ahead of the nearby Ivy Café"). The faux-French styling is laid
on with a bit of a trowel, but the end-result is enveloping and very "stylish";
while the mostly-French brasserie fare steers the typical C&K line between
being very acceptable and merely acceptable. "Terrible acoustics" is an issue
raised in some feedback ("excessively noisy for the elderly St John's Wood
clientele", according to one septuagenarian reporter). / NW8 7SH;
soutine.co.uk; @SoutineStJohn.*

Sparrow SE13 £47 | 3 | 3 | 2 |
Rennell Street   020 8318 6941   1–4D

*"The best restaurant in Lewisham might sound like damning it with faint
praise", but this two-year-old indie is a "convivial neighbourhood spot" that
fits the bill without too much irony. The first venture from husband-and-wife
team Terry Blake and Yohini Nandakumar, it has a "very varied menu"
("mostly small plates") that "divides into dishes with a Sri Lankan heritage
and others with a strong 'St John' vibe (but without too much fusion-
crossover going on"). "It can get a bit cramped, and hot with its big front
windows facing a traffic-clogged and rather unlovely roundabout (currently
being redeveloped with new housing/cinema/retail, etc)". / SE13 7HD;
sparrowlondon.co.uk; @sparrowlondon.*

Spiritland £58 | 3 | 3 | 5 |
9 - 10 Stable Street, N1   9–3C NEW
Royal Festival Hall, Belvedere Road, SE1   020 3146 1980   2–3D NEW

*For the "mind-blowing sound system", or as "a great place to grab a drink
and a bite with your mates", this "groovy", music-led three-year-old,
near Granary Square has won quite a following. (It was founded by music
consultant Paul Noble, who has worked with Monocle and the Beeb;
and Canteen founders Patrick Clayton-Malone and Dominic Lake).
"The new, handy Festival Hall branch has the same vibe as the King's Cross
original, and here they offer really well-prepared cooking to match the cool
sounds, laid-back atmosphere and enthusiastic service... it deserves
to thrive." / spiritland.com; @spiritland.*

The Spread Eagle E9 £40 | 3 | 4 | 4 |
224 Homerton High Street   020 8985 0400   14–1C

*"Top vegan food in town, courtesy of Club Mexicana" is to be found at this
"cool" east Homerton hostelry: London's first 100% vegan pub. Even those
who feel it's "hyped" and only "OK if you're in the area" say
"they must be doing something right as it's packed". / E9 6AS;
www.thespreadeaglelondon.co.uk; @SpreadEagleLDN.*

Spring Restaurant WC2 £85 | 3 | 4 | 5 |
New Wing, Lancaster Pl   020 3011 0115   2–2D

*"A lovely use of a beautiful space" – "with delicate light flowing in, and a
cream-focused colour scheme" – this "open and airy room", within
magnificent Somerset House, properly "lives up to its name", and "is the
perfect setting for the light, fresh and wonderful dishes" created by Skye
Gyngell from her "fine, seasonal" menu. That it's "not cheap" is noted,
but seldom with rancour. "Courteous service" completes a "superb" and
"romantic" experience. / WC2R 1LA; www.springrestaurant.co.uk; @Spring_Rest;
10.30 pm; closed Sun D; credit card required to book.*

The Square W1 £128 3 3 2
6-10 Bruton St 020 7495 7100 3–2C
"A bit starchy, but hard to fault" – Clément Leroy continues to prepare "near-faultless" modern French cuisine at Marlon Abela's celebrated Mayfair temple of gastronomy, whose other major culinary feature is one of the capital's more formidable wine lists. Ambience-wise, it's never exactly been a riotous venue – even during its higher profile Phil Howard days – and now, as it was then, is still most often nominated as an expense-accounter favourite, notwithstanding a "refurbished dining room that's more industrial-chic than stylish-comfort". / W1J 6PU; www.squarerestaurant.com; @square_rest; 10.15 pm, Fri & Sat 10.45 pm; closed Sun L; booking max 8 may apply.

Sri Suwoon SW1 £35 4 4 3
44 Hugh Street 020 7828 0321 2–4B
This "fantastic neighbourhood Thai" is a "local gem (very much part of the Pimlico renaissance)": "the room is delightful", and "the food is exceptional and very good value" from a kitchen that "goes from strength to strength". / SW1V 4EP; www.srisuwoon.com; @sri_suwoon.

St Leonard's EC2 £70 1 2 2
70 Leonard Street 020 7613 5346 13–1B
This potentially "very interesting newcomer" in Shoreditch (on the site long famous as Eyre Brothers, RIP) with a 'fire and ice' theme – a combination of open-hearth, roast dishes with a raw seafood bar – failed to ignite passions amongst our reporters in its first 12 months, despite some adulatory press reviews. Some fans did proclaim its "amazing" dishes, but others said "how I hate this place" citing "terrible food and snotty service". Perhaps the management just didn't gel, as Jackson Boxer unexpectedly severed his ties with the place in August 2019, leaving Andrew Clarke to soldier on solo. / EC2A 4QX; stleonards.london; @stleonardsEC2.

St Martin's Lane Kitchen WC2 NEW £64
St Martin's Lane Hotel, 45 St Martin's Lane 020 7300 5588 5–4B
Spring 2019 temporary replacement for the once-achingly-hip Asia de Cuba (RIP) – the main dining room at one of London's early-wave, boutique hotels (which was opened in 1999 by NYC-supremo Ian Schrager in partnership with designer Philippe Starck). Initial feedback suggests its new Pan-Asian offering is "more neutral" than its previous wacky sharing-plate menu, but that, while it's "lost some of its appeal" it can still be a useful option in the area. A full-time successor is mooted, but no timetable has been announced thus far. / WC2N 4HX; www.morganshotelgroup.com; @StMartinsLDN.

Stecca SW10 £76 2 2 2
14 Hollywood Rd 020 7460 2322 6–3B
Hit and miss feedback on this Italian two-year-old, in a posh side street opposite the entrance to the Chelsea & Westminster hospital. On the plus side, all reports rate the cooking as good or better. But it can also seem pricey for what it is, and meals don't always run like clockwork: "the management and the regular clientele were treating the place as the most remarkable restaurant in this part of the world, but our service was very up and down, to the extent they gave us free puddings". / SW10 9HY; www.stecca.co.uk; 10 pm.

Stem & Glory EC1 NEW £52 3 2 2
60 Bartholomew Close 020 3969 9392 10–2B
"Striking the right balance between recreating 'meaty' dishes and classic vegetarian cooking" – this new, all-day vegan near Barts (offshoot of a Cambridge-based business), scores solid marks for its imaginative, meat-free food in early-days reports. The effect of its contemporary white-and-cream design is somewhere between sparkly-fresh and icily-sparse. / EC1A 7BF; www.stemandglory.uk; @stemandglory.

Stick & Bowl W8 £26 3 2 1
31 Kensington High Street   020 7937 2778   6–1A
"No-fuss" Chinese dive in posh Kensington that's "filled with surprising high-
end customers, particularly given its shared table design" and beyond-retro
1950s decor. "The cheap food's always the same: consistently delicious and
freshly cooked – long may it continue in this expensive area". / W8 5NP;
10.45 pm; Cash only; no booking.

Sticks'n'Sushi £63 3 3 3
3 Sir Simon Milton Sq, Victoria St, SW1   020 3141 8810   2–4B
11 Henrietta St, WC2   020 3141 8810   5–3D
113-115 King's Road, SW3   020 3141 8181   6–3C
Nelson Rd, SE10   020 3141 8220   1–3D
58 Wimbledon Hill Rd, SW19   020 3141 8800   11–2B
Crossrail Pl, E14   020 3141 8230   12–1C
"Not Japanese nor pretending to be" – this Danish fusion-chain offers
a suspicious-sounding-but-successful mix of "fancy sushi" with "plenty
of other stuff on skewers" (i.e. yakitori 'sticks'). "Some of the non-traditional
additions don't quite work, but those that do are lovely"; and as a group,
"where so many others fail, it delivers well on consistency". Its "big and
spacious", Scandi-style branches create a "vibrant and exciting" environment
too, "but, oh my word, the prices…" / www.sticksnsushi.com; @sticksnsushi_UK;
10 pm, Wed-Sat 11 pm.

Sticky Mango at RSJ SE1 £52 2 2 2
33 Coin Street   020 7928 4554   10–4A
Having the "same staff as RSJ" (its predecessor on the site, now RIP)
preserves some continuity at this 30-year stalwart, near the Festival Hall,
whose "brave move to Thai food from classic French" a couple of years ago
has split opinion: "zingy and fresh" to fans, but to critics, "entirely
unremarkable". Its famous cellar of Loire wine has also been transferred
to the new venture: "still the best wine list I know of, but it goes less well
with the Asian food now on offer". The ambience of the room – whose
Reinforced Steel Joist inspired the name of the former operation – has never
been a major plus. / SE1 9NR; www.stickymango.co.uk; @stickymangoldn;
10.30 pm.

Stockwell Continental SW8 £43 3 4 3
169 South Lambeth Road   020 3019 0757   11–1D
"An excellent addition to Vauxhall" – this hip, all-day, café/bar was a new
departure last year for the team behind Anchor & Hope (who run the
nearby Canton Arms, and who have hitherto concentrated purely
on gastropubs). It occupies the characterful site that was once Rebato's
(RIP), with coffee and snacks served in the café at the front (the former
tapas bar) and a dining room to the rear, majoring in pizza alongside other
Mediterranean dishes (and there's "a great selection of classic cocktails"
too). It's regularly "busy and packed with regulars" and solidly rated all-
round, but yet to enjoy the major love inspired by its stablemates.
/ SW8 1XW; www.stockwellcontinental.com.

The Stonhouse SW4 £46 3 3 3
165 Stonhouse St   020 7819 9312   11–1D
"Bright and airy", traditional-ish gastroboozer (plus garden), off Clapham
High Street, "reliably serving good food" (if not of a particularly 'gourmet'
variety). / SW4 6BJ; www.thestonhouse.co.uk; @threecheerspubs; 10.30 pm,
Sun 9 pm.

Story SE1   £122   3 3 3
199 Tooley St   020 7183 2117   10–4D
"Take your taste buds on a stimulating journey" when you sample the "truly memorable, eight-course or ten-course tasting menu spanning three to four hours" at Tom Sellers' "extraordinary" venture, near Tower Bridge; where reporters are "blown away" by the "sensationally presented cuisine prepared with exceptional care and perfect flavours… it's hard to find enough superlatives". "Somehow the staff find a way to do fine gastronomy with the fun but without the pomp" contributing to an all-round "quite magical experience". That's the majority view anyhow, but ratings are again dragged into the middle ground by a determined minority of refuseniks who find it "an overhyped concept": "ill-judged and wildly expensive". STOP PRESS: throughout August and September 2019, Tom and team decamped from London to Cornwall to run 'Story by the Sea'. At the time of this review, the presumption is that after their return, it's then back to business as usual in SE1. / SE1 2UE; www.restaurantstory.co.uk; @Rest_Story; 9.15 pm; closed Mon & Sun.

StreetXO W1   £98   4 3 4
15 Old Burlington St   020 3096 7555   4–3A
"Delicious, different and interesting" – Dabiz Muñoz's "funky" and "very fun" Mayfair three-year-old inspired much more feedback this year, practically all of it adulatory. From the OTT cocktails in the bar, to the full-on, Hispanic-Asian fusion-cuisine emanating from the restaurant's open kitchen, it's a maximalist experience, but one that comes off much more often than not nowadays. Perhaps it's time for the fooderati, who gave it a rough time on its launch, to re-evaluate the place. Top Tip – dip your toe in the water with the £30 express lunch menu. / W1S 2JR; www.streetxo.com; @StreetXO_London; Mon - Fri 11pm, Sat 12, Sun 9.30; No bookings at lunch.

Sub Cult EC2   £14
Container, Finsbury Avenue Sq   13–2A
This June 2019 newcomer opened too late for any survey feedback, although Ben Chancellor and Gaz Phillip's brand is well known to street-food aficionados for its brilliant US deli-style rolls, having operated out of various locations over the last five years. Its first forever-home is in the City, a short walk from Mansion House tube. / EC2M 2PP; www.sub-cult.co.uk; @SubCultSubs.

Sukho Fine Thai Cuisine SW6   £52   5 5 3
855 Fulham Rd   020 7371 7600   11–1B
"Carefully prepared cuisine is served with charm and experience" at this accomplished dining room: West London's top-scoring Thai and, oft-tipped by its fans (from as far afield as Cornwall) as "the best Thai in town", full stop. It occupies a shop conversion deep in Fulham that's attractive but tightly packed. / SW6 5HJ; www.sukhogroups.com; 11 pm.

Suksan SW10   £49   3 3 2
7 Park Walk   020 7351 9881   6–3B
This "charming neighbourhood Thai" in Chelsea serves "food equal to the best in town" according to its fans (although its scores lag behind its smarter sibling, Sukho in Fulham). / SW10 0AJ; www.sukhogroups.com; 10.45 pm, Sun 9.45 pm.

Sumak N8   £40   4 4 2
141 Tottenham Lane   020 8341 6261   1–1C
"Continuing its reign as the best Turkish restaurant in Crouch End, Hornsey and Harringay, beating all opposition in nearby Green Lanes": the "fantastic food" comes with "unlimited, sumac-spiced breads and delicious salads". It "even looks a bit more stylish" since the installation of wall hangings and better lighting. / N8 9BJ; www.sumakrestaurants.co.uk.

The Summerhouse W9 £65 2 3 5

60 Blomfield Rd 020 7286 6752 9–4A

"The perfect summer canalside fish restaurant" – this Little Venice charmer makes the best of *"a delightful waterside setting"*, with *"well-spaced tables and a calm atmosphere"*. The cooking is barely mentioned by reporters, although there are no complaints beyond the suggestion that it's *"a bit overpriced"*. / W9 2PA; www.thesummerhouse.co; @FRGSummerhouse; No Amex.

Sumosan Twiga SW1 £69 2 2 2

165 Sloane Street 020 3096 0222 6–1D

"It's eye-wateringly expensive, but the clientele are so rich that it doesn't matter!" at this deluxe Belgravia outpost of the 20-year-old, Moscow-based Sumosan empire, which shifted a couple of years ago from Mayfair to the stretch of Sloane Street south of Harvey Nicks, seemingly patronised solely by 'citizens of nowhere'. Foodwise, an innovative menu of Italian and Japanese dishes are presented side-by-side (prepared by a chef dedicated to each cuisine): *"lovely… I wasn't paying…"* / SW1X 9QB; www.sumosan.com; @sumosantwiga.

Sunday N1 £31 4 3 3

169 Hemingford Rd 020 7607 3868 9–2D

"Dream of a local gem" on the fringes of Islington, with *"wonderful food and warm, welcoming service"*. *"No bookings at the weekend, so be prepared to queue for your brunch: accept it, deal with it, and enjoy your table when you get it…"* / N1 1DA; @sundaybarnsbury; 10.30 pm; closed Mon, Tue D, Wed D & Sun D; No Amex.

Supawan N1 £48 4 3 2

38 Caledonian Road 020 7278 2888 9–3D

"Superb, zesty southern Thai food" has won a sizeable fanclub for this *"cramped canteen"* in King's Cross and as a result it's *"frequently full"*. It may be *"a bit pricier than many such places in London, but that is reflected in the top-notch quality of the food"*. / N1 9DT; www.supawan.co.uk.

Super Tuscan E1 £56 3 4 3

8a Artillery Passage 020 7247 8717 13–2B

"A little bit of proper, authentic Italy near the City" – this audaciously named trattoria tucked away down a little lane near Spitalfields has won a steady following for its *"original"* approach. Importing specialist ingredients directly from Italy means it's *"not cheap"*, although fans reckon it *"offers very good value for money"*. / E1 7LJ; www.supertuscan.co.uk; @TheSuperTuscan; 10 pm; closed Sat & Sun.

Sushi Atelier W1 £33 5 4 3

114 Great Portland Street 020 7636 4455 2–1B

"Really great sushi with a fusion feel" makes this modern Japanese, just north of Oxford Circus, from the Chisou group *"a great place to become acquainted with Japanese food"*. Sky-high ratings improved further in its second year – a good indication that the *"friendly staff"* are not resting on their laurels. / W1W 6PH; www.sushiatelier.co.uk; @sushiatelierlondon; 11 pm.

Sushi Masa NW2 £41 3 3 2

33b Walm Lane 020 8459 2971 1–1A

"The best place to eat in NW2… keeping up with Sushi Say": its predecessor on this site was a hard act to follow after over twenty years in Willesden Green, and – on limited feedback – this neighbourhood Japanese is a worthy occupant of the site it vacated a couple of years back. / NW2 5SH; 10 pm.

Sushi Tetsu EC1 £90 **5** **5** **3**

12 Jerusalem Pas 020 3217 0090 10–1A

"Prefer it to The Araki…", "the best sushi I've had outside of Tokyo…", "superb…" – Toru Takahashi's Clerkenwell venture is "beyond reproach": "a true neighbourhood sushiya" that rivals London's best-known names, at a fraction of the price, and delivers "astonishing flavours" and the "intimate" experience you'd expect of somewhere with just 7 seats, minded over by "delightful" staff. One perennial complaint though – "the whole dreary booking process". / EC1V 4JP; www.sushitetsu.co.uk; @SushiTetsuUK; 7.45 pm, Thu-Fri 8 pm, Sat 7 pm; closed Mon & Sun.

Sushisamba £89 **3** **2** **3**

Opera Terrace, 35 The Market, WC2 020 3053 0000 5–3D
Heron Tower, 110 Bishopsgate, EC2 020 3640 7330 10–2D

"The lift ride up to the 39th floor is part of the fun", when you visit the "amazing" City branch, in the Heron Tower, of this US-based chain (with siblings in Vegas and Miami): a Hollywood-esque scene, complete with a ritzy cocktail bar; vertigo-inducing outside terrace; and svelte dining room boasting "incredible views". But while it can offer an all-round "great experience" – not least "fabulous" funky, fusion fare – its "pretty-looking" dishes come at extragalactic prices and sceptics feel that "you can eat this style of cuisine better elsewhere" nowadays. (Gripes of an overly "sweet note" to dishes also crept in this year). Its year-old WC2 sibling likewise has a superb setting on top of Covent Garden Market, overlooking the back of the Royal Opera House. But while it, too, is "all very slick and fashionable", it, too, charges "obscene prices albeit for decent food" and – lacking the high-rise glam of the Square Mile – can seem more "clinical" and "pleased with itself". / sushisamba.com; 1.30 am, Wed-Sat 2 am.

Suzi Tros W8 NEW £61

18 Hillgate Street 7–2B

Husband-and-wife team, Adrien Carre and Christina Mouratoglou (of Mazi, just up the road) launched this new bistro and cocktail bar, off Notting Hill Gate, in June 2019: too late for any survey feedback. Named for a cult 1960s Greek film, the venture serves small plates taking their inspiration from northern Greece; plus an exclusively Greek selection of wines and beers. / W8 7SR; www.suzitros.com.

The Swan W4 £53 **3** **3** **4**

1 Evershed Walk,119 Acton Ln 020 8994 8262 8–1A

Slightly "hard to find" on the Chiswick/Acton border, this "lovely" panelled pub serves "surprisingly good", "ambitious", yet "unfussy" food with a distinct Mediterranean accent. Service is "friendly", and there's an "amazing garden" for the summer months. / W4 5HH; www.theswanchiswick.co.uk; @SwanPubChiswick; 9 pm, Fri & Sat 10 pm, Sun 9 pm; closed weekday L.

The Swan at the Globe SE1 £64 **3** **3** **4**

21 New Globe Walk 020 7928 9444 10–3B

"A great view of the river and very competent cuisine" makes this would-be Elizabethan tavern – on the first floor of Shakespeare's Globe theatre – "a delightful find on the tourist trail". Chef Allan Pickett sticks sensibly to modern British rather than cod-historical cooking. / SE1 9DT; www.swanlondon.co.uk; @swanabout; 10.30 pm, Sun 5.30 pm.

Sweet Thursday N1 £43 **3** **2** **2**

95 Southgate Rd 020 7226 1727 14–1A

This "good local pizza place" in De Beauvoir Town "continues to be very popular". There's an "interesting variety of toppings (and bases) and gluten-free/dairy-free options", as well as alternatives such as fish stew. "They also have prosecco on tap" and a smart little bottle shop. / N1 3JS; www.sweetthursday.co.uk; @Pizza_and_Wine; 10 pm, Fri & Sat 10 pm, Sun 9 pm.

Sweetings EC4 £76 3 3 4

39 Queen Victoria St 020 7248 3062 10–3B

"It feels as if one has been decanted into the 1920s but I never fail to enjoy my visits!" – "This unique City institution has a charm and authenticity that can't be imitated" – a "joyous throwback" (founded, on a different site, in 1830) which offers "simple, well-executed British seafood classics" (followed by steamed puddings) at lunchtimes only, to a largely besuited crowd. The "eclectic seating arrangements" can "be a surprise to newbies" – you either perch at "makeshift bar-tops", or cram into the rear dining room where "service is hindered by the lack of room, but everyone mucks in and plates get passed around". "The waiters are nearly as old as the building, but that just adds to its appeal…". "Black Velvet is served in pewter tankards, and a 'bill of fare' serves instead of a menu". The experience comes at "ridiculous prices", but most reckon they're worth paying… "and the place does now take cards". / EC4N 4SA; www.sweetingsrestaurant.co.uk; @SweetingsLondon; 3 pm; L only, closed Sat & Sun; no booking.

Tab X Tab W2 £25 5 4 4

14-16 Westbourne Grove 020 7792 3445 7–1B

"The best coffee in town" is the claim made by fans of Mathew and Charmaine Tabatabai's year-old Bayswater brew-stop, which – with Mavam espresso machine, BOCCA beans, partnership with Ozone coffee roasters, hand-made artisanal cups, yada, yada – is a perfect pitstop for caffeine junkies. It's "a great hang out" too, though, serving simple salads, pancakes, eggs on toast… / W2 4UJ; tabxtab.com; @TABxTABLondon.

Taberna Etrusca EC4 £58 2 2 2

9 -11 Bow Churchyard 020 7248 5552 10–2C

"A cramped City Italian with good food", this traditional venue off Bow churchyard "generally performs well" and is "packed at lunchtime – particularly at the tables outside, when weather permits". "Portions are huge" and there's "a fantastic list of regional Italian wines, some of which you might not find elsewhere". Ratings dropped this year, though, with the odd 'off' report. / EC4M 9DQ; www.etruscarestaurants.com; 9.30 pm; closed Sat & Sun.

The Table SE1 £46 3 3 2

83 Southwark St 020 7401 2760 10–4B

"A firm favourite for breakfast and brunch in Southwark" – this café-style fixture a short stroll from Tate Modern serves "a great menu to suit all tastes", and fans say it's "unbeatable". / SE1 0HX; www.thetablecafe.com; @thetablecafe; 10.30 pm; closed Mon D, Sat D & Sun D; booking weekdays only.

Table Du Marche N2 £53 3 3 2

111 High Road 020 8883 5750 1–1B

"Delicious, reasonably priced food" has won over the East Finchley crowd at this three-year-old bistro in what is otherwise a "culinary wasteland". As a bonus, it's "very French, and therefore romantic". / N2 8AG; www.tabledumarche.co.uk; @TableDuMarche; 11 pm.

Takahashi SW19 £50 5 5 3

228 Merton Rd 020 8540 3041 11–2B

"Some of the best Japanese food in London, at half the price you'd spend in Zone One", is found at this tiny, "surprisingly calming" outfit, in a parade of shops "on a busy road", near South Wimbledon tube station. "Superb fresh sushi" is prepared on site by chef-proprietor Taka, formerly of Nobu, with service by his "charming wife", Yuko. "I've eaten sushi three to four times in Japan – and this is better!". Booking recommended. / SW19; www.takahashi-restaurant.co.uk; @takahashi_sw19; 10 pm, Fri & Sat 10.30 pm, Sun 9 pm.

Tamarind W1 £75 3 4 2
20 Queen St 020 7629 3561 3–3B

"The food speaks volumes" – "sensational grills, exquisite curries and traditional biryanis" – for most (if not all) who report on this pioneering Mayfair venture, which helped validate the whole concept of posh Indian restaurants in the UK. It's "a pity about the basement location" though, and the 2018 refurb designed to give a "light and airy modern" interior has proved "OK, but not really an improvement… if anything noise levels are higher". / W1J 5PR; www.tamarindrestaurant.com; @TamarindMayfair; 10.45 pm, Sun 10.30 pm; closed Sat L; No trainers.

Tamarind Kitchen W1 £62 3 3 3
167-169 Wardour St 020 7287 4243 4–1C

"A hidden pearl in the heart of Soho", this "smart-casual" spin-off from Mayfair's Tamarind has a "lovely, buzzy vibe"; and serves "really impressive and refined modern Indian cooking" – "with a fresh-tasting twist to the traditional dishes" – from "a short menu that changes regularly. / W1F 8WR; tamarindkitchen.co.uk; @tamarindkitchen.

Tamp Coffee W4 £23 3 3 3
1 Devonshire Road no tel 8–2A

"A caffeine hit and empáñadas, obvs" – that's the deal at this well-liked small coffee bar, off Chiswick's main drag, which, as well as its trademark Latino bites, serves a selection of baps, pastries and other brunch-ish fare from early morning till afternoon. / W4; www.tampcoffee.co.uk; @Tampcoffee; 6 pm; L only; booking max 6 may apply.

Tandoor Chop House WC2 £51 4 3 3
Adelaide Street 020 3096 0359 5–4C

A "different take on Indian favourites, which you can watch being made in the open kitchen" combines with "retro glamour" styling to good effect at this two-year-old behind St Martin-in-the-Fields: an "excellent concept", "almost like a copy-cat of Dishoom, but way more relaxed". / WC2N 4HW; tandoorchophouse.com; @tandoorchop; 10 pm, Sun 9 pm; booking max 6 may apply.

Tapas Brindisa £60 3 2 2
46 Broadwick St, W1 020 7534 1690 4–2B
18-20 Southwark St, SE1 020 7357 8880 10–4C

"Authentic and delicious tapas… if you can get a table" has made the bustling, original branch of this Hispanic food importer's chain a well-known feature of Borough Market, and "at busy times, it feels rushed". It has spawned a number of spin-offs over the years, which are generally high quality, if not as vibey as the original: most recently opening in October 2018 in the new Battersea Power Station development.
/ www.brindisakitchens.com; @Brindisa; 11 pm-11.30 pm, EC2 12.30 am; SE1 no booking.

Taqueria W11 £40 3 2 3
141-145 Westbourne Grove 020 7229 4734 7–1B

A pioneer of the London taco boom – this Mexican cantina on the Notting Hill and Bayswater border is "good value for money" and "an excellent choice for lunch". After 15 years, however, its menu seems "less interesting than it used to be" – perhaps standards elsewhere have risen. "But the mojitos are as good as ever". (Oldies may recall that this was the joint David Cameron used to be conscientiously spotted in, to show how chilled he was.) / W11 2RS; www.taqueria.co.uk; @TaqueriaUK; 11 pm, Fri & Sat 11.30 pm, Sun 10.30 pm; No Amex.

Tarantella Ristorante Pizzeria W4 £53 3 3 3
4 Elliot Rd 020 8987 8877 8–2A

"Minuscule" – "but perfectly formed" – this "utterly southern Italian local with a regularly changing menu" is a big "favourite" near Turnham Green. Top Tip – "try the specials straight from Puglia, like ox cheek with turnip tops – amazing". / W4 1PE; www.latarantella.london/chiswick.

Taro £34 322
61 Brewer St, W1 020 7734 5826 4–3C
193 Balham High Rd, SW12 020 8675 5187 11–2C
414 Kennington Road, SE11 020 7735 7772 NEW
44a Cannon St, EC4 020 7236 0399 10–3B
Bustling "no-frills" Japanese canteens that serve "great value" noodles and sushi at an efficient pace. The 20-year-old Soho original has now been joined by branches in the City, Balham and most recently Kennington (which is a little more spacious). / www.tarorestaurants.co.uk; W1F 10.30 pm, Fri & Sat 11 pm, Sun 9.30 pm; W1D 10.30 pm, Fri & Sat 10.45 pm, Sun 9.30 pm, Mon 10 pm; no Amex; Brewer St only small bookings.

Tas £47 222
"They've become a bit boring and rote over the years", but these popular, "cheap 'n' cheerful" Turkish cafés are very affordably priced, and even those who see them as "workaday", can feel they still "have a place as a reasonable-enough option" – especially in a big group, or with the kids – and they also offer "lots of choice for vegetarians". Venues are "well-located for combining with cultural visits" – especially on the South Bank, where Tas originated 20 years ago on The Cut, opposite the Young Vic Theatre. There's also a popular branch, Tas Pide (see also), next door to Shakespeare's Globe. / www.tasrestaurant.com; 11.30 pm, Sun 10.30 pm; EC4 Sat 5 pm; 72 Borough High St 6 pm, Sat & Sun 4 pm; EC4 closed Sat D & Sun, cafe SE1 closed Sun.

Tas Pide SE1 £40 234
20-22 New Globe Walk 020 7928 3300 10–3B
"You can't fault the service or location" at this "reasonably priced" offshoot of useful Turkish chain Tas, next to Shakespeare's Globe, whose cosy, distinctive decor follows an Anatolian theme. 'Pide' is the Turkish equivalent to pizza, the branch speciality. / SE1 9DR; www.tasrestaurants.co.uk; @TasRestaurants; 11.30 pm, Sun 10.30 pm.

**Tate Modern,
Kitchen & Bar, Level 6 SE1** £43 224
Level 6 Boiler House, Bankside 0207 401 5108 10–3B
"Beautiful views – adequate but unexciting food": that's the perennial trade-off at Tate Modern's original, elevated dining room – a simple space, but with a stunning vantagepoint for viewing The Thames, St Paul's and the City. It aims to be a showcase for top British ingredients and drinks but results can border on the mundane. / SE1 9TG; www.tate.org.uk; @TateFood; 9 pm; Sun-Thu L only, Fri & Sat open L & D.

Tayyabs E1 £30 422
83 Fieldgate St 020 7247 6400 10–2D
"Queues are mad!" at this "always crazy" and "fantastically good-value" 500-seater, Punjabi BYO in the East End, which is "busy even into the late hours", and a serious rival to the older Lahore five minutes' walk away. Everything is "simply delicious", with "the real highlights being the sizzling and smoking tandoori plates": lamb chops in particular "always hit the mark", but "everything is so fresh". / E1 1JU; www.tayyabs.co.uk; @1tayyabs; 11.30 pm.

Tell Your Friends SW6 £47 334
175 New King's Road 020 7731 6404 11–1B
TYF is the year-old café-style creation of Made in Chelsea sisters Lucy and Tiffany Watson, which brings vegan living to Parsons Green: feedback is still limited, but skips cynicism to laud a "lovely" place with "wonderful", healthy dishes. / SW6 4SW; www.tellyourfriendsldn.com.

temper £49 [3][3][4]
25 Broadwick Street, WI 020 3879 3834 4–1C
5 Mercers Walk, WC2 020 3004 6669 5–2C
Angel Court, EC2 020 3004 6984 10–2C
"Huge cuts of carefully sourced meat, such as great Barnsley chops,
are expertly cooked over wood" at Neil Rankin's "loud and atmospheric"
Soho basement with a 6-metre fire pit, which nowadays also has two similar
satellites in Covent Garden and near Bank: the set-up – "an open kitchen",
"with all the meat on display" creates "some real theatre and buzz". And
in WC2, the venue's wood-fired oven is also pressed into service to deliver
some "incredible deep-dish pizza". There remain one or two reporters who
consider the experience "totally overhyped", but the general impression is of
"a time to remember" and with "a surprisingly reasonable bill for such big
hunks of meat". / temperrestaurant.com; @temperldn.

The 10 Cases WC2 £60 [3][4][3]
16 Endell St 020 7836 6801 5–2C
"A real find so close to the Opera House", this independent Covent Garden
wine bar/bistro offers a "sometimes brilliant but always good – eccentric and
eclectic – wine list", which is "ever changing" as only 10 cases of each wine
are stocked at any point in time. "Friendly and knowledgeable staff" are
on hand to advise on your choice and to present a short menu
of "beautifully crafted small plates and charcuterie", with "particularly
enticing blackboard specials". / WC2H 9BD; www.the10cases.co.uk; @10cases;
11 pm; closed Sun.

10 Greek Street WI £62 [4][3][2]
10 Greek St 020 7734 4677 5–2A
A "great (and ever-changing) range of fairly priced wines", together with
a handwritten 'Black Book' of fine wines at low mark-ups, make this
"fun and friendly" – but also "crowded" and "noisy" – modern Soho wine
bar a regular haunt for wine trade insiders. The food is also "great",
"reliably delicious, and avoids cliches", which makes it an ideal spot
to "enjoy a long, relaxed, indulgent lunch". A number of fans caution though
that "prices seem to be creeping higher…" / W1D 4DH;
www.10greekstreet.com; @10GreekStreet; 10 pm; closed Sun; booking L only.

10 Heddon Street WI NEW
10 Heddon Street 4–3B
In Crown Estates's little restaurant enclave, just off Regent Street, the site
that was Magpie (RIP) was relaunched in summer 2019 under an 'agile
approach' that envisages 'the ability to invite more creative partners on a
short-term basis to add fresh, exciting ideas to London's dining scene'.
We think that may mean a series of pop-ups. First up: Chris Leach
(Pitt Cue, Kitty Fishers et al) and David Carter (of Smokestak), whose menu
will feature various hand-made salumi and hand-rolled pasta dishes.
/ W1B 4BX; 10heddonst.co.uk.

Tendido Cero SW5 £55 [3][3][4]
174 Old Brompton Road 020 7370 3685 6–2B
"Some of the most reliably good tapas in London" – "delicious and perfectly
executed" – plus "an interesting, if pricey wine list" can be found at this
"vibrant", black-and-red liveried offshoot of Cambio de Tercio, the South Ken
fixture, directly opposite. "Constant innovation" in the kitchen means there's
"always something different and appetising" on the menu. / SW5 0BA;
www.cambiodetercio.co.uk; @CambiodTercio; 11 pm.

Terra Rossa N1 £58 3 4 2
139 Upper Street 020 7226 2244 9–3D
"There's no better choice if you're going to Islington's Almeida Theatre" than
this "cheerful Puglian" nearby, which serves "way better food than its
touristy appearance suggests": "simple, flavourful Italian dishes" washed
down with "sensibly-priced, rustic, southern Italian wines". "The atmosphere
is unfussy, friendly and easygoing: you get a great meal and a very
reasonable bill". / N1 1QP; terrarossa-restaurant.co.uk.

Terroirs £54 2 2 3
5 William IV St, WC2 020 7036 0660 5–4C
38 Lordship Lane, SE22 1–4D
"Tucked away off Trafalgar Square, you'd need to know about this very
buzzy wine bar to find it… but sadly many people do as it's normally
packed out". Ten years ago, when it opened, it was a major sensation
thanks to its then-novel combination of "really adaptable", gutsy, Gallic
tapas ("plates of meat, cheese, paté, etc") washed down with "a superb
(if somewhat baffling and esoteric) wine selection, featuring some very
interesting natural wines" (it's actually owned by wine importers, Les Caves
de Pyrenes). Nowadays the prevailing view is that it's "good but very
expensive for what is in effect an uncomfortable and noisy café".
/ terroirswinebar.com; @TerroirsWineBar.

Texture W1 £122 5 4 3
34 Portman St 020 7224 0028 2–2A
Aggi Sverrisson's "sublime", Icelandic-inspired cuisine – in particular
"a refreshing and very imaginative twist on fish" – again wins one of the
survey's highest food-ratings for his well-established flagship, just off Portman
Square. To the odd reporter, the low-key space (actually part of a hotel,
although you only find out when you look for the WC) can seem "dull and
cold", but most reporters like the fact that "there's something a bit different
about the style of the place". "Very warm and welcoming" service only adds
to its refreshingly un-poncy approach. / W1H 7BY; www.texture-restaurant.co.uk;
@TextureLondon; 10.30 pm; closed Mon & Sun.

Thali SW5 £47 4 3 2
166 Old Brompton Rd 020 7373 2626 6–2B
"Subtle, aromatic and utterly delicious food" based around "family recipes"
are on the menu at this unusual, family-run Indian café decked out with
vintage Bollywood posters, on the outer fringe of South Kensington.
"I just don't understand how this place isn't better known", it's a "real gem".
/ SW5 0BA; @thaliLondon; 11.30 pm, Sun 10.30 pm.

The Buxton E1 NEW £47
42 Osborn Street awaiting tel 13–2C
From the team behind the nearby Culpeper, this new (June 2019)
gastroboozer occupies a cleverly rebuilt seven-storey site near the foot
of Brick Lane, whose redevelopment has allowed the addition of 15
bedrooms. It opened too late for survey feedback: The Standard's David
Sexton found the ground floor bar a little "cramped" and "not for lingering",
but a good value, if "lonely pioneer of bourgeois taste" in this grungy 'hood.
/ E1 6TD; www.thebuxton.co.uk.

The Chipping Forecast £47 3 3 3
58 Greek Street, W1 5–2A
29 All Saints Road, W11 020 7460 2745 7–1B
"Reliable fish 'n' chips – and fun hosts" – earn solid ratings for this new-
wave Notting Hill chippy, where the sustainable seafood is sourced directly
from Cornish fishermen. A Soho sibling opened in 2018, close to the
business's origin as a stall in Berwick Market.

The Crown W4 £59 **3 3 4**
210 Chiswick High Road   020 3330 7131   8–2A

With its "lovely sunny courtyard" and gracious interior, Harcourt Inns' Chiswick yearling represents a successful realisation of the potential of this big, very characterful building (formerly Carvosso's RIP, and originally Chiswick's Victorian police station) as a chichi neighbourhood gastropub. But while the food's consistently well-rated, anyone expecting to experience the magic of the place's much PR'd associations with Harcourt's chef-director Henry Harris (erstwhile patron of Knightsbridge's legendary, but long-defunct, Racine) will likely leave disappointed by food that's creditable pub grub for W4, but nowt more. / W4 1PD; thecrownchiswick.co.uk.

The Good Egg £58 **4 3 4**
Unit G9 Kingly Court, W1   4–2B
93 Church St, N16   020 7682 2120   1–1C

"Utterly magic shakshuka served with chunks of roasted sourdough…", "stand-out salt beef bagels…", "incredible coffee with a selection of babka sweet breads (in different flavours!)…", "ZFC – 'za'atar fried chicken' – to die for!…" – these "bustling" Israeli delis in Stoke Newington and Soho's Kingly Court create queues (especially at brunch) with their "quite exceptional and startlingly fresh Middle-Eastern-cum-north-American food. They also make a worthwhile destination at dinner, when the pace is more sedate, the natural wines are flowing and you can actually book a table". "Casual and relaxed", they look "gorgeous" too. / thegoodeggn16.com; @TheGoodEgg_.

The Petersham Restaurant TW10 £66 **2 3 5**
Nightingale Lane   020 8003 3602   1–4A

"Brilliant views over the Thames at the window tables", from a "unique" vantagepoint overlooking Petersham Meadows, add to the "tranquil" atmosphere at this impressive-looking hotel (built in 1865 by the same architect as Portland Place's Langham Hotel). On most accounts, "decent" cooking creates "a real experience" (if in a rather old-fashioned mould), but there's also the odd report of "perfunctory" standards. Top Tip – "a fantastic location for a relaxed afternoon tea". / TW10 6UZ; petershamhotel.co.uk/restaurant; @thepetersham; 9.45 pm.

The Restaurant at The Capital SW3 NEW £91
22-24 Basil St   020 7591 1202   6–1D

Following the departure of Nathan Outlaw, Adam Simmonds is to take over the stoves in the dining room of this luxury hotel, a short walk from the back of Harrods. The new venture will open in autumn 2019. Simmonds's pedigree is good, and he's the latest in a succession of star names to hold the position in the hotel. The main limitation on enjoyment here has historically been the dimensions of the dining room itself: it's a small space, where it's hard to generate much in the way of spark. / SW3 1AT; www.capitalhotel.co.uk; @hotelcapital; 10 pm; closed Sun.

The Yard,
Great Scotland Yard Hotel SW1 NEW
Great Scotland Yard   020 7925 4700   2–3C

Chef and Restaurateur Robin Gill (The Dairy, Sorella, Darby's) will oversee this new dining room – one of four F&B outlets he will help manage (along with partner Alex Harper) within the Great Scotland Yard Hotel built on the site of the Met's original HQ, just off Trafalgar Square; it's due to open in late 2019. As well as two bars, there is also 'The Parlour', which will be big on afternoon tea. / SW1A 2HN; www.hyatt.com/en-US/hotel/united-kingdom/great-scotland-yard/lhrub.

Theo Randall W1 £78 442
InterContinental Hotel, 1 Hamilton Pl 020 7318 8747 3–4A
"Exemplary Italian ingredients cooked to perfection" and "served impeccably
by delightful people" has earned a glowing reputation for the English-born
former River Café chef, whose dining room off the foyer of the 1970s-built
Intercontinental Hotel tower near Hyde Park Corner provides some
of London's best Italian cuisine. The "soulless setting" always attracts
adverse comment, although it is "much improved" since its renovation a few
years back. / W1J 7QY; www.theorandall.com; @theorandall; 11 pm, Sun 10.30 pm;
closed Sat L & Sun.

Theo's SE5 £41 442
2 Grove Ln 020 3026 4224 1–3C
"Lovely pizzas with great crusty bases" have won a thumbs-up from
aficionados for this independent pizzeria in Camberwell (which also has
a much less commented-on outpost in Elephant and Castle). They also serve
panuozzo, or wood-fired sandwiches, at lunchtime. / SE5;
www.theospizzeria.com; @theospizzaldn; 10.30 pm, Fri & Sat 11 pm, Sun 10 pm
; No Amex; May need 6+ to book.

34 Mayfair W1 £94 333
34 Grosvenor Sq 020 3350 3434 3–3A
This swish New York-style grill, appropriately round the corner from the ex-
US Embassy in Mayfair, has a lower profile than its siblings in Richard
Caring's stable, remaining "so under the radar" for almost a decade. The
"safe and easy menu" is "a little uninspiring and expensive, which
is unsurprising given the location", but its "unobtrusively attentive service"
helps make it a "dependable" all-rounder. / W1K 2HD; www.34-restaurant.co.uk;
@34_restaurant; 11 pm, Sun 10 pm.

The Thomas Cubitt SW1 £68 333
44 Elizabeth St 020 7730 6060 2–4A
On Belgravia's smart Elizabeth Street, this "bright and airy" destination
is "more decent-restaurant than good-gastropub" with its "accomplished
cooking" and "light" first-floor dining room. / SW1W 9PA;
www.thethomascubitt.co.uk; @TheThomasCubitt; 10 pm, Sun 9.30 pm.

tibits £43 323
12-14 Heddon St, W1 020 7758 4110 4–3B
124 Southwark St, SE1 10–4B
"For a perfect vegetarian food experience at a fair price, look no further"
than this increasingly popular, Swiss-owned, self-service operation,
with branches off Regent Street and on Bankside. There's "an amazing
choice" of "very fresh food that changes daily", run under an "unusual
system whereby you serve yourself from buffet (aka 'the food boat') and pay
by weight". The Bankside branch, near Tate Modern, has been revamped
to offer a range of seating, from high bar stools or conventional tables
to comfy armchairs. / www.tibits.co.uk; @tibits_uk.

TING SE1 £103 224
Level 35, 31 St Thomas St 020 7234 8108 10–4C
"The view's the thing" at this 35th-floor all-day restaurant and lounge in The
Shard, with 360-degree vistas over London and the Home Counties –
"including from the loos!". Some reporters also rate the "well-presented and
thoughtful menu", which they say contributes to "a fantastic experience".
Sceptics, though, reckon the "food is so-so, service patronising, the bill eye-
watering: strictly for well-heeled tourists!". / SE1 9RY; www.ting-shangri-la.com;
@ShangriLaShard; 11 pm; No trainers; credit card required to book.

Tish NW3 £73 3 4 4
196 Haverstock Hill   020 7431 3828   9–2A
"Unusually smart for a kosher restaurant" – this yearling in Belsize Park, from property developer David Levin, has "real aspirations". A large and impressively kitted-out all-day brasserie, it still attracts the odd gripe that "the food doesn't live up to the setting", but most reports say it's "improved and hitting its stride". / NW3 2AG; www.tish.london; @tish_london.

Titu W1 £55 4 5 4
1A Shepherd Street   020 7493 8746   3–4B
"Possibly the smallest restaurant I've ever been in but BIG on flavours and service" – this "wonderful" Japanese-inspired, 15-seater yearling in Mayfair's pretty Shepherd Market is piloted by Kiwi chef Jeff Tyler (ex-Novikov), and specialises in luxury gyoza dumplings, stuffed with foie gras and wagyu beef. "It's like being back in Tokyo". Top Tip – "Book – it's tiny". / W1J 7HJ; www.titurestaurant.com; @titulondon.

Toff's N10 £39 3 3 2
38 Muswell Hill Broadway   020 8883 8656   1–1B
"Popular, and sometimes crowded institution, in the culinary wilderness of Muswell Hill", well known as one of north London's best "good, old-fashioned" chippies. Run by brothers George and Costas Georgiou: "their fish is always fresh, and perfectly cooked, and the chips are good too". / N10 3RT; www.toffsfish.co.uk; @toffsfish; 10 pm; closed Sun.

Tokimeite W1 £116 3 2 2
23 Conduit St   020 3826 4411   3–2C
Owned by Zen-Noh, Japan's agricultural cooperative, and specialising in high-grade Japanese wagyu, alongside sushi, sashimi, tempura and other more creative fare, this Mayfair three-year-old is centred around an open counter kitchen, controlled by chef Daisuke Hayashi. Fans are "keen for it to be better known" saying its ownership "really shows up in the superb food", but it still has a surprisingly tiny following, perhaps because it's "very expensive (probably too expensive)". / W1S 2XS; www.tokimeite.com; @tokimeitelondon; 10.30 pm.

Tokyo Diner WC2 £27 3 3 3
2 Newport Place   020 7287 8777   5–3B
"I just love it: it's so cheap 'n' cheerful" chorus the many fans of this down-to-earth Japanese canteen in Chinatown, which has been for yonks "a great place for the freshest sushi and yummy tofu". / WC2H 7JJ; www.tokyodiner.com; 11.30 pm; No Amex; No bookings.

Tom Simmons SE1 £64 3 3 2
2 Still Walk   020 3848 2100   10–4D
"Solid cooking" of some ambition – with "clean and distinct flavours" – helps inspire good reports on this Welsh chef's South Bank venue, most particularly as "a handy option for a high-quality meal prior to heading for the Bridge Theatre". "The experience can sometimes feel no more than functional", however, as "the modern setting does not contribute much character", but "friendly service" is some compensation. / SE1 2UP; tom-simmons.co.uk; @TomSimmons_TB; 11 pm, Sun 6 pm; closed Sun D.

Tom's Kitchen £61 2 2 3
27 Cale St, SW3   020 7349 0202   6–2C
Last year's makeover has failed to transform Tom Aikens's casual dining venture in a Chelsea backstreet, which remains a handy amenity for breakfast or a bite in the area, but is "not what it used to be" as a destination (and inspires modest feedback nowadays). Meanwhile, its sister venues in Canary Wharf and Somerset House have closed down, amid little sign of the standards that made Aikens the youngest British chef to earn two Michelin stars at 26. / www.tomskitchen.co.uk; @TomsKitchens; SW3 10.30 pm, Sun 9.30 pm; WC2 10 pm; E14 9.30 pm; SE1 6 pm; B1 10.30 pm, Sun 5 pm; WC2, E14, B1 closed Sun D.

Tommi's Burger Joint £30 3 4 3
30 Thayer St, W1   020 7224 3828   3–1A
37 Berwick Street, W1   020 7494 9086   4–2D

"His simple burgers are perfect", say fans of Tómas Tómasson, who has been grilling over charcoal in his native Iceland since 1981. His "straightforward" outlets in Soho and Marylebone are now part of a European and Scandi chain spanning from Iceland to Italy.
/ www.burgerjoint.co.uk; @BurgerJointUk; 10.30 pm, Sun 9 pm; booking: min 5.

Tomoe SW15 £37 4 3 1
292 Upper Richmond Road   020 3730 7884   11–2B

"Teeming with Japanese customers and Putney locals in the know", this "great little sushi bar", presided over by its "eagle-eyed chef/owner" ("sit up at the sushi bar to see the main man calmly in action") is "just like being in Tokyo". Results are "fabulous": there are "not many places in London where the fish on the sushi is actually thicker than the rice!". Another indie Japanese, Cho-San (RIP) was on the same site, and the "rather tired" interior either "works against it" or adds authenticity, depending on your viewpoint. / SW15; 9.30 pm.

Tonkotsu £44 3 3 2
Selfridges, 400 Oxford St, W1   020 7437 0071   3–1A
63 Dean St, W1   020 7437 0071   5–2A
7 Blenheim Cr, W11   020 7221 8300   7–1A
14 New Broadway, W5   020 8810 1414   1–3A NEW
4 Canvey St, SE1   020 7928 2228   10–4B
Arch 755, Battersea Power Station Arches, SW8   11–1C
133 Rye Lane, SE15   020 7732 5256   NEW
Unit 1, Endeavour Square, E20   020 8534 6809   14–1D
382 Mare St, E8   020 8533 1840   14–1B
Arch 334, 1a Dunston St, E8   020 7254 2478   14–2A

"Healthy ramen bowls" and "the best karaage fried chicken in town" are the secrets behind the rapid growth of the cramped Japanese pitstops, of which there are now 10 in London – the most recent openings, in Shoreditch and Peckham, having followed a £5million investment in 2019. They provide "a meal that could fill you up for a day", with "excellent service from a really friendly team who go the extra mile".
/ www.tonkotsu.co.uk; @TonkotsuSoho; 10 pm - 11 pm, Sun earlier some branches; SW11 closed Mon; no bookings.

Top Cuvee N5 NEW £57 4 4 3
177b Blackstock Road   020 3294 1665   9–1D

"A brilliant addition to Norf Landon": this "buzzy" and "notably hip" new Highgate wine bar and bistro offers a fashionable formula, combining a curt menu of "lovely small plates" – showing "real depth of flavour" – with an "excellent wine list, which may tend a tad to the 'natural', but which offers plenty of choice". "Knowledgeable and enthusiastic staff" add to the picture. "Only slight issue is acoustics: this is a hard-walled box, so noise-sensitive folk may want to pass... but I'm looking forward to returning soon". / N5 2LL; www.topcuvee.com.

Tozi SW1 £49 3 3 3
8 Gillingham St   020 7769 9771   2–4B

"Delicious food just keeps coming" at this rather "unique" Venetian cicchetti (small-plates) outfit, attached to a hotel near Victoria station, whose "fun" style has helped it acquire a major following. There's "charming service from a close-knit Italian team" who treat children with "welcoming joy".
/ SW1V 1HN; www.tozirestaurant.co.uk; @ToziRestaurant; 10 pm.

The Tramshed EC2 £57 3 2 4
32 Rivington St   020 7749 0478   13–1B
"Not that cheap but pretty cheerful": Mark Hix's converted Victorian tramshed in Shoreditch is an atmospheric high-ceilinged space, dominated by a stuffed Damien Hirst cow in a tank, presumably meant to symbolise a menu which majors in steak and chicken – "simple dishes, cooked to perfection". / EC2A 3LX; www.hixrestaurants.co.uk/restaurant/tramshed; @the_tramshed; 11 pm, Wed-Sat midnight, Sun 9.30 pm.

Trangallan N16 £48 4 4 3
61 Newington Grn   020 7359 4988   1–1C
"Lovely, rich, authentic Spanish fare (octopus to die for)" with Galician specialities, again wins praise for this "somewhat shabby-chic" tapas haunt in Newington Green: "it can get refreshingly noisy!" / N16 9PX; www.trangallan.com; @trangallan_n16; 10.30 pm; closed Mon; No Amex; No trainers.

Tredwell's WC2 £66 3 3 3
4 Upper St Martin's Ln   020 3764 0840   5–3B
With its "dark" decor, there's an "NYC-diner feel" to Marcus Wareing's quirky, Theatreland venue, whose "lively and buzzy" (if sometimes "noisy") style and "friendly and welcoming" staff helped improve its ratings this year. For somewhere in the beating heart of the touristy West End, there's a dizzying range of culinary options created by Kiwi chef Chantelle Nicholson (an offbeat mix of ambitious tasting menus and more down-to-earth dishes, like steaks or roasts); and although there are disappointments, a majority this year do extol its "fantastic culinary creations". / WC2H 9NY; www.tredwells.com; @tredwells; 10 pm, Fri & Sat 11 pm.

Trinity SW4 £76 5 5 4
4 The Polygon   020 7622 1199   11–2D
Adam Byatt's "classy" Clapham star is "at the top of its game" and there are only a few restaurants south of the river that give it a run for its money: "a trip always feels special, no matter what the occasion". "Outstanding", contemporary cuisine (from a three-course, or four-course menu) is at the heart of a "wonderful", straightforward formula incorporating "service that's always on point", plus the "relaxing atmosphere" of a room whose "exterior view is much improved now the public WC has been demolished and the area landscaped!". "Really good cocktails" and a "diverse and interesting wine list" complete the picture – look out for vintages marked 'Chef's Cellar'. See also Trinity Upstairs and Charlie's at Browns. / SW4 0JG; www.trinityrestaurant.co.uk; @TrinityLondon; 10 pm, Sun 9 pm; closed Mon L & Sun D.

Trinity Upstairs SW4 £62 5 4 4
4 The Polygon   020 3745 7227   11–2D
The "buzzy, relaxed sibling of the fancier place downstairs"; some fans of chef Adam Byatt's modern British cuisine may even prefer Upstairs for its "informal atmosphere" and "keen prices", which means they can visit more often than down below. There are "delightful small plates to share" with "food of the same quality as the main restaurant", along with "the same wine list". Byatt is very much a man of the moment, having added the role of chef-director at Brown's Hotel in Mayfair in September 2019 (see also). / SW4 0JG; www.trinity-upstairs.co.uk; @trinityupstairs ; 10 pm.

Trishna W1 £88 4 3 3
15-17 Blandford St   020 7935 5624   2–1A
"Original, flavour-packed and utterly delicious" – the cuisine at Karam Sethi's original Marylebone venture (the first in the JKS stable) is a fine homage to the Mumbai venue from which it takes its name, and even if "sister-restaurant Gymkhana has the edge" nowadays, it remains one of the capital's top Indian destinations. It's "really buzzy when full" (to an extent one or two reporters find "disturbing" of enjoyment). / W1U 3DG; www.trishnalondon.com; @TrishnaLondon; 10.30 pm, Sun 9.45 pm.

Trivet SE1 NEW
36 Snowsfields, Melior Street   10–4C
Former Fat Duck duo – head chef Jonny Lake and sommelier Isa Bal, who worked together for 12 years – will open this restaurant and wine bar in Bermondsey later in 2019, in the new Snowsfields Yard development (and the former site of Londrino, RIP). Bal said of the opening, 'The design and experience of the restaurant will also be inspired from our travels, juxtaposing Nordic functionality with the warmth of the Mediterranean and a dose of fun'. / SE1 3QQ.

La Trompette W4   £85   5 4 3
5-7 Devonshire Rd   020 8747 1836   8–2A
"We schlep across town from E18 two or three times a year and we always have a wonderful experience!" – this "consistently fabulous" destination occupies a low-profile location in a Chiswick sidestreet, but remains the "go-to-choice in West London" for many reporters and "rivals many more high-profile West End temples of gastronomy". Like its even-more-famous stablemate, Chez Bruce, its "bright", neighbourhood-style interior is smart but far from flash – the "spoiling experience" it delivers derives from its "seriously imaginative and beautifully executed" modern cuisine and its "seamless and charming" service. And it offers "very good value", too: "this is exactly what every restaurant at this price point should aspire to". On the downside, the table layout can seem "too crowded", and there were also very occasional good-but-not-great meals reported this year: "are they a bit stretched since they added more covers?" / W4 2EU; www.latrompette.co.uk; @LaTrompetteUK; 10.30 pm, Sun 9.30 pm.

Trullo N1   £64   3 3 3
300-302 St Paul's Rd   020 7226 2733   9–2D
"A gem, well worth a visit to darkest Highbury Corner": as it enters its 10th year, Tim Siadatan and Jordan Frieda's "great neighbourhood Italian" remains the survey's most-mentioned destination in north London, buoyed by its "excellent, simple fare" and "efficient service", served in a "compact" but romantic setting that "exudes a tremendous warmth" ("want a first date in a light airy space? Book upstairs, especially in summer; want a sexy tryst? Book a booth downstairs, especially in winter"). On the downside, some former fans feel it's "dropped to middling" of late: "a local place, but with a centre-of-town bill". / N1 2LH; www.trullorestaurant.com; @Trullo_LDN; 10.15 pm; closed Sun D; No Amex.

Tsunami SW4   £48   5 3 3
5-7 Voltaire Rd   020 7978 1610   11–1D
"Exquisite Japanese fusion food as well as fabulously creative cocktails" have made this slick Clapham operation "a perennial favourite" for two decades; and it still gives West End names a run for their money. Top Tip – "gin dara – black cod with sweet miso. I know it's a Nobu original but this is the best version in town". / SW4 6DQ; www.tsunamirestaurant.co.uk; @TsunamiRest; 11 pm, Fri-Sun midnight; closed Sat L & Sun; No Amex.

1251 N1   £46   3 3 3
107 Upper Street   07934 202269   9–3D
"A much-needed alternative to the usual Upper Street fare" – James Cochran's ambitious yearling is a ray of sunshine in N1, and even the less impressed minority who feel "it's not quite up to the celebrity chef hype" generally feel "it's nice to have something a bit different in the local area". Quibbles also include the "cramped", "corridor-like" space and service that can sometimes seem like "amateur's hour", but at its best this part-Scottish, part-Jamaican chef provides "exceptional dishes, with cleverly combined ingredients and subtle spicing". Top Tip – "The £15 lunch deal is the gastronomic bargain of the year": "extraordinary food, lovingly crafted, and at silly prices". / N1 1QN; www.1251.co.uk; @cochran_ja.

28 Church Row NW3 £56 4 4 4
28 Church Row 020 7993 2062 9–2A
A "revelation" – well, by the standards of Hampstead anyhow – this cute basement tapas bar with an open kitchen occupies a cellar space, near the church of St John-at-Hampstead, and has taken the area by storm with its "constantly changing menu, intriguing wine list and very friendly service". There's no booking, but they'll phone you if you wait in the pub opposite.
/ NW3 6UP; www.28churchrow.com; @28churchrow.com; 10.30 pm, Sun 9.30 pm.

28-50 W1 £74 3 2 2
15-17 Marylebone Ln 020 7486 7922 3–1A
"Useful pre-Wigmore Hall" – this Marylebone original is now the sole surviving branch of what for a few years become a chain, but which retrenched last year. The space – with large windows and dominated by the bar – "doesn't encourage you to linger", but the "simple dishes are well executed, at a good price". Really, though, it's "all about the wines by the glass" (15 reds and 15 whites), plus a 'Collector's List' of rare vintages by the bottle. / W1U 2NE; www.2850.co.uk; @2850restaurant.

24 The Oval SW9 £46 4 3 3
24 Clapham Road 0207 735 6111 11–1D
"Finally a great neighbourhood restaurant in Oval!" – "a parched part of London where average offerings abound" – this bistro yearling comes courtesy of Matt Wells (co-owner of The Dairy, Clapham) and Andrew Bradford (from SW4 steakhouse, Knife). A modern bistro-type place, with the benefit of an outside terrace, it provides an "exciting" modern British menu and there's a "committed team making it all happen".
/ SW9 0JG; www.24theoval.co.uk; @24theoval.

Twist W1 £67 5 4 3
42 Crawford St 020 7723 3377 2–1A
"Very surprisingly delicious, every mouthful – way beyond expectations" – Eduardo Tuccillo's tucked-away Marylebone venture (on the site that ages ago was Garbo's, RIP) is arguably "very underrated due to its location" in a "so-loud, as it's so-small" two-floor space. But while it feels "too casual to be a very special night out, the food and service can't be beaten": "a different approach with tapas that aren't just Spanish" delivering "some inspired food combinations". "On the pricey side, but consistently well worth it."
/ W1H 1JW; www.twistkitchen.co.uk; @twistkitchen; closed Sun.

Two Brothers N3 £32 3 2 2
297-303 Regent's Park Rd 020 8346 0469 1–1B
This "reliable local favourite" has "prepared fish freshly to order" at a consistent level for more than a quarter of a century, while the site itself has hosted a traditional fish 'n' chippy for 60 years or so. / N3 1DP; www.twobrothers.co.uk; 10 pm; closed Mon.

Two Lights E2 £63 3 4 3
28-30 Kingsland Road 020 3976 0076 13–1B
If it wasn't backed by the Clove Club, it's hard to know how much buzz this rather functional, Shoreditch-vibe newcomer (on the busy Kingsland Road) would otherwise have generated. The website describes the cooking as 'modern American', in line with the starry NYC-focused CV of chef Chase Lovecky, but if the words 'modern European' were substituted, probably no-one would ever notice the difference. Terminology aside: feedback on the deliciousness of the resulting small plates themselves – while surprisingly limited – has all been upbeat, but, to be harsh, only middling judged by the red-hot standards for this kind of dining in the area generally. / E2 8DA; www.twolights.restaurant.

222 Veggie Vegan W14 £46 4 3 2
222 North End Rd 020 7381 2322 8–2D
"Don't wait for Veganuary or your vegan friend to visit!" – hurry along now to this "little, unpretentious gem": a "fairly functional" café that's a well-established fixture on the edge of West Kensington (just north of the gyratory where the Lillie Road and North End Road cross). "There's a vast array of beautifully fresh dishes that are vibrant, tasty and wholesome, and it's brilliant value for money". / W14 9NU; www.222vegan.com; @222VeganCuisine.

2 Veneti W1 £52 3 3 2
10 Wigmore Street 020 7637 0789 3–1B
For those who say it's "handy for the Wigmore Hall", this well-established Italian is "a good staple", with "professional service" that helps overcome its "lack of atmosphere", and "offering typical Italian fare". Become a regular, though, and the more you appreciate "an absolute gem", with "incredibly attentive" staff, and the more you value its Venetian cuisine ("specialities like bigoli con acciughe, fegato ...all delicious"). / W1U 2RD; www.2veneti.com; @2Veneti; 10.30 pm, Sat 11 pm; closed Sat L & Sun.

Uli W11 £61 3 3 4
5 Ladbroke Road 020 3141 5878 7–2B
This "popular and unpretentious" Singaporean/pan-Asian near Notting Hill Gate has earned a very solid local following in its 22 years – boss Michael Lim "makes it special". The original All Saints Road site closed down in 2015, but the venture was resurrected three years later in this "cool new setting". / W11 3PA; www.ulilondon.com; @ulilondon; 11.45 pm; D only, closed Sun.

Umu W1 £120 4 4 4
14-16 Bruton Pl 020 7499 8881 3–2C
"Yoshinori Ishii is the perfect chef and artist... unique" and goes from strength to strength at this fairly small, hidden-away Japanese – in a quirky Mayfair mews, with little exterior signage – where he's been head chef since 2010. Traditional gripes about the larcenous pricing are notable by their absence this year: instead, feedback could not be more positive about his Kyoto-style kaiseki cuisine, placing it firmly in contention amongst London's top Japanese destinations. Owned by Marlon Abela's M.A.R.C. group – this is head-and-shoulders his best property. / W1J 6LX; www.umurestaurant.com; 10.30 pm; closed Sat L & Sun; No trainers; booking max 14 may apply.

Union Street Café SE1 £65 2 2 2
47-51 Great Suffolk St 020 7592 7977 10–4B
Gordon Ramsay's "Italian-leaning" warehouse conversion in Southwark, with an indoor 'olive grove' complete with trees, pleases some with its "giant portions of great food" and "fantastic cocktails". Far too many reporters this year, though, complain of a "sterile" aspect to its "industrial" decor, and dismiss the fare as mightily "uninspired". / SE1 0BS; www.gordonramsayrestaurants.com/union-street-cafe; @unionstreetcafe; 10.45 pm; closed Sun D.

Unwined SW17 £29 3 4 4
21-23 Tooting High Street 02035839136 11–2C
"Little wine bar and kitchen, with a great vibe in Tooting Market" – "a consistently delightful gem" with "regularly changing guest chefs" and "a fun and quirky wine list to accompany whatever's on the menu". (There's a spin-off wine bar in a shipping container by Waterloo station.) / SW17 0SN; www.unwinedbars.co.uk/tooting; @UnwinedSW17.

Le Vacherin W4 £65 3 3 3
76-77 South Parade   020 8742 2121   8–1A
"Consistently good food" and a "lovely French atmosphere" earn solid ratings for this long-running bistro – an unusually "authentic Gallic experience" by Acton Green. It's "excellent value", too, "if you choose carefully". / W4 5LF; www.levacherin.co.uk; @Le_Vacherin; 10.30 pm, Sun 9 pm; closed Mon L

Vagabond Wines £42 2 3 3
Unit 77, Nova Building, SW1   020 7630 7693   2–4B
25 Charlotte Street, W1   020 3441 9210   2–1C
4 Northcote Road, SW11   020 7738 0540   11–2C
18-22 Vanston Place, SW6   020 7381 1717   6–4A
A "wealth of wines by the glass" and "tasty nibbles", help make this growing group of self-service wine bars a "fun way to try a selection of vintages from a multitude of small producers". At the Battersea Power Station branch's school you can educate your palate towards Wine & Spirit Education Trust certification and watch wine being made from grapes grown in Oxfordshire and Surrey. / www.vagabondwines.co.uk; @VagabondWines.

Vanilla Black EC4 £77 4 3 3
17-18 Tooks Ct   020 7242 2622   10–2A
"Who needs meat when you can eat like this?" – You don't have to "be in touch with your green tea side" to be "seriously seduced by the grown-up vibe" and "exciting cooking" at this "sophisticated" and ambitious meat-free operation, "tucked away in a corner just outside the City". "I'm a meat-eater and always thought vegetarian meals were about lentils and beans, but the food here is delicious, creative and elegant without being pretentious or fussy". / EC4A 1LB; www.vanillablack.co.uk; @vanillablack1; 10 pm; closed Sun; No Amex.

Vardo SW3 NEW
9 Duke of York Square   6–2D
From the team behind Caravan, this autumn 2019 newcomer (the name comes from Romany travelling wagons) is set to open in a striking, purpose-built, new cylindrical building, on Duke of York Square off the King's Road, with a public roof garden and a fully retractable glass wall (the UK's first apparently). The food – described as top British ingredients prepared using 'low and slow' cooking techniques – looks set to echo the wild-and-wacky global style of its older stablemates. / SW3 4LY; www.caravanrestaurants.co.uk/vardo.html.

Vasco & Piero's Pavilion W1 £65 3 3 2
15 Poland St   020 7437 8774   4–1C
"Pleasingly old-fashioned in style and cooking", this long-serving traditional Soho Italian keeps its many regulars happy with "a simple Umbrian menu, done well", including "excellent home-made pasta". There's a "comfortable and friendly ambience, and the occasional luvvie dining before his/her show". Top Tip – "the chef will do zabaglione at the end if the kitchen isn't too busy – a treat!". / W1F 8QE; www.vascosfood.com; @Vasco_and_Piero; 9.30 pm; closed Sat L & Sun.

Veeraswamy W1 £86 3 3 3
Victory Hs, 99-101 Regent St   020 7734 1401   4–4B
Despite a vintage stretching back to 1926, London's oldest Indian (part of the same group as Chutney Mary) doesn't merely trade on its guidebook potential, with "subtle" and "original" cuisine, "dedicated" service, and a first-floor setting, whose agreeable looks are thoroughly modern. It seems to have become "a wee bit pricey" of late, though, "but it is in the heart of the West End, so perhaps not excessively so". / W1B 4RS; www.veeraswamy.com; @theveeraswamy; 10.45 pm, Sun 10:15 pm; booking max 12 may apply.

Verdi's E1 £52 **3 4 4**
237 Mile End Rd 020 7423 9563 14–2B
"A relaxing, high-class restaurant in an area offering mostly junk food and takeaways"; white tablecloths help set a 'proper' tone at this Stepney Green trattoria of about five years' standing, which serves genuine Italian food – a particular shout-out to the pizzas. / E1 4AA; www.verdislondon.com; @verdislondon.

Vermuteria N1 £48 **2 2 3**
Coal Drops Yard 020 3479 1777 9–3C
"An exemplary range of vermouths" and "a very approachable style by the rather strained hipster standards of Coal Drops Yard" help win praise for Anthony Demetre's all-day bar/café in the new development, where his stated aim is to ape the best points of his favourite bars in Italy, France and Spain; and where "the food is standard modern small plates fare, decently done". The odd all-round disastrous report, however, somewhat takes the gloss off its ratings. / N1C 4AB; vermuteria.cc.

Via Emilia N1 £37 **3 2 2**
37a Hoxton Square 020 7613 0508 13–1B
"Delicious filled pasta" made exclusively with ingredients from Emilia-Romagna in northern Italy: that's the proposition at this "tiny, Spartan place just off Hoxton Square", which has earned solid ratings in its first year. It has also introduced the region's fried bread, gnocco fritto, to London, apparently. Sister establishment Parma in Fitzrovia focuses on cheese, charcuterie and Lambrusco wine. / N1 6NN; www.via—emilia.com.

Il Vicolo SW1 £55 **3 3 3**
3-4 Crown Passage 020 7839 3960 3–4D
Among the plutocrats' dining rooms of St James's, this "consistently good and friendly family-restaurant", tucked away down an alley, stands out as a "reliable Italian local" with earth-bound prices. / SW1Y 6PP; www.ilvicolorestaurant.co.uk; 10 pm; closed Sat L & Sun.

The Victoria SW14 £55 **2 2 3**
10 West Temple Sheen 020 8876 4238 11–2A
A ten-minute stroll from the Sheen Gate entrance to Richmond Park, this "pleasant gastropub" with a massive dining conservatory is ideal for a family meal, and "its USP is the small but useful outdoor play area for younger sprogs". The food is generally of "good quality", but there's some dispute as to whether it's "losing its spark" or "recovering having gone downhill". / SW14 7RT; victoriasheen.co.uk; @TheVictoria_Pub; 10 pm, Sun 9 pm; No Amex.

Viet Food W1 £38 **3 3 2**
34-36 Wardour St 020 7494 4555 5–3A
"Amazing Vietnamese street food", courtesy of ex-Hakkasan chef Jeff Tan, is "swiftly and efficiently served" at this spacious Chinatown operation. It can get "hectic… just like Vietnam". / W1D 6QT; www.vietnamfood.co.uk; @vietfoodlondon; 10.30 pm, Fri & Sat 11 pm.

Vijay NW6 £36 **4 3 1**
49 Willesden Ln 020 7328 1087 1–1B
"Delicious South Indian food at bargain prices", including "lovely, tasty vegetarian dishes", has, for decades, drawn a devoted following to this Kilburn institution, which claims to have been Britain's first Keralan restaurant when it opened in 1964. Little has changed since then, lending it a "greasy spoon atmosphere", but nobody's fussed. BYO recommended. / NW6 7RF; www.vijayrestaurant.co.uk; 10.45 pm, Fri & Sat 11.45 pm; no booking.

Villa Bianca NW3 £69 2 2 2

1 Perrins Ct 020 7435 3131 9–2A

This "very traditional Italian" in a prime Hampstead spot "hasn't changed much (except the prices)" for the past 30 years. Its enviable location, tucked away off the main drag, explains much of its appeal, as does a "formal but un-snooty" style that's not to all tastes, but helps attract "lots of buzz (and some celebs!)". Some fans applaud the fare as "well-cooked in generous portions", others say it's merely "fair". / NW3 1QS; villabiancagroup.com/villabianca; @VillaBiancaNW3; 11.30 pm, Sun 10.30 pm.

Villa Di Geggiano W4 £79 3 4 4

66-68 Chiswick High Road 020 3384 9442 8–2B

"A taste of the real Tuscany in W4" can be "a just fantastic experience" at this "lovely Chiswick local". Named after the ancestral home near Siena of the owners, a 500-year-old Chianti dynasty who wanted a London showcase, its strengths are a "warm welcome", "some real ambience" and – as you might expect – "a great wine list". / W4 1SY; www.villadigeggiano.co.uk; @VilladiGeggiano; 10 pm; closed Mon.

The Vincent Rooms,
Westminster Kingsway College SW1 £42 3 3 2

76 Vincent Sq 020 7802 8391 2–4C

"London's best-kept secret" offers cut-price haute cuisine prepared by "the stars of the future" – student chefs and waiters at Kingsway College in Westminster. "The food is always great value, and can be excellent", while "watching people being put through their paces and learning the trade is a fun way to spend an evening". "The main room could be a bit less municipal – maybe get some design students in!". / SW1P 2PD; www.thevincentrooms.co.uk; @thevincentrooms; 7 pm; closed Mon D, Tue D, Fri D, Sat & Sun; No Amex.

Vinegar Yard SE1 NEW

Saint Thomas Street 10–4C

A new 'eating, drinking, shopping and art space' from the founders of Flat Iron Square, also not far from London Bridge, with vintage shops, street food stalls and bars in shipping containers and a large garden. Million Pound Menu stars Baba G's have a stall here, selling their naanwiches and Indian burgers. / SE1 3QU; www.vinegaryard.london; @vinegaryardldn.

Vinoteca £61 2 2 2

15 Seymour Pl, W1 020 7724 7288 2–2A
18 Devonshire Rd, W4 020 3701 8822 8–2A
One Pancras Sq, N1 020 3793 7210 9–3C
7 St John St, EC1 020 7253 8786 10–1B
Bloomberg Arcade, Queen Victoria Street, EC2 awaiting tel 10–3C

"The wine list's brilliant" at these modern-industrial bars: "a huge range" that's "regularly added to, with some unusual vintages", "plenty at affordable prices" and "excellent options by the glass". And this "wine focus attracts a more interesting crowd than some other chains", all making the group "the perfect standby any night of the week". "All branches are recommended", with the one that's super-handy for King's Cross perhaps the most popular (though, being "always busy", it can seem "squashed and hurried", and booking is advisable). Perhaps the "food's a bit average", but practically all feedback actually focuses on its success as a "tasty" complement to the vino. Top Tip – "even better on a Sunday or Monday, when the wine's sold close to retail price". / www.vinoteca.co.uk; 11 pm, W1H & W4 Sun 4 pm; W1F 10.45 pm, Sun 9.30 pm; EC1 and W1H closed Sun.

Vivat Bacchus £60 3 3 2
4 Hay's Ln, SE1   020 7234 0891   10–4C
47 Farringdon St, EC4   020 7353 2648   10–2A
*"There's no better place to try South African wine – from cheap 'n' cheerful
to exceptional vintages" – than at this duo of SA-owned City wine bars,
with walk-in cellars for your deliberation. The Saffa-inspired food is "fairly
hearty" (steaks are a good bet), with a shout-out to the "brilliant cheese
room" in each venue.* / www.vivatbacchus.co.uk; 10.30 pm; closed Sun.

VQ £45 2 3 3
St Giles Hotel, Great Russell St, WC1   020 7636 5888   5–1A
325 Fulham Rd, SW10   020 7376 7224   6–3B
24 Pembridge Road, W11   020 3745 7224   7–2B
152-156 North Gower Street, NW1   020 3301 1224   9–4C
122 Clapham High Street, SW4   020 3096 5956   11–2D NEW
9 Aldgate High St, EC3   020 3301 7224   10–2D
*"Handy… especially when other places are shut!" – these "round-the-clock"
diners have grown from their SW10 base (which has been around for
yonks) to bring their late-night formula of "decent food, a good vibe, friendly
service and dependable value" to ever-more 'hoods: recent additions include
sites in Euston and Clapham. Only Chelsea, Bloomsbury and Aldgate are
actually 24/7.* / www.vingtquatre.co.uk; @Vqrestaurants; Mon-Sun 2 am; booking:
max 6 online.

Vrisaki N22 £43 3 3 2
73 Middleton Rd   020 8889 8760   1–1C
*This Greek-Cypriot taverna in Bounds Green is "famous across North
London for the ridiculous size of its mezze". The food, from Andreas and
Anthony Antoniou, "is reasonably tasty, service is pleasant enough and the
decor plain and uninspiring" – but "all this pales into insignificance if you
go very hungry!".* / N22 8LZ; vrisakirestaurant.com; @vrisakiuk; 11.30 pm,
Sun 9 pm; closed Mon; No Amex.

Wagamama £43 2 2 2
*"Our cheap, go-to choice when out and about" – this famous noodle chain's
ratings picked up this year after its October 2018 acquisition by The
Restaurant Group, who seem to be re-establishing its core virtues as "an OK
place to eat in a hurry", with a "solid and reliable bowl of ramen" that "fills
a hole", in a "collective" and "busy" canteen setting, all at a "reasonable
price". They're particularly "a firm family-favourite" – "kids love the
experience, the service is quick, and it's nice for them to have something
that's more exciting than a pizza/pasta/burger". The branch by the Royal
Festival Hall is notably handy – "a great option on the South Bank".*
/ www.wagamama.com; 10 pm - 11.30 pm; EC2 Sat 9 pm; EC4 closed Sat & Sun;
EC2 closed Sun; no bookings.

Wahaca £37 3 3 3
*"An ever-evolving, fun take on Mexican street food offering zingy flavours
(plus a damn fine margarita)" all "efficiently served" in a "bright and
buzzy" environment seems to have protected Thomasina Miers's popular
chain from much of the casual dining fall-out of recent times; and it remains
"the most dependable of fast(ish) food chains" for many reporters.
In particular, it's "perfect for kids", and families appreciate that "you fill
up well for the price".* / www.wahaca.com; 11 pm, Sun 10.30 pm; W12, Charlotte
St, SW19 Sun 10 pm; no booking or need 6+ to book.

The Wallace,
The Wallace Collection W1 £59 ②③⑤

Hertford Hs, Manchester Sq 020 7563 9505 3–1A

A "real hidden gem" – the spectacular glass-ceilinged atrium at the Wallace Collection is a "great place to bring visitors to London", just off Oxford Street; and serves breakfast, coffee and lunch every day, plus dinner on Fridays and Saturdays. For a full-blown meal, its "unhurried" service can grate, as can cooking that's only "so so". But where it undoubtedly scores is as a "lovely setting for a classic relaxed afternoon tea" – "all very nice and proper" – "with an excellent museum attached..." / W1U 3BN; www.peytonandbyrne.co.uk; @peytonandbyrne; 9.30 pm; Sun-Thu closed D; No Amex; booking max 10 may apply.

Wander N16 £48 ④④③

214 Stoke Newington High Street 020 7249 7283 1–1C

"The perfect neighbourhood restaurant", say fans of this Stoke Newington yearling, where "a daily/weekly-changing seasonal menu of Italian-influenced food with, say, a Portuguese twist and an Australian sensibility, is provided courtesy of Aussie chef-proprietor, Alexis Noble". "Wines are unusual, cleverly chosen, and invariably delicious. Service is sweet and helpful. A delight." / N16 7HU; www.wanderrestaurant.com.

The Watch House SE1 £9 ④②④

199 Bermondsey St 020 7407 6431 10–4D

"A wonderful location off Bermondsey Street" – a "quirky", ancient, tiny shelter originally built for watchmen guarding the graves of nearby St Mary Magdalene Church – helps win fans for this small coffee house (which has since spawned a couple of spin-offs at Tower Bridge and Fetter Lane). It wins many nominations for its "top coffee" too (supplied by Shoreditch roasters, Ozone) and "delicious food". One quibble: service can be "so laid back, it's almost horizontal". / SE1 3UW; www.thewatchhouse.com; @thewatchhouseUK.

The Wells Tavern NW3 £58 ③③④

30 Well Walk 020 7794 3785 9–1A

"Ultra reliable" cooking "a notch above usual gastropub fare" and "very friendly staff" have long made this handsome, dog-friendly Grade II listed tavern a Hampstead favourite. "The food is far from groundbreaking – but that is part of the classic appeal" – "been going for years and never had a bad meal". It's run by Beth Coventry, sister of veteran restaurant critic Fay Maschler (as you'll know if you read her pieces, as she's always giving it a plug!). / NW3 1BX; thewellshampstead.london; @WellsHampstead; 10 pm, Sun 9.30 pm.

Westerns Laundry N5 £56 ③②②

34 Drayton Park 020 7700 3700 9–2D

"Innovative food" in a "hard and echoey" space still packs in the crowds at this hipster hit of a couple of years ago, just off the Holloway Road, which fans feel has a "great vibe" (even despite the fact that "when the place is full, conversation can be close to impossible"). The venue has always had its detractors, though, and there were more vocal complaints this year that the whole approach is "a little too cool for its own good" (i.e. "pleased with itself" and "disappearing up its own fundament"); which results in food that's "not bad but underwhelming, so hard to see what all the fuss is about". Also the natural wine list, "while pleasingly ambitious and different, has a high percentage of misses" (to the extent it can seem "plain daft"). / N5 1PB; www.westernslaundry.com; @WesternsLaundry; 10.30 pm, Sun 5 pm.

The Wet Fish Café NW6 — £54 — 3 3 4

242 West End Lane   020 7443 9222   1–1B

"A West Hampstead standard bearer": this converted 1930s fishmonger is not, despite its name, a fish restaurant – it operates as an all-day bistro, and fans say it's "hit the spot for the last 15 years, with the high-quality food, great ambience and friendly service you'd hope for from a great local"; or that it's "busy most of the time, especially at weekend brunch" when "you may need to queue". The critiques of last year weren't repeated this time: the worst anyone says is that it's "nothing special but OK". / NW6 1LG; www.thewetfishcafe.co.uk; @thewetfishcafe; 10 pm; No Amex; Booking evening only.

The White Onion SW19 — £62 — 3 4 2

67 High St   020 8947 8278   11–2B

This spin-off from Eric and Sarah Guignard's redoubtable French Table in Surbiton can offer "first-class" cuisine with "professional and attentive service", and – about to enter its fifth year – practically all reports agree that it's been a "very welcome addition to the SW London restaurant scene". It does take some flak, though, for "cooking that's hit and miss – some dishes distinctly mediocre, but others excellent". / SW19 5EE; www.thewhiteonion.co.uk; @thewhiteonionSW; 10.30 pm; closed Mon, Tue L, Wed L & Thu L.

The Wigmore, The Langham W1 — £50 — 4 4 5

15 Langham Place, Regent Street   020 7965 0198   2–1B

"Setting the standards for a central London bar" – Michel Roux's two-year-old near Oxford Circus "has found a real niche" as a top West End rendezvous ("almost too successful for its own good" during peak times, when it risks becoming too thronging and loud). "You wouldn't know that it is part of a hotel" (it's actually carved out from – and a partnership with – the neighbouring five-star hotel, The Langham) and the unusually "classy" conversion of the space "burnishes the large, pub-style setting". "Its food is stretching the concept of gastropub food" in terms of ambition, but "definitely worth the money". / W1B 3DE; www.the-wigmore.co.uk; @Wigmore_London; Mon - Wed Midnight, Thurs - Sat 1am.

Wild Food Cafe WC2 NEW — £46 — 3 2 2

First Floor, 14 Neal's Yard   020 7419 2014   5–2C

"An ageless vegetarian": if you haven't been to this "no bookings and shared tables" café – tucked away on the first-floor of quaint Neal's Yard – in the last three years, you might easily miss the fact that it's changed its name and gone veggie (it was fka the World Food Café). For a snack near Covent Garden, it provides a smallish menu of "lovely genuine organic salads, veg burgers" and other fare. It also has a less commented-on Islington spin-off, with a good proportion of seating at the open kitchen counter, which features a dedicated brunch menu and a small selection of pizzas. / WC2H 9DP; www.wildfoodcafe.com; @WildFoodCafe.

Wild Honey St James SW1 — £79

Sofitel, 8 Pall Mall   020 7758 9160   3–2C

Anthony Demetre upped sticks and re-located his well-liked Mayfair establishment into the Sofitel, just off Trafalgar Square, taking over the attractive space that was formerly Balcon (RIP). It opened in August 2019, too late for survey feedback, but he's a deft and very accomplished chef, and his presence at this very handily situated venue seems likely to deepen its longstanding appeal as a quality rendezvous just away from the bustle of the West End. Fay Maschler's early days review was rapturous. / SW1Y 5NG; www.wildhoneyrestaurant.co.uk; @WildHoneySJ; 10.30 pm; closed Sun.

Wild Rice & Mamasan W1 NEW £50 3 4 3
28 Brewer Street 020 7434 3777 4–2D
Pan Serirak and Mike Asavarut created this duo of Thai-influenced, late-2018 newcomers in Soho: Wild Rice is on the ground floor, and focuses on small plates to share (Thai flavours with seasonal British ingredients). Mamasan is the basement restaurant, offering street food dishes. Early feedback suggests it's finding its feet, but worth a go: "we went and it was empty – I'm not sure why it wasn't packed as it deserved to be". / W1F 0SR; www.wildricelondon.com.

The Wilmington EC1 £55 3 3 3
69 Rosebery Avenue 020 7837 1384 10–1A
"Our local – we're so lucky!" Near the foodie mecca of Exmouth Market, this "busy" Clerkenwell corner-boozer receives a consistent thumbs-up in reports: "the standard of the food is high". / EC1R 4RL; www.wilmingtonclerkenwell.com; @wilmingtonec1; 10pm, Fri & Sat 10.30pm , Sun 9pm.

Wiltons SW1 £98 4 5 4
55 Jermyn St 020 7629 9955 3–3C
"The Best of British" – London's oldest restaurant (founded 1742, but not on this site) feels – with its "muffled conversations and refined decor mixing deep reds, browns and greens" – "akin to a compact version of an old-fashioned club"; and its St James's quarters provide a "top drawer", "old-school" experience for those of an "old-fashioned" disposition ("jackets are required for men"). "Acoustics are civilised" and "tables are very discreet, so it's perfect for business lunches or dinners"; while service operates "with class and efficiency", yet "without being unctuous". "If you want first-class, traditional cuisine", in particular fish and seafood (also game in season), this is the place for you – "sublime ingredients" are "presented impeccably, but without frills". Do try to ensure you are there at the invitation of your tax advisor or art dealer, however: "the bill is always brutal". / SW1Y 6LX; www.wiltons.co.uk; @wiltons1742; 10.15 pm; closed Sat L & Sun.

The Windmill W1 £56 3 3 3
6-8 Mill St 020 7491 8050 4–2A
"Excellent home-made pies" make this "always enjoyable" classic pub in Mayfair "worth a visit". They're backed up by a "super selection of ales, craft beers and wine", a "gin terrace" and a "great pubby atmosphere" – "what more could you ask for?" / W1S 2AZ; www.windmillmayfair.co.uk; @windmillpubW1; 10 pm, Sun 5 pm; closed Sat D & Sun.

The Wine Library EC3 £40 2 3 5
43 Trinity Sq 020 7481 0415 10–3D
This ancient cellar near Tower Hill has a "brilliant selection of wines at retail prices", accompanied by charcuterie and cheeses – "basically drinks-party food, but none the worse for that". With its "highly knowledgeable staff", it's a great place for oenophiles to while away an hour or two (if not in huge comfort, given the not-particularly-comfortable seating). / EC3N 4DJ; www.winelibrary.co.uk; 7.30 pm; closed Mon D, Sat & Sun.

The Wolseley W1 £68 2 3 5
160 Piccadilly 020 7499 6996 3–3C
"Always buzzing whatever the time of day": Corbin & King's "magnificent" Grand Café near The Ritz remains a linchpin of metropolitan life; the capital's No. 1 venue for a business meal – especially breakfast; and "a must-visit" for anyone getting to know London. "The space always impresses" – a converted Edwardian car-showroom that provides a "uniquely London" take on a "vast Belle-Époch-style brasserie". It has "the right cosmopolitan feel" to lend an air of sophistication to any meal, plus "familiar faces from media and TV" to inject further excitement. "There's a huge menu, so you'll always find something you fancy", but while its "retro", "comfort" cuisine (with a Mittel-European twist) is "served with

urbane panache", it is widely acknowledged by regulars that the dishes themselves are "uninspired" and taste "to be honest, average". But who cares? "It is hard not to love this place". Top Tip – "A grand setting for a quintessential and well-priced afternoon tea experience". / W1J 9EB; www.thewolseley.com; @TheWolseley; midnight, Sun 11 pm.

Wong Kei W1 £32 3 1 1
41-43 Wardour St   020 7437 8408   5–3A

"Go through the doors and instantly get barked at – how many? Then, an instruction is growled: 'Upstairs!'" The ritual of a meal at this famous Chinatown veteran, has elements of self-conscious parody (you can actually buy a T-shirt saying 'upstairs'), but remains relatively 'real': a loose pact between its infamously "rude" and dismissive staff and students, theatre-goers and hungry workers in search of cheap, Chinese chow. "You are unlikely to get any smiles as you find yourself at a shared table, in a crammed-in dining area with plates piled high with deliciously smelly food being slammed onto various tables – they want you to be decisive, eat, and get out as soon as possible" – but it's "a fantastic filler". / W1D 6PY; www.wongkeilondon.com; 11.15 pm, Sun 10.30 pm; Cash only.

Workshop Coffee £37 3 4 3
1 Barrett Street, St Christopher's Place, W1   020 7253 5754   3–1B
80a Mortimer St, W1   020 7253 5754   3–1C
25 London Street, W2   7–1D NEW
1 Old Street Yard, EC1   020 7253 5754   13–1A

"Perfect coffee every time" keeps caffeine fiends crawling back to this small and serious chain. "Baking from Fortitude Bakehouse is a good complement". / workshopcoffee.com; @workshopcoffee; EC1M 6 pm, Tue-Fri 7 pm; W1U & W1W 7 pm, Sat & Sun 6 pm; EC1A 6 pm; EC1 closed Sat & Sun; no bookings.

Wright Brothers £68 3 3 3
13 Kingly St, W1   020 7434 3611   4–2B
56 Old Brompton Rd, SW7   020 7581 0131   6–2B
11 Stoney St, SE1   020 7403 9554   10–4C
26 Circus Road West, SW8   020 7324 7734   11–1C
8 Lamb St, E1   020 7377 8706   10–2D

"The best and freshest oysters by far, with seasonal varieties from time to time…"; "superb plateau de fruits de mer"; and "super-fresh fish" from an "ever-changing selection of specials", all make this small group of seafood bistros "easy to love". The style is "busy and jostling" throughout – "be prepared to share your table with other diners" in some locations – in others "some of the tables are so close, you'll make new friends whether you want to or not!". The Borough Market original and South Kensington spin-off attract most (and most favourable) reports – other branches (including at Battersea) can seem "a welcome addition but nothing remarkable". / SE1 10 pm, Sat 11 pm; W1 11 pm, Sun 10 pm; E1 10.30 pm, Sun 9 pm; SW7 10.30 pm, Sun 9.30 pm; booking: max 7 online.

Wulf & Lamb SW1 £50 4 2 2
243 Pavilion Road   0203 948 5999   6–2D

"Never thought vegan food could be so guilt-inducing!": this self-consciously decadent plant-based two-year-old – under ex-Vanilla Black chef Franco Casoli in a "lovely" mews off Sloane Square – is "just a damn good restaurant in many ways… unlike many other vegans that seem to equate vegan food with a depressing ambience!". "The only grumble is the need to go downstairs to order". / SW1X 0BP; www.wulfandlamb.com; @wulfandlamb; No bookings.

Wun's W1 £34
24 Greek Street   020 8017 9888   5–2A
The Soho branch of Bun House changed to Wun's in late July 2019 – too late for this year's survey – and, still under the ownership of Z He and Alex Peffly, is now a '1960s-style tea room and late night bar'. Set across two floors in Soho, it aims to mimic the communal, open-air cafes and restaurants in Hong Kong known as 'dai pai dong'. / W1D 4DZ; tearoom.bar; @8unhouse.

Xi'an Biang Biang E1 £35   3 3 3
62 Wentworth Street   020 8617 1470   13–2C
"Oodles of noodles… and fun, too": this "bustling, happy-making eatery" – year-old sibling to Highbury's Xi'an Impression – occupies a canteen-style space in Spitalfields and "specialises in spicy, hand-pulled noodles"; "yum!". / E1 7AL; xianbiangbiangnoodles.com; @xianbiangbiang1.

Xi'an Impression N7 £33   5 2 1
117 Benwell Rd   020 3441 0191   9–2D
"Lip-smackingly good, seriously authentic" dishes from Xi'an in central China, with "a great chilli kick in every mouthful", can be found at this "small and cramped" venue by the Arsenal stadium "with the ambiance of a transport caff". "Some dishes are alien to the European palate", but it's "better – and cheaper – than anywhere in Chinatown", so "always full of Chinese students from the local college, who know a good thing". Top Tip – "scrumptious noodles and dumplings: follow the chef's recommendations". / N7; www.xianimpression.co.uk; @xianimpression; 10 pm.

Xier W1 NEW £121   4 3 4
13-14 Thayer Street   020 7486 3222   3–1A
Sharing a building with XR (see also) – the first floor of Carlo Scotto's highly ambitious Marylebone newcomer is much less casual than the ground-floor – a "very elegant room" that's a symphony of whites and neutrals. A ten-course tasting menu is the centrepiece of its evening offer, with British ingredients used to create modern European dishes with Japanese riffs. The odd sceptic feels results are "interesting, but not all of them are delicious", but most diners are total converts, extolling an all-round, exceptional, gastronomic experience. / W1U 3JR; www.xierlondon.com.

XR W1 NEW £67   3 3 2
13-14 Thayer Street   0207 486 3222   3–1A
The ground-floor of Carlo Scotto's Marylebone newcomer (see also Xier) – formerly a branch of PizzaExpress – isn't as warmly greeted as the more ambitious upstairs by reporters. Early days feedback rates the dishes – a more casual version of the fine food above – consistently well, but there's only the odd rave, and the atmosphere here seems more elusive too. / W1U 3JR; www.xierlondon.com.

XU W1 £69   4 3 4
30 Rupert St   020 3319 8147   4–3D
"Sublime, very different, Taiwanese cuisine" delivering "flavourful and stylish" dishes in a "super-cool setting" (evoking a 1930s tea parlour) makes this "tiny but beautiful" two-year-old on the edge of Chinatown many reporters' "new favourite place for Chinese-style food". Owned by the people behind Bao, its "subtly flavoured delights" include "brilliant tea-based cocktails" and a "lovely selection of the teas themselves". / W1D 6DL; xulondon.com; @XU_london; 11 pm.

Yalla Yalla £42 3 2 2
1 Green's Ct, W1   020 7287 7663   4–2D
12 Winsley St, W1   020 7637 4748   3–1C
"Cheap 'n' cheerful" Beirut-style street-food duo that offer "a top Lebanese experience" in a hidden Soho alleyway and Fitzrovia. "The food is very good and very good value", with some "unusual and delicious choices – try the mixed fish with za'atar and sumac". / www.yalla-yalla.co.uk; W1W 11.30 pm, Sat 11pm, Sun 8 pm, W1F 11 pm, Sun 10 pm; booking min 10.

Yama Momo SE22 £57 3 2 3
72 Lordship Ln   020 8299 1007   1–4D
The "very good cooking at this Japanese fusion place" – an offshoot of stalwart Clapham hotspot, Tsunami – makes it a popular option in East Dulwich. Service, though "sweet", has slipped a notch, though: "they sometimes seem more interested in serving cocktails than getting the food sorted". / SE22 8HF; www.yamamomo.co.uk; @YamamomoRest; 10 pm, Fri & Sat 10.30 pm, Sun 9.30 pm; closed weekday L.

Yard Sale Pizza £42 4 3 2
54 Blackstock Road, N4   020 7226 2651   9–1D
622 High Road Leytonstone, E11   020 8539 5333   1–1D
15 Hoe Street, E17   020 8509 0888   1–1D
105 Lower Clapton Rd, E5   020 3602 9090   14–1B
"Unusual toppings that actually work" ("BBQ sauce!") and "the best-ever, super-thin crusts" are hallmarks of this "achingly East London trendy" quartet of "excellent" and "inventive" pizza-stops. / yardsalepizza.com; @YardSalePizza; 11 pm, Sun 10 pm; no bookings.

Yashin £98 3 2 2
117-119 Old Brompton Rd, SW7   020 7373 3990   6–2B
1a Argyll Rd, W8   020 7938 1536   6–1A
Backstreet sushi restaurant in High Street Kensington of high ambition which typically elicits high praise, but which curiously inspired practically no feedback this year. By contrast its South Kensington spin-off, which occupies a characterful landmark (formerly Brompton Library) is usually ignored, but inspired a number of reports, mostly adulatory regarding its "exceptionally good" (if pricey) cuisine: "the chef asked us if we wanted him to do something special, he did, and it was the best sushi we have ever had". / 10 pm.

Yauatcha £88 4 2 3
Broadwick Hs, 15-17 Broadwick St, W1   020 7494 8888   4–1C
Broadgate Circle, EC2   020 3817 9888   13–2B
"Silky-fine cheung fun, filled with sweet fresh prawns"... "dumplings wrapped in translucent skins"... "delicious venison puffs"... – "you can't go back to Chinatown dim sum after a trip" to one of these "hip and happening", Chinese-inspired haunts, whose "addictive bites keep reeling you in". The "flash" Soho original, created by Alan Yau, "still feels fresh after all these years" – with its moody basement and lighter ground floor – while the Broadgate spin-off is much larger in scale, more conventionally glam, and with a big cocktail terrace overlooking Broadgate Circle. Any drawbacks? Service is "efficient" but "sometimes brusque". Top Tips – Soho also serves tea, and has a line in "gorgeous, elegant patisserie"; EC2 does "exceptional-value weekend lunches". / www.yauatcha.com; 10 pm - 11.30 pm; EC2 closed Sun.

The Yellow House SE16 £48 3 4 3
126 Lower Rd   020 7231 8777   12–2A
"We're so lucky this place exists, in SE16 of all places!" – so says a local fan of this oasis in the culinary badlands surrounding Surrey Quays Station. Wood-fired pizza is a highpoint on the wide-ranging and "affordably priced" menu. / SE16 2UE; www.theyellowhouse.eu; @Theyellowhouse_; 10 pm, Sun 8 pm; closed Mon, Tue-Sat D only, Sun open L & D.

Yen WC2 £98 **4 4 4**
190 Strand, 5 Arundel Street   020 3915 6976   2–2D

In the soulless environs of Temple, it's a surprise to discover this stark, stylish Japanese in a new development – the year-old spin-off from a well-established Parisian venture (and ultimately part of one of Japan's largest fashion houses, Onward). The brand is "famed for their soba noodles which are created on-site, but the sushi and sashimi are also things of real beauty". Reports are still limited, but such as we have remain ecstatic: "very difficult to fault, from the attentive, elegant service, to the mouthwatering food, to the stunning interiors (and Japanese toilets!)". STOP PRESS: In summer 2019, the chef who makes the soba-noodles had to return to Paris. The date of his return is currently unknown, and – until he does – the trademark noodles are off the menu. / WC2R 3DX; www.yen-london.co.uk; @YenRestaurant.*

Yeni W1 NEW £66 **4 3 3**
55 Beak Street   020 3475 1903   4–2C

"As good as that we ate when in the Turkish original" – this stylish-looking Soho newcomer is a London sibling to one of Istanbul's hottest properties, and (at odds with some press reviews) it impresses all early reporters (notwithstanding the odd incident of "shaky service" or "lack of ambience"), with "interesting" cuisine produced by star chef Civan Er. / W1F 9SH; www.yeni.london.

Yi-Ban E16 £59 **2 2 2**
London Regatta Centre, Dockside Rd, Royal Albert Dock   020 7473 6699   12–1D

Watching take-offs and landings at London City Airport provides distraction at this dock-side Chinese near Royal Albert Dock DLR, which continues to divide opinion between fans who hail its "top dim sum" and sceptics who feel it's merely "average". Sadly, everyone agrees that "neither service, nor other elements of the experience live up to the food". / E16 2QT; www.yi-ban.co.uk; 11 pm, Sun 10.30 pm.

Yipin China N1 £50 **4 2 1**
70-72 Liverpool Rd   020 7354 3388   9–3D

"Nobody comes for the decor or service" when choosing this Chinese canteen near Angel, which has "zero charm", to the extent some find it "a strange place". But it's definitely "worth a visit", so long as you "stick to Hunanese and Sichuan dishes in which they specialise – spicy and challenging but very good". / N1 0QD; www.yipinchina.co.uk; 11 pm; Cash only.

Yming W1 £55 **4 4 3**
35-36 Greek St   020 7734 2721   5–2A

"William (the maitre d') always has a warm welcome" at this "long-term favourite": a Soho "oasis" whose "calm and friendly" atmosphere ("without the feeling we need to rush and free the table") provides a quiet-but-stark contrast with the frenzy of Chinatown a couple of blocks south. Foodwise "it attempts nothing new or extraordinary – just good Chinese cooking that's always wholesome and satisfying", with "decent wine at un-greedy prices". / W1D 5DL; www.yminglondon.com; 11.45 pm.

Yopo W1 NEW £72
20-21 Newman Street   020 3146 8880   3–1D

With its lush and somewhat 'out-there' styling, Fitzrovia's Mandrake Hotel makes an attractive destination for a meal, but recently closed its former restaurant Serge et Le Phoque (RIP). In its place came this spring 2019 newcomer, hailed as 'modern European with a South American accent' (and named for a powerful hallucinogen). One early report – in keeping with upbeat press reviews from the likes of The Telegraph's William Sitwell – suggests it's well worth a trip. / W1T 1PG; www.themandrake.com; @MandrakeHotel.

York & Albany NW1 £59 2 2 2
127-129 Parkway 020 7592 1227 9–3B

Gordon Ramsay's "beautiful" Regency tavern on the Camden Town corner of Regent's Park, is a large venue incorporating both a big bar, plus a sizeable dining area and basement. It doesn't receive a perfect scorecard from reporters, with some feedback describing it as "disappointing" or "overpriced", but its ratings climbed more into the middle-ground this year. / NW1 7PS; www.gordonramsayrestaurants.com/york-and-albany; @yorkandalbany; 10.30 pm, Sun 10 pm.

Yoshi Sushi W6 £45 3 4 2
210 King St 020 8748 5058 8–2B

"The best kimchi in London" – apparently "voted by the South Korean Embassy!" – is found at this drab-looking stalwart, near Ravenscourt Park tube. Despite the name, the place is Korean-owned and run – and it's the "fantastic Korean dishes" that garner the plaudits this year: "sweet, savoury, spicy and with generous portions". But the Japanese dishes are also excellent and "service is always personal". / W6 0RA; www.yoshisushi.co.uk; 11 pm, Sun 10.30 pm; closed Sun L

Yoshino W1 £49 3 3 2
3 Piccadilly Pl 020 7287 6622 4–4C

"Good, simple Japanese food" has drawn a steady crowd to this offbeat, two-storey outfit for 35 years; its trump card is "location, location and location" – a little alleyway between Regent Street and Piccadilly. Cooking standards have "varied over the years", but most reporters still approve the overall experience and "sensible prices for Mayfair". / W1J 0DB; www.yoshino.net; @Yoshino_London; closed Sun.

Yum Bun EC2 £22 5 3 2
Dinerama, 19 Great Eastern St 07919 408 221 13–2B

"Perfect fluffy pillows of yumminess" with a range of "classic Asian street-food stuffings" have recruited an army of fans for Lisa Meyer's Chinese-inspired steamed bun stalls in the past 10 years. They can now be found at Spitalfields Market Kitchens and the various Street Feast venues. Top Tip – "do not miss the signature roast pork belly, served with cucumber and a sticky dark sauce exploding with umami". / EC2A 3EJ; www.yumbun.com; @yumbun; closed Mon D, Tue D, Wed D, Sat L & Sun; No bookings.

Zafferano SW1 £99 3 2 2
15 Lowndes St 020 7235 5800 6–1D

"Pricey but always 'comme il faut'" sums up the still-accomplished cuisine at this once-famous Belgravian, a short walk from Knightsbridge. That said, 20 years ago under founding chef Giorgio Locatelli, it was "the doyenne of Italian restaurants", while now it's simply "reliable" – if at a high level – and "resting on its laurels". / SW1X 9EY; www.zafferanorestaurant.com; 10.30 pm, Sun 10 pm.

Zaffrani N1 £53 3 3 2
47 Cross St 020 7226 5522 9–3D

An "excellent local Indian", close to the Almeida Theatre, that wins consistently solid ratings for its cuisine, and – for non-carnivores – has "enough vegetarian dishes to be interesting". / N1 2BB; www.zaffrani.co.uk; 10.30 pm.

Zaibatsu SE10 £32 4 4 2
96 Trafalgar Rd 020 8858 9317 1–3D

This "buzzy, family-owned Asian" dishes up "really fresh Japanese fusion food" that's "cheap and delicious", including "super-value sushi". It's "basic" and "functional", with "dog-eared menus" and Formica tables, but "service is efficient" and you can BYO. / SE10 9UW; www.zaibatsufusion.co.uk; @ong_teck; 11 pm; closed Mon; Cash only.

Zaika of Kensington W8 £71 **4** **3** **3**
1 Kensington High Street 020 7795 6533 6–1A

The forgotten sibling of Mayfair's swanky Tamarind inspires shockingly little feedback nowadays, but all reports continue to applaud this posh nouvelle Indian, which occupies an impressive converted banking hall near Kensington Palace Gardens: "top cuisine, with excellent service, and grand style". / W8 5NP; www.zaikaofkensington.com; @ZaikaLondon; 10.45 pm, Sun 9.45 pm; closed Mon L; credit card required to book.

Zelman Meats £64 **3** **3** **3**
Harvey Nichols, Fifth Floor, 109-125 Knightsbridge, SW1 020 7201 8625 6–1D
2 St Anne's Ct, W1 020 7437 0566 4–1D

"Barbecue perfection!", insist fans of Misha Zelman's "good value" Soho steakhouse (with a Knightsbridge offshoot in Harvey Nichols). The "atmosphere's a bit industrial", but "the cocktails are good" and the "meat fantastic" – "I prefer the steak to Hawksmoor's and Goodman's despite it being reliably half the price". / zelmanmeats.com; W1 10.30 pm, Sun 9 pm; SW1 10 pm, Sun 7 pm; W1 closed Mon L, N4 closed Mon-Fri L.

Zeret SE5 £34 **4** **4** **3**
216-218 Camberwell Road 020 7701 8587 1–3C

"You get to practically eat the plate (as the food is served on a large injera flatbread)" when you sample the cooking at this "lovely local Ethiopian" in Camberwell. Don't miss out on the coffee ceremony at the end of the meal. / SE5 0ED; www.zeretkitchen.com ; 11 pm ; No Amex.

Zero Degrees SE3 £47 **3** **3** **3**
29-31 Montpelier Vale 020 8852 5619 1–4D

"Amazing pizzas" are a culinary highlight on the sizeable menu (moules, salads, pasta…) at this early-wave microbrewery in Blackheath which is celebrating its 20th year in 2020, and where you can also sample, of course, a wide variety of brews fermented in the adjoining stainless steel tanks. Over the years it's spawned spin-offs in Cardiff, Reading and Bristol. / SE3 0TJ; www.zerodegrees.co.uk; @Zerodegreesbeer; midnight, Sun 11.30 pm.

Zheng SW3 £65 **4** **3** **2**
4 Sydney St 020 7352 9890 6–2C

"Great but under-rated Malaysian/Singaporean food", "executed with real style", has earned consistently high marks for this sleek sibling of a successful Oxford venue, since it took over the Chelsea site of Brasserie Gustave (RIP) two years ago. / SW3 6PP; www.zhengchelsea.co.uk; @zhengchelsea; 11.30 pm, Sun 10 pm.

Zia Lucia £36 **4** **4** **3**
61 Blythe Road, W14 8–1C **NEW**
157 Holloway Road, N7 020 7700 3708 9–2D

"The queuing is now almost part of the trip" to the "frenetic-but-we-love-it" Holloway original: "a terrific local pizzeria that's always packed" thanks to its "inventive, delicious chewy bases (including charcoal dough), generously finished off with a variety of flavoursome toppings", and washed down with "great local beers". Its sibling, north of Brook Green, is in a much less happening location, but already winning feedback as "a great addition to the area, with friendly staff; and where everything on the menu is fresh, and portions are generous".

Ziani's SW3 £63 **2** **3** **2**
45 Radnor Walk 020 7351 5297 6–3C

Squashed trattoria off the King's Road that's long been a staple of the Chelsea crowd, who find it fun packing in like sardines next to their neighbours. In the year that saw the death of founder and long-term owner, Roberto Colussi, feedback has become a little more mixed than once it was, but it's still tipped by fans as a "favourite", especially by those with kids in tow. / SW3 4BP; www.ziani.co.uk; 11 pm, Sun 10 pm.

Zobler's,
The Ned EC2

2 3 3

27 Poultry   020 3828 2000   10–2C

"A great choice for a quick catch-up in the City" – this NYC-style Jewish deli operation vies with Cecconi's within The Ned's humongous food court as its most popular destination, and grabbing a dog, Reuben or burger here is also popular for a casual business meal (although conditions can be "extremely noisy"). Some of the dishes can be "ordinary" – its best feature is actually breakfast: "good coffee" (with unlimited refills) and lots of yummy options ("the Challah French toast is fantastic!") / EC2R 8AJ; www.thened.com; @TheNedLondon.

Zoilo W1

£64   4 4 3

9 Duke St   020 7486 9699   3–1A

"Much underrated", this Argentinian tapas and wine bar behind Oxford Street is the perfect place to sample "steaks from the Pampas, cooked to perfection". "Lunchtime specials are terrific value", and the "mini beef burgers dripping with homemade chimichurri are worth a journey". / W1U 3EG; www.zoilo.co.uk; @Zoilo_London; 10.30 pm; closed Sun.

Zuma SW7

£82   5 3 5

5 Raphael St   020 7584 1010   6–1C

Arjun Waney and Rainer Becker's "well-oiled" glamour-magnet, just off Knightsbridge, "has kept its high standards for more than 15 years now" (it opened in 2002, nowadays with spin-offs around the globe). "The cocktail bar is a bit of a zoo", but that just adds energy to its "buzzy" ("so noisy!"), "casual and comfortable" overall style; and even if Japanese-fusion cuisine doesn't today seem like quite the genius-magic it did on opening, the "sublime" dishes here still feel as fresh as a daisy: "wonderous bites" of sushi, black cod and other "supreme" creations. / SW7 1DL; www.zumarestaurant.com; 10.45 pm, Sun 10.15 pm; booking max 8 may apply.

AREA OVERVIEWS

CENTRAL

Soho, Covent Garden & Bloomsbury
(Parts of W1, all WC2 and WC1)

Price	Name	Cuisine	Ratings
£190+	Aulis London	British, Modern	5 5 4
£120+	Maison Bab & Kebab Queen	Turkish	5 4 3
£100+	The Northall	British, Modern	3 2 3
	The Savoy Hotel	British, Traditional	2 3 3
	Smith & Wollensky	Steaks & grills	2 3 2
£90+	The Baptist Grill	British, Modern	3 4 4
	Bob Bob Ricard	"	2 3 5
	The Petersham	"	2 1 4
	Kaspar's Seafood and Grill	Fish & seafood	3 4 4
	The Savoy Hotel	Afternoon tea	2 3 4
	Yen	Japanese	4 4 4
£80+	Christopher's	American	2 2 3
	The Ivy	British, Modern	2 2 3
	Social Eating House	"	2 2 4
	Spring Restaurant	"	3 4 5
	Simpson's in the Strand	British, Traditional	2 2 3
	Neptune	Fish & seafood	2 2 2
	J Sheekey	"	4 4 4
	Clos Maggiore	French	3 4 5
	Frenchie	"	3 2 2
	Sushisamba	Fusion	3 2 3
	Evelyn's Table	International	4 5 3
	Cakes and Bubbles	Spanish	3 4 4
	Hawksmoor	Steaks & grills	4 3 3
	Oscar Wilde Lounge	Afternoon tea	3 4 5
	Cecconi's Pizza Bar	Pizza	2 2 4
	Yauatcha	Chinese	4 2 3
	aqua kyoto	Japanese	2 2 4
	Roka	"	5 4 4
£70+	Balthazar	British, Modern	2 2 4
	Frog by Adam Handling	"	5 5 3
	Garden Room	"	2 2 3
	Hix	"	1 2 2
	The Portrait	"	2 3 4
	Holborn Dining Room	British, Traditional	3 2 3
	Rules	"	3 3 5
	J Sheekey Atlantic Bar	Fish & seafood	3 3 4
	Gauthier Soho	French	4 4 3
	Otto's	"	4 4 3
	Gezellig	International	4 3 2
	Laurent at Cafe Royal	"	– – –
	Nopi	Mediterranean	4 3 2
	Eneko Basque Kitchen & Bar	Spanish	4 4 3
	Heritage	Swiss	– – –
	Dalloway Terrace	Afternoon tea	3 2 4

	Lima Floral	*Peruvian*	3	3	2
£60+	Big Easy	*American*	3	2	3
	Hubbard & Bell	"	3	3	3
	Andrew Edmunds	*British, Modern*	3	3	5
	Bryn Williams	"	3	3	3
	Cora Pearl	"	3	2	3
	Dean Street Townhouse	"	2	3	5
	Ducksoup	"	4	3	4
	The French House	"	3	4	5
	Ham Yard Restaurant	"	2	3	4
	Heliot Steak House	"	3	3	3
	The Ivy Market Grill	"	2	2	4
	Quo Vadis	"	3	3	5
	10 Greek Street	"	4	3	2
	Tredwell's	"	3	3	3
	George in the Strand	*British, Traditional*	3	3	3
	The Ivy Soho Brasserie	"	2	2	4
	The Delaunay	*East & Cent. European*	2	4	4
	Fishworks	*Fish & seafood*	3	2	2
	The Oystermen	"	4	3	3
	Parsons	"	4	3	2
	Randall & Aubin	"	4	3	5
	Wright Brothers	"	3	3	3
	Cigalon	*French*	4	4	4
	L'Escargot	"	3	2	4
	The 10 Cases	*International*	3	4	3
	Bocca Di Lupo	*Italian*	5	4	3
	Café Murano	"	2	2	2
	Luce e Limoni	"	4	4	3
	Margot	"	2	4	3
	Vasco & Piero's Pavilion	"	3	3	2
	Cigala	*Spanish*	2	2	1
	Tapas Brindisa Soho	"	3	2	2
	Sophie's Steakhouse	*Steaks & grills*	2	2	3
	Zelman Meats	"	3	3	3
	Burger & Lobster	*Burgers, etc*	3	2	3
	Cantina Laredo	*Mexican/TexMex*	2	2	2
	Ceviche Soho	*Peruvian*	3	3	4
	The Palomar	*Middle Eastern*	4	3	4
	Yeni	*Turkish*	4	3	3
	The Duck & Rice	*Chinese*	3	2	3
	Tamarind Kitchen	*Indian*	3	3	3
	Sticks'n'Sushi	*Japanese*	3	3	3
	Jinjuu	*Korean*	4	4	3
	St Martin's Lane Kitchen	*Pan-Asian*	–	–	–
	Patara Soho	*Thai*	3	4	3
	XU	*Taiwanese*	4	3	4
£50+	Joe Allen	*American*	2	2	3
	Coopers Restaurant & Bar	*British, Modern*	3	4	3
	Noble Rot	"	3	4	4
	The Norfolk Arms	"	3	3	3
	Terroirs	"	2	2	3
	Cork & Bottle	*British, Traditional*	2	2	4
	Bonnie Gull Seafood Shack	*Fish & seafood*	5	3	3

Blanchette	French	4 2 3
Bon Vivant	"	3 2 3
Le Garrick	"	3 3 4
Henrietta Bistro	"	3 3 3
Mon Plaisir Restaurant	"	3 3 4
The Good Egg	Fusion	4 3 4
Boulevard	International	2 3 3
Da Mario	Italian	2 3 3
Dehesa	"	2 2 3
Fumo	"	3 3 3
La Goccia	"	2 2 4
Mele e Pere	"	3 3 3
Polpo	"	1 2 2
San Carlo Cicchetti	"	3 3 4
Barrafina	Spanish	5 5 5
Ember Yard	"	3 3 4
Opera Tavern	"	4 4 3
Rambla	"	3 3 2
St Moritz	Swiss	3 4 4
Casita Andina	Peruvian	4 3 3
Señor Ceviche	"	3 3 2
The Barbary	North African	5 5 4
Berenjak	Persian	4 4 4
Red Farm	Chinese	3 2 3
Yming	"	4 4 3
Dum Biryani	Indian	3 2 2
Fatt Pundit	"	3 3 2
Kricket	"	4 4 4
Little Kolkata	"	4 3 2
Tandoor Chop House	"	4 3 3
Chotto Matte	Japanese	4 3 4
Flesh and Buns	"	2 3 3
Inko Nito	"	3 3 4
Wild Rice & Mamasan	Thai	3 4 3

£40+			
Hoppers	Sri Lankan	4 3 3
Bodean's	American	2 2 2
Breakfast Club	"	3 3 3
Shampers	British, Modern	3 4 4
VQ	"	2 3 3
Brasserie Zédel	French	2 3 5
Café Monico	"	2 2 4
Prix Fixe	"	3 2 2
Relais de Venise L'Entrecôte	"	3 3 3
Savoir Faire	"	3 4 3
La Fromagerie Bloomsbury	International	3 4 3
Bancone	Italian	5 4 3
Casa Tua	"	4 3 3
Ciao Bella	"	3 4 4
Pastaio	"	3 3 2
Blacklock	Steaks & grills	3 4 4
Macellaio RC	"	4 3 3
Mildreds	Vegetarian	3 3 3
Wild Food Cafe	"	3 2 2
Haché	Burgers, etc	3 4 2
The Chipping Forecast	Fish & chips	3 3 3

	Name	Cuisine			
	North Sea Fish	"	3	4	2
	Poppies	"	3	3	3
	Pizza Pilgrims	Pizza	4	3	3
	Rossopomodoro	"	2	2	2
	temper Covent Garden	"	3	3	4
	Chick 'n' Sours	Chicken	4	3	3
	Bodean's	BBQ	2	2	2
	temper Soho	"	3	3	4
	Breddos Tacos	Mexican/TexMex	4	2	3
	Corazón	"	3	4	3
	Yalla Yalla	Lebanese	3	2	2
	Le Bab	Turkish	4	2	3
	Barshu	Chinese	4	2	2
	Four Seasons	"	4	1	1
	Golden Dragon	"	3	2	2
	Joy King Lau	"	3	3	2
	Cinnamon Bazaar	Indian	3	3	3
	Darjeeling Express	"	4	3	3
	Dishoom	"	3	4	5
	Gopal's of Soho	"	3	3	2
	Malabar Junction	"	3	3	3
	Punjab	"	3	4	3
	Salaam Namaste	"	3	3	2
	Bone Daddies	Japanese	3	3	3
	Ichi Buns	"	2	2	3
	Ippudo London	"	3	3	3
	Jugemu	"	5	2	3
	Oka	"	4	3	2
	Robata	"	–	–	–
	Shackfuyu	"	4	3	3
	Shoryu Ramen	"	3	2	2
	Tonkotsu	"	3	3	2
	Freak Scene	Pan-Asian	5	4	4
	Cay Tre	Vietnamese	3	3	2
£35+	Gordon's Wine Bar	International	2	2	5
	Lina Stores	Italian	4	4	4
	Princi	"	3	2	3
	MEATliquor	Burgers, etc	3	3	3
	Homeslice	Pizza	4	3	3
	Ceru	Middle Eastern	4	3	4
	Chilli Cool	Chinese	4	2	1
	Sagar	Indian	3	3	2
	Kanada-Ya	Japanese	5	3	2
	Koya-Bar	"	4	4	3
	Kulu Kulu	"	3	2	1
	On The Bab	Korean	3	3	2
	Hare & Tortoise	Pan-Asian	3	3	2
	Kiln	Thai	5	4	4
	Lao Cafe	"	3	2	2
	Viet Food	Vietnamese	3	3	2
	Bao	Taiwanese	4	3	3
£30+	Café in the Crypt	British, Traditional	2	1	4
	Bar Italia	Italian	2	3	5
	Flat Iron	Steaks & grills	4	4	4

			Rating		
	Shake Shack	Burgers, etc	3	2	2
	Tommi's Burger Joint	"	3	4	3
	50 Kalò di Ciro Salvo	Pizza	4	3	2
	Wong Kei	Chinese	3	1	1
	Wun's	"	–	–	–
	Eat Tokyo	Japanese	3	2	2
	Taro	"	3	2	2
	Bibimbap Soho	Korean	3	3	2
	C&R Café	Malaysian	4	2	2
£25+	Jacob the Angel	British, Modern	3	3	3
	Patty and Bun Soho	Burgers, etc	4	3	3
	Coqfighter	Chicken	5	3	2
	India Club	Indian	2	2	2
	Sen Viet	Japanese	3	4	2
	Tokyo Diner	"	3	3	3
£20+	Master Wei	Chinese	4	3	2
	The Kati Roll Company	Indian	4	2	2
	Jidori	Japanese	4	3	2
£15+	The Halal Guys	American	3	3	2
	Curry House Coco Ichibanya	Japanese	–	–	–
£10+	Nordic Bakery	Scandinavian	3	2	2
	Bageriet	Sandwiches, cakes, etc	4	3	3
	Flat White	"	4	4	3
	Bun House	Chinese	4	3	3
£5+	Maison Bertaux	Afternoon tea	4	4	5
	Monmouth Coffee Company	Sandwiches, cakes, etc	3	5	4

Mayfair & St James's (Parts of W1 and SW1)

			Rating		
£360+	The Araki	Japanese	5	3	2
£150+	Hélène Darroze	French	3	4	4
	Sketch	"	3	3	4
£140+	Hide	British, Modern	3	5	4
	Le Gavroche	French	4	5	4
	The Greenhouse	"	3	3	3
£130+	Alain Ducasse	French	2	3	3
	The Promenade	Afternoon tea	2	4	4
	Park Chinois	Chinese	2	2	3
£120+	The Ritz	British, Traditional	3	4	5
	Galvin at Windows	French	3	3	5
	The Square	"	3	3	2
	Cut	Steaks & grills	3	2	2
	Kai Mayfair	Chinese	3	2	2
	Umu	Japanese	4	4	4

£110+					
	Pollen Street Social	*British, Modern*	3	3	3
	La Petite Maison	*French*	4	3	4
	Seven Park Place	*"*	4	4	3
	The Ritz	*Afternoon tea*	3	4	5
	Tokimeite	*Japanese*	3	2	2
	Jean-Georges	*Pan-Asian*	2	3	3

£100+					
	Alyn Williams	*British, Modern*	4	5	3
	Dorchester Grill	*"*	3	4	4
	Ormer Mayfair	*"*	4	4	2
	Corrigan's Mayfair	*British, Traditional*	3	3	3
	Sexy Fish	*Fish & seafood*	1	2	2
	Bocconcino Restaurant	*Italian*	2	2	2
	Novikov (Italian restaurant)	*"*	2	2	2
	Ikoyi	*West African*	4	2	2
	China Tang	*Chinese*	3	3	4
	Hakkasan Mayfair	*"*	4	2	3
	Benares	*Indian*	2	2	2
	Nobu	*Japanese*	3	2	2
	Nobu Berkeley	*"*	3	2	2
	Novikov (Asian restaurant)	*Pan-Asian*	3	2	4

£90+					
	Hush	*British, Modern*	2	2	3
	The Game Bird	*British, Traditional*	3	5	3
	Wiltons	*"*	4	5	4
	Bentley's	*Fish & seafood*	3	3	3
	Estiatorio Milos	*"*	3	2	4
	Sketch	*French*	1	2	3
	StreetXO	*International*	4	3	4
	Murano	*Italian*	4	5	3
	Goodman	*Steaks & grills*	4	3	3
	34 Mayfair	*"*	3	3	3
	Ruya	*Turkish*	3	3	3
	Ginza Onodera	*Japanese*	3	3	2

£80+					
	Colony Grill Room	*American*	2	2	3
	Gridiron	*British, Modern*	–	–	–
	Hide Ground	*"*	3	4	4
	Scott's	*Fish & seafood*	4	4	4
	Onima	*Fusion*	3	3	4
	The American Bar	*International*	2	4	3
	Cecconi's	*Italian*	2	2	4
	Chucs Dover Street	*"*	2	3	3
	Ristorante Frescobaldi	*"*	3	3	2
	Aquavit	*Scandinavian*	3	2	3
	Hawksmoor	*Steaks & grills*	4	3	3
	Rowley's	*"*	2	2	3
	Ella Canta	*Mexican/TexMex*	3	3	3
	Coya	*Peruvian*	4	3	4
	Indian Accent	*Indian*	5	4	2
	Jamavar	*"*	3	3	3
	Veeraswamy	*"*	3	3	3
	Roka	*Japanese*	5	4	4
	Sake No Hana	*"*	4	3	3

£70+					
	Le Caprice	*British, Modern*	2	4	4
	Galvin at the Athenaeum	"	1	2	2
	Kitty Fisher's	"	3	3	3
	Langan's Brasserie	"	2	2	4
	No. 5 Social	"	–	–	–
	Quaglino's	"	2	3	5
	Brown's Hotel	*British, Traditional*	3	4	4
	Black Roe	*Fish & seafood*	3	3	3
	Boudin Blanc	*French*	3	3	4
	Boulestin	"	2	2	2
	Emilia	*Italian*	4	4	3
	Sartoria	"	3	3	3
	Theo Randall	"	4	4	2
	The Guinea Grill	*Steaks & grills*	3	3	3
	Fortnum & Mason	*Afternoon tea*	3	4	4
	Momo	*Moroccan*	4	3	4
	Bombay Bustle	*Indian*	4	3	3
	Gymkhana	"	5	4	4
	Tamarind	"	3	4	2
	Lucky Cat	*Pan-Asian*	–	–	–
£60+	Bellamy's	*British, Modern*	3	4	4
	The Keeper's House	"	2	2	3
	The Punchbowl	"	3	3	4
	The Wolseley	"	2	3	5
	Fishworks	*Fish & seafood*	3	2	2
	Les Platanes	*French*	–	–	–
	Café Murano	*Italian*	2	2	2
	Franco's	"	3	4	4
	Pucci Mayfair	*Mediterranean*	3	3	3
	Sabor	*Spanish*	5	4	4
	Burger & Lobster	*Burgers, etc*	3	2	3
	Chisou	*Japanese*	4	4	2
	Sakagura	"	3	3	2
	Patara Mayfair	*Thai*	3	4	3
£50+	The Avenue	*American*	3	3	3
	The Windmill	*British, Traditional*	3	3	3
	Al Duca	*Italian*	2	2	2
	Il Vicolo	"	3	3	3
	maze Grill	*Steaks & grills*	2	2	2
	Delfino	*Pizza*	3	3	2
	Lucknow 49	*Indian*	4	4	3
	Titu	*Pan-Asian*	4	5	4
£40+	El Pirata	*Spanish*	2	3	3
	tibits	*Vegetarian*	3	2	3
	Shoryu Ramen	*Japanese*	3	2	2
	Yoshino	"	3	3	2
£35+	Rasa	*Indian, Southern*	3	4	2

Fitzrovia & Marylebone (Part of W1)

			Rating
£170+	Bubbledogs, Kitchen Table	British, Modern	4 4 4
£120+	Xier	British, Modern	4 3 4
	Texture	Scandinavian	5 4 3
£100+	The Chiltern Firehouse	American	1 1 3
	Pied À Terre	French	4 4 4
	Beast	Steaks & grills	2 2 2
	Hakkasan	Chinese	4 2 3
£90+	The Berners Tavern	British, Modern	2 1 4
	Roganic	"	5 4 2
	Roux at the Landau	"	4 5 4
	Locanda Locatelli	Italian	4 4 3
£80+	AOK Kitchen	British, Modern	2 2 4
	Portland	"	4 4 2
	Mere	East & Cent. European	4 5 4
	Clarette	French	3 3 3
	Les 110 de Taillevent	"	2 3 3
	Orrery	"	3 3 3
	Arros QD	Spanish	4 4 4
	Trishna	Indian	4 3 3
	Defune	Japanese	4 3 2
	Roka	"	5 4 4
£70+	Clipstone	British, Modern	4 4 3
	Roast	"	3 2 4
	Noizé	French	4 5 4
	28-50	"	3 2 2
	Yopo	Fusion	– – –
	Caffè Caldesi	Italian	3 2 3
	The Ninth London	Mediterranean	5 4 3
	Palm Court	Afternoon tea	3 3 4
	Lima	Peruvian	3 3 2
	The Bright Courtyard	Chinese	3 2 2
	Royal China Club	"	4 3 3
	Jikoni	Indian	3 3 4
	OOTY	Indian, Southern	5 4 3
	Dinings	Japanese	5 4 2
£60+	Brasserie of Light	British, Modern	2 2 4
	Vinoteca Seymour Place	"	2 2 2
	XR	"	3 3 2
	Fischer's	East & Cent. European	2 2 4
	Fancy Crab	Fish & seafood	3 3 2
	Fishworks	"	3 2 2
	Twist	Fusion	5 4 3
	Meraki	Greek	4 4 4
	Bernardi's	Italian	3 4 3
	Fucina	"	– – –
	Harry's Bar	"	2 2 3
	Blandford Comptoir	Mediterranean	3 3 3

	Mortimer House Kitchen	"	3	3	4
	ROVI	"	5	4	4
	The Harcourt	Scandinavian	3	4	4
	Lurra	Spanish	3	3	4
	Burger & Lobster	Burgers, etc	3	2	3
	Daylesford Organic	Sandwiches, cakes, etc	3	1	2
	Zoilo	Argentinian	4	4	3
	Pisqu	Peruvian	3	3	2
	Honey & Co	Middle Eastern	5	3	3
	Kyseri	Turkish	4	4	2
	The Greyhound Cafe	Thai	3	2	3
£50+	Bubbledogs	American	3	4	4
	Caravan	British, Modern	2	2	3
	The Ivy Café	"	1	1	3
	The Lore of the Land	"	3	3	4
	The Wigmore	British, Traditional	4	4	5
	Bonnie Gull	Fish & seafood	5	3	3
	The Wallace	French	2	3	5
	Carousel	Fusion	4	4	3
	Opso	Greek	3	3	3
	Foley's	International	4	4	2
	Briciole	Italian	3	3	2
	2 Veneti	"	3	3	2
	Riding House Café	Mediterranean	2	3	3
	Mac & Wild	Scottish	3	3	3
	Barrica	Spanish	3	3	3
	Donostia	"	4	4	3
	Ibérica	"	3	2	3
	Salt Yard	"	4	4	3
	Boxcar Butcher & Grill	Steaks & grills	4	4	3
	The Gate	Vegetarian	4	2	2
	Maroush	Lebanese	3	2	2
	Honey & Smoke	Middle Eastern	4	3	2
	Ishtar	Turkish	3	3	2
	Royal China	Chinese	3	1	2
	Flesh and Buns Fitzrovia	Japanese	2	3	3
	Laksamania	Malaysian	3	2	2
	Cocochan	Pan-Asian	3	2	2
£40+	Hoppers	Sri Lankan	4	3	3
	Passyunk Avenue	American	4	4	3
	Lantana Café	Australian	3	3	3
	The Long Bar	British, Modern	2	4	4
	La Fromagerie Café	International	3	4	3
	Circolo Popolare	Italian	–	–	–
	Made in Italy James St	"	4	2	3
	Rossopomodoro	"	2	2	2
	Vagabond Wines	Mediterranean	2	3	3
	Le Relais de Venise	Steaks & grills	3	3	3
	Santa Maria	Pizza	4	3	3
	Yalla Yalla	Lebanese	3	2	2
	Delamina	Middle Eastern	4	4	2
	Chettinad	Indian	4	3	2
	Roti Chai	"	4	3	3
	Bone Daddies	Japanese	3	3	3

	Sushiology by Atari-Ya	"	4 2 1
	Tonkotsu	"	3 3 2
	Bao & Bing	Taiwanese	3 3 4
£35+	MEATLiquor	Burgers, etc	3 3 3
	Golden Hind	Fish & chips	3 2 2
	Homeslice	Pizza	4 3 3
	Workshop Coffee	Sandwiches, cakes, etc	3 4 3
	Sanxia Renjia	Chinese	3 2 2
	Ragam	Indian	4 4 2
	Sagar	"	3 3 2
	Bao Fitzrovia	Taiwanese	4 3 3
£30+	Ethos	Vegetarian	4 2 3
	Tommi's Burger Joint	Burgers, etc	3 4 3
	Sushi Atelier	Japanese	5 4 3
	Bibimbap Soho	Korean	3 3 2
£25+	Patty and Bun	Burgers, etc	4 3 3
£15+	Icco Pizza	Italian	4 2 1
	Kaffeine	Sandwiches, cakes, etc	3 5 4
	Patogh	Middle Eastern	4 3 2

Belgravia, Pimlico, Victoria & Westminster (SW1, except St James's)

£130+	Celeste at The Lanesborough	French	2 2 4
£120+	Marcus	British, Modern	3 3 3
	Dinner	British, Traditional	2 2 2
£110+	Pétrus	French	3 4 3
£100+	Siren	Fish & seafood	– – –
	Rib Room	Steaks & grills	3 2 3
	Imperial Treasure	Chinese	2 2 2
£90+	Kerridge's Bar & Grill	British, Modern	3 3 4
	Roux at Parliament Square	"	4 4 3
	The Dining Room	British, Traditional	3 5 4
	Sette	Italian	– – –
	Zafferano	"	3 2 2
	The Collins Room	Afternoon tea	2 3 4
	Hunan	Chinese	4 2 1
	The Cinnamon Club	Indian	3 2 3
£80+	Enoteca Turi	Italian	3 4 2
	Olivocarne	"	3 2 2
	Santini	"	2 3 3
	Ametsa	Spanish	3 3 2
	The Crystal Moon Lounge	Afternoon tea	2 4 4
	Mr Chow	Chinese	2 1 2
	Amaya	Indian	5 3 3

271

	Chutney Mary	"	**4**	**4**	**3**

£70+	45 Jermyn Street	British, Modern	**3**	**3**	**4**
	Hans' Bar & Grill	"	**2**	**3**	**3**
	The Rex Whistler Restaurant	"	**3**	**3**	**5**
	Wild Honey St James	"	–	–	–
	Olivomare	Fish & seafood	**3**	**3**	**2**
	Bar Boulud	French	**3**	**3**	**3**
	Colbert	"	**2**	**2**	**4**
	Olivo	Italian	**3**	**3**	**2**
	Boisdale of Belgravia	Scottish	**3**	**2**	**3**
	M Restaurant Victoria Street	Steaks & grills	**2**	**2**	**2**
	Drawing Room, Dukes	Afternoon tea	–	–	–
	Kahani	Indian	**5**	**4**	**3**
	Quilon	Indian, Southern	**5**	**5**	**2**

£60+	The Alfred Tennyson	British, Modern	**3**	**3**	**3**
	Aster Restaurant	"	**2**	**2**	**2**
	Daylesford Organic	"	**3**	**1**	**2**
	Lorne	"	**5**	**5**	**3**
	The Orange	"	**3**	**2**	**3**
	Rail House Café	"	**2**	**2**	**2**
	Scully	"	**5**	**4**	**3**
	The Thomas Cubitt	"	**3**	**3**	**3**
	La Poule au Pot	French	**3**	**3**	**5**
	Cambridge Street	International	**3**	**3**	**4**
	Caraffini	Italian	**3**	**5**	**4**
	Il Convivio	"	**3**	**4**	**3**
	Hai Cenato	"	**3**	**2**	**2**
	Osteria Dell'Angolo	"	**3**	**3**	**2**
	Quirinale	"	**3**	**4**	**3**
	Sale e Pepe	"	**3**	**4**	**3**
	San Carlo	"	**3**	**4**	**4**
	Signor Sassi	"	**3**	**3**	**3**
	Zelman Meats	Steaks & grills	**3**	**3**	**3**
	Burger & Lobster	Burgers, etc	**3**	**2**	**3**
	Oliveto	Pizza	**4**	**3**	**2**
	Abd El Wahab	Lebanese	**3**	**3**	**2**
	Ken Lo's Memories	Chinese	**3**	**2**	**2**
	Sticks'n'Sushi	Japanese	**3**	**3**	**3**
	Sumosan Twiga	"	**2**	**2**	**2**
	Salloos	Pakistani	**3**	**2**	**3**

£50+	Granger & Co	Australian	**3**	**2**	**3**
	The Botanist	British, Modern	**2**	**2**	**2**
	The Other Naughty Piglet	"	**4**	**3**	**2**
	Rochelle Canteen at the ICA	"	**4**	**4**	**2**
	Ottolenghi	Mediterranean	**3**	**2**	**2**
	About Thyme	Spanish	**3**	**4**	**3**
	Ibérica	"	**3**	**2**	**3**
	Wulf & Lamb	Vegetarian	**4**	**2**	**2**
	Seafresh	Fish & chips	**3**	**2**	**2**
	O'ver	Pizza	**4**	**3**	**3**
	Kazan	Turkish	**3**	**3**	**2**
	A Wong	Chinese	**5**	**5**	**3**
	Farzi Cafe	Indian	**4**	**4**	**4**

£40+	The Jones Family Kitchen	British, Modern	4 3 3
	The Vincent Rooms	"	3 3 2
	Grumbles	International	3 3 4
	Gustoso	Italian	3 3 3
	Tozi	"	3 3 3
	Vagabond Wines	Mediterranean	2 3 3
	Goya	Spanish	3 2 3
	Cyprus Mangal	Turkish	4 3 2
	Bone Daddies	Japanese	3 3 3
	Machiya	"	3 2 2
£35+	Market Hall Victoria	International	4 2 2
	Kanada-Ya	Japanese	5 3 2
	Sri Suwoon	Thai	4 4 3
£30+	Shake Shack	Burgers, etc	3 2 2
£20+	Bleecker Burger	Burgers, etc	5 2 1
£15+	Regency Cafe	British, Traditional	3 3 5

WEST

Chelsea, South Kensington, Kensington, Earl's Court & Fulham (SW3, SW5, SW6, SW7, SW10 & W8)

£160+	Gordon Ramsay	*French*	3 3 2
£130+	Bibendum	*French*	3 3 4
£110+	The Five Fields	*British, Modern*	5 5 4
£90+	Restaurant at The Capital	*Fish & seafood*	– – –
	Yashin Ocean House	*Japanese*	3 2 2
£80+	Bluebird	*British, Modern*	2 3 4
	Elystan Street	"	5 5 3
	Launceston Place	"	4 4 4
	No. Fifty Cheyne	"	3 4 4
	Le Colombier	*French*	3 4 3
	Chucs	*Italian*	2 3 3
	Scalini	"	2 3 3
	Hawksmoor Knightsbridge	*Steaks & grills*	4 3 3
	Min Jiang	*Chinese*	3 3 5
	Akira at Japan House	*Japanese*	2 3 3
	Koji	"	3 3 4
	Zuma	"	5 3 5
£70+	Clarke's	*British, Modern*	4 5 4
	Harwood Arms	"	4 3 3
	Kitchen W8	"	4 4 3
	Medlar	"	4 4 3
	Belvedere Restaurant	*French*	2 4 5
	Daphne's	*Italian*	2 3 4
	Frantoio	"	3 4 4
	Lucio	"	3 3 2
	Manicomio	"	3 2 3
	Stecca	"	2 2 2
	Bombay Brasserie	*Indian*	3 3 2
	Zaika of Kensington	*Indian, Southern*	4 3 3
	Dinings	*Japanese*	5 4 2
£60+	Big Easy	*American*	3 2 3
	Brinkley's	*British, Modern*	2 2 3
	Daylesford Organic	"	3 1 2
	The Enterprise	"	2 3 4
	Harlequin	"	4 4 4
	The Ivy Chelsea Garden	"	2 2 4
	Park Terrace Restaurant	"	2 3 3
	Tom's Kitchen	"	2 2 3
	Maggie Jones's	*British, Traditional*	2 3 4
	The Sea	*Fish & seafood*	4 4 4
	Wright Brothers	"	3 3 3
	Mazi	*Greek*	4 4 3
	Suzi Tros	"	– – –

Gallery Mess	International	2	3	3
The Kensington Wine Rooms	"	2	3	3
Enoteca Rosso	Italian	2	2	3
La Famiglia	"	2	3	4
Harry's Dolce Vita	"	3	3	5
La Mia Mamma	"	3	3	3
Il Portico	"	3	5	4
Ziani's	"	2	3	2
Cambio de Tercio	Spanish	4	3	3
Sophie's Steakhouse	Steaks & grills	2	2	3
Geales	Fish & chips	2	2	2
Chicama	Peruvian	4	2	4
Good Earth	Chinese	3	3	2
Romulo Café	Filipino	3	4	3
Kutir	Indian	5	4	4
Chisou	Japanese	4	4	2
Sticks 'n' Sushi	"	3	3	3
Zheng	Malaysian	4	3	2
Patara	Thai	3	4	3
£50+	The Abingdon	British, Modern	3	3	4
	Brook House	"	3	2	4
	The Builders Arms	"	–	–	–
	The Cross Keys	"	3	4	4
	maze Grill	"	2	2	2
	Rabbit	"	3	2	3
	The Sands End	"	3	3	4
	The Shed	"	3	3	3
	Bumpkin	British, Traditional	2	2	3
	Bibendum Oyster Bar	Fish & seafood	3	3	4
	Bistro Mirey	Fusion	4	3	3
	The Admiral Codrington	International	3	3	3
	maze Grill	"	2	2	2
	Polpo	Italian	1	2	2
	Riccardo's	"	3	2	2
	San Pietro	"	3	2	2
	Daquise	Polish	2	2	2
	Ognisko Restaurant	"	3	4	5
	Casa Brindisa	Spanish	3	3	4
	Tendido Cero	"	3	3	4
	Pizzicotto	Pizza	4	5	3
	Maroush	Lebanese	3	2	2
	Royal China	Chinese	3	1	2
	Pure Indian Cooking	Indian	3	4	2
	E&O Chelsea	Pan-Asian	3	3	3
	Sukho Fine Thai Cuisine	Thai	5	5	3
	Go-Viet	Vietnamese	4	3	2
£40+	Bodean's	American	2	2	2
	VQ	British, Modern	2	3	3
	Aglio e Olio	Italian	3	3	2
	Chelsea Cellar	"	4	4	4
	Da Mario	"	3	3	3
	Made in Italy	"	4	2	3
	Nuovi Sapori	"	3	3	3
	The Atlas	Mediterranean	4	4	4

	Haché	*Steaks & grills*	3 4 2
	Macellaio RC	"	4 3 3
	Rocca Di Papa	*Pizza*	3 3 4
	Rossopomodoro	"	2 2 2
	Lupita West	*Mexican/TexMex*	3 2 2
	Melabes	*Middle Eastern*	3 2 2
	Best Mangal	*Turkish*	4 3 2
	Dishoom	*Indian*	3 4 5
	Flora Indica	"	4 4 4
	Malabar	"	3 3 2
	Noor Jahan	"	3 4 3
	Thali	"	4 3 2
	Bone Daddies	*Japanese*	3 3 3
	Oka	"	4 3 2
	Suksan	*Thai*	3 3 2
£35+	Churchill Arms	*British, Traditional*	3 2 5
	Mona Lisa	*International*	3 3 2
	Pappa Ciccia	*Italian*	3 3 2
	Ceru	*Middle Eastern*	4 3 4
	Addie's Thai Café	*Thai*	4 3 2
£30+	Eat Tokyo	*Japanese*	3 2 2
	Phat Phuc	*Vietnamese*	3 3 2
£25+	Stick & Bowl	*Chinese*	3 2 1
£10+	Jollibee	*Chicken*	1 2 1

Notting Hill, Holland Park, Bayswater, North Kensington & Maida Vale (W2, W9, W10, W11)

£150+	The Ledbury	*British, Modern*	5 5 4
£120+	Core by Clare Smyth	*British, Modern*	5 4 4
£80+	104 Restaurant	*British, Modern*	4 3 3
	Chucs Westbourne Grove	*Italian*	2 3 3
	Caractère	*Mediterranean*	5 5 4
£70+	108 Garage	*British, Modern*	4 3 2
	London Shell Co.	*Fish & seafood*	3 3 5
	Angelus	*French*	3 4 2
£60+	Daylesford Organic	*British, Modern*	3 1 2
	The Frontline Club	"	2 2 4
	Gold	"	– – –
	The Hero of Maida	"	2 2 3
	The Ladbroke Arms	"	3 3 3
	Six Portland Road	"	4 4 3
	The Summerhouse	*Fish & seafood*	2 3 5
	Cepages	*French*	4 3 4
	The Cow	*Irish*	3 3 4
	Assaggi	*Italian*	3 3 1

	Assaggi Bar & Pizzeria	"	3 3 3	
	Edera	"	3 3 3	
	Mediterraneo	"	3 2 3	
	The Oak W2	"	3 3 4	
	Osteria Basilico	"	4 3 2	
	Farmacy	Vegetarian	4 4 3	
	Flat Three	Japanese	3 3 3	
	Maguro	"	4 3 2	
	Uli	Pan-Asian	3 3 4	
£50+	Electric Diner	American	2 2 3	
	Granger & Co	Australian	3 2 3	
	Julie's	British, Modern	– – –	
	Paradise, Kensal Green	"	2 2 5	
	Pomona's	"	3 4 4	
	7 Saints	"	4 4 4	
	Hereford Road	British, Traditional	4 4 3	
	Snaps & Rye	Danish	4 4 3	
	Bucket	Fish & seafood	3 4 3	
	Ida	Italian	3 4 3	
	Polpo	"	1 2 2	
	Portobello Ristorante	"	3 3 3	
	Ottolenghi	Mediterranean	3 2 2	
	Orasay	Scottish	4 4 4	
	Lockhouse	Burgers, etc	3 3 3	
	Pizza East Portobello	Pizza	3 2 4	
	Andina Picanteria	Peruvian	4 3 3	
	Maroush	Lebanese	3 2 2	
	Kateh	Persian	4 3 2	
	Pearl Liang	Chinese	4 2 2	
	Royal China	"	3 1 2	
	E&O	Pan-Asian	3 3 3	
£40+	VQ	British, Modern	2 3 3	
	The Chipping Forecast	Fish & seafood	3 3 3	
	Raoul's Café	Mediterranean	3 2 4	
	Taqueria	Mexican/TexMex	3 2 3	
	The Cedar Restaurant	Lebanese	3 3 2	
	Four Seasons	Chinese	4 1 1	
	Mandarin Kitchen	"	4 3 1	
	Bombay Palace	Indian	5 4 3	
	Noor Jahan	"	3 4 3	
	Tonkotsu	Japanese	3 3 2	
	The Heron	Thai	4 3 1	
	MAM	Vietnamese	4 4 3	
£35+	MEATliquor	Burgers, etc	3 3 3	
	Workshop Coffee	Sandwiches, cakes, etc	3 4 3	
£30+	Gold Mine	Chinese	4 2 2	
£25+	Tab X Tab	British, Modern	5 4 4	
	Patty and Bun	Burgers, etc	4 3 3	
	Fez Mangal	Turkish	5 4 3	
£10+	Lisboa Pâtisserie	Sandwiches, cakes, etc	3 2 3	

277

Hammersmith, Shepherd's Bush, Olympia, Chiswick, Brentford & Ealing (W4, W5, W6, W12, W13, W14, TW8)

£180+	Endo at Rotunda	Japanese	5 5 4
£100+	The River Café	Italian	3 3 3
£80+	La Trompette	French	5 4 3
£70+	Villa Di Geggiano	Italian	3 4 4
£60+	The Anglesea Arms	British, Modern	4 4 4
	Duke of Sussex	"	2 2 3
	Vinoteca	"	2 2 2
	Michael Nadra	French	4 3 2
	Le Vacherin	"	3 3 3
	Cibo	Italian	4 5 3
	The Oak W12	"	3 3 4
	Popeseye	Steaks & grills	4 3 2
	Little Bird Chiswick	Pan-Asian	3 3 4
£50+	Brackenbury Wine Rooms	British, Modern	2 3 3
	The Carpenter's Arms	"	3 3 3
	Charlotte's W4	"	3 2 3
	City Barge	"	3 3 3
	The Colton Arms	"	2 3 4
	The Dartmouth Castle	"	3 4 4
	Eat 17 Hammersmith	"	3 3 3
	The Havelock Tavern	"	3 2 3
	The Princess Victoria	"	3 3 3
	The Hampshire Hog	British, Traditional	2 3 3
	Albertine	French	3 3 5
	Annie's	International	3 4 4
	L'Amorosa	Italian	4 4 3
	Pentolina	"	4 5 3
	Tarantella Ristorante Pizzeria	"	3 3 3
	Cumberland Arms	Mediterranean	3 3 3
	The Swan	"	3 3 4
	The Crown	"	3 3 4
	The Gate	Vegetarian	4 2 2
	The Bird in Hand	Pizza	4 3 4
	Shikumen	Chinese	4 2 2
	Indian Zing	Indian	4 3 2
£40+	222 Veggie Vegan	Vegan	4 3 2
	High Road Brasserie	British, Modern	2 3 3
	The Pear Tree	"	3 4 4
	Soane's Kitchen	"	2 2 3
	Le Petit Citron	French	3 2 3
	The Andover Arms	International	3 4 4
	Pasta Remoli	Italian	3 3 3
	Santa Maria	Pizza	4 3 3
	Angie's Little Food Shop	Sandwiches, cakes, etc	3 2 2
	Best Mangal	Turkish	4 3 2
	North China	Chinese	4 3 3

	Potli	*Indian*	4	4	3
	Atari-Ya	*Japanese*	4	2	1
	Kiraku	"	4	3	2
	Tonkotsu	"	3	3	2
	Yoshi Sushi	"	3	4	2
£35+	Homeslice	*Pizza*	4	3	3
	Oro Di Napoli	"	4	4	3
	Zia Lucia	"	4	4	3
	Sagar	*Indian*	3	3	2
	Shilpa	*Indian, Southern*	5	3	1
	Hare & Tortoise	*Pan-Asian*	3	3	2
	101 Thai Kitchen	*Thai*	5	2	2
	Saigon Saigon	*Vietnamese*	3	2	3
£30+	Adams Café	*Moroccan*	3	5	3
	Abu Zaad	*Syrian*	3	3	2
	Anarkali	*Indian*	3	2	2
	Eat Tokyo	*Japanese*	3	2	2
£25+	Kerbisher & Malt	*Fish & chips*	3	2	2
	Alounak	*Persian*	3	3	3
£20+	Tamp Coffee	*Sandwiches, cakes, etc*	3	3	3
£5+	Bears Ice Cream	*Ice cream*	–	–	–

Hampstead, West Hampstead, St John's Wood, Regent's Park, Kilburn & Camden Town (NW postcodes)

£80+	The Landmark	British, Modern	2 3 5

£70+	The Booking Office	British, Modern	2 1 4
	The Gilbert Scott	British, Traditional	3 2 4
	L'Aventure	French	3 4 5
	Tish	Kosher	3 4 4
	Kaifeng	Chinese	3 2 2

£60+	Bradley's	British, Modern	2 2 2
	Odette's	"	4 4 3
	Michael Nadra	French	4 3 2
	Oslo Court	"	3 5 4
	Bull & Last	International	3 3 3
	Morso	Italian	3 4 3
	The Rising Sun	"	3 3 3
	Villa Bianca	"	2 2 2
	Delicatessen	Middle Eastern	3 2 2
	Good Earth	Chinese	3 3 2
	Phoenix Palace	"	3 2 2
	Patara	Thai	3 4 3

£50+	The Clifton	British, Modern	3 4 4
	Ham	"	3 2 3
	The Ivy Café	"	1 1 3
	Parlour Kensal	"	3 4 4
	Searcys St Pancras Grand	"	1 2 3
	The Wells Tavern	"	3 3 4
	The Wet Fish Café	"	3 3 4
	Holly Bush	British, Traditional	2 2 3
	York & Albany	"	2 2 2
	Lemonia	Greek	1 4 4
	The Savannah	International	– – –
	Soutine	"	3 3 4
	La Collina	Italian	2 3 2
	28 Church Row	Spanish	4 4 4
	The Gate	Vegetarian	4 2 2
	Manna	"	2 2 2
	The Sea Shell	Fish & chips	3 2 2
	Pizza East	Pizza	3 2 4
	Crocker's Folly	Lebanese	3 3 4
	Bonoo	Indian	4 4 3
	Singapore Garden	Malaysian	4 4 2

£40+	VQ Euston	British, Modern	2 3 3
	Lure	Fish & seafood	3 4 3
	Authentique Epicerie & Bar	French	3 4 3
	La Ferme	"	3 3 3
	Anima e Cuore	Italian	5 5 2
	L'Artista	"	3 3 3

	Giacomo's	"	3	3	2
	Quartieri	"	4	3	3
	El Parador	Spanish	3	3	3
	Beef & Brew	Steaks & grills	3	4	3
	Haché	"	3	4	2
	Mildreds	Vegetarian	3	3	3
	Purezza	"	4	3	3
	Harry Morgan's	Burgers, etc	3	3	3
	Poppies Camden	Fish & chips	3	3	3
	L' Antica Pizzeria	Pizza	4	4	3
	L'Antica Pizzeria da Michele	"	3	2	3
	Rossopomodoro	"	2	2	2
	Greenberry Café	Sandwiches, cakes, etc	3	3	4
	The Cedar Restaurant	Lebanese	3	3	2
	Skewd Kitchen	Turkish	4	3	3
	Great Nepalese	Indian	3	3	2
	KoolCha	"	–	–	–
	Paradise Hampstead	"	4	5	4
	Saravanaa Bhavan	"	4	3	2
	Atari-Ya	Japanese	4	2	1
	Jin Kichi	"	5	4	3
	Oka	"	4	3	2
	Sushi Masa	"	3	3	2
	The Petite Coree	Korean	4	3	2
	Bang Bang Oriental	Pan-Asian	2	2	3
£35+	Fiddie's Italian Kitchen	Italian	3	3	2
	Nautilus	Fish & chips	4	4	1
	Sacro Cuore	Pizza	4	3	2
	Kuku Riku	Chicken	–	–	–
	Guglee	Indian	3	3	2
	Vijay	"	4	3	1
	Anjanaas	Indian, Southern	4	2	2
£30+	Shake Shack	Burgers, etc	3	2	2
	Ravi Shankar	Indian	3	2	2
	Asakusa	Japanese	5	2	2
	Eat Tokyo	"	3	2	2
£25+	Ali Baba	Egyptian	3	2	2
	Ariana II	Afghani	3	3	2
	Diwana Bhel-Poori House	Indian	3	2	1
	Sakonis	"	3	2	1
	Roti King	Malaysian	5	2	1
£20+	Balady	Middle Eastern	3	4	2
	Chutneys	Indian	3	2	2
£15+	Icco Pizza	Pizza	4	2	1
	E Mono	Turkish	4	2	1
£10+	Ginger & White Hampstead	Sandwiches, cakes, etc	3	3	3

Hoxton, Islington, Highgate, Crouch End, Stoke Newington, Finsbury Park, Muswell Hill & Finchley (N postcodes)

£90+	Cub	British, Modern	4	4	3
£70+	The Frog Hoxton	British, Modern	5	5	3
	Plum + Spilt Milk	"	2	3	3
	German Gymnasium	German	2	2	4
	Salut	International	4	3	3
£60+	Frederick's	British, Modern	3	4	5
	Jolene	"	3	2	3
	The Lighterman	"	3	2	4
	Perilla	"	4	4	3
	Prawn on the Lawn	Fish & seafood	4	3	2
	Bistro Aix	French	2	2	3
	Radici	Italian	2	2	2
	Trullo	"	3	3	3
	Vinoteca	Mediterranean	2	2	2
	Parrillan	Spanish	3	4	4
	Casa Pastór & Plaza Pastór	Mexican/TexMex	3	2	3
£50+	Granger & Co	Australian	3	2	3
	The Bull	British, Modern	3	4	3
	Caravan King's Cross	"	2	2	3
	The Drapers Arms	"	3	3	4
	Granary Square Brasserie	"	2	1	3
	Humble Grape	"	3	4	3
	Jones & Sons	"	3	4	3
	Moio	"	3	3	3
	Oldroyd	"	4	3	2
	Pig & Butcher	"	3	4	3
	The Red Lion & Sun	"	3	3	3
	Rotunda Bar & Restaurant	"	3	3	4
	Season Kitchen	"	3	3	2
	Spiritland	"	3	3	5
	Top Cuvee	"	4	4	3
	Westerns Laundry	"	3	2	2
	St Johns	British, Traditional	3	2	3
	Petit Pois Bistro	French	4	3	3
	Sardine	"	4	3	3
	Table Du Marche	"	3	3	2
	The Good Egg	Fusion	4	3	4
	Banners	International	2	3	4
	Primeur	"	3	3	3
	Il Guscio	Italian	3	4	3
	Osteria Tufo	"	4	3	2
	Terra Rossa	"	3	4	2
	Coal Office	Mediterranean	3	4	4
	Ottolenghi	"	3	2	2
	Bar Esteban	Spanish	3	4	3
	Barrafina	"	5	5	5
	Camino King's Cross	"	2	2	2
	La Lluna	"	3	3	2
	Smokehouse Islington	Steaks & grills	3	3	3

	Black Axe Mangal	*Turkish*	4	3	3
	Yipin China	*Chinese*	4	2	1
	Zaffrani	*Indian*	3	3	2
£40+	Breakfast Club Hoxton	*American*	3	3	3
	Wander	*Australian*	4	4	3
	Chriskitch	*British, Modern*	4	3	3
	Hicce	*"*	2	3	4
	Linden Stores	*"*	3	3	2
	1251	*"*	3	3	3
	Snooty Fox	*British, Traditional*	3	2	3
	Kipferl	*East & Cent. European*	3	2	3
	Le Sacré-Coeur	*French*	3	2	3
	Vrisaki	*Greek*	3	3	2
	Aleion	*International*	3	3	3
	La Fromagerie	*"*	3	4	3
	500	*Italian*	3	3	3
	Pasta Remoli	*"*	3	3	3
	Lady Mildmay	*Mediterranean*	3	3	3
	Café del Parc	*Spanish*	5	5	3
	Trangallan	*"*	4	4	3
	Vermuteria	*"*	2	2	3
	Beef & Brew	*Steaks & grills*	3	4	3
	Mildreds	*Vegetarian*	3	3	3
	Rossopomodoro	*Pizza*	2	2	2
	Sweet Thursday	*"*	3	2	2
	Yard Sale Pizza	*"*	4	3	2
	Chick 'n' Sours	*Chicken*	4	3	3
	Plaquemine Lock	*Cajun/creole*	2	4	3
	Gallipoli	*Turkish*	2	3	3
	Sumak	*"*	4	4	2
	Kaki	*Chinese*	3	2	1
	Dishoom	*Indian*	3	4	5
	Farang	*Thai*	4	4	2
	Supawan	*"*	4	3	2
£35+	Lina Stores	*Italian*	4	4	4
	Passione e Tradizione	*"*	3	2	2
	Pizzeria Pappagone	*"*	3	3	3
	Via Emilia	*"*	3	2	2
	Cut + Grind	*Burgers, etc*	3	3	3
	MEATLiquor Islington	*"*	3	3	3
	Olympus Fish	*Fish & chips*	3	3	2
	Toff's	*"*	3	3	2
	Sacro Cuore	*Pizza*	4	3	2
	Zia Lucia	*"*	4	4	3
	Fink's Salt and Sweet	*Sandwiches, cakes, etc*	3	4	3
	Max's Sandwich Shop	*"*	5	4	3
	Gem	*Turkish*	3	3	2
	Indian Rasoi	*Indian*	3	2	2
	Jashan	*"*	4	4	2
	Rasa	*Indian, Southern*	3	4	2
	Kanada-Ya	*Japanese*	5	3	2
	Dotori	*Korean*	4	3	2
	Sambal Shiok	*Malaysian*	3	3	1
	CôBa	*Vietnamese*	4	3	2

£30+	Sunday	British, Modern	4 3 3
	Two Brothers	Fish & seafood	3 2 2
	Le Mercury	French	2 2 3
	Flat Iron	Steaks & grills	4 4 4
	MEATmission	Burgers, etc	3 3 4
	BabaBoom	Middle Eastern	3 2 2
	Gökyüzü	Turkish	2 2 2
	Xi'an Impression	Chinese	5 2 1
	Shahi Pakwaan	Indian	4 4 3
£25+	EartH Kitchen	British, Modern	3 2 2
	Afghan Kitchen	Afghani	3 3 2
	Delhi Grill	Indian	3 3 2
£20+	Piebury Corner	British, Traditional	3 2 2

SOUTH

South Bank (SE1)

£120+	Story	British, Modern	3 3 3
£110+	Aqua Shard	British, Modern	1 1 4
£100+	Oblix	British, Modern	2 2 4
	Oxo Tower	"	1 1 1
	TING	International	2 2 4
	Hutong	Chinese	2 2 5
£80+	Hawksmoor	Steaks & grills	4 3 3
	Duddell's	Chinese, Dim sum	3 2 3
£70+	Oxo Tower	British, Modern	1 1 3
	Sea Containers	"	2 3 3
	Skylon	"	2 3 4
	Butlers Wharf Chop House	British, Traditional	3 3 4
	Roast	"	3 2 4
	Le Pont de la Tour	French	2 2 3
£60+	Blueprint Café	British, Modern	3 3 4
	The Ivy Tower Bridge	"	2 2 4
	The Swan at the Globe	"	3 3 4
	Tom Simmons	"	3 3 2
	Union Street Café	"	2 2 2
	Applebee's Fish	Fish & seafood	4 2 2
	fish!	"	4 2 2
	Wright Brothers	"	3 3 3
	Vivat Bacchus	International	3 3 2
	La Barca	Italian	3 3 3
	Baltic	Polish	3 3 4
	LOBOS Meat & Tapas	Spanish	4 3 3
	Pizarro	"	4 3 3
	Tapas Brindisa	"	3 2 2
	Pique Nique	Chicken	3 2 3
	Santo Remedio	Mexican/TexMex	3 3 3
	Rabot 1745	Afro-Caribbean	2 3 2
	Bala Baya	Middle Eastern	3 2 2
£50+	The Anchor & Hope	British, Modern	4 3 2
	Caravan Bankside	"	2 2 3
	Elliot's Café	"	4 4 4
	40 Maltby Street	"	4 4 4
	The Garrison	"	3 3 3
	House Restaurant	"	2 3 2
	Lupins	"	4 3 2
	Menier Chocolate Factory	"	2 2 3
	Native	"	3 3 2
	Casse-Croute	French	4 4 4
	Spiritland	Fusion	3 3 5
	Arthur Hooper's	International	3 3 3
	Bar Douro	Portuguese	4 4 4

	Camino Bankside	*Spanish*	2	2	2
	José	"	5	4	5
	Meson don Felipe	"	2	2	3
	Mimo	"	–	–	–
	The Coal Shed	*Steaks & grills*	3	3	3
	O'ver	*Pizza*	4	3	3
	London Grind	*Sandwiches, cakes, etc*	3	4	4
	Paladar	*South American*	4	3	3
	Arabica Bar and Kitchen	*Lebanese*	3	4	3
	Sticky Mango at RSJ	*Pan-Asian*	2	2	2
	Champor-Champor	*Thai*	3	3	2
£40+	Lantana London Bridge	*Australian*	3	3	3
	The Garden Cafe	*British, Modern*	3	2	3
	The Green Room	"	2	2	2
	Hello Darling	"	2	3	3
	The Table	"	3	3	2
	Tate Modern	"	2	2	4
	Boro Bistro	*French*	2	3	3
	Flour & Grape	*Italian*	4	3	3
	Macellaio RC	"	4	3	3
	Casa do Frango	*Portuguese*	3	4	4
	Mar I Terra	*Spanish*	2	3	3
	tibits	*Vegetarian*	3	2	3
	El Pastór	*Mexican/TexMex*	4	3	4
	Tas Pide	*Turkish*	2	3	4
	Est India	*Indian*	3	3	3
	Gunpowder	"	4	3	3
	Tonkotsu Bankside	*Japanese*	3	3	2
	Kin and Deum	*Thai*	5	2	3
£35+	BOB's Lobster	*Fish & seafood*	3	4	3
	Bao Borough	*Taiwanese*	4	3	3
£30+	Flat Iron	*Steaks & grills*	4	4	4
£25+	Mercato Metropolitano	*Italian*	4	2	3
	Padella	"	5	4	3
	Patty and Bun	*Burgers, etc*	4	3	3
	Masters Super Fish	*Fish & chips*	3	2	1
£5+	Monmouth Coffee Company	*Sandwiches, cakes, etc*	3	5	4
	The Watch House	"	4	2	4

Greenwich, Lewisham, Dulwich & Blackheath
(All SE postcodes, except SE1)

£60+	Craft London	*British, Modern*	4	4	3
	Llewelyn's	"	3	2	2
	Rivington Grill	"	2	2	2
	Brasserie Toulouse-Lautrec	*French*	–	–	–
	Sticks'n'Sushi	*Japanese*	3	3	3

£50+	The Camberwell Arms	*British, Modern*	5	3	3
	The Crooked Well	"	3	3	3
	Levan	"	5	5	4
	Louie Louie	"	3	2	3
	The Rosendale	"	3	3	3
	Terroirs	"	2	2	3
	Peckham Bazaar	*Greek*	3	3	3
	Con Gusto	*Italian*	3	4	4
	Forza Win	"	4	4	3
	Luciano's	"	4	3	2
	Coal Rooms	*Steaks & grills*	4	4	3
	Kudu	*South African*	4	4	4
	Babur	*Indian*	5	5	4
	Kennington Tandoori	"	3	4	3
	Yama Momo	*Japanese*	3	2	3
£40+	Babette	*British, Modern*	3	3	3
	Black Prince	"	3	3	2
	Catford Constitutional Club	"	3	3	4
	The Guildford Arms	"	3	4	3
	Sparrow	"	3	3	2
	Next Door	*Fish & seafood*	4	3	2
	Brookmill	*International*	2	3	3
	The Yellow House	"	3	4	3
	Artusi	*Italian*	4	3	2
	Marcella	"	3	3	3
	Le Querce	"	4	3	3
	Mamma Dough	*Pizza*	3	3	3
	Rocca Di Papa	"	3	3	4
	Theo's	"	4	4	2
	Zero Degrees	"	3	3	3
	Dragon Castle	*Chinese*	4	3	3
	Ganapati	*Indian*	4	4	3
	Bone Daddies	*Japanese*	3	3	3
	The Begging Bowl	*Thai*	4	3	2
	Bánh Bánh	*Vietnamese*	3	3	2
£35+	MEATliquor ED	*Burgers, etc*	3	3	3
	Olley's	*Fish & chips*	3	3	2
	FM Mangal	*Turkish*	3	4	2
	Sanxia Renjia	*Chinese*	3	2	2
	Everest Inn	*Indian*	3	3	3
	Mr Bao	*Taiwanese*	5	3	3
£30+	500 Degrees	*Pizza*	3	2	2
	Zeret	*Ethiopian*	4	4	3
	Zaibatsu	*Japanese*	4	4	2
£25+	The Lido Café	*British, Modern*	3	3	4
	Goddards At Greenwich	*British, Traditional*	3	4	3
	400 Rabbits	*Pizza*	4	3	2
	Café East	*Vietnamese*	5	2	2
£20+	Silk Road	*Chinese*	5	2	2
	Paranhodu	*Korean*	3	4	2

£15+	Peckham Levels	*International*	– – –
£5+	Kappacasein	*Sandwiches, cakes, etc*	4 3 2

Battersea, Brixton, Clapham, Wandsworth
Barnes, Putney & Wimbledon
(All SW postcodes south of the river)

£80+	Chez Bruce	*British, Modern*	5 5 4
£70+	Hatched	*British, Modern*	5 4 2
	Trinity	"	5 5 4
	Darby's	*Irish*	4 4 4
£60+	Black Radish	*British, Modern*	4 4 3
	Brunswick House Café	"	3 2 5
	Cannizaro House	"	1 1 3
	Home SW15	"	3 3 2
	The Oak SW11	"	3 3 4
	Trinity Upstairs	"	5 4 4
	Fox & Grapes	*British, Traditional*	3 2 4
	Rick Stein	*Fish & seafood*	3 3 4
	Wright Brothers	"	3 3 3
	Bistro Vadouvan	*French*	4 4 3
	Sinabro	"	3 3 3
	The White Onion	"	3 4 2
	London House	*International*	2 2 2
	Fiume	*Italian*	2 2 4
	Riva	"	4 4 1
	Good Earth	*Chinese*	3 3 2
	Sticks'n'Sushi	*Japanese*	3 3 3
	Little Bird Battersea	*Pan-Asian*	3 3 4
	Patara	*Thai*	3 4 3
£50+	The Avalon	*British, Modern*	3 4 4
	Bistro Union	"	3 2 2
	The Brown Dog	"	3 3 3
	The Dairy	"	5 4 5
	Earl Spencer	"	3 2 3
	Hood	"	4 3 3
	Humble Grape	"	3 4 3
	The Ivy Café	"	1 1 3
	Lamberts	"	4 5 4
	Manuka Kitchen	"	3 3 3
	Nutbourne	"	2 2 3
	Olympic	"	2 2 3
	Salon Brixton	"	4 4 3
	The Victoria	"	2 2 3
	Canton Arms	*British, Traditional*	4 3 4
	Roe	*Fish & seafood*	– – –
	Augustine Kitchen	*French*	4 4 3
	Gazette	"	3 3 3
	Soif	"	3 3 3
	Cent Anni	*Italian*	3 3 3

	Maremma	"	–	–	–
	Osteria Antica Bologna	"	3	2	2
	Sapori Sardi	"	3	3	2
	Sorella	"	4	3	4
	Boqueria	Spanish	4	3	3
	Knife	Steaks & grills	4	4	3
	Naughty Piglets	"	5	5	3
	Addomme	Pizza	4	3	3
	Santa Maria del Sur	Argentinian	3	4	3
	Chokhi Dhani London	Indian	3	4	3
	Cinnamon Kitchen Battersea	"	4	3	3
	Takahashi	Japanese	5	5	3
£40+	Bodean's	American	2	2	2
	The Abbeville	British, Modern	3	3	3
	Counter Culture	"	4	4	2
	Plot	"	4	3	3
	Smoke & Salt	"	5	4	3
	24 The Oval	"	4	3	3
	VQ Clapham	"	2	3	3
	Sea Garden & Grill	Fish & seafood	4	4	4
	The Light House	International	3	3	3
	The Plough	"	2	2	4
	The Stonhouse	"	3	3	3
	Italo	Italian	4	3	4
	Made in Italy	"	4	2	3
	Pizza Metro	"	4	3	3
	Stockwell Continental	"	3	4	3
	Vagabond Wines	Mediterranean	2	3	3
	Little Taperia	Spanish	3	3	3
	Arlo's	Steaks & grills	3	3	3
	Macellaio RC	"	4	3	3
	Tell Your Friends	Vegetarian	3	3	4
	Haché	Burgers, etc	3	4	2
	Al Forno	Pizza	3	4	4
	Dynamo	"	4	3	3
	Mamma Dough	"	3	3	3
	Mother	"	3	3	4
	Pizza da Valter	"	3	2	2
	Rossopomodoro	"	2	2	2
	Santa Maria	"	4	3	3
	Indian Moment	Indian	3	2	2
	Kashmir	"	3	3	2
	Ma Goa	"	3	4	3
	Hashi	Japanese	3	4	2
	Oka	"	4	3	2
	Tonkotsu Battersea	"	3	3	2
	Tsunami	"	5	3	3
	Bánh Bánh	Vietnamese	3	3	2
£35+	Flotsam and Jetsam	Australian	3	3	3
	Fish in a Tie	Mediterranean	3	3	3
	MEATliquor	Burgers, etc	3	3	3
	Eco	Pizza	3	3	3
	Orange Pekoe	Sandwiches, cakes, etc	3	3	4
	Chit Chaat Chai	Indian	4	4	3

	Tomoe	Japanese	4	3	1
	Hare & Tortoise	Pan-Asian	3	3	2
	Mien Tay	Vietnamese	3	2	2
£30+	Amrutha	Vegan	4	4	2
	Dip & Flip	Burgers, etc	3	2	2
	Dirty Burger	"	3	3	2
	Chicken Shop & Dirty Burger	Chicken	3	3	2
	Meza	Lebanese	3	2	2
	BabaBoom	Middle Eastern	3	2	2
	Indian Ocean	Indian	3	4	3
	Taro	Japanese	3	2	2
	Awesome Thai	Thai	3	4	2
	Daddy Bao	Taiwanese	4	3	3
£25+	Unwined	Chinese	3	4	4
	Hot Stuff	Indian	3	4	2
	Munal Tandoori	"	4	4	2
	Jaffna House	Indian, Southern	3	2	2
	Mirch Masala	Pakistani	4	2	2
	Kaosarn	Thai	4	2	3
£15+	Joe Public	Pizza	4	3	2
	Milk	Sandwiches, cakes, etc	3	2	3

Outer western suburbs
Kew, Richmond, Twickenham, Teddington

£80+	The Glasshouse	British, Modern	4	3	3
	Petersham Nurseries Cafe	"	2	2	5
£70+	The Dysart Petersham	British, Modern	3	4	4
	M Bar & Grill Twickenham	Steaks & grills	2	2	2
£60+	The Bingham	British, Modern	3	4	5
	The Petersham Restaurant	"	2	3	5
	Al Boccon di'vino	Italian	4	4	5
£50+	Black Dog Beer House	British, Modern	4	3	3
	The Ivy Café	"	1	1	3
	Petit Ma Cuisine	French	3	3	3
	A Cena	Italian	3	4	3
	Bacco	"	3	3	2
£40+	Le Salon Privé	French	3	3	3
	Matsuba	Japanese	4	3	2
£35+	Dastaan	Indian	5	4	3
	Moksha	"	4	4	3

EAST

Smithfield & Farringdon (EC1)

£180+	The Clove Club	British, Modern	3 3 2
£100+	Club Gascon	French	4 4 3
£90+	Sushi Tetsu	Japanese	5 5 3
£80+	Luca	Italian	3 3 4
£70+	Anglo	British, Modern	5 3 2
	The Quality Chop House	British, Traditional	4 4 4
	Bleeding Heart Restaurant	French	3 3 4
	The Drunken Butler	"	4 4 4
	Smiths of Smithfield	Steaks & grills	3 2 4
£60+	The Coach	British, Modern	4 2 3
	The Jugged Hare	"	3 2 2
	The Modern Pantry	"	2 2 2
	Vinoteca	"	2 2 2
	St John Smithfield	British, Traditional	5 4 3
	Palatino	Italian	4 3 2
	Moro	Spanish	3 3 2
	Hix Oyster & Chop House	Steaks & grills	2 2 2
	Burger & Lobster	Burgers, etc	3 2 3
	Ceviche Old St	Peruvian	3 3 4
£50+	Stem & Glory	Vegan	3 2 2
	Granger & Co	Australian	3 2 3
	Bourne and Hollingsworth	British, Modern	3 2 4
	Caravan	"	2 2 3
	Lino	"	3 4 2
	The Wilmington	"	3 3 3
	Café du Marché	French	3 3 5
	Comptoir Gascon	"	3 2 3
	Bowling Bird	International	4 4 3
	Niche	"	3 3 2
	Apulia	Italian	3 3 2
	Da Giua	"	3 4 2
	Polpo	"	1 2 2
	Santore	"	3 2 2
	Fare	Mediterranean	3 3 4
	Ibérica	Spanish	3 2 3
	The Gate	Vegetarian	4 2 2
	Berber & Q Shawarma Bar	Middle Eastern	4 4 4
£40+	Bodean's	American	2 2 2
	Lantana Café	Australian	3 3 3
	La Ferme London	French	3 3 3
	Monsieur Le Duck	"	4 3 3
	Macellaio RC	Italian	4 3 3
	The Eagle	Mediterranean	4 3 3
	Morito	Spanish	4 3 3

			Rating
	Pizza Pilgrims	*Pizza*	4 3 3
	Breddos Tacos	*Mexican/TexMex*	4 2 3
	The Sichuan	*Chinese*	3 3 2
	Bone Daddies	*Japanese*	3 3 3
	Pham Sushi	"	4 3 3
	Cây Tre	*Vietnamese*	3 3 2
£35+	Fish Central	*Fish & seafood*	3 4 3
	Le Cellar	*French*	3 4 3
	Homeslice	*Pizza*	4 3 3
	Workshop Coffee	*Sandwiches, cakes, etc*	3 4 3
	On The Bab	*Korean*	3 3 2
£10+	Department of Coffee	*Sandwiches, cakes, etc*	3 4 3
	Prufrock Coffee	"	3 3 2

The City (EC2, EC3, EC4)

			Rating
£120+	La Dame de Pic London	*French*	4 4 3
£110+	Mei Ume	*Japanese*	3 3 3
	Nobu Shoreditch	"	2 2 2
£90+	City Social	*British, Modern*	3 3 3
	Fenchurch Restaurant	"	4 3 4
	Angler	*Fish & seafood*	4 3 3
	Goodman City	*Steaks & grills*	4 3 3
	Lutyens Grill	"	3 3 3
£80+	Duck & Waffle	*British, Modern*	2 2 4
	Helix	"	2 3 5
	1 Lombard Street	"	2 2 2
	Bob Bob Cité	*French*	– – –
	Coq d'Argent	"	2 3 4
	Cecconi's	*International*	2 2 4
	Hawksmoor	*Steaks & grills*	4 3 3
	Coya	*Peruvian*	4 3 4
	Yauatcha City	*Chinese*	4 2 3
	Sushisamba	*Japanese*	3 2 3
£70+	Bread Street Kitchen	*British, Modern*	2 2 3
	Darwin Brasserie	"	2 2 5
	St Leonard's	"	1 2 2
	Fish Market	*Fish & seafood*	2 2 2
	Sweetings	"	3 3 4
	Cabotte	*French*	4 5 4
	Manicomio	*Italian*	3 2 3
	Boisdale of Bishopsgate	*Scottish*	3 2 2
	M Restaurant	*Steaks & grills*	2 2 2
	Vanilla Black	*Vegetarian*	4 3 3
	Mint Leaf Lounge	*Indian*	3 3 4
£60+	The Don	*British, Modern*	3 3 3
	Fortnum's Bar & Restaurant	"	2 3 3

	High Timber	"	3 3 3
	The Ivy City Garden	"	2 2 4
	The Mercer	"	3 2 2
	Merchants Tavern	"	2 2 3
	Vinoteca City	"	2 2 2
	Paternoster Chop House	British, Traditional	2 2 2
	Vivat Bacchus	International	3 3 2
	Caravaggio	Italian	3 2 2
	Hispania	Spanish	3 3 3
	José Pizarro	"	4 3 2
	Aviary	Steaks & grills	2 2 3
	Burger & Lobster	Burgers, etc	3 2 3
	Red Rooster	Chicken	2 2 3
	Nanashi	Japanese	3 2 2
£50+	The Anthologist	British, Modern	2 2 2
	The Botanist	"	2 2 2
	Caravan	"	2 2 3
	Humble Grape	"	3 4 3
	Leroy	"	3 4 3
	Northbank	"	2 2 3
	Gloria	Italian	3 3 4
	Osteria	"	3 3 2
	Popolo	"	5 4 3
	Taberna Etrusca	"	2 2 2
	Ekte Nordic Kitchen	Scandinavian	3 2 2
	Mac & Wild	Scottish	3 3 3
	Camino Shoreditch	Spanish	2 2 2
	The Jones Family Project	Steaks & grills	3 3 4
	The Tramshed	"	3 2 4
	Haz	Turkish	2 2 2
	Oklava	"	4 4 3
	Kym's by Andrew Wong	Chinese	4 3 3
	Brigadiers	Indian	5 4 4
	Cinnamon Kitchen	"	4 3 3
£40+	Bodean's	American	2 2 2
	Coppa Club Tower Bridge	British, Modern	2 3 5
	VQ	"	2 3 3
	Simpson's Tavern	British, Traditional	3 3 4
	The Wine Library	International	2 3 5
	Rucoletta	Italian	4 2 2
	Blacklock	Steaks & grills	3 4 4
	Relais de Venise L'Entrecôte	"	3 3 3
	Haché	Burgers, etc	3 4 2
	Pizza Pilgrims	Pizza	4 3 3
	Ozone Coffee Roasters	Sandwiches, cakes, etc	3 3 4
	temper City	BBQ	3 3 4
	Shoryu Ramen	Japanese	3 2 2
£35+	Café Below	British, Modern	3 3 3
	Homeslice	Pizza	4 3 3
	Koya	Japanese	4 4 3
	On The Bab	Korean	3 3 2
	Hare & Tortoise	Pan-Asian	3 3 2

£30+	Flat Iron	Steaks & grills	4 4 4
	Shake Shack	Burgers, etc	3 2 2
	K10	Japanese	3 2 2
	Taro	"	3 2 2
	Bibimbap	Korean	3 3 2
£25+	Patty and Bun	Burgers, etc	4 3 3
£20+	Bleecker Burger	Burgers, etc	5 2 1
	Yum Bun	Japanese	5 3 2
£10+	Sub Cult	Sandwiches, cakes, etc	– – –

East End & Docklands (All E postcodes)

£180+	Mãos	Portuguese	5 5 4
£90+	Lyle's	British, Modern	4 3 2
	Galvin La Chapelle	French	4 4 5
	Goodman	Steaks & grills	4 3 3
£80+	Cecconi's Shoreditch	Italian	2 2 4
	Hawksmoor	Steaks & grills	4 3 3
	Roka	Japanese	5 4 4
£70+	Bright	British, Modern	5 4 3
	Galvin HOP	"	3 3 3
	Pidgin	"	5 3 2
	Smith's Wapping	"	4 4 5
£60+	Big Easy	American	3 2 3
	Bistrotheque	British, Modern	3 2 4
	The Culpeper	"	3 2 4
	The Gun	"	2 2 4
	The Narrow	"	1 2 3
	Rochelle Canteen	"	3 3 3
	Two Lights	"	3 4 3
	The Marksman	British, Traditional	4 3 3
	St John Bread & Wine	"	3 2 3
	Cornerstone	Fish & seafood	5 4 4
	Wright Brothers	"	3 3 3
	Plateau	French	3 3 3
	Brat	Fusion	5 5 4
	Canto Corvino	Italian	3 2 3
	Brawn	Mediterranean	5 3 4
	Boisdale of Canary Wharf	Scottish	2 3 4
	Burger & Lobster	Burgers, etc	3 2 3
	Buen Ayre	Argentinian	4 3 2
	Café Spice Namaste	Indian	5 4 3
	Sticks'n'Sushi	Japanese	3 3 3
£50+	Corner Room	British, Modern	3 2 3
	Duke of Richmond	"	3 2 3
	Eat 17	"	3 3 3

	The Empress	"	3	4	3
	Humble Grape	"	3	4	3
	Madame Pigg	"	3	4	4
	Mare Street Market	"	3	2	5
	Bumpkin	British, Traditional	2	2	3
	Forman's	Fish & seafood	4	3	3
	Blanchette East	French	4	2	3
	Chez Elles	"	4	4	4
	Angelina	Fusion	5	4	3
	Blixen	International	2	2	3
	Casa Fofó	"	5	3	3
	Dokke	"	3	4	3
	Eat 17	"	3	3	3
	Lagom	"	4	3	3
	The Laughing Heart	"	2	3	3
	Il Bordello	Italian	3	3	3
	Capeesh	"	3	3	3
	Lardo	"	3	2	2
	Super Tuscan	"	3	4	3
	Verdi's	"	3	4	4
	Ottolenghi	Mediterranean	3	2	2
	Ibérica	Spanish	3	2	3
	Burger & Beyond	Burgers, etc	5	3	3
	Pizza East	Pizza	3	2	4
	Smokestak	BBQ	5	3	3
	Andina	Peruvian	4	3	3
	Berber & Q	Middle Eastern	4	4	4
	Haz	Turkish	2	2	2
	Lahpet	Burmese	3	2	3
	Royal China	Chinese	3	1	2
	Yi-Ban	"	2	2	2
	Grand Trunk Road	Indian	4	3	2
	Smoking Goat	Thai	5	4	4
	Som Saa	"	3	2	3
£40+	Breakfast Club	American	3	3	3
	P Franco	British, Modern	4	2	3
	The Buxton	"	–	–	–
	Provender	French	3	3	3
	Campania & Jones	Italian	4	4	3
	Emilia's Crafted Pasta	"	4	4	3
	Pasta Remoli	"	3	3	3
	Morito	Spanish	4	3	3
	Mao Chow	Vegetarian	–	–	–
	Mildreds	"	3	3	3
	The Spread Eagle	"	3	4	4
	Ark Fish	Fish & chips	3	4	2
	Poppies	"	3	3	3
	Pizza Pilgrims	Pizza	4	3	3
	Yard Sale Pizza	"	4	3	2
	Chick 'n' Sours	Chicken	4	3	3
	Lupita	Mexican/TexMex	3	2	2
	Delamina East	Middle Eastern	4	4	2
	Sichuan Folk	Chinese	4	2	2
	Dishoom	Indian	3	4	5
	Gunpowder	"	4	3	3

	Ippudo London	*Japanese*	3 3 3
	Tonkotsu	"	3 3 2
£35+	Xi'an Biang Biang	*Chinese*	3 3 3
	Mien Tay	*Vietnamese*	3 2 2
	Sông Quê	"	3 3 2
	Bao Bar	*Taiwanese*	4 3 3
£30+	Da Terra	*Fusion*	5 4 4
	Flat Iron	*Steaks & grills*	4 4 4
	Dirty Burger Shoreditch	*Burgers, etc*	3 3 2
	Shake Shack	"	3 2 2
	Crate Brewery and Pizzeria	*Pizza*	4 3 4
	Gökyuzu	*Turkish*	2 2 2
	Lahore Kebab House	*Pakistani*	5 2 2
	Tayyabs	"	4 2 2
£25+	E Pellicci	*Italian*	3 5 5
	Patty and Bun	*Burgers, etc*	4 3 3
	Mangal 1	*Turkish*	5 2 2
	Needoo	*Pakistani*	4 3 2
£20+	Bleecker Burger	*Burgers, etc*	5 2 1
	Jidori	*Japanese*	4 3 2
	Singburi Royal Thai Café	*Thai*	4 3 3
£15+	The Duck Truck	*Burgers, etc*	5 3 3
£10+	Black Bear Burger	*Burgers, etc*	5 3 –
	The Rib Man	"	5 3 –
	Pavilion Cafe & Bakery	*Sandwiches, cakes, etc*	4 2 4
£5+	Brick Lane Beigel Bake	*Sandwiches, cakes, etc*	4 1 1

MAPS

MAP 1 – LONDON OVERVIEW

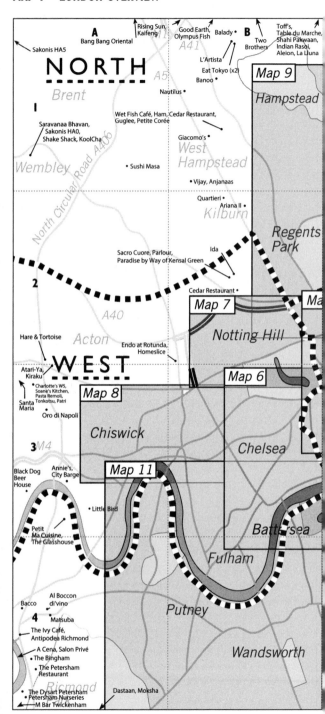

A

Sakonis HA5

Bang Bang Oriental

Rising Sun, Kaifeng

Good Earth, Olympus Fish

Balady

B

Two Brothers

Toff's, Table du Marche, Shahi Pakwaan, Indian Rasoi, Aleion, La Lluna

NORTH

Brent

L'Artista

Eat Tokyo (x2)

Banoo

Map 9

Hampstead

Nautilus

1

Saravanaa Bhavan, Sakonis HA0, Shake Shack, KoolCha

Wembley

Wet Fish Café, Ham, Cedar Restaurant, Guglee, Petite Corée

Giacomo's

West Hampstead

Sushi Masa

Vijay, Anjanaas

Quartieri

Ariana II

Kilburn

Ida

Regents Park

Sacro Cuore, Parlour, Paradise by Way of Kensal Green

Map [Ma

2

A40

Cedar Restaurant

Map 7

Acton

Notting Hill

Hare & Tortoise

Endo at Rotunda, Homeslice

WEST

Atari-Ya, Kiraku

Map 6

Charlotte's W5, Soane's Kitchen, Pasta Remoli, Tonkotsu, Patri

Santa Maria

Map 8

Oro di Napoli

Chiswick

Chelsea

3 *M4*

Black Dog Beer House

Annie's, City Barge

Map 11

Little Bird

Petit Ma Cuisine, The Glasshouse

Battersea

Fulham

Al Boccon di'vino

Bacco

4

Matsuba

Putney

The Ivy Café, Antipodea Richmond

A Cena, Salon Privé

The Bingham

Wandsworth

The Petersham Restaurant

The Dysart Petersham

Petersham Nurseries

M Bar Twickenham

Richmond

Dastaan, Moksha

North Circular Road A406

MAP I – LONDON OVERVIEW

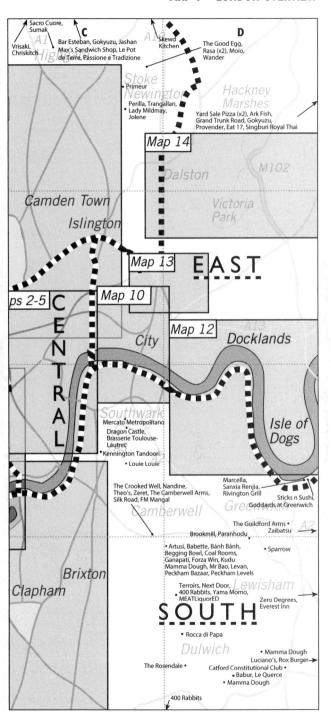

Sacro Cuore, Sumak

Vrisaki, Chriskitch

A1 High

C

Bar Esteban, Gokyuzu, Jashan Max's Sandwich Shop, Le Pot de Terre, Passione e Tradizione

Skewd Kitchen

D

The Good Egg, Rasa (x2), Moio, Wander

Primeur

Stoke Newington

Hackney Marshes

Perilla, Trangallan, Lady Mildmay, Jolene

Yard Sale Pizza (x2), Ark Fish, Grand Trunk Road, Gokyuzu, Provender, Eat 17, Singburi Royal Thai

Map 14

M102

Dalston

Victoria Park

Camden Town

Islington

Map 13

E A S T

Map 10

Map 12

City

Docklands

ps 2-5

C
E
N
T
R
A
L

Southwark

Mercato Metropolitano

Dragon Castle, Brasserie Toulouse-Lautrec

Kennington Tandoori

Louie Louie

Isle of Dogs

Marcella, Sanxia Renjia, Rivington Grill

Greenwich

Sticks n Sushi, Goddards at Greenwich

The Crooked Well, Nandine, Theo's, Zeret, The Camberwell Arms, Silk Road, FM Mangal

Camberwell

The Guildford Arms • Zaibatsu

A2

Brookmill, Paranhodu

• Sparrow

• Artusi, Babette, Bánh Bánh, Begging Bowl, Coal Rooms, Ganapati, Forza Win, Kudu Mamma Dough, Levan, Peckham Bazaar, Peckham Levels

Brixton

Clapham

Terroirs, Next Door, 400 Rabbits, Yama Momo, MEATLiquorED

Lewisham

Zero Degrees, Everest Inn

S O U T H

• Rocca di Papa

Dulwich

• Mamma Dough

Luciano's, Rox Burger

Catford Constitutional Club •

The Rosendale •

• Babur, Le Querce

• Mamma Dough

400 Rabbits

MAP 2 – WEST END OVERVIEW

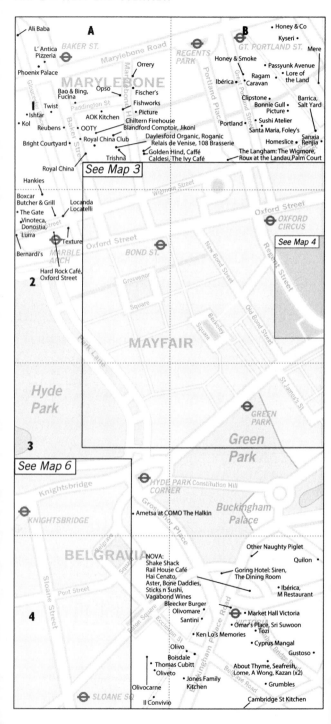

A

- Ali Baba
- L' Antica Pizzeria
- Phoenix Palace

BAKER ST.

Marylebone Road

- Orrery
- Bao & Bing, Fucina
- Opso
- Fischer's
- Fishworks
- Picture

MARYLEBONE

Paddington St

- Twist
- Ishtar
- Kol
- Reubens
- AOK Kitchen
- OOTY
- Bright Courtyard
- Royal China Club
- Royal China
- Chiltern Firehouse
- Blandford Comptoir, Jikoni
- Daylesford Organic, Roganic
- Relais de Venise, 108 Brasserie
- Golden Hind, Caffè
- Caldesi, The Ivy Café
- Trishna

See Map 3

- Hankies
- Boxcar Butcher & Grill
- The Gate
- Vinoteca, Donostia,
- Lurra
- Bernardi's
- Locanda Locatelli
- Texture

MARBLE ARCH

Oxford Street

BOND ST.

Grosvenor Square

- Hard Rock Café, Oxford Street

B

- Honey & Co
- Kyseri
- Mere
- Honey & Smoke
- Passyunk Avenue
- Lore of the Land
- Ragam
- Ibérica
- Caravan
- Clipstone
- Bonnie Gull
- Picture
- Portland
- Sushi Atelier
- Santa Maria, Foley's
- Barrica, Salt Yard
- Sanxia Renjia
- Homeslice
- The Langham: The Wigmore,
- Roux at the Landau, Palm Court

GT. PORTLAND ST.

REGENTS PARK

Portland Place

Wigmore Street

Oxford Street

OXFORD CIRCUS

New Bond Street

Regent Street

See Map 4

2

MAYFAIR

Park Lane

Berkeley Square

Old Bond Street

Hyde Park

3

GREEN PARK

Green Park

St. James's St.

See Map 6

Knightsbridge

KNIGHTSBRIDGE

HYDE PARK CORNER

Constitution Hill

Grosvenor Place

Buckingham Palace

BELGRAVIA

Sloane Street

Pont Street

- Ametsa at COMO The Halkin

NOVA:
Shake Shack
Rail House Café
Hai Cenato,
Aster, Bone Daddies,
Sticks n Sushi,
Vagabond Wines

- Bleecker Burger
- Olivomare
- Santini
- Olivo
- Boisdale
- Thomas Cubitt
- Oliveto
- Olivocarne
- Il Convivio
- Jones Family Kitchen
- Ken Lo's Memories

Eaton Square

Ebury St

Elizabeth St

Buckingham Palace Road

- Other Naughty Piglet
- Quilon
- Goring Hotel: Siren, The Dining Room
- Ibérica, M Restaurant
- Market Hall Victoria
- Omar's Place, Sri Suwoon
- Tozi
- Cyprus Mangal
- Gustoso
- About Thyme, Seafresh, Lorne, A Wong, Kazan (x2)
- Grumbles
- Cambridge St Kitchen

4

Sloane Square

SLOANE SQ

MAP 2 – WEST END OVERVIEW

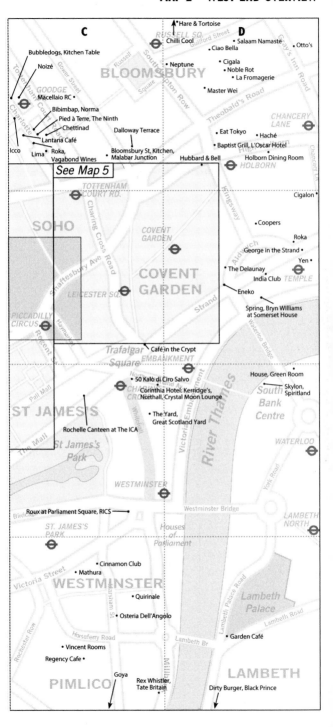

C

D

• Hare & Tortoise

RUSSELL SQ.

• Chilli Cool

• Salaam Namaste

• Otto's

Bubbledogs, Kitchen Table

• Ciao Bella

Noizé

• Cigala

• Neptune

• Noble Rot

• La Fromagerie

BLOOMSBURY

GOODGE

Macellaio RC •

• Master Wei

Bibimbap, Norma

Pied à Terre, The Ninth

CHANCERY
LANE

Chettinad

• Eat Tokyo

• Haché

Lantana Café

• Baptist Grill, L'Oscar Hotel

Icco

Lima • Roka, Vagabond Wines

Dalloway Terrace

• Holborn Dining Room

Bloomsbury St, Kitchen,
Malabar Junction

Hubbard & Bell

HOLBORN

See Map 5

TOTTENHAM
COURT RD.

SOHO

Cigalon

COVENT
GARDEN

• Coopers

• Roka

COVENT
GARDEN

George in the Strand •

• Yen

LEICESTER SQ.

• The Delaunay

India Club

TEMPLE

PICCADILLY
CIRCUS

Eneko

Spring, Bryn Williams
at Somerset House

Café in the Crypt

Trafalgar
Square

EMBANKMENT

• 50 Kalò di Ciro Salvo

House, Green Room

Corinthia Hotel: Kerridge's,
Northall, Crystal Moon Lounge

Skylon,
Spiritland

South
Bank
Centre

ST JAMES'S

• The Yard,
Great Scotland Yard

Rochelle Canteen at The ICA

WATERLOO

St James's
Park

River Thames

WESTMINSTER

Roux at Parliament Square, RICS

Westminster Bridge

LAMBETH
NORTH

ST. JAMES'S
PARK

Houses
of
Parliament

• Cinnamon Club

• Mathura

WESTMINSTER

Lambeth
Palace

• Quirinale

• Osteria Dell'Angolo

• Vincent Rooms

• Garden Café

Regency Cafe •

PIMLICO

Goya

Rex Whistler,
Tate Britain

LAMBETH

Dirty Burger, Black Prince

MAP 3 – MAYFAIR, ST. JAMES'S & WEST SOHO

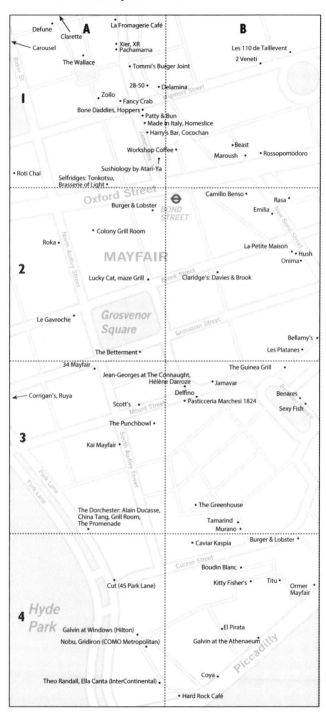

A

Defune
Clarette
Carousel
The Wallace

La Fromagerie Café

B

Les 110 de Taillevent
2 Veneti

Xier, XR
Pachamama

Tommi's Burger Joint

28-50
Delamina
Zoilo
Fancy Crab
Bone Daddies, Hoppers
Patty &Bun
Made in Italy, Homeslice
Harry's Bar, Cocochan

Wigmore Street

1

Workshop Coffee
Beast
Maroush
Rossopomodoro

Sushiology by Atari-Ya

Roti Chai
Selfridges: Tonkotsu,
Brasserie of Light

Oxford Street

Camillo Benso
Rasa
Burger & Lobster
BOND
STREET
Emilia

Colony Grill Room

MAYFAIR

Roka
La Petite Maison
Hush
Onima

2

Lucky Cat, maze Grill
Claridge's: Davies & Brook

Le Gavroche

*Grosvenor
Square*

Grosvenor Street

Bellamy's
Les Platanes

The Betterment

34 Mayfair
The Guinea Grill

Jean-Georges at The Connaught,
Hélène Darroze
Jamavar
Delfino
Benares
Corrigan's, Ruya
Scott's
Pasticceria Marchesi 1824
Sexy Fish
Mount Street

3

The Punchbowl

Kai Mayfair

Park Lane
Park Lane

The Greenhouse

Tamarind
The Dorchester: Alain Ducasse,
China Tang, Grill Room,
The Promenade
Murano

Caviar Kaspia
Burger & Lobster

Curzon Street

Boudin Blanc

Cut (45 Park Lane)
Kitty Fisher's
Titu
Ormer
Mayfair

*Hyde
Park*

4

Galvin at Windows (Hilton)
El Pirata
Nobu, Gridiron (COMO Metropolitan)
Galvin at the Athenaeum

Piccadilly

Theo Randall, Ella Canta (InterContinental)
Coya

Hard Rock Café

MAP 3 – MAYFAIR, ST. JAMES'S & WEST SOHO

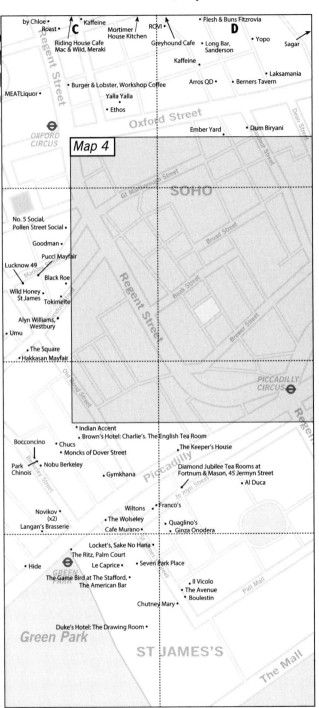

by Chloe •
Roast • • Kaffeine **C**
Riding House Cafe
Mac & Wild, Meraki
Mortimer
House Kitchen
ROVI •
Greyhound Cafe
• Flesh & Buns Fitzrovia **D**
• Long Bar,
Sanderson
• Yopo
Sagar

Kaffeine •

• Laksamania
Arros QD • • Berners Tavern

MEATLiquor •

• Burger & Lobster, Workshop Coffee
Yalla Yalla
• Ethos

Oxford Street

*OXFORD
CIRCUS*

Map 4

Ember Yard • • Dum Biryani

SOHO

No. 5 Social,
Pollen Street Social •

• Goodman •

Pucci Mayfair
Lucknow 49
Black Roe

Wild Honey •
St James
Tokimeite

Alyn Williams,
Westbury
• Umu

• The Square
• Hakkasan Mayfair

*PICCADILLY
CIRCUS*

• Indian Accent
• Brown's Hotel: Charlie's. The English Tea Room
Bocconcino • • Chucs
• Moncks of Dover Street
• The Keeper's House
Park
Chinois
• Nobu Berkeley
• Gymkhana
Diamond Jubilee Tea Rooms at
Fortnum & Mason, 45 Jermyn Street
• Al Duca

Wiltons • Franco's
Novikov
(x2)
Langan's Brasserie
• The Wolseley
Cafe Murano •
• Quaglino's
• Ginza Onodera

Locket's, Sake No Hana •
The Ritz, Palm Court
• Hide
Le Caprice • • Seven Park Place
The Game Bird at The Stafford, •
The American Bar
• Il Vicolo
• The Avenue
• Boulestin
Chutney Mary •

Duke's Hotel: The Drawing Room •

Green Park

ST JAMES'S

The Mall

MAP 4 – WEST SOHO & PICCADILLY

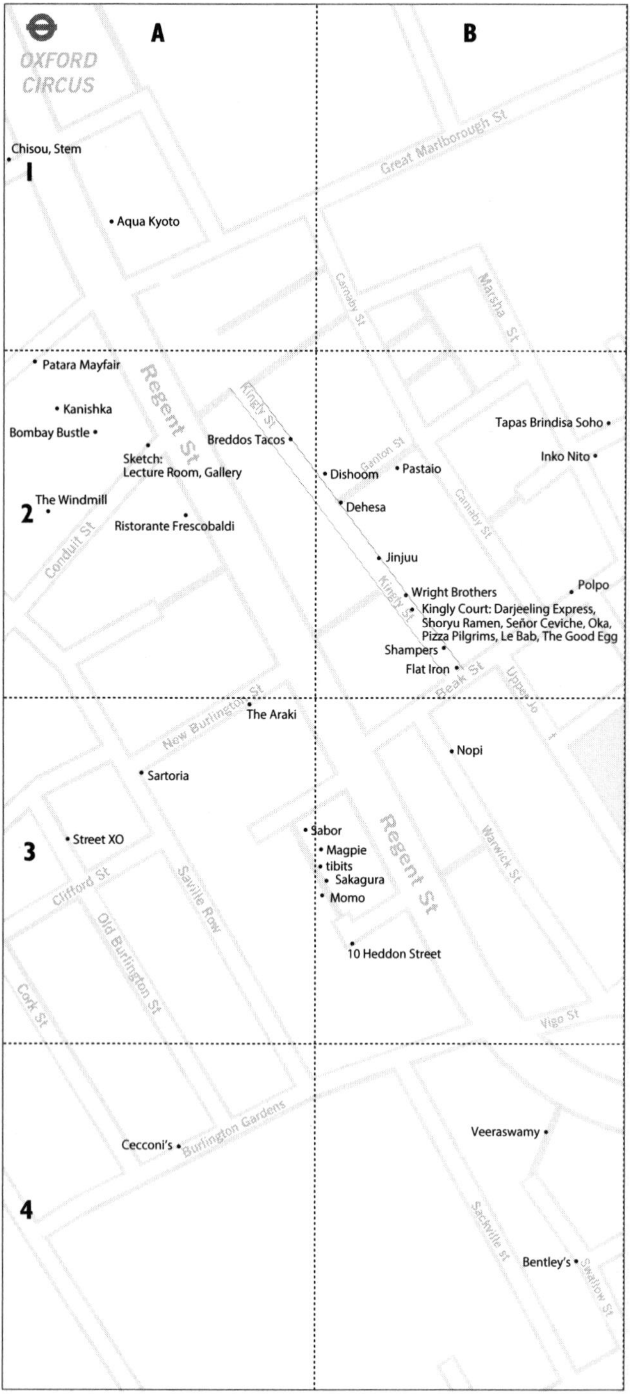

OXFORD CIRCUS

A

B

Great Marlborough St

I

Chisou, Stem

• Aqua Kyoto

Carnaby St

Marsha St

2

• Patara Mayfair

Regent St

Kingly St

Tapas Brindisa Soho •

• Kanishka

Inko Nito •

Bombay Bustle •

Breddos Tacos •

Ganton St

• Dishoom

• Pastaio

Sketch:
Lecture Room, Gallery

• Dehesa

The Windmill •

• Jinjuu

Carnaby St

Ristorante Frescobaldi •

• Wright Brothers

Polpo •

Conduit St

Kingly St

• Kingly Court: Darjeeling Express,
Shoryu Ramen, Señor Ceviche, Oka,
Pizza Pilgrims, Le Bab, The Good Egg

Shampers •

Flat Iron •

Beak St

Upper Jo

3

New Burlington St

The Araki •

• Nopi

• Sartoria

Regent St

• Street XO

• Sabor

Warwick St

• Magpie

Clifford St

• tibits

Old Burlington St

Saville Row

• Sakagura

• Momo

• 10 Heddon Street

Cork St

Vigo St

4

Burlington Gardens

Cecconi's •

Veeraswamy •

Sackville St

Bentley's •

Swallow St

MAP 4 – WEST SOHO & PICCADILLY

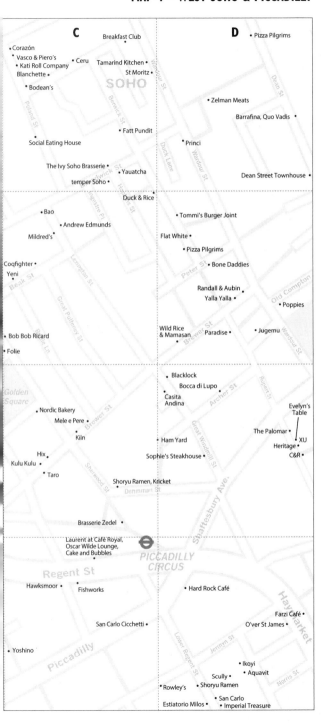

C

Breakfast Club

• Corazón
• Vasco & Piero's
• Kati Roll Company   • Ceru
Blanchette •   Tamarind Kitchen •
                      St Moritz •
  • Bodean's   SOHO

                    • Fatt Pundit
  •
Social Eating House

The Ivy Soho Brasserie •
                    • Yauatcha
  temper Soho •

              Duck & Rice

  • Bao
    • Andrew Edmunds
Mildred's •

Coqfighter •
Yeni

  • Bob Bob Ricard
• Folie

Golden
Square
  • Nordic Bakery
    Mele e Pere •
          Kiln •

  Hix •
Kulu Kulu •
    • Taro

        Shoryu Ramen, Kricket

    Brasserie Zedel •

  Laurent at Café Royal,
  Oscar Wilde Lounge,
  Cake and Bubbles
                    PICCADILLY
                    CIRCUS
Regent St

Hawksmoor •   Fishworks

        San Carlo Cicchetti •

• Yoshino
        Piccadilly

D   • Pizza Pilgrims

                    • Zelman Meats

              Barrafina, Quo Vadis •

        • Princi

              Dean Street Townhouse •

  • Tommi's Burger Joint

Flat White •
    • Pizza Pilgrims
        • Bone Daddies

    Randall & Aubin •
    Yalla Yalla •
                    • Poppies

Wild Rice
& Mamasan   Paradise •   • Jugemu

  • Blacklock
    Bocca di Lupo •
  Casita
  Andina
                    Evelyn's
                    Table
        The Palomar •
                    ↓ XU
        Ham Yard   Heritage •
  Sophie's Steakhouse •   C&R •

• Hard Rock Café

                    Farzi Café •
        O'ver St James •

                • Ikoyi
        Scully •   • Aquavit
  • Rowley's • Shoryu Ramen
        • San Carlo
  Estiatorio Milos • • Imperial Treasure

MAP 5 – EAST SOHO, CHINATOWN & COVENT GARDEN

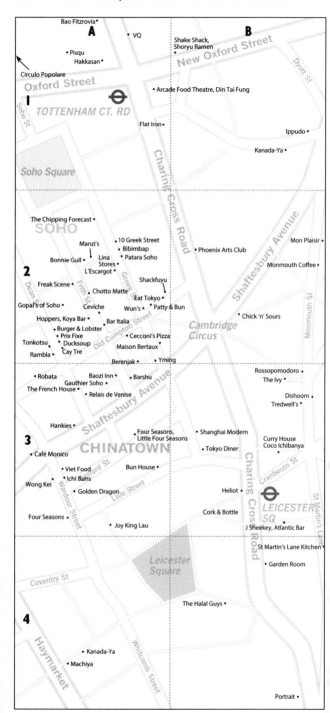

A

B

Bao Fitzrovia •

• VQ

Shake Shack,
Shoryu Ramen

New Oxford Street

Dyott St

• Pisqu

Hakkasan •

Circulo Popolare

Oxford Street

Soho St

1

TOTTENHAM CT. RD

• Arcade Food Theatre, Din Tai Fung

Flat Iron •

Ippudo •

Kanada-Ya •

Soho Square

The Chipping Forecast •

SOHO

Manzi's

• 10 Greek Street

• Bibimbap

• Patara Soho

• Phoenix Arts Club

Mon Plaisir •

Monmouth Coffee •

Bonnie Gull •

Lina
Stores

L'Escargot •

2

Freak Scene •

Shackfuyu •

Chotto Matte •

Eat Tokyo •

Charing Cross Road

Shaftesbury Avenue

Monmouth St

Gopal's of Soho •

Ceviche •

Wun's •

Patty & Bun

Chick 'n' Sours •

Dean Street

Frith St

Greek Street

Old Compton Street

Hoppers, Koya Bar •

Burger & Lobster •

• Prix Fixe

Bar Italia •

Cambridge
Circus

Tonkotsu •

• Ducksoup

• Cecconi's Pizza

Rambla •

Cay Tre

Maison Bertaux •

Berenjak •

• Yming

• Robata

Baozi Inn •

• Barshu

Rossopomodoro •

The Ivy •

Gauthier Soho •

The French House •

• Relais de Venise

Shaftesbury Avenue

Dishoom •

Tredwell's •

Hankies •

3

CHINATOWN

Four Seasons,
Little Four Seasons

• Shanghai Modern

Curry House
Coco Ichibanya

• Café Monico

Gerrard St

• Tokyo Diner

Wardour Street

• Viet Food

• Ichi Buns

Bun House •

Cranbourn St

Heliot •

LEICESTER
SQ

Wong Kei •

• Golden Dragon

Lisle Street

Cork & Bottle

Charing Cross Road

St Martin's Lane

Four Seasons •

• Joy King Lau

J Sheekey, Atlantic Bar

St Martin's Lane Kitchen

Leicester
Square

• Garden Room

Coventry St

4

The Halal Guys •

Haymarket

• Kanada-Ya

Whitcomb Street

• Machiya

Portrait •

MAP 5 – EAST SOHO, CHINATOWN & COVENT GARDEN

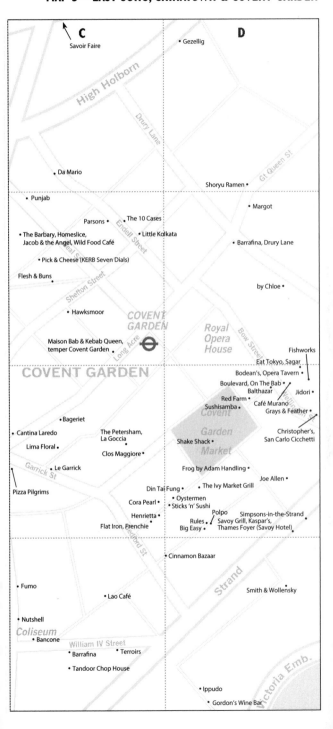

C

D

Savoir Faire

• Gezellig

High Holborn

Drury Lane

Gt Queen St

• Da Mario

Shoryu Ramen •

• Punjab

• Margot

Parsons • • The 10 Cases

• Little Kolkata

• The Barbary, Homeslice,
Jacob & the Angel, Wild Food Café

Endell Street

• Barrafina, Drury Lane

• Pick & Cheese (KERB Seven Dials)

Flesh & Buns

Shelton Street

by Chloe •

• Hawksmoor

**COVENT
GARDEN**

Royal
Opera
House

Maison Bab & Kebab Queen,
temper Covent Garden

Long Acre

Bow Street

Fishworks

Eat Tokyo, Sagar

COVENT GARDEN

Bodean's, Opera Tavern •

Boulevard, On The Bab •
Balthazar

Wellington St

Jidori •

Red Farm •

Café Murano •

Sushisamba •

Grays & Feather •

Covent

• Bageriet

Garden

Christopher's,
San Carlo Cicchetti

• Cantina Laredo

The Petersham,
La Goccia

Market

Shake Shack •

Lima Floral •

Clos Maggiore •

Garrick St

• Le Garrick

Frog by Adam Handling •

Joe Allen •

Pizza Pilgrims

Din Tai Fung • • The Ivy Market Grill

Cora Pearl • • Oystermen

Polpo

Simpsons-in-the-Strand

• Sticks 'n' Sushi

Henrietta • Rules • Savoy Grill, Kaspar's,

Flat Iron, Frenchie

Big Easy • Thames Foyer (Savoy Hotel)

Bedford St

• Cinnamon Bazaar

Strand

• Fumo

• Lao Café

Smith & Wollensky

• Nutshell

Coliseum

• Bancone

William IV Street

• Barrafina • Terroirs

• Tandoor Chop House

Victoria Emb.

• Ippudo

• Gordon's Wine Bar

MAP 6 – KNIGHTSBRIDGE, CHELSEA & SOUTH KENSINGTON

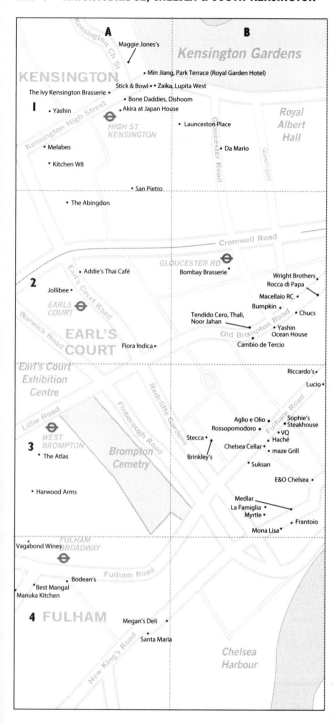

MAP 6 – KNIGHTSBRIDGE, CHELSEA & SOUTH KENSINGTON

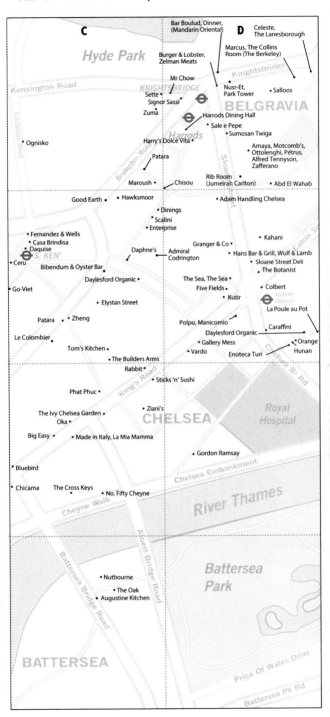

C

D

Hyde Park

Bar Boulud, Dinner,
(Mandarin Oriental)

Celeste,
The Lanesborough

Marcus, The Collins
Room (The Berkeley)

Burger & Lobster,
Zelman Meats

Knightsbridge

Kensington Road

Mr Chow

KNIGHTSBRIDGE

Nusr-Et,
Park Tower

Salloos

Sette

Signor Sassi

BELGRAVIA

Zuma

Harrods Dining Hall

Ognisko

Sale e Pepe

Sumosan Twiga

Harry's Dolce Vita

Harrods

Amaya, Motcomb's,
Ottolenghi, Pétrus,
Alfred Tennyson,
Zafferano

Patara

Brompton Road

Maroush

Chisou

Rib Room
(Jumeirah Carlton)

Abd El Wahab

Good Earth

Hawksmoor

Adam Handling Chelsea

Dinings

Scalini

Enterprise

Kahani

Fernandez & Wells

Casa Brindisa

Daquise

S. KEN'

Daphne's

Granger & Co

Admiral
Codrington

Hans Bar & Grill, Wulf & Lamb

Sloane Street Deli

The Botanist

Ceru

Bibendum & Oyster Bar

Daylesford Organic

The Sea, The Sea

Go-Viet

Five Fields

Colbert

Elystan Street

Kutir

SLOANE
SQUARE

La Poule au Pot

Patara

Zheng

Le Colombier

Polpo, Manicomio

Caraffini

Daylesford Organic

Tom's Kitchen

Gallery Mess

Orange

The Builders Arms

Vardo

Enoteca Turi

Hunan

Rabbit

Sticks 'n' Sushi

King's Road

Phat Phuc

Royal
Hospital

The Ivy Chelsea Garden

Ziani's

CHELSEA

Oka

Big Easy

Made in Italy, La Mia Mamma

Gordon Ramsay

Bluebird

Chelsea Embankment

Chicama

The Cross Keys

No. Fifty Cheyne

River Thames

Cheyne Walk

Battersea
Park

Nutbourne

The Oak

Augustine Kitchen

Albert Bridge Road

Battersea Bridge Road

BATTERSEA

Price Of Wales Drive

Battersea Pk Rd

Eaton Square

Sloane Street

Chelsea Br Rd

MAP 7 – NOTTING HILL & BAYSWATER

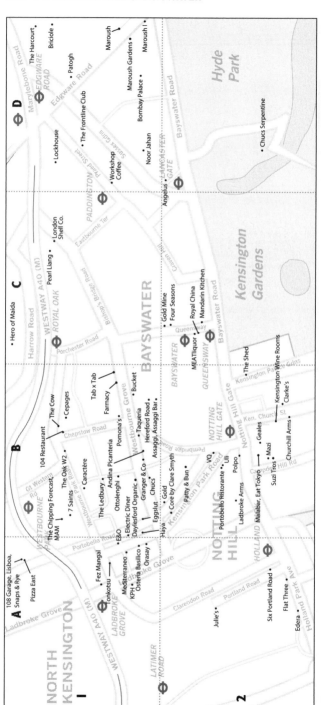

NORTH KENSINGTON

BAYSWATER

NOTTING HILL

Hyde Park

Kensington Gardens

108 Garage, Lisboa, Snaps & Rye
Pizza East
Fez Mangal
Tonkotsu
Mediterraneo
KPH
Osteria Basilico
Orasay
E&O
Electric Diner
Daylesford Organic
Eggslut
Haya
Gold
Chucs
Core by Clare Smyth
Granger & Co
Assaggi, Assaggi Bar
Hereford Road
Taqueria
Pomona's
Andina Picanteria
The Ledbury
Ottolenghi
7 Saints
Caractere
The Oak W2
MAM
The Chipping Forecast
104 Restaurant
The Cow
Cepages
Tab x Tab
Farmacy
Bucket
Hero of Maida
Pearl Liang
London Shell Co.
Lockhouse
Workshop Coffee
The Frontline Club
The Harcourt
Bricole
Maroush
Patogh
Maroush Gardens
Bombay Palace
Maroush I
Noor Jahan
Angelus
Chucs Serpentine
Gold Mine
Four Seasons
Royal China
Mandarin Kitchen
MEATliquor
The Shed
Kensington Wine Rooms
Clarke's
Geales
Malabar, Eat Tokyo
Suzi Tros
Mazi
Churchill Arms
VQ
Portobello Ristorante
Polpo
Uli
Ladbroke Arms
Patty & Bun
Julie's
Six Portland Road
Flat Three
Edera

LATIMER ROAD
LADBROKE GROVE
WESTBOURNE PARK
ROYAL OAK
PADDINGTON
LANCASTER GATE
QUEENSWAY
BAYSWATER
NOTTING HILL GATE
HOLLAND PARK
EDGWARE ROAD

A   B   C   D

1

2

MAP 8 – HAMMERSMITH & CHISWICK

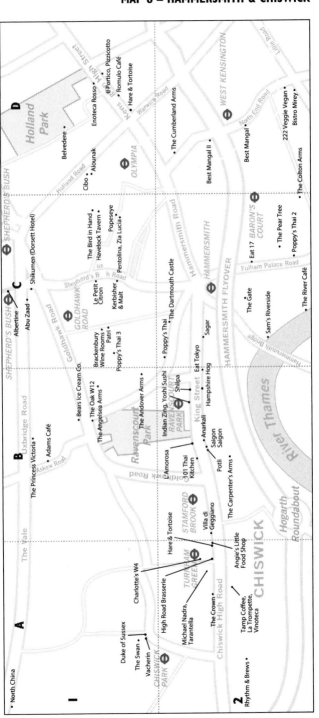

MAP 9 – HAMPSTEAD, CAMDEN TOWN & ISLINGTON

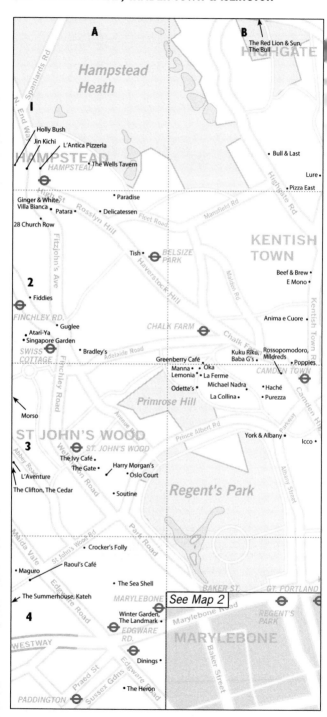

A

Hampstead Heath

B

The Red Lion & Sun,
The Bull

HIGHGATE

1

Holly Bush
Jin Kichi
L'Antica Pizzeria

HAMPSTEAD
HAMPSTEAD

The Wells Tavern

Bull & Last

Lure •

• Pizza East

• Paradise

Ginger & White,
Villa Bianca
• Patara   • Delicatessen

28 Church Row

KENTISH
TOWN

Fitzjohn's Ave
Rosslyn Hill
Fleet Road
Mansfield Rd

Tish •   BELSIZE
PARK

Haverstock Hill

Beef & Brew •
E Mono •

2

• Fiddies

FINCHLEY RD.

CHALK FARM

Chalk Farm Rd

Kentish Town Rd

Anima e Cuore •

Guglee

• Atari-Ya
• Singapore Garden

SWISS
COTTAGE

Finchley Road

Adelaide Road

• Bradley's

Greenberry Café •

Manna •   • Oka
Lemonia •   • La Ferme

Odette's •

Kuku Riku,   Rossopomodoro,
Baba G's •   Mildreds
• Poppies

CAMDEN TOWN

Michael Nadra •

La Collina •

• Haché

• Purezza

Morso

ST JOHN'S WOOD

Wellington Road

ST. JOHN'S WOOD

Primrose Hill

Prince Albert Rd

York & Albany •

Albany Street

Icco •

3

The Ivy Café •
The Gate •   Harry Morgan's
• Oslo Court

L'Aventure

The Clifton, The Cedar

Abbey Road

• Soutine

Regent's Park

Maida Vale

St John's Wood Rd

• Crocker's Folly

Raoul's Café

• Maguro

Park Road

Edgware Road

• The Sea Shell

BAKER ST.   GT. PORTLAND

The Summerhouse, Kateh

MARYLEBONE   *See Map 2*

4

Winter Garden,
The Landmark •

EDGWARE
RD.

WESTWAY

Marylebone Road

REGENT'S
PARK

MARYLEBONE

Baker Street

Dinings •

Praed St   Sussex Gdns

PADDINGTON   • The Heron

MAP 9 – HAMPSTEAD, CAMDEN TOWN & ISLINGTON

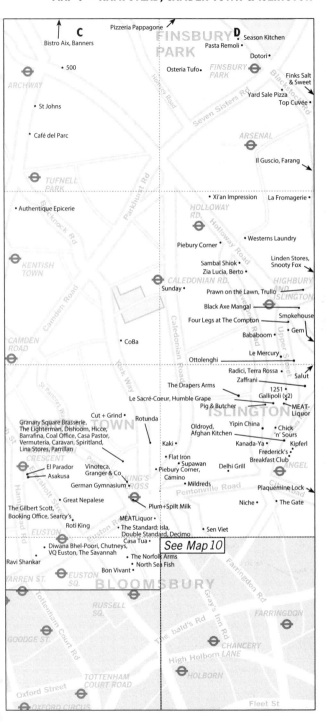

MAP 10 – THE CITY

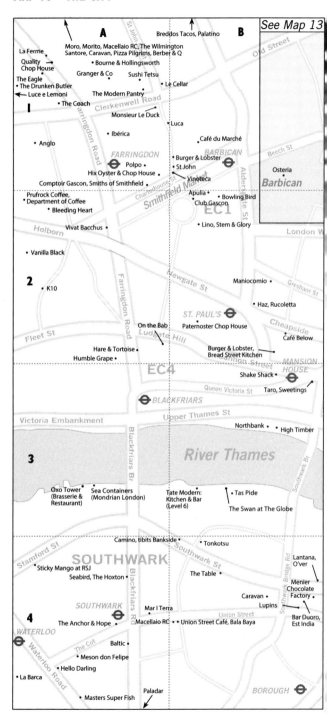

See Map 13

A

B

Breddos Tacos, Palatino

Old Street

La Ferme

Moro, Morito, Macellaio RC, The Wilmington
Santore, Caravan, Pizza Pilgrims, Berber & Q

Quality
Chop House

• Bourne & Hollingsworth

The Eagle
• The Drunken Butler
← Luce e Lemoni

• Granger & Co

Sushi Tetsu

• Le Cellar

• The Modern Pantry

1

• The Coach

Clerkenwell Road

Monsieur Le Duck

• Luca

• Anglo

• Ibérica

• Café du Marché

BARBICAN

Beech St

Farringdon
Road

FARRINGDON

Burger & Lobster •

Polpo •

• St John

Osteria

Hix Oyster & Chop House

Vinoteca

Barbican

Comptoir Gascon, Smiths of Smithfield

Aldersgate St

Smithfield Market

Charterhouse St

Apulia •

Prufrock Coffee,
• Department of Coffee
• Bleeding Heart

• Bowling Bird

Club Gascon

EC1

London W

Vivat Bacchus •

• Lino, Stem & Glory

Holborn

• Vanilla Black

2

Newgate St

Maniocomio •

Gresham St

• K10

Farringdon Road

ST. PAUL'S

• Haz, Rucoletta

Cheapside

Fleet St

On the Bab •

Ludgate Hill

Paternoster Chop House

Café Below •

Hare & Tortoise •

Humble Grape •

Burger & Lobster,
Bread Street Kitchen

Cannon Street

**MANSION
HOUSE**

EC4

Shake Shack •

Queen Victoria St

Taro, Sweetings

BLACKFRIARS

Upper Thames St

Victoria Embankment

Northbank •

• High Timber

Blackfriars Br

River Thames

Southwark Br

3

Oxo Tower
(Brasserie &
Restaurant)

Sea Containers
(Mondrian London)

Tate Modern:
Kitchen & Bar
(Level 6)

• Tas Pide

The Swan at The Globe

Camino, tibits Bankside •

• Tonkotsu

Lantana,
O'ver

Stamford St

SOUTHWARK

Southwark St

• Sticky Mango at RSJ

The Table •

Menier
Chocolate
Factory

Seabird, The Hoxton

Blackfriars Rd

Caravan •

Lupins

Southwark Bridge Rd

SOUTHWARK

4

Mar I Terra •

Union Street

Bar Duoro,
Est India

WATERLOO

The Anchor & Hope •

• Macellaio RC

• Union Street Café, Bala Baya

WATERLOO

The Cut

Baltic •

• Meson don Felipe

• Hello Darling

• La Barca

Waterloo Road

• Masters Super Fish

Paladar

BOROUGH

MAP 10 – THE CITY

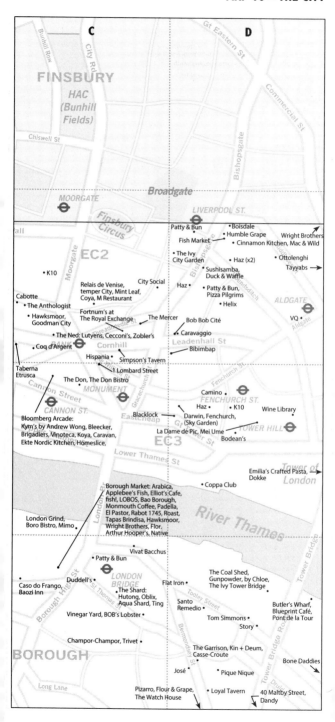

MAP 11 – SOUTH LONDON (& FULHAM)

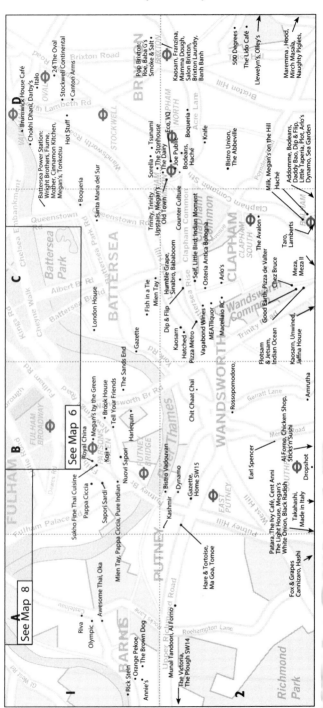

MAP 12 – EAST END & DOCKLANDS

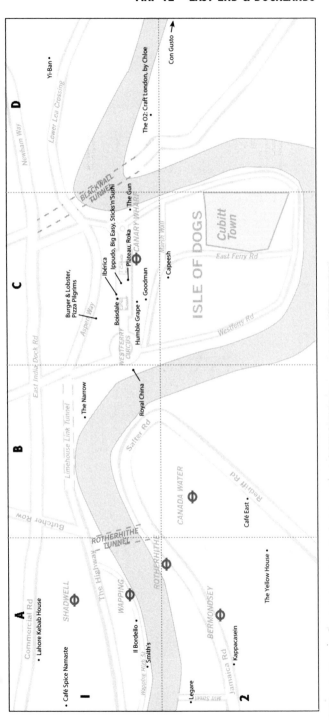

Con Gusto →

Yi-Ban •

Lower Lea Crossing

Newham Way

The O2: Craft London, by Chloe
•

D

BLACKWALL TUNNEL

Ippudo, Big Easy, Sticks'n'Sushi

Plateau, Roka

The Gun

CANARY WHARF

Iberica

Burger & Lobster,
Pizza Pilgrims

Boisdale •

Goodman •

Capeesh •

Humble Grape •

Marsh Wall

C

WESTFERRY CIRCUS

Aspen Way

East Ferry Rd

ISLE OF DOGS

Cubitt
Town

Westferry Rd

East India Dock Rd

The Narrow •

Limehouse Link Tunnel

Royal China

B

Salter Rd

CANADA WATER

Café East •

Redriff Rd

Butcher Row

ROTHERHITHE TUNNEL

The Highway

ROTHERHITHE

A

Commercial Rd

Lahore Kebab House •

Café Spice Namaste •

SHADWELL

WAPPING

Il Bordello •

Smith's •

Wapping High St

Legare •

Mill Street

Jamaica Rd

BERMONDSEY

Kappacasein •

The Yellow House •

1

2

MAP 13 – SHOREDITCH & BETHNAL GREEN

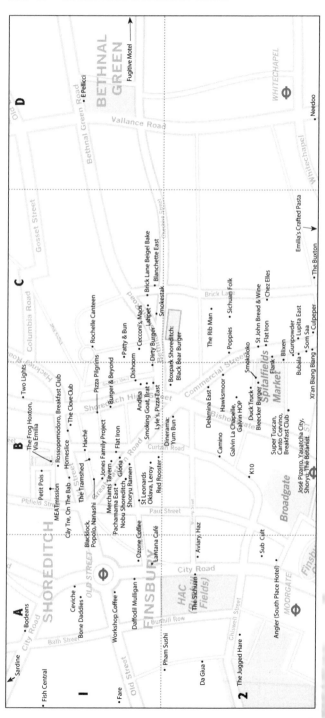

BETHNAL GREEN

WHITECHAPEL

SHOREDITCH

FINSBURY

MOORGATE

Bethnal Green Road

Vallance Road

Gosset Street

Columbia Road

Brick Lane

Commercial Street

Bishopsgate

Old Street

City Road

Bath Street

Bunhill Row

Chiswell Street

Whitechapel

Broadgate

HAC (Fields)

Spitalfields Market

Fugitive Motel
E Pellicci
The Buxton
Emilia's Crafted Pasta
Needoo
Brick Lane Beigel Bake
Blanchette East
Smokestak
Sichuan Folk
St John Bread & Wine
Chez Elles
Cecconi's Macs
Dirty Burger, Lahpet
Boxpark Shoreditch: Black Bear Burger
The Rib Man
Poppies
Flat Iron
Gunpowder
Rochelle Canteen
Patty & Bun
Dishoom
Blixen
Lupita East
Som Saa
Culpeper
Two Lights
Pizza Pilgrims
Burger & Beyond
Andina
Smoking Goat, Brat
Lyle's, Pizza East
Dinerama: Yum Bun
Delamina East
Hawksmoor
Smokoloko
Bubala
Xi'an Biang Biang
The Frog Hoxton, Via Emilia
Rossopomodoro, Breakfast Club
The Clove Club
Hoxton
Haché
Jones Family Project
Flat Iron
St Leonards
Oklava, Leroy
Red Rooster
Duck Truck
Bleecker Burger
Flank
Cây Tre, On The Bab
MEATmission
Homeslice
The Tramshed
Merchants Tavern
Gloria
Pachamama East
Nobu Shoreditch, Shoryu Ramen
Camino
Galvin La Chapelle, Galvin HOP
Super Tuscan, Canto Corvino, Breakfast Club
Petit Pois
Blacklock, Popolo, Nanashi
K10
José Pizarro, Yauatcha City, Shoryu, The Botanist
Ceviche
Bodeans
Daffodil Mulligan
Ozone Coffee
Lantana Café
Aviary, Haz
Sub Cult
Workshop Coffee
Bone Daddies
Sardine
Fish Central
Fare
Pham Sushi
The Sichuan
Da Gua
The Jugged Hare
Angler (South Place Hotel)

MAP 14 – EAST LONDON

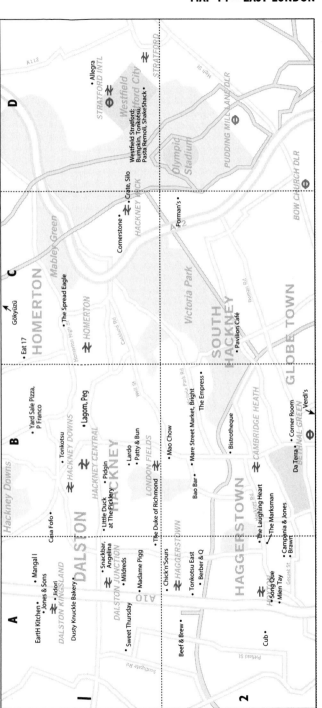